# International Conference on High-Temperature Reactor Technology (HTR 2021)



Journal of Physics: Conference Series Volume 2048

Online
2-5 June 2021

ISBN: 978-1-7138-5019-9
ISSN: 1742-6588

**Printed from e-media with permission by:**

Curran Associates, Inc.
57 Morehouse Lane
Red Hook, NY 12571

**Some format issues inherent in the e-media version may also appear in this print version.**



Institute of Physics
Dirac House, Temple Back
Bristol BS1 6BE UK

Phone: 44 1 17 929 7481
Fax: 44 1 17 920 0979

techtracking@iop.org

**Additional copies of this publication are available from:**

Curran Associates, Inc.
57 Morehouse Lane
Red Hook, NY 12571 USA
Phone: 845-758-0400
Fax: 845-758-2633
Email: curran@proceedings.com
Web: www.proceedings.com

# TABLE OF CONTENTS

HTR 2021
Organized by:
HIMNI
batan
In Cooperation with
IAEA
PROCEEDING OF INTERNATIONAL CONFERENCE
ON HIGH TEMPERATURE REACTOR TECHNOLOGY
2021
2-5 JUNE 2021
VIRTUAL CONFERENCE, INDONESIA
Volume 2

**IOP Journal of Physics: Conference Series**

# PROCEEDING OF INTERNATIONAL CONFERENCE ON HIGH TEMPERATURE REACTOR TECHNOLOGY 2021

**VIRTUAL CONFERENCE, INDONESIA**
**2-5 JUNE 2021**

**Volume 2 of 2**

**Organized By**
Indonesian Nuclear Society (HIMNI)
National Nuclear Energy Agency (BATAN)
Universitas Gadjah Mada

**In Cooperation with**
International Atomic Energy Agency (IAEA)

Journal of Physics: Conference Series **2048** (2021) 011001 doi:10.1088/1742-6596/2048/1/011001

This page intentionally left blank

Journal of Physics: Conference Series **2048** (2021) 011001 doi:10.1088/1742-6596/2048/1/011001

# INTERNATIONAL CONFERENCE ON HIGH TEMPERATURE REACTOR TECHNOLOGY 2021

## PREFACE

The International Topical Meeting on High Temperature Reactor Technology is the sole international conference focusing on high-temperature gas-cooled reactors and process heat application technology. Inaugurated in 2002 by the European High Temperature Reactor Technology Network HTR-TN at Petten, The Netherlands, successive meetings were held in China (Beijing, 2004), South Africa (Johannesburg, 2006), USA (Washington DC, 2008), Czech Republic (Prague, 2010), Japan (Tokyo, 2012), China (Weihai, 2014) USA (Las Vegas, 2016) and Poland (Warsaw, 2018).

HTR 2021 International Conference, held virtually on 2-5 June 2021, under the theme of "The Role of HTGR Technology for the First Nuclear Power Plant in Indonesia". This conference discussed various aspects ranging from national policies and HTR applications in Industry to various technical aspects. In addition, these meetings provided ample opportunities to meet and interact with leading scientists, researchers, and experts and promote high-level networking. Keynote speakers will convey the progress in HTR technology in several countries, which are expected to encourage all participants. At the same time, productive discussions are expected to continue to be encouraged, which will keep participants up to date on developments in this technology, and the challenges faced.

This conference is hosted by the Indonesian Nuclear Society (HIMNI), National Nuclear Energy Agency of Indonesia (BATAN), and Universitas Gadjah Mada (UGM). It is organized in cooperation with the International Atomic Energy Agency (IAEA).

More than three hundred participants from Indonesia, USA, Poland, China, Netherland, Austria, Russia, Germany, Japan, and some other countries have participated in this conference. About 50 presentations including 5 keynote speeches and 1 plenary talk are presented. The presentations are grouped into 8 tracks of particular interest: (**Track 1)** National Research Programs and Industrial Projects, (**Track 2)** Industrial Applications and Markets, (**Track 3)** Fuel and Waste, (**Track 4)** Materials, Components and Manufacturing, (**Track 5)** Reactor Physics Analysis, (**Track 6)** Computer Codes and Analysis (Thermal-Hydraulics, Structural, Multiphysics), (**Track 7)** Development, Design and Engineering, (**Track 8)** Safety and Licensing

All submitted papers then peer-reviewed by relevant experts, eventually 50 papers were accepted for publication. We are indebted to all of authors for submitting their original papers. We would like to thank all participants, and express our gratitude to all those who helped the success of this conference.

**Djarot Sulistio Wisnubroto**
(BATAN - National Nuclear Energy Agency of Indonesia / HIMNI - Indonesian Nuclear Society)
Email: djarot@batan.go.id

**Conference Chair:**
**Djarot Sulistio Wisnubroto**
(BATAN - National Nuclear Energy Agency of Indonesia / HIMNI - Indonesian Nuclear Society)

**Conference Co-Chairs:**
1. **Michael A. Fütterer** (European Commission - Joint Research Center)
2. **M. Hadid Subki** (IAEA - International Atomic Energy Agency)

## EDITORIAL BOARD AND REVIEWERS



## DESIGN AND LAYOUT

Nugroho Hary Santosa, Farisy Yogatama S., Muhammad Yunus, Muksin Aji S., Wahid Luthfi

Journal of Physics: Conference Series **2048** (2021) 011001 doi:10.1088/1742-6596/2048/1/011001

HTR 2021

Organized by: HIMNI batan in Cooperation with IAEA

Journal of Physics: Conference Series **2048** (2021) 011002 doi:10.1088/1742-6596/2048/1/011002

# Guidance for HTR2021 Organizing Committees

## Structure

1. The Organizing Committees comprise International Organizing Committee (IOC) and Local Organizing Committee (LOC), both led by a Conference Chair from the host country and supported by a Co-Chair for the IOC and a Technical Program Chair for the LOC.
2. The IOC consists of leading figures and experts from the HTR community, and serves to promote HTR2020, assist the LOC in planning and program execution, and contribute to the review of abstracts and papers. (See the list of reviewer and committee in https://htr2020.org/)
3. The Local Organizing Committee (LOC) consists of representatives and experts from the host institution(s) and local organization(s), and liaises with the IOC prior to and during the Conference in arrangement of the technical program, events, and logistics for participants.

## Review Process

1. Review process of Abstracts and Papers will be grouped into eight (8) Tracks.
2. Each Track will be led by two (2) Track Leaders, i.e. one (1) International Track Leader and one (1) Local Track Leader. Track Leaders are selected from members of the IOC and the LOC, by the Conference Chairs.
3. Track Leaders have the primary responsibility to choose relevant Reviewers from the IOC for each submission, coordinate the review process with the Reviewers, and interact with the Authors.
4. Reviewers should perform the review of abstracts and papers, and report back to the Track Leaders upon completing the task.
5. The conference adopts single blind review, and Reviewers can either submit the results in the open conference peer-Review, abstract, publication and conference management (OpenConf software) or send the comments via email to the Track Leader.
6. Track Leaders and Reviewers should sign up to get access to the abstracts and papers through the following link: https://htr2020.org/paper-submission/.
   - Select Review and Program Committees
   - Go to Sign up using keycode: htr2020review.
   - Fill out the form and click Submit. Notification will be sent to your email.
   - Reviewers will receive notification of new review assignment
   - Go to Sign in and select View Submission.

## Track Session at the Conference

1. Track Leaders will lead the corresponding Track Session during the Conference, prepare the summary, and report to the Conference Chairs.

**Important Timelines:**

Abstract submission (29 February 2020), Review notification (31 March 2020), Full Paper due (20 February 2021), Review notification (28 February 2021), and Final Paper due (31 March 2021).

HTR 2021

Organized by: HIMNI batan

in Cooperation with IAEA International Atomic Energy Agency

Journal of Physics: Conference Series **2048** (2021) 011003 doi:10.1088/1742-6596/2048/1/011003

# Peer Review Declaration Form Guidance

On the following page you will find the declaration form.

- Please answer each question.
- You should submit the form along with the rest of your submission files.
- The deadline is the submission date written in your publishing agreement.

**All conference organisers/editors are required to declare details about their peer review.**

**We will publish the information you provide as part of your proceedings.**

Journal of Physics: Conference Series **2048** (2021) 011003 doi:10.1088/1742-6596/2048/1/011003

# Peer review declaration

All papers published in this volume of Journal of Physics: Conference Series have been peer reviewed through processes administered by the Editors. Reviews were conducted by expert referees to the professional and scientific standards expected of a proceedings journal published by IOP Publishing.

- **Type of peer review: ~~Single-blind~~ / Double-blind / ~~Triple-blind~~ / ~~Open~~ / ~~Other~~ (please describe)**
  **We keep hidden the identity of both the author and reviewer.**

- **Conference submission management system: OpenConf**

- **Number of submissions received: 103**

- **Number of submissions sent for review: 103**

- **Number of submissions accepted: 44**

- **Acceptance Rate (Number of Submissions Accepted / Number of Submissions Received X 100): 42.72%**

- **Average number of reviews per paper: 2**

- **Total number of reviewers involved: 39**

- **Any additional info on review process:**

- **Contact person for queries:**
  Name: Djarot Sulistio Wisnubroto
  Affiliation: BATAN - National Nuclear Energy Agency of Indonesia
  Email: djarot@batan.go.id

# The Challenges of Implementing the Indonesian Experimental Power Reactor (RDE) Program

**D S Wisnubroto, G R Sunaryo, Y S B Susilo, S Bahri, and T Setiadipura**

National Nuclear Energy Agency of Indonesia – BATAN, Puspiptek Serpong, Tangerang Selatan, Banten, Indonesia, 15310 Phone: +62-21-7563142.

Email: djarot@batan.go.id

**Abstract.** This paper shows the effort to implement the RDE and its challenges from 2013 to 2018. RDE was a program to introduce nuclear power plants by building non-commercial power reactors. The RDE program was also used to prove that Indonesian engineers can design a reactor that will later supply electricity and steam for industry. The technology used is a high-temperature gas-cooled reactor. This RDE program is a very strategic intermediate target for energy security and national sovereignty. The development of RDE-based nuclear power plants, in the long run, is expected to have implications for reducing reliance on fossil fuels, more self-sufficiency in energy supply increases national industrial capacity and competitiveness in the global economic order, as well as enhance energy and political diplomacy. Also, RDE can be a reference installation for PeLUIt (Power and Steam Generators for Industry) power plants for small and medium enterprises to meet the demand for electricity and industrial heat in an area's needs. However, many challenges occurred to implement this program; among them were cost estimation and cost-benefit analysis. Although the program has not been realized, mainly for financial reasons, many positive things have been obtained from these activities.

## 1. uction

The idea of developing an experimental power reactor (RDE) was initiated through discussion between National Development Planning Agency (BAPPENAS) and BATAN in June 2013. Then followed up with a trilateral meeting between BATAN, BAPPENAS, and the Ministry of Finance, and has received support from related stakeholders (some universities and technology agencies). Although most Indonesians support the development of nuclear power plants based on a survey conducted [1], it is not easy to get a political decision to implement the nuclear power plant program so that RDE can be a breakthrough to avoid political complications in Indonesia. The Indonesian Government formally stated the RDE in the midterm national development planning 2015-2019 [2]. Nine RDE Pre-Project activities that have been carried out since 2014 to 2018 are (1) land allocation preparation and master plan preparation (coordination with Ministry of Research, Technology and Higher Education), (2) preparation of RDE Blueprint, (3) site permit process, (4) preparation conceptual design documents and Front End Engineering Design, Feasibility Studies, Safety Analysis Report, Reactor Main Data (DUR), and List of Reactor Design Information (DID), (5) International Cooperation (IAEA, Rosatom, INET / Tsinghua University, CNEC, JAEA), (6) HTGR- related workshops, (7) ten draft documents related to construction permits (DUR, DID, RDE Aging Documents, Radiation Protection, and Accident Management), (8) training related to Project Management, technology, and safety both at home and abroad, and (9) the establishment of the Project Management Organization (PMO) Team.

This paper shows the effort to implement the RDE and its challenges from 2013 to 2018. Although the program has not been realized, mainly for financial reasons, many positive things have been obtained from these activities.

## 2. Purpose and Benefits

The purpose of developing RDE is to bring Indonesia to become a technology owner related to electrical energy and heat for the national industry in the long term. RDE development is a very strategic intermediate target for resilience energy, national sovereignty, and the existence of the Indonesian state in the future. Development RDE- based nuclear power plants are expected to have implications in the future for reducing dependence on fossil fuels [3], are more self-reliable in energy supply, increase industrial capabilities nationwide. The Government hopes that this program will also increase Indonesia's competitiveness in the regional and global economic order [4]. Besides, RDE can be a reference plant for small and medium power reactors (50 s / d 600 MWe per unit) to meet electricity and industrial heat demand. The RDE may be compatible with the geographical condition of Indonesia as an archipelago that some areas require small/medium electricity power or those with small power grid capacity [6]. In line with that, the program of RDE may increase the capacity of the national nuclear industry in the field of manufacturing and construction capabilities, reducing dependence on the state other, as well as having a positive impact on increasing public acceptance of Nuclear Power Plant.

Besides that, some of the benefits related to RDE development for Indonesia are:

a. Improve energy security in the long term.
b. Mastery of development project management related to nuclear power plants, which will bring Indonesia, is among the countries for the design of the 4th generation.
c. Increasing the capacity of Indonesian human resources in mastering aspects of nuclear safety and make documents related to nuclear power plant licensing (especially site permits, construction permits, commissioning permits, and operating permits).
d. Increase national human resources (HR) capacity to design, construct, operate, and maintain nuclear power plants.
e. Improved R&D for heat/cogeneration applications.
f. Increase the capacity of local industries to support the nuclear industry.
g. Increase international networks.

The basic idea is that if the RDE project is successful, it will trigger larger commercial HTGR with the power of 50 to 600 MWe in various parts of Indonesia as needed. Thus, Indonesia will become a leading country in the ASEAN region and is expected to become a provider of HTGR type nuclear power plants domestically and in the region.

## 3. Location of RDE and Site Permits

The RDE site was selected in the Serpong Puspiptek Area. This selection streamlines the licensing process related to the site, which may take many years. The location of RDE is not more than 500 meters from RSG GAS 30 MW, which BATAN has managed for nearly 30 years. The land provided for RDE is 8,674 ha. The current status is already obtained a borrow-to-use permit from the Ministry of Research, Technology and Higher Education and the Ministry of Finance. The process of obtaining an RDE site permit has been carried out since 2014, covering seven aspects as required in the regulation on licensing for nuclear installations and utilization of nuclear materials. Namely the seismic aspect, utilities, geotechnical and foundation, meteorology, hydrology, dispersion and distribution population, and human-induced events. The Indonesian national regulatory agency (BAPETEN) approved implementing the RDE site evaluation on February 25, 2015. After that, activities of the site evaluation were carried out until 2016. Finally, the status of the RDE location has met safety terms and criteria and has obtained a site permit from BAPETEN on January 23, 2017. This is the first experience for Indonesia to issue a location permit for a nuclear power plant. It is also unique because the RDE reactor design process was still ongoing, but the location has been approved.

**Figure 1.** The location of the RDE site at Puspiptek Serpong

## 4. Scope of Work Plan and Activity Components

The Project activities have a scope according to the RDE project stages with activity components as follows:

1. RDE Project Initiation Stage
   The scope of pre-project activities includes preparing blueprint, user requirements documents (URD), technology selection, feasibility study (FS), conceptual design, and site permit process.
2. The RDE Project Planning Stage
   The activities in this stage include principal permits, site permits, construction permits, commissioning permits, operating permits, and other permits.
3. RDE Project Implementation Phase
   Components of activities within this scope include basic engineering design and detail design, procurement, construction, process installation, and commissioning. Each stage of implementation is also related to the preparation, monitoring, and evaluation of human resources.
4. RDE Project Completion Stage
   This stage is the final stage of the project RDE development, where all the criteria of the RDE project (contract) have been fulfilled.

Unfortunately, the above plan has only been implemented in the first phase. At that time, the calculation of financing required a very long discussion. As a result, the Government considered this program expensive and ordered a review of the RDE development costs.

## 5. Challenges on The RDE, Cost estimation, and Funding

Costs in the development of RDE are classified into three types: investment costs, operational costs and maintenance costs, and nuclear fuel costs.

1. Investment or Capital Costs.
   Initially, Funding for the RDE program wanted to use the Government's budget. However, since nuclear facilities' construction is expensive, the Government considers loans from foreign financial institutions [7].
2. Operation and Maintenance Costs.
   Operation and maintenance costs consist of salaries for employees, spare parts, costs electricity, water and telecommunications consumables, and cleaning costs.

3. Nuclear Fuel Costs.
   Nuclear fuel costs include purchasing nuclear materials, fabrication, and transport to reactor and storage after use.

One of the RDE Project Initiation Stage results is the estimation cost of building RDE. The estimate is around 300 million US dollars, or equivalent to 4.3 trillion rupiahs. The Government considers these costs too expensive. This led BATAN to switch from a turn-key program to designing its RDE. This change also had a positive impact, namely that BATAN could estimate the cost of RDE development in more detail and at a lower cost. BATAN collaborated with several state-owned enterprises with experience designing and building non-nuclear power plants to calculate the cost of non-nuclear islands. BATAN has received support from the International Atomic Energy Agency (IAEA) and several partner countries for the nuclear island part. The costs for the RDE are as follows:

**Table 1.** Components of RDE Costs

| No. | Component | Unit | Total |
|---|---|---|---|
| 1. | Investment | Billion rupiah | 2.200 |
| 2. | Operation and Maintenance | Billion rupiah/year | 142,57 |
| 3. | Nuclear Fuel | Billion rupiah/year | 36,4 |

Detailed Funding Plan

The detailed funding plan for the RDE development project is based on the needs budget, such as basic and detailed design activities, engineering, procurement and construction (EPC), and supporting activities for implementing the RDE project. Supporting activities include the preparation of human resources, licensing, and project management/management.

Based on calculating the cost per RDE component by the BATAN Team, RDE development needs are 164,805 million USD.

Annual RDE Development Financing Pembangunan

The estimated cost breakdown per year is based on activity and cost optimization, and HR costs are based on the S curve. The first year starts with preparing basic designs to detailed design and site preparation activities with a cost of about 12% of the total funding or 17,777 million USD. In the second year, it continued with site preparation and started the equipment procurement with 29,629 million USD (28% of the total Funding). Finally, the third year requires 41,480 million USD for construction and procurement equipment.

## 6. Cost and Benefit Analysis

One of the biggest challenges in assessing the feasibility of investment in constructing nuclear research facilities is assessing or estimating what benefits will be obtained by the Government in the future [8]. Given the estimated high cost of RDE development, the Government always asked about the benefits for the public. Of course, the most significant benefits provided by R&D facilities such as RDE are intangible or difficult to measure financially and do not directly affect the national economy. The benefits of developing an RDE, both tangible and intangible, are described below.

Tangible benefits:

1. Electricity production
   RDE capacity is designed for 10 MWth, which can produce electricity with a capacity of 2.9 MWe. The estimated use of RDE electricity for internal purposes is only 0.4 MWe, while the majority is 2.5 MWe for public purposes. With an annual operation of 6570 hours, at a capacity factor of 75%, RDE can produce 16,425 MWh per year. Considering the price of electricity by PLN, which is equal to Rp1,139 / kWh, BATAN per year can save as much as Rp.18.7 billion.

2. Nuclear Power Plant Design
   By referring to the RDE design, developing a larger nuclear power plant is possible in the future. The estimated cost for the RDE scale-up from research to final design is likely to be around USD 1.014 million. This profit belongs to the Government of Indonesia.
3. Human resource development
   The existence of the RDE program will increase the capability of human resources not only for BATAN but also for other stakeholders (universities, research institutions, state-owned enterprises, BAPETEN, state electricity companies, and others).
4. Patents
   The RDE program will enhance research on instrumentation and control, materials science, and new technological discoveries. Many patents can arise from these studies.

Intangible benefits**:**

Since intangible benefits are difficult to measure in terms of economic value, so some estimation has been made, i.e.:

1. Increasing Public Acceptance [9].
   With the RDE, the community will be able to accept the presence of the larger NPP. In addition, because of the RDE, promoting nuclear power plants is more comfortable and more effective in explaining safety and security factors because there is an example of a small power reactor operation.
2. Increased self-confidence.
   For a long time, Indonesia has three research reactors located in Bandung, Yogyakarta, and Serpong. However, it still does not have NPP. One of the causes is self-doubt in Indonesia to build and operate nuclear power plants. With the construction of RDE, it is expected to increase self-confidence, especially in decision-makers.
3. Become a referral center.
   Not many countries have developed the HTGR (High Gas Reactor Temperature) [10]. With the construction of RDE, Indonesia will become a reference center, especially for the regional area.
4. Maintain competence.
   Many nuclear human resources in Indonesia are on the verge of retirement, while the younger generation has minimal experience developing and operating nuclear reactors. Therefore, RDE development is significant in maintaining human resource capabilities.

## 7. Operation and Maintenance Plan

In the planning, RDE will operate at full power of 10 MWth, or equivalent electricity production. 2.9 MW. It is planned that, in addition to various experimental activities, RDE's electricity production is used to meet the electricity needs of BATAN's laboratory facilities and possibly for the surrounding community. The experiments, including, among others, study the physical parameters of the HTGR reactor, safety experiments, thorium fuel experiments, and heat/cogeneration applications. It is expected that the RDE will operate in five modes: start-up, mains power operation, shutdown, test demonstration, and maintenance. This operating mode share is 75% for mains power operation and 25% for start-up, shutdown, demonstration or experimentation, and maintenance programs. Some of the experimental and demonstration plans that will be carried out in RDE are zero power experiment, full-power operation, demonstration of RDE's inherent safety, and heat application system (cogeneration experiments). Safety experiments include multiple crash demonstrations (including system outage/SBO accidents) to prove RDE's resistance to accidents such as the Fukushima incident. The scheme of safety experiments is similar to the activities on the HTTR (Japan) and HTR-10 (China) reactors. In addition, it is planned that there will be unique experiments that are not similar to the two reactors from Japan and China. Namely, trials of electricity generation systems that can later be used to design reactors with greater power on a commercial scale. The data obtained from the experimental results will be validated with the Calculation Code created and developed by the

BATAN team for understanding the process in depth. This validated data will be used to develop future nuclear power plant designs for the needs of Indonesia and other countries. The RDE maintenance program that will be carried out includes maintenance for preventive action and corrective action. Maintenance activities will be carried out regularly so that critical components continue to operate in good condition and support the safe, secure, and reliable operation of the RDE.

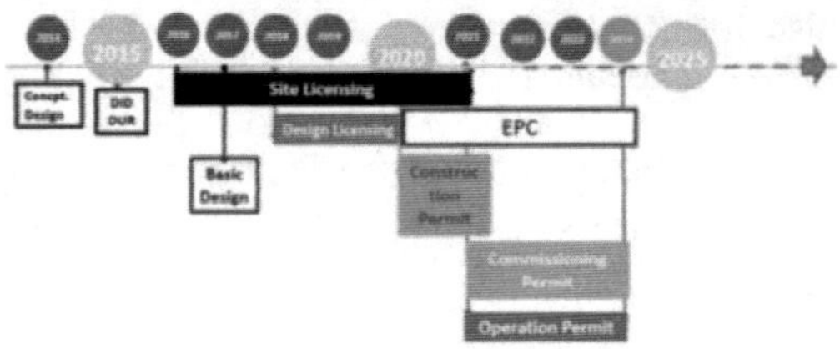


**Figure 2.** Roadmap of RDE

## 8. Conclusion

RDE will bring Indonesia to become a technology provider related to the provision of electrical and heat to support the needs of the national industry and be the leading country in the region. This RDE program is a very strategic intermediate target for energy security and national sovereignty. The development of RDE-based nuclear power plants, in the long run, is expected to have implications for reducing reliance on fossil fuels, more self-sufficiency in energy supply increases national industrial capacity and competitiveness in the global economic order, as well as enhance energy and political diplomacy. In addition, RDE can be a basis for PeLUIt (Power and Steam Generators for Industry) power plants for small and medium-sized businesses to meet industrial electricity and heat needs in an area. With the development of RDE, Indonesia will enter a new era of Generation IV power reactor technology that can bring Indonesia ahead in nuclear technology.

Although the program has not been realized, mainly for financial reasons, many positive things have been obtained from these activities. For example, from the RDE activities for four years, the mapping of stakeholders to build nuclear power plants has become more apparent. Likewise, the collaboration between research institutions, universities, and State-Owned Enterprises will be a vital asset in the future in building nuclear power plants. The special one is, even nuclear energy regulatory agencies can grant RDE site permits. Therefore, it is hoped that the Indonesian Government will reconsider the RDE program in the future.

## References

[1] D. S. Wisnubroto, Ruslan, D. Irawan, and T. Erni, "Public opinion survey on nuclear energy in Indonesia: Understanding public perception on nuclear power plant program," 2019, doi: 10.1063/1.5135551.
[2] BAPPENAS, "Midterm National Development Planning of Indonesia 2015- 2019," 2015.
[3] The Indonesian Government, Indonesian National Energy Policy. 2014.
[4] Indonesian Ministry of National Development Planning (Bappenas) and Indonesia Statistics Bureau (BPS), "Indonesian population projection 2015- 2045," 2018.
[5] Indonesian State Electricity Enterprise, "PLN Statistics 2017," Jakarta, 2018.
[6] Indonesian State Electricity Enterprise, "PLN Statistics 2018," Jakarta, 2019.
[7] The Republic of Indonesia, Act of State Finance, No. 17/2003
[8] The Republic of Indonesia, Act No. 11 /2019 on National System for Science and Technology. Indonesia, 2019, pp. 1–30.
[9] D. Irawan, T. E. Wijayanti, Mudjiono, and M. Busthomi, "Recent Status of Public Response to RDE Development & Utilization," 2019, doi: 10.1088/1742- 6596/1198/2/022051.
[10] T. Setiadipura, S. Bakhri, G. R. Sunaryo, and D. S. Wisnusubroto, "Cooling passive safety features of Reaktor Daya Eksperimental," 2018, doi: 10.1063/1.5046618.

# RDE Design Strategy for Indonesia Experimental NPP

**G R Sunaryo[1], S Bakhri[1], M Subekti[1], T Setiadipura[1], and D S Wisnubroto[2]**

National Nuclear Energy Agency, BATAN
[1]Building 80, [2]Building 50, PUSPITEK, SERPONG, Indonesia

phone: +62-217560912, email: genirina@batan.go.id

**Abstract.** *Reaktor Daya Eksperimental* (RDE) is developed as a chain to enhancing capacity Building. And, this is Indonesia Nuclear Energy Agency (BATAN) Authority. The activity is made based on the basic rules that is written on Act number 17, 2007, Long Term of National Development Plan (RPJPN 2005-2025) and Government Decree number 14, 2015 on Master Plan of National Industry Development 2015-2035 (RIPIN 2015-2035). It is written strongly that Nuclear Energy is considered to be commenced in 2020. Hence, on June 22, 2016, Mr. President Joko Widodo made a statement that RDE is supported fully to be constructed. It may initiate international collaboration among countries, and local as well. The main goal of initiating the RDE design Program, beside developing the national capability as a nuclear reactor technology provider by mastering the design, construction project management, commissioning and operation of a nuclear power reactor, is to mastering nuclear power plant that to be able to be scaled-up and commercialized to support the national energy security. This paper describes the design project strategy, that include design features, Safety Features, Plant Safety and Operational Performances, Instrumentation and Control Systems, Plant Layout Arrangement, Design and Licensing Status, Fuel Cycle Approach, Waste Management and Disposal Plan, finally Development Milestones as well. RDE's design experience has brought Indonesia to the nuclear power plant gate. The site permit process is on hand, and design approval has been started. It is clear that the role of stakeholder involvement is important. And, how the Cooperation has been able to reduce the price of NPP development. Hence, the communication strategy with BAPETEN, is holding another key. Meanwhile, the influences coming from internally BATAN's management, external political, influences, as well as foreign politics, play a strong role in the NPP development scene in Indonesia. Step regulation two, approval design, unfinished. It's still got to go on.

## 1. Introduction

BATAN has entered the age of 62 years in 2020. It has been more than 40 years of fighting for nuclear power plants, but it always leads to antinuclear demos.

There has to be a lesson learnt from this experience. Then, in the Long Term of National Development Plan (RPJPN 2005-2025) and Government Decree number 14, 2015 on Master Plan of National Industry Development 2015-2035 (RIPIN 2015-2035), written the operation of Nuclear Power Plant (NPP). Base on this, in 2012, the head of BATAN and the head of BAPPENAS agreed to conduct NPP development activities. Just for research purposes. Why? Because based on BAPETEN rules, BATAN only has the full role of operating Non-Commercial Nuclear Power Plants. And the reactor type chosen is the 4$^{th}$ generation, HTGR, 10 MWt. Namely Experimental Power Reactor, RDE. Then, on June 22, 2016, Mr. President Joko

Widodo made a statement that RDE is fully supported to be constructed. It is convincing that this activity may initiated international collaboration among countries, and local as well.

Why HTGR? BATAN has a long history related to HTGR studies, more than 20 years.[1] And this type of reactor is believed to be the type that best suits the needs in eastern Indonesia. Where many smelter fields have to be built, and HTGR is able to supply electricity and hot steam as lighters of industrial processes of mineral management.

RDE will be built as a turn key project. And for the purposes of design evaluation that will come from vendors, it is thought to conduct design activities independently. The goal is to make human resources more skilled in evaluating design. Also, this standalone RDE design, is a first step to design with higher power, and commercial purposes.

The concept design has been bid, and won by RENUKO. In cooperation with Rosatom Russia. Based on that, concept design is obtained. The next development process was hampered, with political winds changing. So, the activity of describing the concept design into basic and detailed design, becomes the main activity of RDE.

The design activities were financed by DIPA BATAN and also flagship of the Ministry of Research and Technology for two years. The next challenge approached, with the replacement of BATAN's head, because his term was up. The support of the highest leadership of the institution plays an important role in improving BATAN's human resources capability. The less conducive direction of the replacement leadership, led to the hibernation of RDE design activities.

In this paper will describe how the RDE design safety features. In addition, how the working team system in completing basic and detailed design, how the strategy of supply Fuel Chain, and how is the Construction Regulation, and waste management concept, is also explained plainly and well.

## 2. RDE Technology

RDE design feature is shown in Table 1, below. The RDE, is designed based on an established pebble-bed reactor principle. The design employs the TRISO-based fuel which provide a sound fission product retention capability resulting in slow release of radioactive material to the environment in any condition of the core including the most severe postulated accident.[3]

## 3. Design Project Strategy

### *3.1. Human Resources*

In completing the design, a team is required. It consists of various disciplines. Where human resources are available, scattered in various work units in BATAN. Therefore, the formation of a team consisting of personnel from across work units, became the main strategy of the success of this project.

In addition to cross-center, Cooperation with Non-Ministry Institutions such as the Agency for the Assessment and Application of Technology (BPPT). Also, several public universities (UGM, ITB, IPB, Hassanuddin), and private (Pertamina University, Swiss German University, Pamulang University etc.). Triple Helix system. It is also a pattern of teamwork, by including Government-Owned Enterprises (SOEs) such as PT Pembangunan Perumahan (PT PP) and PT Rekadaya Listrika Consult (Reconsult).

Why should it be with state own company? First, because they are very skilled in designing and building coal plants. His experience is very high. The design of the coal plant is exactly the same as the NPP design on the non-nuclear island side. Therefore, by cooperating, it is expected, can accelerate the completion of the design process. Also, it will speed up the process of obtaining a design license from bada regulation, BAPETEN.

In addition, this cooperation will be able to increase local participation. Some parts of the design, which are non-nuclear island, use local product. Like turbines, pumps and so on.

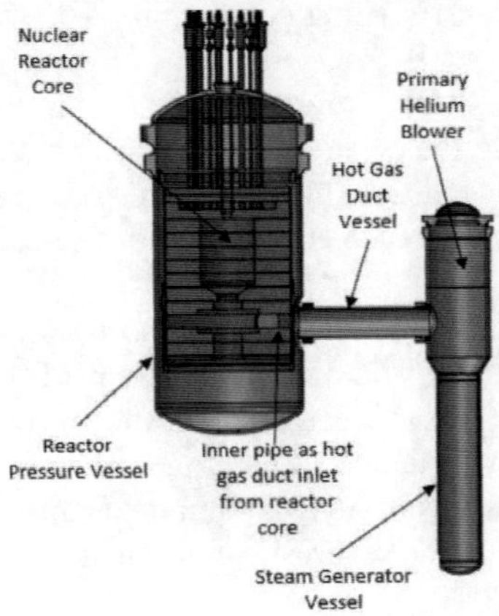


**Table 1.** RDE design Feature.[2]

**MAJOR TECHNICAL PARAMETERS**

| Parameter | Value |
|---|---|
| Technology developer, country of origin | National Nuclear Energy Agency (BATAN), Indonesia |
| Reactor type | Pebble bed high temperature gas-cooled reactor |
| Coolant/moderator | Helium/graphite |
| Thermal/electrical capacity, MW(t)/MW€ | 10/3 |
| Primary circulation | Forced circulation |
| NSSS Operating Pressure (primary/secondary), MPa | 3 / 6 |
| Core Inlet/Outlet Coolant Temperature (°C) | 250/750 |
| Fuel type/assembly array | Spherical elements with coated particle fuel |
| Number of fuel assemblies in the core | 27,000 |
| Fuel enrichment (%) | 17 |
| Core Discharge Burnup (GWd/ton) | 80 |
| Refuelling Cycle (months) | On-line refueling |
| Reactivity control mechanism | Control rod and small absorber sphere |
| Approach to safety systems | Combined active and passive |
| Design life (years) | 40 |
| Plant footprint ($m^2$) | ~24000 |
| RPV height/diameter (m) | 11.1/4.2(inner) |
| RPV weight (metric ton) | 180 |
| Seismic Design (SSE) | 0.26 (g) |
| Fuel cycle requirements / Approach | LEU, open cycle, spent fuel intermediate storage at plant |
| Distinguishing features | Inherent safety, no need for offsite emergency measures |
| Design status | Site license was already approved in 2017. Detail design development is in progress as part of Design Approval phase. |

*3.2. Working Strategy*

How does the design work? By implementing Work Breakdown Structure (WBS) System. What about location? This related issue is very sensitive and often invites counter communities around the location. Therefore, it was decided to take the R&D area as its land, PUSPIPTEK. This is reasonable, because RDE is a non-commercial nuclear power plant and for experimental or experimental scales. By taking the location of R&D, it is expected that the site licensing process, will be faster. It is proved. In a total of 2.5 years, or 1.5 years on the BAPETEN side, the site permit can be obtained. Valid for five (5) years, after which it must be re-evaluated related to the impact of increasing the population of the surrounding community. The site permit was obtained in 2017.

BATAN started RDE design activities in 2015. The main goal of the RDE Program is to develop the national capability as a nuclear reactor technology provider by mastering the design, construction project management, commissioning and operation of a nuclear power reactor. In addition, the nuclear reactor type chosen in the program should become the master nuclear power plant to be up-scaled and commercialized to secure the national energy security.

Pebble bed reactor (PBR) type of High temperature gas-cooled reactor (HTGR) was chosen as the technology to be applied in the RDE Program.[4] A sound safety feature and flexible applications of the PBR technology are among the reasons of this decision. PBR has a high safety level which is shown by a small radioactive release to the environment on any probable accident. In particular, it has a passive safety feature, the capability of nuclear reactors to maintain its cooling performances only by natural mechanisms with no external support, which is very important feature to survive even in the severest condition as occur in Fukushima accident.

As described above, the Site Licensing was received from the National Nuclear Regulatory Body (BAPETEN) in January 2017. It should be followed by the next step, Design Approval. For this purpose, BATAN should submit pile documents related to detail design and safety analysis report. An unofficial discussion meeting with BAPETEN has been held. The goal is to equalize perceptions related to safety features.

## 4. Co-Generation Application

The RDE is owned by BATAN as an experimental research reactor. Which is basically focus on demonstrating the operational and safety performance of a pebble bed high temperature gas-cooled reactor. Includes the demonstration on its capability to handle the most severe accident scenarios, such as depressurized loss of forced cooling (DLOFC).

As cogeneration, RDE is designed have multi functions. Not only electrical production, but also utilization of its high steam as an output. For RDE itself, does not consider the cogeneration for commercial application. However, for the following phase of design, it is considered to developed for the industrial application.

Based on the discussion, particularly with PT. Pembangunan Perumahan (PT. PP) and PT. Rekadaya Elektrika Consult (Reconsult), a direct utilization of a small 3MWe as electric source for many islands in Indonesia, could be used as a replacing plant of an expensive diesel fuel was foreseen.

Therefore, the name of Micro-PeLUIt is generated. PeLUIt is stand for *Pembangkit Listrik dan Uap-panas Industri*, for Power and Industrial Hot Steam Plant. While RDE, is kept to be a name name of the reactor, which sited at the Puspiptek SERPONG.

## 5. Plant Layout Arrangement

The nuclear island contains reactor building, reactor auxiliary building, as shown in Fig. 1. The steam turbo-generator is housed in the turbine building. The other plant auxiliary systems are shown as well.

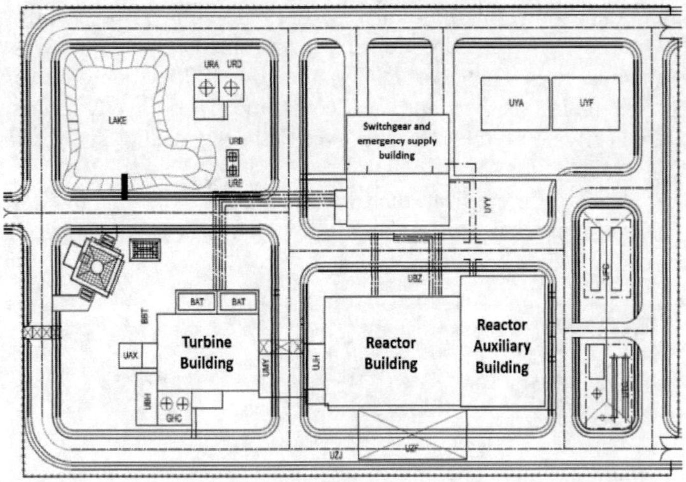


**Figure 1.** Plant Layout of the RDE. While for the Micro-PeLUIt a more compact layout (maintaining main component as in RDE) is under developed.[2]

## 6. Site and Design Licensing Status

What is site permit and design licensing? Base on BAPETEN regulations, there 5 phases that have to be proceeded and pass. Site licensing, design approval, construction permit, commissioning permit and operation permit.

The first permit stating is related with location. Where RDE will be constructed? Chairman BATAN decided to selected PUSPIPTEK, the R&D area. Just 500m from the RSG GAS 30MW research reactor. Please note that different types of reactors and power, so different site permits. And every five years, the site permit must be revised, especially in the safety analysis. One of them is safety for residents around the NPP.

The Site Licensing was already approved by the Nuclear Energy Regulatory Agency (BAPETEN) in 2017 and will be expired on 2021.

Then, before going to the Construction License the RDE, need to pass the second phase, Design Approval phase. Starts from the end of 2018. Detail design and Safety Analysis Report should be is prepared. in progress of completion as part of the Design Approval requirement. In working the detail design, BATAN cooperate with national engineering company PT. Pembangunan Perumahan (PT. PP) and PT. Rekadaya Elektrika Consult (ReConsult). Beside of accelerating the design project, contributing those stakeholders could increase in TKDN (local manufacture contribution). Therefore, design was made by supporting facilities available in Indonesia. Such as pumps, turbines, and others. This is because the price is competitive and the quality is good. And guaranteed the safety of its operation. As a result, the estimated RDE construction price is cheaper. Even less than half when compared with the price bid from the vendor.

Besides that, BATAN cooperates with several universities, International Atomic Energy Agency (IAEA) and the Nuclear Energy Supervisory Agency (BAPETEN) as regulators, as well. This is implemented, because to build a nuclear power plant, the rules are very strict.

## 7. Fuel Safety and Supply Chain

The supply chain of fuel is a parameter that should be considered. Especially, for the construction of commercial nuclear power plants. Therefore, fuel safety guarantees become a record of the acceptable type of nuclear power plant.

Besides that, the safety philosophy in NPP, either RDE, involves the principles of work safety. How the surrounding community and the environment are safe, if unwanted or unexpected things happen, such as the Chernobyl and Fukushima cases. However, RDE is the G-4 NPP, it should be very safe. The design is created to protect people, including workers and local community, and the environment as well.

The heart of the safety is relying on fuel. How safe the fuel design is holding the first priority on safety. And either RDE.

Its fuel design is completely different from the Chernobyl and Fukushima nuclear power plants, which is like a small ball. Consist of more than eleven thousand kernels, that are covered or coated with a layer of silicon carbide (SiC) or carborundum compounds. (Fig.2.)

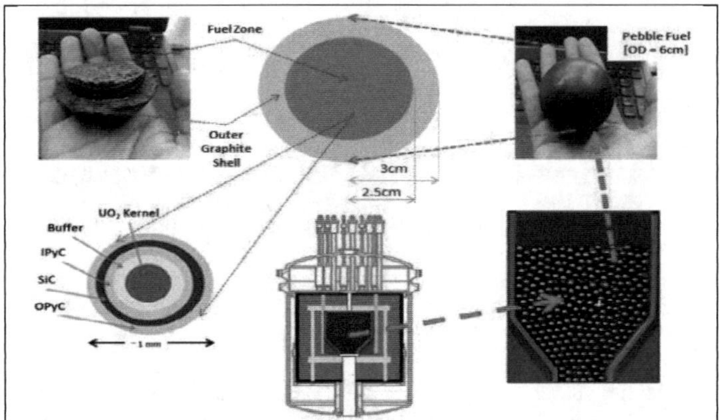


**Figure 2.** Schematic TRISO-based particle fuel, pebble fuel, and the reactor core.[6]

SiC is very rare compound, that's why is made synthetically. It is known to be very strong and high heat resistance, reaches 3500 degrees Celsius.

So, in the event of an accident, RDE fuel (U-235 kernel with SiC coating, 1.0 mm diameter) remains confined. It may not induce any radioisotopes and radiation come out and poisoning the environment. Not like Fukushima case, which is U-235 pellet, inserting into zircaloy rod. The melting point of zirconium only 1855 degrees Celsius. Severely lower than the melting point of silicon carbide compounds which is 3500 degrees Celsius.

Hence, RDE fuel is cooled by a passive cooling system.[5] It means that if the reactor stop operation suddenly, the rest of heat will cool down by itself. Helium gas that is used for coolant, will only melt when cooled to extreme temperatures, minus 268.9 degrees Celsius. Meanwhile, to compact it, the temperature needed is even more extreme: minus 272.2 degrees Celsius. Very safe. That is why RDE design experts use helium as a reactor coolant.

RDE, also HTGR, has been included in the IAEA ARIS booklet released on 2020, as one of three types of Small Medium Reactors that already have their fuel license. So, RDE development will not encounter any constraints related to fuel supply. And please note that in order to obtain a fuel permit or certificate, you must go through a series of radiation experiments accompanied by testing to understand whether or not there is a radioactive release from the fuel. If it happens, how big and what kind of actinide it is, should be classified. This is why it is called that fuel is the heart of the NPP. If the heart is unhealthy, easily leaky, then the health of the NPP will also be very weak. Then, the safety side of its NPP operations is very worrying. This is the regulatory philosophy regarding the operation of the NPP. In conclusion, the supply chain of fuel for RDE is safe.

## 8. Waste Management and Disposal Plan

Waste disposal should be defined from the beginning. Because this issue is very sensitive, and will affect public support. For RDE, the spent fuel, or burned fuel is designed to be collected into the spent fuel cask, in the fuel cycle system. That will be placed in the in the spent fuel storage room, that located in the reactor building. Again, safety to the environment is playing a key role, especially from the radiation effect. Therefore, the tight monitor related to radiation and temperature, is applied in the spent fuel storage room. Avoiding criticality is the basic thinking on this safety design.

Transport cask is design for handling the spent fuel. And, since RDE is belong to BATAN, so, the final storage will be in BATAN facility. No, re-processing is considered.

The definition of waste management in the RDE, include particular active liquid waste collection, low level and inactive liquid waste. Also, the monitoring tanks, that is used for collecting liquid waste below the statutory limiting values for disposal, and water extraction system for helium supporting systems as well.

Hence, in the accident condition, collecting and storage of the condensate from post-accident water separator is available. Disposal of the active liquid waste is planned to be at the BATAN's nuclear waste processing center, near the RDE site.

## 9. Conclusion

RDE's design experience has brought Indonesia to the nuclear power plant gate. Where the site permit process has been obtained, and started into the second phase, design approval. This activity has opened the eyes of real how to cooperate with local stakeholders related to the completion of NPP design, playing a very important role. How the Cooperation has been able to reduce the price of NPP development. How to communicate with BAPETEN in the process of obtaining a site permit and also heading to design approval. Also, how BATAN's own internal and external political influences, as well as foreign politics, play a strong role in the NPP development scene in Indonesia. Step regulation two, approval design, unfinished. It's still got to go on.

## Acknowledgement

Thank you very much to Prof. Dr. Djarot Sulistio Wisnubroto, head of BATAN for the period of 2012-2018, for his initiative to create an Experimental Power Reactor (RDE) construction project. Also, for design team members who gallantly, tread together to start RDE design activities. Not to forget, it is noted that the financing of activities comes from DIPA BATAN and also Flagship from the ministry of higher education. Finally, to all the administrative colleagues who helped a lot in the neatness of RDE administration.

## References

[1] GR Sunaryo, Febrianto, Sumijanto, RPH Ismuntoyo, "Application of high temperature reactor (HTR) in securing the water supplies", Seminar on HTR technology and application II, Jakarta, 19-20, 1995.
[2] IAEA Advance Reactor Information System 2020 edition, p 191-194.
[3] PM Udiyani, S Kuntjoro, GR Sunaryo, H Susiati, "Atmospheric dispersion Analysis for Expected Radiation dose due to Normal Operation of RSG-GAS and RDE Reactors", Atom Indonesia, Vol 44. No 3, p 115-121.
[4] T Setiadipura, "Equilibrium Core Design of Reaktor Daya Eksperimental", Journal of Physics: Conference Series, Vol 1198, 2, p 022076
[5] T Setiadipura, S Bakhri, GR Sunaryo, DS Wisnubroto, "Cooling passive safety features of Reaktor Daya Eksperimental", AIP Conference Proceedings 1984 (1), 020034, 2018.
[6] T Taryo, R Ridwan, GR Sunaryo, M Rachmawati, "The Strategy to Support HTGR fuels for The 10 MW Indonesia's Experimental Power Reactor (RDE)", Urania Jurnal Ilmiah Daur Bahan Bakar Nuklir 24 (1), 2018, DOI: http://dx.doi.org/10.17146/urania.2018.24.1.3729

# Uranium Exploration, Deposit and Resources: The Key of Nuclear Power Plant Development Program in Indonesia

**H Syaeful, I G Sukadana, Y S B Susilo, F D Indrastomo, A G Muhammad, and Ngadenin**

Centre for Nuclear Minerals Technology, National Nuclear Energy Agency, Jl. Lebak Bulus Raya No. 9, Pasar Jumat, Jakarta Selatan, Indonesia

phone: +62-816607921, email: syaeful@batan.go.id

**Abstract.** Uranium deposit in Indonesia was found in almost all Indonesian Archipelago, mainly in Kalimantan, Sulawesi, Sumatera, Papua, Bangka Belitung and Riau islands. Uranium exploration activities started in the 1960s to recent, conducted in many exploration stages. The exploration in prospects area are completed with drilling activities to delineate the mineralization zone and continued to resources estimation. In Kalan Area, the research had been completed with underground/tunneling mining. The uranium resources are classified into discovered or undiscovered based on exploration stages, and conventional or unconventional based on sources of primary/secondary/by-product mineral production. The resources are calculated from Kalan Area and its surroundings (Kalimantan) with addition of Mamuju Area (West Sulawesi) and Sibolga Area (North Sumatera). Uranium identified resource in Indonesia is 13,503 tU while the undiscovered is 62,330 tU. Meanwhile, categorized by uranium source, the conventional and unconventional resources are 48,388 tU and 27,445 tU respectively. The uranium resources categories should be increased and completed with feasibility study to increase the resources to reserve classification. The exploration, deposit, and resources are the key to ensure the readiness of developing nuclear power plants in Indonesia, where one of them is Experimental Power Reactor (EPR) or Reaktor Daya Eksperimental (RDE) with domestic uranium fuel.
Keywords: uranium, deposit, exploration, geology, resources, RDE

## 1. Uranium Exploration and Mine Development

National Nuclear Energy Agency (BATAN) has launched the program to develop Experimental Power Reactor (EPR) or generally known as Reaktor Daya Eksperimental (RDE) in year 2015. This program has increased the enthusiasm for various supporting sectors to contribute, one of which is the uranium resources as baseline for nuclear fuel support in future development.

The uranium resources itself, was first investigated by the Directorate Survey of Geology, now Center for Nuclear Minerals Technology (PTBGN), was formed in 1969 in order to explore the uranium deposits in Indonesia. The uranium exploration stages, applied the scheme of IAEA, from Preliminary Prospection, General Prospection, Detail Prospection, and Systematic Prospection. Nowadays with the terminology of United Nations Frameworks Classification (UNFC), the stages is more general and also nationally in line with Indonesian National Standard (SNI) [1]–[3] (Table 1).

The uranium exploration in Indonesia is started in 1960s. Important stage in exploration activity is in 1969 when uranium exploration cooperation signed by Indonesia (National Nuclear Energy Agency-BATAN) and France (Commissariat a l'energie atomique-CEA). The exploration cooperation started with general exploration in Schwaner Mountain and surrounding region in West to East Kalimantan which covers area of 266,000 km$^2$. The exploration cooperation is successfully found some area contained uranium deposit, named Kalan and Mahakam Hulu. In 1974 exploration cooperation focused in Kalan and Melawi-Mahakam. In 1977 cooperation is terminated and the exploration activity is done solely by BATAN.

**Table 1.** Exploration stages of BATAN and comparison to others standard

| | BATAN | IAEA (1988) | SNI (2002) | UNFC (2009) |
|---|---|---|---|---|
| EXPLORATION STAGES | Reconnaissance Survey<br>Preliminary Prospection (scale 1:250.000) | Planning and Area Selection | Reconnaissance Survey | Reconnaissance Survey |
| | General Prospection (scale 1:100.000) | Reconnaissance Phase (scale 1:250.000-1.100.000) | Prospection | Prospection |
| | Detail Prospection (scale 1:5000-1:10000) | Follow-Up Phase (Scale 1:50.000-1:25.000) | General Exploration | General Exploration |
| | Systematic Prospection (1:1000-1:2000) | Detailed Phase (1:5.000-1:500) | Detail Exploration | Detail Exploration |

After the period of collaboration between BATAN and France's CEA in 1977, the exploration program focused on Kalan Area, West Kalimantan which had the most significant uranium mineralization indication by that time. Research of exploration, mining and processing is on its peak in 1981 when Eko-Remaja tunnel started. The tunnel cut the ore body and the Eko Hill as the same time. In 1986 main tunnel is reached other slope-front of Eko Hill for the length of 618 m. The tunnel continues for research of mining and processing. Also started in 1981, processing pilot plant is started in Lemajung for processing ore from Eko-Remaja. Research processing is running for 10 years and it's ended in 1996 with 740 kg of yellow cake produced.

After the ceased of the Eko-Remaja, exploration rate is decreased but still focused in Kalan and its surrounding area, includes Mentawa (Central Kalimantan) consisted of systematic geological and radiometric mapping, and radon survey. In early 2000's, additional exploration drilling was started in Kalan at Jumbang, Mentawa, and Semut sectors [4]. In 2009, systematic prospection in the Kawat area, Mahakam, was carried out. General prospection in Bangka Belitung Province was also undertaken.

Uranium and thorium exploration re-focused to Mamuju, West Sulawesi after first major discovery in 2012 from program of regional environmental radiation dose-rate mapping. In 2013 preliminary survey is conducted in Mamuju region and successfully delineated several interesting sectors for further exploration target [5]. Detailed ground radiometric mapping was conducted in the Takandeang, Taan, Ahu, Pangasaan, and Hulu Mamuju sectors. Geophysical resistivity and induced polarisation surveys conducted in the Botteng and Takandeang sectors were followed by reconnaissance drilling in 2015 for a total depth of 1,600 m. Drilling targets were anomalous uranium occurring as stratabound and supergene enrichment in volcanic deposits. In the same year of 2015 exploration in the Ella Ilir area, West Kalimantan included geological and radiometric mapping, and reconnaissance drilling with 400 m of total depth is conducted. The drilling in this area focused on uranium veins in metapelite schistose and metatuff.

Regional geophysical survey includes ground geomagnetic, gravity, resistivity measurements, and seismic had started in the Mamuju area. In 2019, reconnaissance drilling for total length of 425 m is conducted in Pasa'bu and Takandeang sector.

Year of 2019 is the last year of 2015 - 2019 strategic plans, and the 3$^{rd}$ year of new Indonesian government policy in research program of National Research Priority (PRN) 2017-2045. The PRN is expecting actual and deliverable research target. In the sense of exploration project, it is consistently adding the scoping study for every project. More economic deposit has to be prioritizing to allow near future development. The basin uranium exploration is firstly implemented and some radon anomaly is found in Melawi Basin, West Kalimantan as model for further basin approach development.

## 2. Uranium Deposit and Resources

Uranium occurrences by definition are a naturally occurring or anomalous concentration of uranium. Uranium deposit is a mass of naturally occurring mineral from which uranium could be exploited at present or in the future, and resources is total amount of uranium in the deposit [6], [7]. In resources reporting, generally it is divided into Identified Resources and Undiscovered Resources (Table 2).

Identified resources composed by Reasonably Assured Resources (RAR) and Inferred Resources (IR), it is referring to uranium deposits delineated by sufficient direct measurement to conduct pre-feasibility studies, and in some cases feasibility studies. In term of RAR, high confidence in estimates of grade and tonnage are generally compatible with standards for making the decision to proceed with of the project. Inferred Resources (IR) are not defined with a high a degree of confidence and generally require further direct measurement prior to making a decision to develop the project [8].

Undiscovered resources (prognosticated and speculative) refer to resources that are expected to occur based on geological knowledge of previously discovered deposits and regional geological mapping. Prognosticated resources (PR) refer to those expected to occur in known uranium provinces, generally supported by some direct evidence. Speculative resources (RS) refer to those expected to occur in geological provinces that may host uranium deposits. Both prognosticated and speculative resources require significant amounts of exploration before their existence can be confirmed and grades and tonnages can be more accurately determined. All PR and SR are reported as in situ resources [8], [4]. Intended for the ease of understanding of the resource category, comparison to other resources reporting is described in Table 2. The comparison is made to Australian Joint Ore Reserve Committee (JORC) code, United States Department of Energy, and United Nations Framework Classification.

**Table 2.** Approximate correlation of term used in resources classification system [9]

| | **Identified Resources (Known Conventional Resources)** | | | **Undiscovered Resources (Undiscovered Conventional Resources)** | |
|---|---|---|---|---|---|
| OCD-NEA/IAEA 2005 | Reasonably Assured Resources (RAR) | | Inferred (EAR-I) | Prognosticated (EAR-II) | Speculative (speculative) |
| Australia | Demonstrated<br>Measured | Demonstrated<br>Indicated | Inferred | Undiscovered | |
| United States (DOE) | Reasonably assured | | Estimated additional | | Speculative |
| UNFC | G1 | | G1+G2 | G3 | G4 |

The description of uranium resources in Indonesia will be describe based on characteristic of deposit and potential production, which is conventional and unconventional. Conventional resources are defined as "resources from which uranium is recoverable as a primary product, a co-product or an important by-product, while unconventional resources are resources from which uranium is only recoverable as a minor by-product" [10].

### *2.1. Conventional Resources*

Uranium as a conventional resource found as metamorphic, volcanic, and sandstone deposit in Indonesia (Table 3 and Fig.1). In West Kalimantan, Kalan is the most important uranium mineralization area. Geographically it is located in up-stream part of Kalan River. Beside Kalan also there is Iban, Nanga Kepayang, and Ella Hilir. Kalan is situated in the northern margin of the Schwaner Mountains, Kalan geologically consists of Pinoh Metamorphic Group (PMG) rocks that were intruded by later granitic rocks of Sepauk Tonalite and Sukadana Granite in some parts. The Protolith of the Pinoh Metamorphic was the volcanogenic sediments that suggested to be formed during subduction at the Paleo-Pacific margin after collision of South West Borneo to Sundaland in Early Cretaceous (130 Ma) [11].

The uranium hosting Paleozoic Kalan Basin is located some 300 km ESE of Pontianak, the capital city of west Kalimantan. The basin fill consists largely of fine-grained, variably, epi to mesozonally metamorphosed volcano-sedimentary strata, which are separated into two series, an upper series, about 3,000–4,000 m thick, comprises metamorphosed sedimentary, volcano-sedimentary, and volcanic rocks of relatively monotonous nature and fine grain size, and the Lower Series is dominated by metapelite and metasiltstone of amphibolite grade facies with biotite, andalusite, cordierite, and sillimanite [9], [12]. According to IAEA geological classification of uranium deposit, the Kalan is included in metamorphic type of deposit [7], [13].

General stratigraphy, Kalan is divided into 5 units, which are lower series of volcano sedimentary, Rabau quartzite, upper Kalan volcano sedimentary, Amir Engkala felsic volcanic, and Bukitbiru meta-argillite [14], [15]. The most significant resources are located in Kalan Hulu volcanic sediment which is sector of Eko-Remaja, Lembah Hitam, and Lemajung.

Eko-Remaja and Lembah Hitam located close to each other, separated only by Kalan River. Intensive exploration activity in Kalan is focussed in both of these sectors; include more than 33,000 m of coring and non-coring drilling and also supported by exploration tunnel of 618 m length in Eko-Remaja.

Host rock of mineralization is metasiltstone and metapelite schistose, as interlayer in sterile rock metapelite Jeronang. Thickness of host rock is 80–100 m, with mineralization is controlled by structural opening, tectonic breccia, and some is in schistose layer [14]. Another study on mineralization control in the Eko-Remaja tunnel, it is first brittle deformation resulting open-mode fractures and schistosity planes that later filled by U-rich solution forming U veins, veinlets and breccia mineralization. The ductile deformation observed from N 70° E fold plunging 30° NE that generate schistosity plane dipping 70-80° relatively to the north [16], [17]. Resources of Eko Remaja is 3.220 in Reasonably Assured category [14], [18]. Lembah Hitam has almost the same host rock and mineralization style with Eko-Remaja, and has total resources of 1,994 tons U in Reasonably Assured category. Another same type of host rock and mineralization style is Lemajung sector, located 3 km NE from Eko-Remaja sector. More than 12.000 m exploration drilling has been done in this sector. Uranium resources in Lemajung is 769 ton U in Reasonably Assured category [19], [20].

Others important sector in Kalan is Rabau. Stratigraphically it is composed of Quarzite Rabau, with uranium mineralization in favourable rock of quartzite micro biotite and also controlled by tectonic plane. Total of 33 drillholes with total run of more than 4,700 m has been done in the area. Total resources in Rabau is 268 ton U with reasonably assured category [15], [21]. Another sector with identified uranium resources in Kalan area is Kalan Ketungau, Rirang, Amir Engkala, Tanah Merah, Jeronang Hulu, Semut, and Sarana [14], [22], [23]. Some high grades uranium and rare earth element (REE) in Rirang boulder is geologically very interesting; it is hosted in monazite boulder. The chemical analysis of the boulder indicates high rare earth element which is up to 59%, high phosphate contents, low alumina and silica content in monazite type [24]–[26].

In Ella Ilir Area, Batubulan sector, West Kalimantan, uranium mineralisation is trending NW-SE with 1-30 cm thickness with a radiometric anomaly ranging from 250-15.000 cps, hosted in metapelite schistose and metatuff rocks. The mineralization present as boudinage vein with uraninite as the radioactive mineral, associated with quartz tourmaline, feldspar, pyrite, iron oxide and hematite. Resource estimation results of 458 tU as inferred category of resources [27].

In East Kalimantan, the volcanic rock of Nyaan and Kawat riolite in up-stream of Mahakam River are the host for the uranium deposit. Uranium is stratabound dominated or majorly controlled by lava flow, and some also effected by later tectonic and mobilization to open tectonic fracture. Uranium minerals are pitchblende and autunite. Uranium resources are 9,247 ton U in Kawat sector, and 5,890 ton U in Paluq and Nyaan sectors [28], [29].

In Central Kalimantan, Darab area also hosted uranium on its metamorphic and granitic rocks. The mineralization is closed to contact as tectonic breccia filling and veins. Radioactive minerals in the mineralized rocks are uraninite, monazite, and probably thoriano-uraninite. Uranium resources are 528 ton U in inferred category [30]. Mentawa area hosted uranium in its quartzite rocks. Uranium mineralization associated with tourmaline, quartz and sulfide, lenses in form, and has the same direction with schistosity plane. Resources is 8,194 ton U in prognosticated category [9], [31].

**Table 3.** Conventional uranium resources in Indonesia

| No | Sector | Identified Resources | | Undiscovered Resources | |
|---|---|---|---|---|---|
| | | RAR | Inferred | Prognosticated | Speculative |
| **West Kalimantan** | | | | | |
| 1 | Eko-Remaja | 3,220 | - | - | - |
| 2 | Rabau | 249 | - | - | - |
| 3 | PC-15 (Kalan Ketungau) | 42 | - | - | - |
| 4 | Rirang | 30 | - | - | - |
| 5 | Lembah Hitam | 1,994 | - | - | - |
| 6 | Lemajung | 769 | - | - | - |
| 7 | Amir Engkala | 319 | 462 | - | - |
| 8 | Tanah Merah | 210 | - | 525 | - |
| 9 | Jeronang Hulu | - | 775 | - | - |
| 10 | Semut | 197 | - | - | - |
| 11 | Jumbang | - | - | 3,336 | - |
| 12 | Prembang Kanan | - | - | 206 | - |
| 13 | Dendang Arai | - | - | 118 | - |
| 14 | Bubu | - | - | 93 | - |
| 15 | Ririt | - | - | 8 | - |
| 16 | Sarana | - | 775 | - | - |
| 17 | Batu Bulan (Ella Ilir) | - | 458 | - | - |
| **East Kalimantan** | | | | | |
| 18 | Kawat | - | - | 9,247 | - |
| 19 | Paluq dan Nyaan | - | - | 5,890 | - |
| **Central Kalimantan** | | | | | |
| 20 | Mentawa | - | - | 8,194 | - |
| 21 | Darab | - | 528 | - | - |
| **West Sulawesi** | | | | | |
| 22 | Salumati, Takandeang | - | 165 | 2,562 | - |
| 23 | Rantedunia. Takandeang | - | 56 | - | - |
| 24 | Taan | - | 431 | - | - |
| 25 | Hulu Mamuju | - | - | - | 1,096 |
| 26 | Ampalas | - | - | - | 6,017 |
| **North Sumatera** | | | | | |
| 27 | Aloban, Sibolga | - | 415 | - | - |
| | **TOTAL** | **7,031** | **4,065** | **30,179** | **7,113** |

In Mamuju, West Sulawesi, first high dose rate radiation reported in 2007 when regional dose rate mapping took place. In 2012 data confirmation is conducted. Geologically, the area with the high radiation dose rate can be localized in geological Formation of Adang Volcanic. This formation is composed of alkaline volcanic rocks with basic to intermediates composition, and result of several volcanic events. Ever since 2013, the area has been intensively explored to identify uranium, thorium and other potential co and by-product elements. In 2015, first drilling activities were carried out in the Botteng, Takandeang, and Taan Sectors. A total of 21 boreholes were drilled for a total of 1.600 m. In 2019, the drilling continued in Ahu and Takandeang Sectors with total 6 boreholes and 750 m total depth. Resources estimated in Salumati are 165 tU in inferred category and 2,562 tU in prognosticated category. In Rantedunia Sector, uranium is estimated as 56 tU, while in Taan Sector, resources is estimated as 431 tU in inferred category. [5], [32]–[34]. Radioactive mineral identified in the area until now is thorite [35], davidite, thorianite, gummite, and autunite [36]. Higher concentration of thorium and rare earth are also typical on alkaline rocks, and could allow benefit development of this area. Hulu Mamuju Sector probably the most interesting target where the highest grade of uranium, thorium, and rare earth element found in the region. Nevertheless, despite the accessibility and steep morphology feature, only limited radiometric and geological mapping, and radon survey could be conducted. The uranium resources in Hulu Mamuju and Ampalas Sectors are estimated 1,096 tU and 6,017 tU respectively as undiscovered speculative resources.

In North Sumatera, 22 drillholes have been conducted to characterize uranium mineralization in the Aloban sector. Uranium deposit located in the small localized intra-basin sediment which is restricted by a normal fault from surrounding granitic rocks. Uranium dominantly is absorbed by organic material in fine grains sediment, and formed the black shale type of deposit, while also in the interbedded sandstone and conglomerate, some anomaly also present. Uranium mineral is uraninite, carnotite, and coffinite. Resources estimated as 415 tU in Inferred category [37], [38].

### *2.2. Unconventional Resources*

Uranium as unconventional resources dominated in monazite as by-product of tin and zircon mining (Table 4 and Fig. 1). In Semelangan, West Kalimantan, area of potential deposit is distributed in drainage area of Pawan, Tulak, and Laur River of more than 25,000 Ha area. S-type Sukadana granite is identified as source rock of this deposit. Resource in the area estimated 624 tU in Prognosticated category [13], [39]. In Central Kalimantan, Katingan has also the same condition as in Ketapang. The monazite is present as by-product of zircon mining as the main product of mine. Resources are estimated 485 tU in prognosticated category.

Bangka and Belitung are dominated the resources of uranium of unconventional deposit. Several limited surface explorations are done in the islands, which is geological and radiometric mapping, and heavy mineral geochemistry. Relatively simple geological setting, simple mining method, and high economic value of placer deposit brought so many interests of tin mining in the island. Radioactive mineral as by-product of tin mining is dominated by monazite and scarce of xenotime. Speculative resources in Bangka-Belitung are estimated 21,792 tU. Prognosticated resources is in Bangka Selatan 293 tU, in Bangka Tengah and Pangkalpinang (PKP) 263 tU, in Tumbang Rusa 415 tU, and in Cerucuk Belitung is 66 tU [40], [41]. Bangka Island is estimated as 2,407 tU.

Uranium in Singkep, is associated in the same tin-belt with Bangka-Belitung and other Riau islands. Monazite present also as by-product of tin mining. Resources are estimated 1,100 tU in the prognosticated category. Distribution of uranium (and thorium) resources, of both discovered and discovered resources category, can be seen in Figure 1.

**Table 4.** Unconventional Uranium Resources

| No | Sektor | Identified Resources | | Undiscovered Resources | |
|---|---|---|---|---|---|
| | | **RAR** | **Inferred** | **Prognosticated** | **Speculative** |
| **West Kalimantan** | | | | | |
| 1 | Semelangan | - | - | 624 | - |
| **Central Kalimantan** | | | | | |
| 2 | Katingan | - | - | 485 | - |
| **Tin Belt** | | | | | |
| 3 | Bangka-Belitung | - | - | - | 21,792 |
| 4 | Bangka Selatan | - | - | 293 | - |
| 5 | Bangka Tengah & PKP | - | - | 263 | - |
| 6 | Tumbang Rusa | - | - | 415 | - |
| 7 | Cerucuk, Belitung | - | - | 66 | - |
| 8 | Bangka | 2,407 | - | - | - |
| 9 | Singkep | - | - | 1,100 | - |
| **TOTAL** | | **2,407** | **-** | **3,246** | **21,792** |

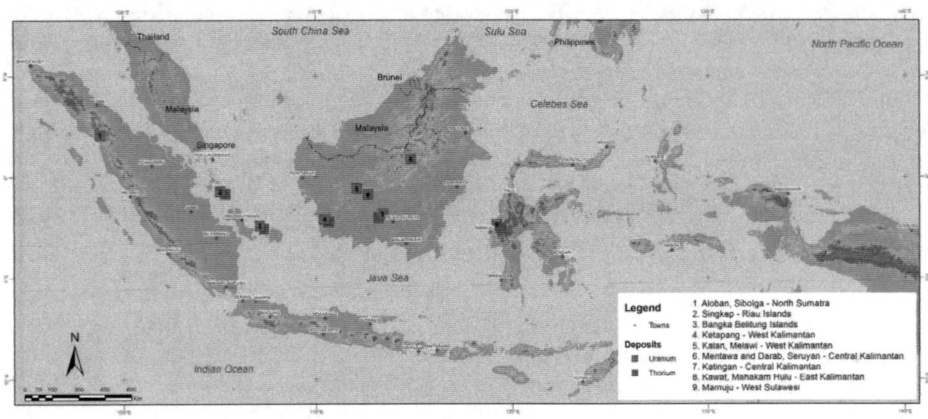


**Figure 1.** Distribution of uranium and thorium deposits in Indonesia.

## 3. Conclusion

Uranium exploration had been conducted for more than 50 years to support nuclear power plant program in Indonesia. There are several prospect areas for uranium deposit and been intensively explored to support the nuclear fuel. Uranium resources are grouped into identified and undiscovered resources from their exploration status. The resources in these categories are 13,503 tU and 62,330 tU respectively. Based on characteristic of deposit and potential production, the resources are grouped into conventional and unconventional resources. The resources in these categories are 48,388 tU and 27,445 tU respectively. Total uranium resources are 75,833 tU in all categories. Exploration programs still continuous in some prospect Area in Indonesia. The result of uranium resources should be developed to increase the classification of resources and conducting the feasibility study to increase the resources to reserve classification. The exploration, deposit, and resources are the key to ensure the readiness of developing nuclear power plants with uranium fuel in Indonesia.

## References

[1] B. S. Nasional, *Klasifikasi Sumberdaya Mineral dan Cadangan, Amandemen 1-SNI 13-4726-1998*. Jakarta, 1998.

[2] United Nation, *Guidelines for Application of the United Nations Framework Classification for Fossil Energy and Mineral Reserves and Resources 2009 for Uranium and Thorium Resources*, no. ECE/ENERGY/2015/7. 2015.

[3] S. K. Haldar, *Mineral exploration : principles and applications*. 2013.

[4] OECD Nuclear Energy Agency and International Atomic Energy Agency (IAEA), *Uranium 2014: Resources, Production and Demand*. 2014.

[5] H. Syaeful, I. G. Sukadana, and A. Sumaryanto, "Radiometric Mapping for Naturally Occurring Radioactive Materials (NORM) Assessment in Mamuju, West Sulawesi," *Atom Indones.*, vol. 40, no. 1, pp. 33–39, 2014, doi: 10.17146/aij.2014.263.

[6] International Atomic Energy Agency (IAEA), *World Distribution of Uranium Deposits (UDEPO) with Uranium Deposit Classification*. 2009.

[7] International Atomic Energy Agency (IAEA), *Geological Classification of Uranium Deposits and Description of Selected Examples, IAEA-TECDOC-1842*. 2018.

[8] U. Nations, *Guidelines for Application of the United Nations Framework Classification for Fossil Energy and Mineral Reserves and Resources 2009 for Uranium and Thorium Resources*, no. ECE/ENERGY/2015/7. 2015.

[9] F. J. Dahlkamp, *Uranium Deposits of the World: Asia*. 2009.

[10] P. Bruneton and M. Cuney, "Geology of uranium deposits," in *Uranium for Nuclear Power: Resources, Mining and Transformation to Fuel*, no. 1956, Elsevier Ltd, 2016, pp. 11–52.

[11] J. Hennig, H. T. Breitfeld, R. Hall, and A. M. S. Nugraha, "The Mesozoic tectono-magmatic evolution at the Paleo-Pacific subduction zone in West Borneo," *Gondwana Res.*, vol. 48, pp. 292–310, 2017, doi: 10.1016/j.gr.2017.05.001.

[12] Ngadenin, A. Sumaryanto, H. Syaeful, and I. G. Sukadana, "Geologi dan Mineralisasi Uranium di Daerah Kalan, Kabupaten Melawi, Kalimantan Barat," in *Seminar Nasional Kebumian XII, Fakultas Teknologi Mineral, Universitas Pembangunan Nasional "Veteran" Yogyakarta*, 2017, pp. 108–114.

[13] International Atomic Energy Agency (IAEA), *Descriptive Uranium Deposit and Mineral System Models*. 2020.

[14] S. Tjokrokardono, B. Sutopo, L. Subiantoro, and K. Setiawan, "Geologi dan Mineralisasi Uranium Kalan, Kalimantan Barat: Model Termostratografi," in *Kumpulan Laporan Hasil Penelitian Tahun 2005*, 2005, pp. 27–52.

[15] H. Syaeful and Suharji, "Geostatistics Application on Uranium Resources Classification: Case Study of Rabau Hulu Sector, Kalan, West Kalimantan," *Eksplorium*, vol. 39, no. 2, pp. 131–140, 2018, doi: 10.17146/eksplorium.2018.39.2.4960.

[16] H. S. Karyono, "Analisis Kontrol Tektonik pada Vein Mineralisasi di Bukit Eko, Kalan, Kalimantan Barat," in *Prosiding Pertemuan Ilmiah Tahunan ke-20 IAGI*, 1991, pp. 115–128.

[17] A. G. Muhammad, R. C. Saputra, and H. Syaeful, "Fracture Analysis of Uranium-Bearing Rock in Eko-Remaja Exploration Tunnel at Depth 50-200 Meters, Kalan, West Kalimantan," *J. Phys. Conf. Ser.*, vol. 1363, no. 1, 2019, doi: 10.1088/1742-6596/1363/1/012013.

[18] J. Baratha, D. S. Muljono, A. Sumaryanto, and H. Supalal, "The Actual Status of Uranium Ore Resources at Eko Remaja Sector: The Need of Verification of Resources Computation and Geometrical Form of Mineralization Zone by Mining Test," in *Meeting on Uranium Exploration, Mining, and Extraction*, 1995, pp. 47–60.

[19] Ngadenin and P. Sularto, "Evaluasi Model Struktur Geologi dan Pola Mineralisasi Uranium Sektor Lemajung Barat, Cekungan Kalan, Kalimantan Barat," in *Prosiding Presentasi Ilmiah Daur Bahan Bakar Nuklir V*, 2000, pp. 41–53.

[20] H. Syaeful, Suharji, and A. Sumaryanto, "Pemodelan Geologi dan Estimasi Sumber Daya Uranium di Sektor Lemajung, Kalan, Kalimantan Barat," in *Prosiding Seminar Nasional Teknologi Energi Nuklir Tahun 2014*, 2014, pp. 329–342.

[21] B. Soetopo, R. Witjahyati, and Y. Wusana, "Sintesa Geologi dan Pemineralan Uranium Sektor Rabau Hulu, Kalan, Kalimantan Barat," in *Seminar Geologi Nuklir dan Sumberdaya Tambang Tahun 2004*, 2004, pp. 84–99.

[22] Suharji, "Re-evaluasi Sumber Daya Uranium di Sektor Semut, Kalan, Kalimantan Barat," in *Prosiding Seminar Nasional Geologi Nuklir dan Sumber Daya Tambang Tahun 2014*, 2014, pp. 35–50.

[23] Sartapa and I. G. Sukadana, "Geologi dan Mineralisasi Uranium di Sektor Sarana Kalan, Kalimantan Barat berdasarkan Data Pemboran," *Eksplorium*, vol. 32, no. 2, pp. 91–102, 2011, doi: http://dx.doi.org/10.17146/eksplorium.2011.32.2.2816.

[24] H. Syaeful, K. S. W, I. G. Sukadana, and A. G. M, "Rare Earth Element Exploration in Indonesia," in *Proceedings of Sundaland Resources 2014 MGEI Annual Convention*, 2014, no. November, pp. 205–217.

[25] Ngadenin, Suyadi, M. Gunawan, and Safrodin, "Peningkatan Kualitas Estimasi Cadangan Uranium dan Unsur Tanah Jarang di SubSektor Rirang Tengah, Kalimantan Barat," in *Prosiding Presentasi Ilmiah Daur Bahan Bakar Nuklir VI*, 2001, pp. 61–74.

[26] Suharji and M. Widodo, "Studi Cebakan Bijih Uranium dari Paritan Dalam di Sektor Rirang, Kalan, Kalimantan Barat," in *Prosiding Presentasi Ilmiah Daur Bahan Bakar Nuklir VI*, 2001, pp. 43–54.

[27] OECD Nuclear Energy Agency and I. A. E. Agency, *Uranium 2018: Resources, Production and Demand*. 2018.

[28] Ngadenin, I. G. Sukadana, A. G. Muhammad, and Suripto, "Eksplorium," *Eksplorium*, vol. 32, no. 2, pp. 65–76, 2011.

[29] I. G. Sukadana, "Eksplorium," *Eksplorium*, vol. 33, no. 2, pp. 129–145, 2012.

[30] R. Witjahjati, S. Tjokrokardono, and M. Widodo, "Metamorphic Rock of Darab Related to Uranium Mineralization," *Atom Indones.*, vol. 17, no. 1, pp. 13–27, 1991.

[31] Widiyanta, Tugijo, Boman, S. Darmono, R. Iswanto, and A. Sutriyono, "Inventarisasi Sektor Potensial Uranium Mentawa Kalimantan Tengah, Tahapan Prospeksi Sistematik," in *Prosiding Presentasi Ilmiah Daur Bahan Bakar Nuklir V*, 2000, pp. 17–28.

[32] I. G. Sukadana, A. Harijoko, and L. D. Setijadji, "Tataan Tektonika Batuan Gunungapi di Komplek Adang, Kabupaten Mamuju, Provinsi Sulawesi Barat," *Eksplorium*, vol. 36, no. 1, pp. 31–44, 2015, doi: 10.17146/eksplorium.2015.36.1.2771.

[33] F. D. Indrastomo, I. G. Sukadana, A. Saepuloh, A. H. Harsolumakso, and D. Kamajati, "Interpretasi Volkanostratigrafi Daerah Mamuju Berdasarkan Analisis Citra Landsat-8," *Eksplorium*, vol. 36, no. 2, pp. 71–88, 2015, doi: 10.17146/eksplorium.2015.36.2.2772.

[34] I. G. Sukadana, H. Syaeful, Suharji, D. Haryanto, and Widodo, "Radioactive Elements Resources and Rare Earth Potency in Taan Sector, Mamuju, West Sulawesi," in *MGEI Southwest Pacific Resources 2018*, 2018, pp. 103–108.

[35] M. I. N. Said, M. Anggraini, M. Z. Mubarok, and K. S. Widana, "Studi Ekstraksi Bijih Thorit dengan Metode Digesti Asam dan Pemisahan Thorium dari Logam Tanah Jarang dengan Metode Oksidasi-Presipitasi Selektif," *Eksplorium*, vol. 38, no. 2, p. 109, 2018, doi: 10.17146/eksplorium.2017.38.2.3930.

[36] I. G. Sukadana, H. Syaeful, F. D. Indrastomo, K. S. Widana, and E. Rakhma, "Identification of Mineralization Type and Specific Radioactive Minerals in Mamuju, West Sulawesi," *J. East China Univ. Technol.*, vol. 39, pp. 36–45, 2016.

[37] R. Witjahjati and H. Supalal, "Perhitungan Sumber Daya Uranium di Daerah Rabau Hulu Kalimantan Barat," in *Internal Report of PPBGN BATAN*, Jakarta, 1991.

[38] R. C. Ciputra, A. G. Muhammad, T. B. Adimedha, H. Syaeful, and I. G. Sukadana, "Estimasi Sumber Daya Uranium Tipe Batupasir di Sektor Aloban, Sibolga, Tapanuli Tengah," *Eksplorium*, vol. 40, no. 1, pp. 1–10, 2019, doi: 10.17146/eksplorium.2019.40.1.5360.

[39] L. Subiantoro, B. Soetopo, and D. Haryanto, "Kajian awal prospek bahan galian monasit mengandung uranium dan elemen asosiasinya di Semelangan, Ketapang, Kalimantan Barat," *Eksplorium*, vol. XXXII, no. 155, pp. 1–16, 2011.

[40] S. Raharjo, "Eksplorasi Logam Tanah Jarang di Jalur Timah Indonesia," in *Unconventional Exploration Target & Latest Technique and New Tools in Mineral and Coal Exploration*, 2016, pp. 116–124.

[41] Ngadenin, H. Syaeful, K. S. Widana, and M. Nurdin, "Potensi Thorium Dan Uranium Di Kabupaten Bangka Barat," *Eksplorium*, vol. 35, no. 2, pp. 69–84, 2014.

Journal of Physics: Conference Series **2048** (2021) 012004 doi:10.1088/1742-6596/2048/1/012004

# Technoeconomic analysis of High Temperature Reactors for industrial applications in Poland

**BChmielarz[1,2], A Bredimas[1], and C Herpson[2]**

[1]Ultra Safe Nuclear Corporation Europe 2 route de la Noue, 91190 Gif sur Yvette, France phone: +33 782 76 77 88
[2]Sorbonne Université, 4 place Jussieu, 75252 Paris Cedex 05, France

Coresponding author's e-mail : blazej.chmielarz@usnc.com

**Abstract.** The paper analyses Polish industrial energy market requirements and the economic boundary conditions of for High Temperature Reactor (HTR)-based hybrid energy systems for electricity, heat, and hydrogen production. The Polish industry suffers from high imported gas prices and high dependence on domestic coal sector. Most industrial coal boilers are ageing and will need replacement within two decades. Increasing emission prices will soon cripple the profitability of coal in favour of natural gas and leave an opening for HTRs. HTRs can be competitive for both heat and electricity generation if used at load factors above 90% and constructed within budget and on time. The competitiveness of HTRs grows further with rising fossil fuels and CO2 emission prices. For industrial hydrogen, steam methane reforming (SMR) is competitive against any other alternative. Large-scale hydrogen production with HTR-based Sulphur Iodine cycle may compete with SMR if capital and operational costs can be decreased. High temperature steam electrolysis requires more durable materials and lower capital cost. Electrolysis, given its relatively low CAPEX and scalability, can be competitive when electricity is cheap as a result of over-production from intermittent power capacities. Other fossil-based hydrogen production methods appear more costly and CO2-intensive than SMR. The study was done as a part of the GEMINI+ project.

## 1. Introduction

One of long-envisioned prospects of the nuclear community included in the technology roadmap of the Generation IV International Forum is expansion of the use nuclear energy beyond electricity production. GEMINI+ and Next Generation Nuclear Plant (NGNP) Alliance are initiatives to accelerate introduction of nuclear energy into industrial cogeneration [1].

HTRs have the advantage over other nuclear technologies of addressing a much wider array of technological processes which comprise the industrial heat generation market. It is one of the few technologically and economically feasible sustainable ways of generating high-quality heat. This quality, combined with the fact that non-electric energy requirements are larger than the entire electricity market [2] and the emission prices are expected to increase in the future [3], creates a major opportunity in regions with carbon taxes and/or with emission allowance trading schemes, like the European Union Emissions Trading System (EU ETS).

Poland is an example of a country subject to EU ETS which has a sizeable chemical industry with large demand for high quality heat, which is currently dependent on fossil fuels, and a vested interest in HTR technology [4]. Its case study is the focus of this technoeconomic analysis.

## 2. Polish Market Requirements

Poland is a major player in the European mineral fertilizer market with 19,6% of phosphate and 18,2% of nitrogen fertilizer production shares in the EU [5]. In addition, it houses several refineries, one of which, PKN Orlen, is among the largest in Europe, with over 2,1 GWt of installed generating capacity [6] and 18,7 megatons of crude oil processing capacity per year [7]. Another sector with demand for sub-550°C heat is the pulp and paper industry, with large coal consumption and a major facility with 692 MWt of installed capacity near Kwidzyń. The combined installed heat generating capacity of large facilities with demand for heat in the range between 250-550°C is over 7 GWt (Table 1).

**Table 1.** List of Polish facilities with the largest heat consumption in the range of 250-550°C [4]

| **Facility** | **Installed capacity [MWt]** |
|---|---|
| PKN Orlen | 2153 |
| Anwil S.A. – Grupa Orlen | 997 |
| Grupa Azoty Puławy | 755 |
| Grupa Azoty Police | 481 |
| Grupa LOTOS | 465 |
| Grupa Azoty Tarnów | 558 |
| Grupa Azoty Kędzierzyn | 557 |
| International Paper Kwidzyń | 692 |
| PCC Rokita | 160 |
| Orlen Południe Zakład Trzebinia | 93 |
| LOTOS Jasło | 74 |
| Orlen Południe Zakład Jedlicze | 62 |
| **Total** | **7047** |

Most primary energy in cogeneration systems in Poland comes from hard coal (see Figure 1). The importance of coal in the industry is further underlined by the fact that Poland has the largest fleet of industrial coal boilers in the EU, though the installations are old with less than 10% being under 30 years old, and relatively small, averaging about 100 MW each [8]. It creates a major problem for the country as there is an upcoming demand for new installations which, depending on regulations, may need to be not coal-fired. The most readily available alternatives are natural gas installations but both fuel prices and the security of supply are not favourable for Poland in that case as the country is currently still largely dependent on Russia for its supply.

Many efforts are made to bolster the stability of pricing and security of natural gas supply through construction of *Baltic Pipe* gas transmission pipeline and further expansion of a Liquefied Natural Gas Terminal in Świnoujście [9][10][11].

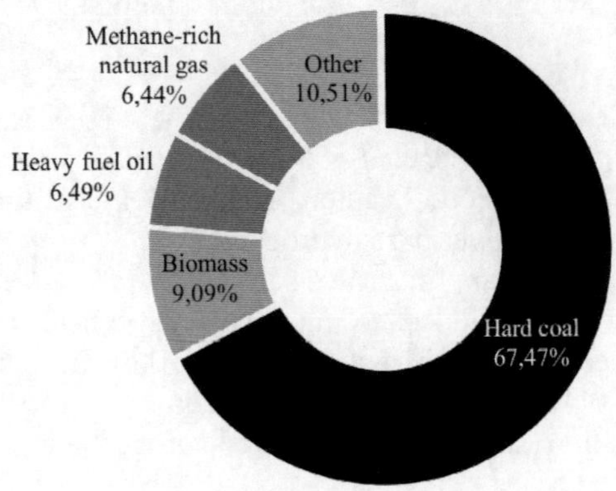


**Figure 1.** Heat in cogeneration systems by fuel in Poland in 2017 [12]

## 3. Methodology

The paper analyses several heat generating technologies for both CHP and hydrogen production applications. Economic assessment is based around comparison of levelized costs of heat, electricity, and hydrogen and the sensitivity of the costs to changes in selected variables.

### *3.1. Technologies selected for the analysis*

The assessment focused on comparing ready-to- market solutions with those close to deployment, both for heat and hydrogen generation. It includes pulverized coal boilers, gas boilers, Combined Cycle Gas Turbines and High Temperature Gas-cooled Reactors for heat generation. Hydrogen production technologies include electrolysis, High Temperature Steam Electrolysis (HTSE), Sulphur-Iodine Cycle (SI) and Steam Methane Reforming (SMR). With exceptions for CCGT and natural gas boilers, which will be explained later, all the heat-generating technologies were matched with each hydrogen generating technology for cost analysis. Gas boilers and CCGT contain exceptions – gas-fired SMR is a standalone solution not utilizing either heat source, SI cycle was done with NG boiler only and electrolysis together with HTSE were not considered with gas boilers.

Each technology considered in the analysis has some advantages and drawbacks.

- Pulverized coal boiler.
  Most used technology in Poland for industrial heat generation. Relatively high flexibility, moderate capital cost and very high emissions
- Gas-fired boiler.
  Mature technology with very high flexibility and quick deployment with low capital cost
- Combined Cycle Gas Turbine.
  Very high efficiency for electricity production with relatively low emissions and average flexibility – high share of primary energy must always be converted to electricity
- High Temperature Gas-cooled Reactor.
  Not yet commercially utilized but with many reactor- years of experience and potentially short market deployment, the least flexible heat generation technology with the highest capital cost and the lowest fuel cost and potentially highest availability factor.
  Given that the paper is an outlook for hybrid energy systems within the next few decades, for the purpose of this analysis it is assumed that HTGR can deliver temperatures sufficiently high for hydrogen production methods which follow:
  - Steam Methane Reforming.
    Mature technology, the most employed dedicated hydrogen production method, with very high thermodynamic efficiency, low capital cost and innate $CO_2$ production when

processing its feedstock – methane [13][14]. Hydrogen requires purification for fuel cell applications

- Electrolysis.
  Mature and flexible technology with somewhat higher capital cost than SMR at large scale and very high electric energy demand despite being near its theoretical efficiency limit [15][16]. Its specific capital cost is not significantly affected by scale of deployment. It can deliver pure hydrogen
- High Temperature Steam Electrolysis.
  Technology recently added to market with considerably higher efficiency than conventional electricity [17] but with lower flexibility, high capital, and operational expenses [15], [18], [19] as well as requirement of very high temperature source for efficient operation [20]. Can deliver pure hydrogen at high pressure for fuel cells
- Sulphur-Iodine Cycle.
  Thermochemical method of hydrogen generation pursued by several countries, can offers high thermodynamic efficiency over 50%. Efficiency drops rapidly with temperatures lower than 850°C and the process stops completely below 700°C [21][22]. High capital and operational cost. Can deliver pure hydrogen at high pressure for fuel cell applications [20]

### *3.2. Hybrid Energy Systems*

The definition of Hybrid Energy Systems is broad it is an energy system utilizing more than one energy generation technology and/or outputting more than one product [23]. The simplest system which can be called *hybrid* is Combined Heat and Power, commonly found in chemical plants or for district heating. The paper limits investigation to simple CHP and cogeneration with hydrogen production without regard for stochastics of demand variations. A deeper investigation into more complex hybrid energy systems (HES), including analyses of impact of varying loads, energy storage, virtual plants comprised of energy generation technologies, suchas nuclear with coal or gas boilers and CCGT and/or renewables, as well as other cogeneration use cases, such as district heating or desalination, should follow this study to help determine economically and ecologically optimal solutions.

### *3.3. Model equations*

The analysis is based around comparison of levelized costs of electricity, heat, and hydrogen. The investigated hybrid systems have different cost structures and energy requirements for hydrogen production - calculation of levelized costs permits more straightforward comparison of financial feasibility of each technology despite the differences.

The first element of the calculation is calculation of the Capital Recovery Factor (CRF) (Equation 1) [24].

$$CRF = \frac{r(1+r)^T}{(1+r)^{T-1}} \qquad (1)$$

Where $r$ is discount rate expressed as a fraction and T is operational lifetime.
Once obtained, the levelized cost (LC) can be calculated (Equation 2) [24]:

$$LC = \frac{\sum_{i=1}^{CT} f_i \, x \, (1+r)^{CT-(i-1)}}{8760 \, x \, LF \, x \, (SOCC \, x \, CRF)^{-1}} + O\&M + FC \qquad (2)$$

Where $CT$ is construction time (in years), $f_i$ is fraction of capital investment in year $i$ , $LF$ is load factor, expressed as a fraction of effective full power hours in a year, $SOCC$ is Specific Overnight Capital Cost, expressed in EUR/MW for energy installations and EUR/(t/h) for hydrogen facilities, O&M is Operations and Maintenance cost, expressed as EUR/MWh for energy installations and EUR/t for hydrogen facilities, and FC is fuel cost per obtained MWh for energy installations and per ton of hydrogen in case of hydrogen facilities.

The analysis linearizes the sensitivity of levelized cost to changes of cost components around standard model assumptions (see Table 2), as shown in Equation 3.

$$Nominal\ sensitvity = \frac{|LC(v_f) - LC(v_0)|}{\left(\frac{|v_f - v_0|}{v_{ref}}\right) x\ 100\%} \quad (3)$$

Where $\boldsymbol{LC(v)}$ is levelized cost under standard assumptions except for the variable $\boldsymbol{v}$ , $\boldsymbol{v0}$ is the lowest value of respective variable, $\boldsymbol{vf}$ is the highest value of the respective variable and $\boldsymbol{vref}$ is the reference value under standard assumptions.

## 4. Standard model assumptions

The model assumes current pricing of rules and state- of-the-art efficiencies and load factors for each technology. The chosen discount rate is relatively low but not unprecedented in energy cost analyses, thus creating favourable conditions for HTRs. Given the long-term nature of environmental policies and predictable baseload operation envisioned in these scenarios, however, the value is justifiable. The price of emission is ~5 EUR/t$CO_2$eq higher than around the time of writing but is likely to increase past the chosen value within the decade.

The analysis assumes following price margins for fuels: 6,0-11,5 EUR/GJ for natural gas, 2,75-4,00 EUR/GJ for coal [25] and 0,94-2,81 EUR/GJ for HTGR fuel [20][26]. Load factors are between 60 and 99% for the purpose of sensitivity analysis. Sensitivity of construction time is subject to ± 2 years uncertainty.

**Table 2.** Standard assumptions for external factors and operational parameters [3], [8], [26]–[30]

| Variable | Value |
|---|---|
| Discount rate | 5% |
| Load factor | 90% |
| Operational lifetime | 60 years - HTRs<br>40 years - coal and hydrogen units 30 years - gas units |
| Construction time | 5 years - HTRs<br>3 years - other technologies |
| Fuel prices (without taxes or transport fees) | 1,87 EUR/GJ - HTGR fuel<br>2,79 EUR/GJ - hard coal 8,67 EUR/GJ - natural gas |
| Emission prices | 30 EUR/tCO2eq |
| Electric efficiency | 61,0% - CCGT<br>43,3% - other technologies |

Capital cost and operational lifetime sensitivity ranges are between 50 and 150% of standard assumptions (see Table 3).

**Table 3.** Specific Overnight Capital Cost of technologies selected in the analysis [4], [20], [31]–[33]

| Specific Overnight Capital Cost of | Value |
|---|---|
| Pulverized coal boiler | 390,0 EUR/kWt |
| Gas boiler | 235,4 EUR/kWt |
| Combined Cycle Gas Turbine facility | 947,3 EUR/kWe |
| High Temperature Reactor | 2636,4 EUR/kWt |
| Steam turbine | 140,0 EUR/kWe |
| Sulphur-Iodine cycle hydrogen facility | 71,1 MEUR/($t_{H2}$/h) |
| Electrolysis facility | 26,5 MEUR/($t_{H2}$/h) |
| High Temperature Steam Electrolysis facility | 49,0 MEUR/($t_{H2}$/h) |
| Gas-fired Steam Methane Reforming facility | 13,7 MEUR/($t_{H2}$/h) |
| Unconventional Steam Methane Reforming facility | 26,5 MEUR/($t_{H2}$/h) |

Operational costs and process energy requirements are summarized in Table 4. The values were constant throughout the analysis.

**Table 4.** Operational costs and process energy requirements of investigated technologies [14], [20], [34]–[36]

| **Variable** | **Value** | |
|---|---|---|
| O&M as a share of standard CAPEX | 33 % for coal and gas<br>5,8% for HTGR | |
| **O&M cost per ton of $H_2$** | | |
| Electrolysis facility | 134,3 EUR/$tK_2$ | |
| High Temperature Steam Electrolysis facility | 1071,7 EUR/$tK_2$ | |
| Sulphur-iodine Iodine hydrogen facility | 602,4 EUR/$tK_2$ | |
| Unconventional Steam Methane Reforming facility | 100,8 EUR/$tK_2$ | |
| Steam Methane Reforming facility | 67,2 EUR/$tK_2$ | |
| **Technology** | **Energy requirement [GJ/tH$_2$]** | |
| Sulphur-Iodine hydrogen facility | **Thermal** | **Electric** |
| High Temperature Steam Electrolysis facility | 254,2 | 0,0 |
| Electrolysis facility | 24,0 | 124,7 |
| Steam Methane Reforming facility | 0,0 | 180,0 |
| Unconventional Steam Methane Reforming facility | 63,7 | 2,0 |
| Sulphur-Iodine hydrogen facility | 70,7 | 2,3 |

Some cost components were treated as variables, others were kept constant throughout the analysis. Overnight cost, fuel price, carbon emission price, load factor, discount rate, construction time and operational lifetime were treated as variables whereas efficiencies, O&M costs, output power, cost of desalinated water and grid electricity cost were kept constant. The output power was set to 165 MWt, which in the case of CCGT meant a gas turbine connected to a 165 MWt heat recovery steam generator (HRSG) and in case of hydrogen installations, input of 165 MWt of process heat combined with its equivalent in electricity for the respective electricity generation method. Cost of distilled water was fixed at 1,84 EUR/t. Levelized price of electricity from the grid was kept at 70 EUR/MWh [37]. The specific capital cost of a large steam turbine added to CHP installations was 140 EUR/KWe [31].

## 5. Results

The section of results is divided into three sections: discussion on levelized costs of CHP under standard assumptions, analysis of impacts of cost components on the levelized costs of CHP and comparison of different systems for hydrogen production.

### *5.1. Levelized costs of Combined Heat and Power*

Given that the most relevant competitive advantage of HTRs over other nuclear technologies in the context of this technoeconomic analysis is the ability to supply industrial heat at high temperatures, most of the presented results refer to the levelized costs of heat. The analysis is based on Deliverable 3.12 of GEMINI+ [38].

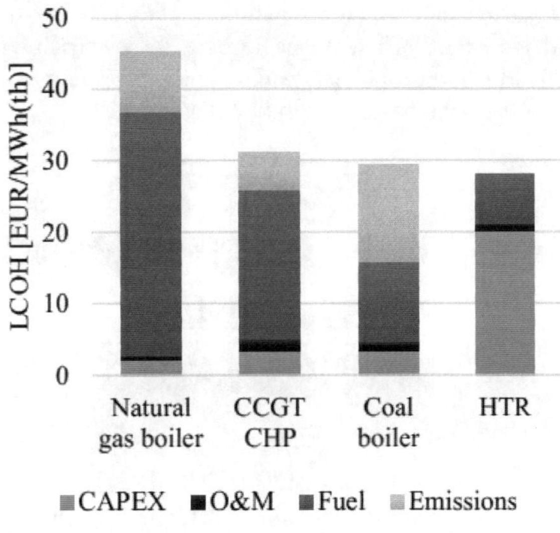


**Figure 2.** Levelized cost of process heat under standard assumptions

Figure 2 provides a breakdown of most relevant cost components for considered heat generating technologies. Under the standard scenario assumptions, the HTR can provide the most affordable industrial heat, followed by coal and CCGT.

For gas boilers, the price of fuel determines 80% of the price. The remaining costs are relatively low, despite the presumed high price of emissions of 30 EUR per ton. In case of CCGT, there is a notably higher capital and operational cost, but the vast majority of the price is related to fuel cost, followed by emissions cost. Coal boilers comprise evenly of fuel and emissions cost, making them highly susceptible to two external variables. 74% of the cost of heat from the HTR is related to its CAPEX, with the rest being related almost solely on fuel. The fuel cost is much lower than in case of competing technologies. The very high share of CAPEX in the levelized cost places most of the investment risk in internal factors related to construction costs and planning as well as financing scheme.

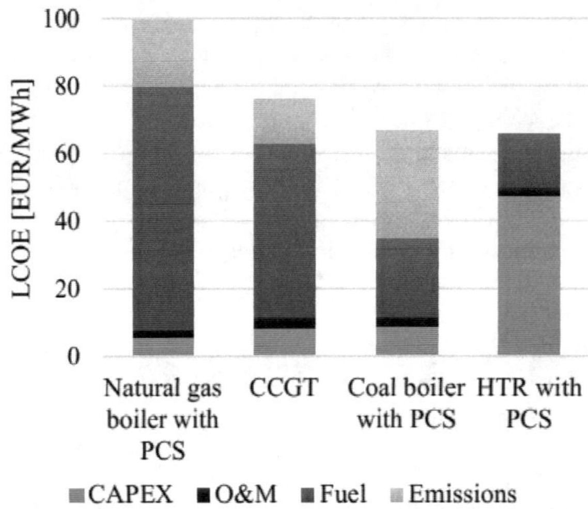


**Figure 3.** Levelized cost of electricity under standard assumptions

Much like in the previous plot, Figure 3 places HTRs on a very similar level as coal boilers for electricity production. CCGT is more costly than coal or HTRs under standard assumptions despite the highest electric efficiency due to very high cost of natural gas. CCGT is best utilized as a cogeneration technology, taking advantage of an efficient gas turbine for electricity production and high fuel utilization factor when delivering industrial heat, leading to lower primary consumption. Gas boilers are significantly more costly for baseload power generation than the rest.

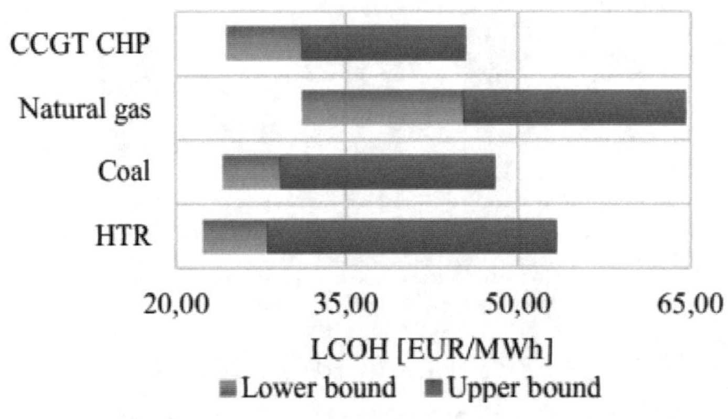


**Figure 4.** Range of LCOH with two most sensitive cost parameters offset by the highest plausible amounts

Taking into consideration the probable ranges of cost components place the technologies on a similar playing field (Figure 4). Natural gas boilers, whose LCOH for baseload energy production is ~ 15 EUR/MWh(th) higher than competition, are an exception. Factors impacting fossil-fired technologies are predominantly external - fuel and emission price, whereas HTRs are impacted by internal factors - construction time, overnight cost, load factor, discount rate.

*5.2. Impact of selected cost components on levelized costs*

The following graphs (Figure 5 to Figure 10) show levelized costs of heat from different technologies under standard assumptions, represented with solid lines, as well as under their respective best- and worst- case scenarios, shown with dotted lines.

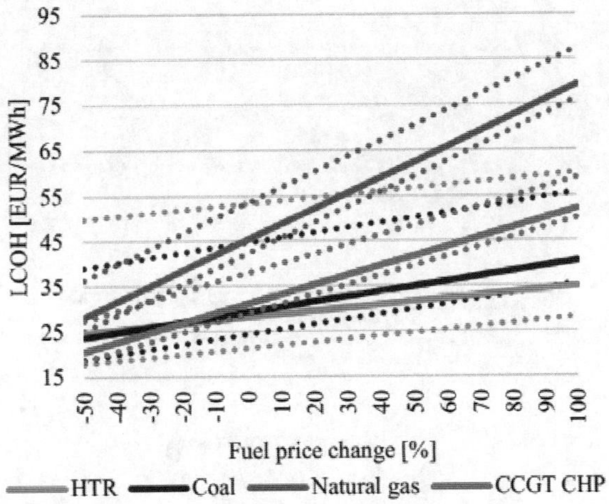


**Figure 5.** Cost of process heat as a function of fuel price

Fuel price has a moderate impact on costs of energy from coal boilers and HTRs. It is by far the most important cost component for gas boilers and CCGT stability of gas prices should have the highest priority to investors when considering the two technologies. It is worth noting that real-world scenarios need to add the fixed costs of transport of fuel, which would impact profitability of coal most notably.

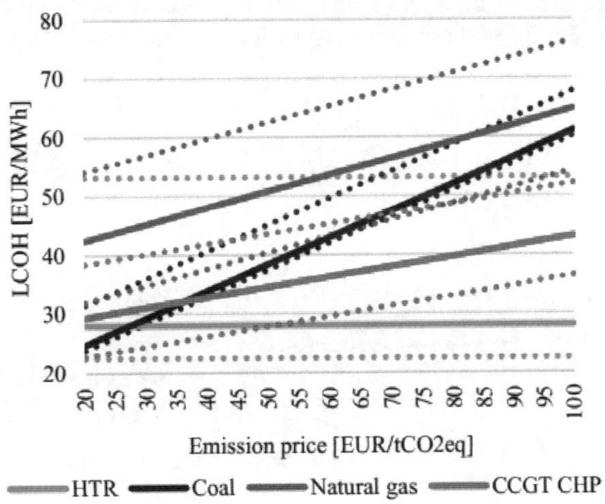


**Figure 6.** Cost of process heat as a function of emission price

Among the greatest advantages of nuclear energy is its independence from emission prices. Rising emission prices can rapidly make.coal uncompetitive –the model price of 30 EUR/tCO2 is about the border of profitability for coal. At 35 EUR/tCO2, it stops being cheaper than heat from CCGT.

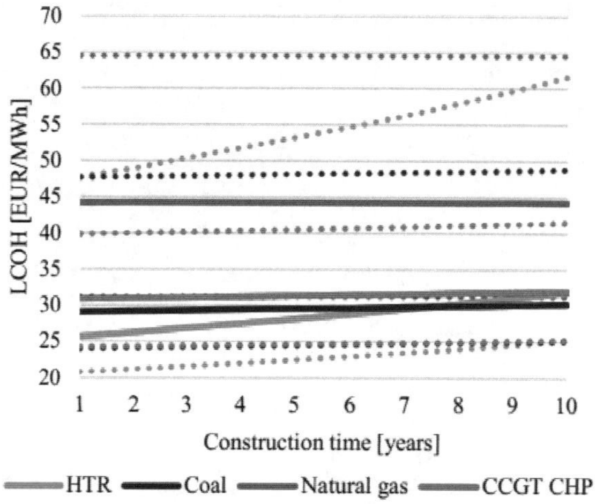


**Figure 7.** Cost of process heat as a function of construction time

Many nuclear projects are famously delayed by several years, leading to increased CAPEX. An effect of such delays on the levelized cost is illustrated in Figure 7. An added consideration is the delayed return on investment in such situations. The graph underlines an importance of good management of a nuclear plant construction as it is the only technology impacted this severely by it. On the other hand, bringing the construction time in line with other technologies at three years is highly favourable for an HTR, showing the potential of modular reactor construction which could lead to faster deployments.

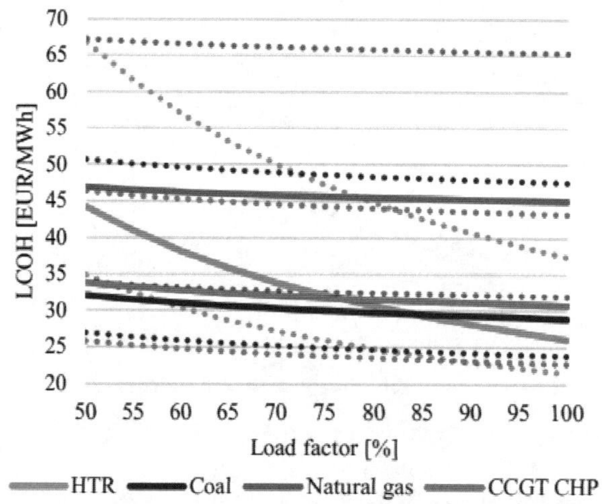


**Figure 8.** Cost of process heat as a function of load factor

The high CAPEX of HTRs can be amortized with high load factors. Very high effective utilization factors exceeding 90% render HTRs the most affordable energy source. On the other hand, load factors below 50% make them uncompetitive even with gas boilers. In cases of very low utilization, the cost of energy increases dramatically, amplified in case of HTRs by their high CAPEX. At very low load factors, below 10%, gas boilers start making economic sense, positioning them as the most suitable backup generators, particularly considering their flexibility with regards of fuels accepted and short start-up times.

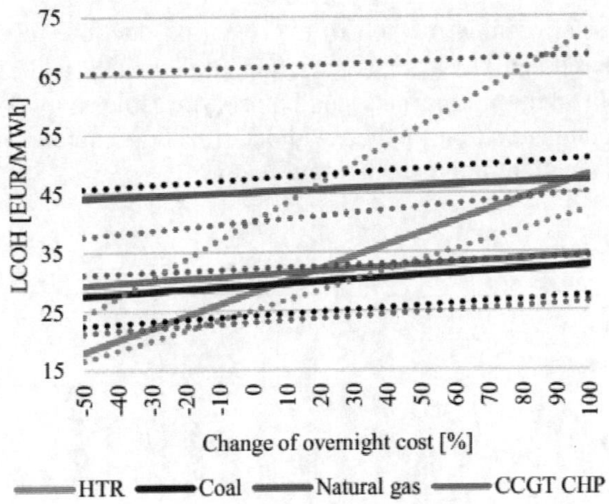


**Figure 9.** Cost of process heat as a function of overnight cost

Much like in the case of load factor, Figure 9 shows the severe impact of changes in overnight cost on the economic feasibility boundaries of HTRs. Even in our scenario which favours HTRs, an overnight cost increase of 20% could render an HTR uncompetitive with established technologies under otherwise standard assumptions.

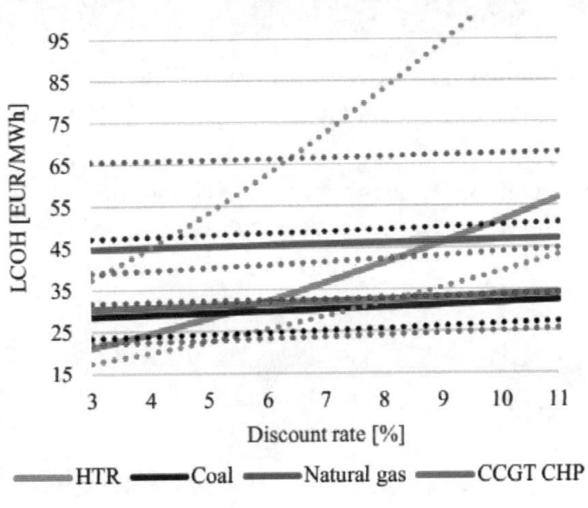


**Figure 10.** Cost of process heat as a function of discount rate

While being a secondary consideration for fossil-fired technologies, the discount rate is among the deciding factors for the levelized costs of energy from HTRs at 3% discount rate, which would imply increase value of long-term investment and low risk, it is by far the most affordable heat and electricity source.

At 7% discount rate, an HTR becomes 30% more costly than heat from coal or CCGTs. Figure 10 shows that discount rate determines the economic feasibility of HTRs. Unlike most variables, discount rate is both known and fixed once project financing is established therefore it was not considered in best- and worst- case scenario calculations.

### *5.3. Costs of hydrogen*

SMR remains the most affordable method of hydrogen production, regardless of implementation method. Its advantage exceeds 1 EUR/kg$H_2$ (Figure 11). SI with HTR is the most affordable emission-free source of hydrogen. In addition, it is the second most affordable source of hydrogen after SMR.

Any non-SMR hydrogen generation method without an HTR generates more emission than SMR, furthering the established position of the technology.

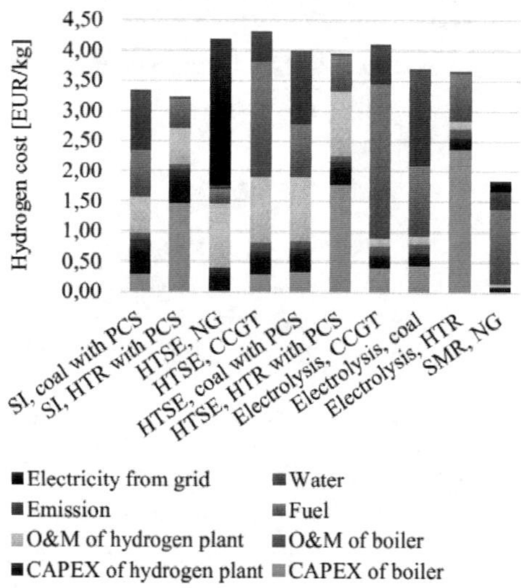


**Figure 11.** Levelized cost of hydrogen for selected technologies under standard assumptions

It is difficult to compete with SMR due to its very high thermodynamic efficiency, even in worst-case scenarios (Figure 12). Improvements to efficiency of SI or lowering its CAPEX and O&M could make it competitive with SMR.

The O&M combined with CAPEX of HTSE make it currently prohibitively expensive

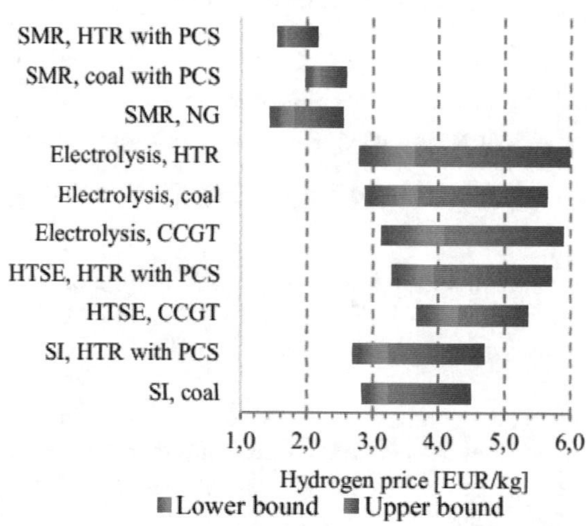


**Figure 12.** Range of hydrogen prices with plausible offsets of two most sensitive parameters

Electrolysis is not an effective baseload method of hydrogen production but its relatively low CAPEX enables opportunistic hydrogen production during periods of cheap electricity

## 6. Summary

HTRs can be competitive with coal or gas technologies, particularly in scenarios with higher fuel or emission prices than our standard assumptions. The greatest disadvantage of HTRS is linked to its high CAPEX, which is very sensitive to underutilization or mismanagement during construction and planning which would result in prolonged construction or higher overnight cost. The assumed discount rate is the determining factor which can make or break a nuclear project, though, necessitating an advantageous financing scheme.

Both fuel and emission prices in the upcoming decades remain highly uncertain, particularly for Poland which makes considerable efforts towards higher energy security, partially ensured by domestic coal and gas reserves, leading to an argument for an HTR. In addition, Poland needs new generating capacities, given its large share of aged, coal-fired boilers - the facilities highlighted in Table 1 alone could host 42 units of 165 MWt reactors. If sustainable and captive generating technologies were to be excluded (such as burning sulphur, biomass or oil processing by products) the number of potential units would be between 25 and 35.

Hydrogen from SMR is notably cheaper than from other production methods, even with fuel and emission prices being unfavourable, meaning it will be difficult to replace without innovation in hydrogen generation technologies, fuel or emission prices outside of scope of our analysis or environmental policies limiting use of the technology.

SI and HTSE need development to lower their CAPEX and O&M costs to become competitive with SMR. SI could also compete if it were upscaled over 10 times to lower the specific capital cost.

Electrolysis can take advantage of periods of cheap electricity due to its scalability, flexibility, and low CAPEX, though it is not economically viable as a large-scale baseload hydrogen generation method in the scope of our scenarios.

## References

[1] J. Collins, "Next Generation Nuclear Plant Project Technology Development Roadmaps: The Technical Path Forward for 750°C-800°C Reactor Outlet Temperature," no. January, p. Medium: ED, 2009, [Online]. Available: http://www.osti.gov/bridge/servlets/purl/963 739-u6igyw/.

[2] "Final energy consumption by sector," 2014, doi: 10.1787/9789264214200-graph27-en.

[3] A. Marcu *et al.*, "2019 State of the EU ETS Report," *Carbon Mark. Forum - Think. ahead Eur.*, no. February, pp. 1–20, 2019.

[4] Ministry of Energy of Poland, "Możliwości wdrożenia wysokotemperaturowych reaktorów jądrowych w Polsce," 2017.

[5] FAOSTAT, "Fertilizers by Nutrient," *Food and Agriculture Organization of the United Nations* 2017. http://www.fao.org/faostat/en/#data/RFN (accessed Sep. 30, 2019).

[6] Urząd Regulacji Energetyki, "Koncesje w zakresie innym niż paliwa ciekłe," 2019. https://rejestry.ure.gov.pl/c/1 (accessed Nov. 08, 2019).

[7] Concave, "Refinery Sites in Europe," 2020. https://www.concawe.eu/refineries-map/ (accessed Jun. 30, 2020).

[8] European Commission, *Best Available Techniques (BAT) Reference Document for Large Combustion Plants - Final Draft*. European Comission, 2016.

[9] J. Wiech and M. Zaniewicz, "Skompromitować Polskę, nawet za cenę rzetelności. O ataku dezinformacyjnym na Baltic Pipe [ANALIZA]," *Energetyka24*, 2019. https://www.energetyka24.com/skompromit owac-polske-nawet-za-cene-rzetelnosci-o- ataku-dezinformacyjnym-na-baltic-pipe- analiza (accessed Sep. 25, 2019).

[10] B. Sawicki, "Sawicki: Czy Baltic Pipe się opłaci? (ANALIZA)," *BiznesAlert*, 2018. https://biznesalert.pl/baltic-pipe-koszty- oszczednosci-ure/ (accessed Sep. 25, 2019).

[11] Polskie Radio, "Za 4 lata pożegnamy się z Gazpromem: rosyjski gaz zastąpi LNG i gaz ze złóż

norweskich oraz krajowy surowiec," *Polskie Radio*, 2019. https://polskieradio24.pl/42/3167/Artykul/2299609,Za-4-lata-pozegnamy-sie-z- Gazpromem-rosyjski-gaz-zastapi-LNG-i- gaz-ze-zloz-norweskich-oraz-krajowy- surowiec (accessed Sep. 25, 2019).

[12] Polskie Towarzystwo Elektrociepłowni Zawodowych, "Raport o kogeneracji w ciepłownictwie," 2019. [Online]. Available: https://www.gov.pl/attachment/1b0d1dfe- 9ad4-4e78-a895-21f8413b85d0.

[13] AirScience, "Hydrogen Production," 2009. https://hydrogeneurope.eu/hydrogen- production-0 (accessed Nov. 21, 2019).

[14] Hydrogen tools, "Current Hydrogen Production Efficiencies," 2019. [Online]. Available: https://h2tools.org/hyarc/hydrogen-production.

[15] F. M. Sapountzi, J. M. Gracia, C. J. (Kee. J. Weststrate, H. O. A. Fredriksson, and J. W. (Hans. Niemantsverdriet, "Electrocatalysts for the generation of hydrogen, oxygen and synthesis gas," *Prog. Energy Combust. Sci.*, vol. 58, pp. 1–35, 2017, doi: 10.1016/j.pecs.2016.09.001.

[16] National Renewable Energy Laboratory, "Technology Brief : Analysis of Current-Day Commercial Electrolyzers," *U.S. Dep. Energy Off.*, p. 2, 2004, [Online]. Available: http://www.nrel.gov/docs/fy04osti/36705.pd f.

[17] Sunfire, "Sunfire-HyLink." https://www.sunfire.de/en/products-and- technology/sunfire-hylink (accessed Nov. 15, 2019).

[18] A. Hauch, *Solid Oxide Electrolysis Cells -- Performance and Durability*, vol. 37, no. October. 2007.

[19] R. Hino, K. Haga, H. Aita, and K. Sekita, "38. R&D on hydrogen production by high- temperature electrolysis of steam," *Nucl. Eng. Des.*, vol. 233, no. 1–3, pp. 363–375, 2004, doi: 10.1016/j.nucengdes.2004.08.029.

[20] A. Antony *et al.*, "Examining the Technoeconomics of Nuclear Hydrogen Production and Benchmark Analysis of the IAEA HEEP Software," 2018.

[21] S. Goldstein, X. Vitart, and J. M. Borgard, "General comments about the efficiency of the iodine-sulphur cycle coupled to a high temperature gas-cooled reactor," *Nucl. Prod. Hydrog.*, no. April, pp. 85–98, 2004, doi: 10.1787/9789264107717-7-en.

[22] M. Jaszczur, M. A. Rosen, T. Śliwa, M. Dudek, and L. Pieńkowski, "Hydrogen production using high temperature nuclear reactors: Efficiency analysis of a combined cycle," *Int. J. Hydrogen Energy*, vol. 41, no. 19, pp. 7861–7871, 2016, doi: 10.1016/j.ijhydene.2015.11.190.

[23] R. Ståhl, "Compilation and evaluation of non-conventional hybrid energy options," no. 755478, 2019, [Online]. Available: http://gemini-initiative.eu/.

[24] W. D'haeseleer, "Synthesis on the Economics of Nuclear Energy - Study for the European Commission," 2013, [Online]. Available: https://www.mech.kuleuven.be/en/tme/research/energy_environment/Pdf/wpen2013- 14.pdf.

[25] U.S. EIA, "Annual Energy Outlook 2019 with projections to 2050," *Annu. Energy Outlook 2019 with Proj. to 2050*, vol. 44, no. 8, pp. 1–64, 2019, doi: DOE/EIA-0383(2012) U.S.

[26] A. M. Gandrik, "HTGR Cost Model Users ' Manual," *Idaho Natl. Lab.*, no. January, 2012, [Online]. Available: https://art.inl.gov/NGNP/INL Documents/Year 2012/HTGR Cost Model Users Manual rev 1.pdf.

[27] Polski Rynek Węgla, "Indeks PSCMI 1," 2019. https://polskirynekwegla.pl/indeks- pscmi-1 (accessed Aug. 06, 2019).

[28] European Energy Exchange, "European Emission Allowances," 2019. https://www.eex.com/en/market-data/environmental-markets/spot-market/european-emission-allowances (accessed Nov. 25, 2019).

[29] Eurostat, "Natural gas prices, second semester of 2016-2018," *Eurostat*,2019. https://ec.europa.eu/eurostat/statistics-explained/index.php/Natural_gas_price_statistics #Natural_gas_prices_for_non- household_consumers (accessed Jun. 17, 2019).

[30] ORLEN Press office, "ORLEN completes the Włocławek CCGT project," 2017.

https://www.orlen.pl/EN/PressOffice/Pages/ORLEN-completes-the-Włocławek-CCGT-project.aspx (accessed Sep. 19, 2019).

[31] D. Pauschert, "Study of Equipment Prices in the Power Sector," 2009. [Online]. Available: https://esmap.org/sites/default/files/esmap-files/TR122-09_GBL_Study_of_Equipment_Prices_in_th e_Power_Sector.pdf.

[32] L. Kaiwen, Y. Bin, and Z. Tao, "Economic analysis of hydrogen production from steam reforming process: A literature review," *Energy Sources, Part B Econ. Plan. Policy*, vol. 13, no. 2, pp. 109–115, 2018, doi: 10.1080/15567249.2017.1387619.

[33] M. Wittenstein and G. Rothwell, "Projected Costs of Generating Electricity," 2015. [Online]. Available: https://www.oecd- nea.org/ndd/pubs/2015/7057-proj-costs- electricity-2015.pdf.

[34] A. J. Seebregts, "Gas-Fired Power," *IEA ETSAP - Technol. Br. E02 – April 2010*, no. April, pp. 1–5, 2010, [Online]. Available: http://www.iea-etsap.org/web/E- TechDS/PDF/E02-gas_fired_power-GS-AD- gct.pdf.

[35] A. J. Seebregts, "Gas-Fired Power," no. September 2009, pp. 2007–2010, 2009.

[36] NREL, "Current (2009) State-of-the-Art Hydrogen Production Cost Estimate Using Water Electrolysis (NREL/BK-6A1-46676)," no. September, p. 44, 2009, doi: 10.1016/0305-4403(88)90035-0.

[37] C. Schnell and M. Roszkowski, "Instytut Jagielloński : Ceny energii . Trwały wzrost cen energii zmieni dopiero modyfikacja polskiego miksu energetycznego . Czy stać nas na marnowan ie czasu ?," 2018.

[38] B. Chmielarz and A. Bredimas, "Market requirements , technical feasibility , required economic boundary conditions for HES," 2020.

# Cost Analysis of Nuclear Hydrogen Production Using IAEA-HEEP 4 Software

**E Dewita, R Prassanti, K S Widana, and Y S B Susilo**

Center for Nuclear Minerals Technology (PTBGN)- BATAN, Jalan Lebak Bulus Raya No. 9, Ps. Jumat, Jakarta, Indonesia, 12440

phone: +12-345-67891011, email: erland@batan.go.id

**Abstract.** Hydrogen is a commercially important element. Basically, there are several methods of hydrogen production that have been commercially used, such as Steam Methane Reforming (SMR), High Temperature Steam Electrolysis (HTSE), and thermochemical cycles, like Sulphur-Iodine (SI). Among these methods, SMR is the most widely used for large-scale hydrogen production, with conversion efficiency between 74–85% and it has commercially used in some fertilizer industries in Indonesia. Steam reforming is a method to convert alkane (natural gas) compounds to hydrogen and carbon dioxide (synthetic gas) by adding moisture at high pressure and temperature (35-40 bar; 800-900$^0$C). These hydrogen production technologies can be coupled with different nuclear reactors based on the heat required in the process. The High Temperature Gas-cooled Reactor (HTGR) using helium as a coolant, has a high outlet temperature (900$^o$C), so it can potentially be used to supply for process heat for hydrogen production, coal liquefaction/ gasification or for other industrial processes requiring high temperature heat. Hydrogen production cost from SMR method is influenced by a range of technical and economic factors. The fuel component of natural gas needed in the SMR method can be replaced by nuclear heat from a nuclear power plant (NPP) operating in cogeneration mode (i.e. simultaneous producing electric power and heat), hence contributing to the reduction of carbon dioxide in the process.

In the SMR method, fuel costs are the largest cost component, accounting for between 45% and 75% of production costs. Therefore, there is opportune to assess the economics of hydrogen production by using nuclear heat. The economic evaluation is done by using IAEA HEEP-4 Software.

The results comprise cost break up for 2 cases, coupling SMR process for hydrogen production with: (1) 2 HTGRs of 170 MWth/unit; and (2) 1 HTGR of 600 MWth/unit. The cost of hydrogen production is highly depend on the scale of the NPP as energy source and results indicated that hydrogen production cost of the 1 HTGR Unit600 $MW_{th}$ (Case 2) has a lower value (1.72 US\$/kg$H_2$), than the cost obtained when 2 HTGR units of 170 MWth each (case 1) are considered (2.72 US\$/kg$H_2$). For comparison, the hydrogen production cost by using SMR with carbon capture and storage (CCS) with natural gas as fuel is 2.27 US\$/kg$H_2$.

Keywords: nuclear, cogeneration, hydrogen, HTGR, HEEP-4, economy, steam methane reforming

## 1. Introduction

As of 2019, roughly 70 million tons of hydrogen are produced annually worldwide [7] mostly used in oil refining (~25%) and for the production of ammonia (~55%) and fertilizers. Other applications are in methanol production (~10%), the steel industry, food processing and electronics sectors [1].

There is various method for hydrogen production, namely: Steam Methane Reforming (SMR), natural gas reforming/ gasification, electrolysis, renewable liquid reforming, and fermentation [2,3]. Among these methods, SMR is the most common and developed method used for large-scale hydrogen production. SMR uses natural gas both as raw material and fuel with conversion efficiency between 74–85% [4]. Ratio of natural gas used as raw material to natural gas used as a fuel is 40%:60%. Therefore, it is opportune to seek solutions to replace natural gas fuel by other energy sources, one of which being nuclear heat. This contributes to reducing the greenhouse gas emissions released in the hydrogen production process and also to the economy of natural gas reserves.

Steam reforming converts alkane (natural gas) compounds to hydrogen and carbon dioxide (synthetic gas) by adding moisture at high pressure and temperature (35-40bar; 800-900°C). The process is achieved through four main steps: desulfurization, catalytic reforming, CO conversion, and gas separation [5]. The process requires heating the gas to between 700–1100 °C in the presence of steam and a nickel catalyst. The resulting endothermic reaction breaks up the methane molecules and forms carbon monoxide CO and hydrogen $H_2$. The CO gas can then be passed with steam over iron oxide or other oxides and undergo a water gas shift reaction to obtain further quantities of $H_2$. The downside to this process is that its major byproducts are CO, $CO_2$ and other greenhouse gases, depending on the quality of the feedstock (natural gas, naphtha, etc.).

Therefore, considering environmental impact and a drive for saving natural gas reserves in Indonesia, investigation of replacing the natural gas used as fuel in the SMR process for hydrogen production with nuclear heat is opportune.

Nuclear energy is an excellent source of process heat for various industrial applications including desalination, synthetic and unconventional oil production, oil refining, biomass-based ethanol production, and hydrogen production. One of the nuclear power reactors that has the potential to be used to supply high temperature steam for hydrogen production process is High Temperature Gas Cooled Reactor (HTGR). HTGR is helium- cooled and graphite-moderated and uses a thermal neutron spectrum, with an outlet coolant temperature of ~800°C [8,9]. Due to a high coolant outlet temperature, HTGR can be used for the generation of hydrogen through several endothermic processes, such as steam reforming. It has also potential for cogeneration purposes, wherein part of the heat is used to produce electricity and part of the other is used to produce hydrogen, so electricity and hydrogen can be simultaneously produced. The use of nuclear power plants (NPPs) in cogeneration systems provides many economic, environmental and efficiency related benefits [10].

This study was conducted to analyze the economics of nuclear hydrogen using IAEA HEEP-4 Software.

## 2. Methodology

The economic evaluation of hydrogen production cost using cogeneration of HTGR with a SMR plant was carried out by using the IAEA HEEP Software. HEEP stands for Hydrogen Economic Evaluation Programme and is a tool provided freely by IAEA to Member States to analyze economics of the most promising processes for hydrogen production (high and low-temperature electrolysis, thermo-chemical processes including Sulphur–Iodine (S-I) process, and steam reforming). A literature review of hydrogen production by SMR was performed to determine to most representative input parameters for the economic model.

## 3. Theory

### *3.1. Hydrogen Production Methods*
Hydrogen can be produced from diverse, domestic resources including fossil fuels, biomass, and water electrolysis with electricity. The environmental impact and energy efficiency of hydrogen depends on how it is produced.

There are a number of ways to produce hydrogen: [11,12,13,14]

- Natural Gas Reforming/Gasification: synthesis gas, which is a mixture of hydrogen, carbon monoxide, and a small amount of $CO_2$, is created by reacting natural gas with high-temperature steam. The CO gas is reacted with water to produce additional hydrogen. This method is the cheapest, most efficient, and most common. Natural gas reforming using steam accounts for the majority of hydrogen produced in the United States annually.
  A synthesis gas can also be created by reacting coal or biomass with high-temperature steam and oxygen in a pressurized gasifier, which is converted into gaseous components—a process called gasification. The resulting synthesis gas contains hydrogen and carbon monoxide, which is reacted with steam to separate the hydrogen.
- Electrolysis: An electric current splits water into hydrogen and oxygen. If the electricity is produced by renewable sources, such as solar or wind, the resulting hydrogen will be considered renewable as well, and has numerous emissions benefits. Power-to-hydrogen projects are taking off, where excess renewable electricity, when it's available, is used to make hydrogen through electrolysis.
- Renewable Liquid Reforming: Renewable liquid fuels, such as ethanol, are reacted with high-temperature steam to produce hydrogen near the point of end use.
- Fermentation: Biomass is converted into sugar-rich feedstocks that can be fermented to produce hydrogen.

Several hydrogen production methods are in development [12]:

- High-Temperature Water Splitting: High temperatures generated by solar concentrators or nuclear reactors drive chemical reactions that split water to produce hydrogen.
- Photobiological Water Splitting: Microbes, such as green algae, consume water in the presence of sunlight, producing hydrogen as a byproduct.
- Photoelectrochemical Water Splitting: Photoelectrochemical systems produce hydrogen from water using special semiconductors and energy from sun.

### *3.2. Cogeneration System*
Cogeneration systems refer to energy systems that have the ability to produce two useful commodities simultaneously. Cogeneration systems are combined heat and power plants, where electricity and useful heat are both produced from one plant. Cogeneration is a highly efficient energy orientation that can achieve primary energy savings compared to conventional power and heat supply.

Furthermore, aside from electricity and heat combination, commodities include heat for desalination, hydrogen production and other applications. In essence, Cogeneration system is a process that produces electricity and heat simultaneously. The schematic diagram of Cogeneration of HTGR type reactor with hydrogen production plant of SMR is shown in Figure 1.

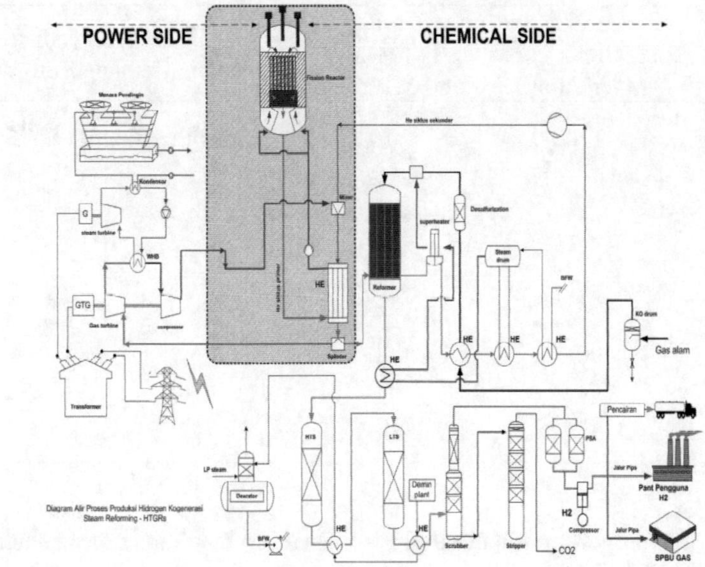


**Figure 1**. Schematic diagram of nuclear heat supply for hydrogen plant [15].

**Table 1.** Input data for NPP and Hydrogen Production Plant [16]

| NPP | Case-1 2 HTGRs of 170 MWth/unit | Case-2, 1 HTGR of 600 MWth/unit | Hydrogen Production Plant (Steam Methane Reforming Method) | |
|---|---|---|---|---|
| Thermal rating (MWth/unit) | 170 | 600 | $H_2$ generation rate (kg $H_2$/s) | 4.2 |
| Heat for $H_2$ plant (MWth/ unit) | 65.3 | 170 | $H_2$ generation per unit (kg/unit) | 5.9E+7 |
| Electricity rating (MWe/ unit) | 21.3 | 202 | Heat consumption (MWth/unit) | 65.3 |
| Number of units | 2 | 1 | Electricity required (MWe/unit) | 33 |
| Initial fuel load (kg/unit) | 2396 | 7090 | Number of units | 2 |
| Annual fuel feed (kg/unit) | 767 | 1773 | Capital cost (USD/kg $H_2$) | 2.0E+8 |
| Capital cost (CC) (USD/unit) | 6.0E+8 | 5.47E+8 | Energy Usage cost (USD) | 6.15E+6 |
| CC fraction for electricity infrastructure (%) | 10 | 10 | Other O&M cost (% of CC) | 7.78 |
| Fuel cost (USD/kg fuel) | 22937 | 5800 | Decommissioning cost (% of CC) | 10 |
| O&M cost (% of CC) | 4 | 3.81 | Annual water consumption(L/yr) | 0 |

| NPP | Case-1 2 HTGRs of 170 MWth/unit | Case-2, 1 HTGR of 600 MWth/unit | Hydrogen Production Plant (Steam Methane Reforming Method) | |
|---|---|---|---|---|
| Decommissioning cost (% of CC) | 2.5 | 10 | Capability factor (%) | 90 |
| Construction period (years) | 5 | 3 | | |
| Operation period (years) | 40 | 40 | Availability factor (%) | 100 |
| Capacity factor (%) | 90 | 90 | | |
| Availability factor (%) | 100 | 100 | | |

*3.3. Economic Analysis*

The production cost of hydrogen from natural gas is influenced by a range of technical and economic factors. Input data for economic evaluation of hydrogen production by using HEEP software is shown in Table 1 and input data for financial parameter is as shown in Table 2.

**Table 2.** Financial Parameter

| | |
|---|---|
| Discount Rate | 10% |
| Inflation Rate | 3% |
| Equity/ Debt | 70%/30% |
| Borrowing Interest | 5% |
| Tax rate | 25% |

## 4. Results and Discussion

Hydrogen is a commercially important element. It is used for many industrial applications and to provide a lower carbon emission technology for its production, this study investigated the option of using nuclear heat to replace the fuel component of gas in the SMR process.

Hydrogen production cost will strongly depend on the price of feedstocks and process efficiency, as well as a wide variety of other parameters such as nuclear plant size and plant availability, maturity of the technology, and physical distance to end-use markets. The nuclear power plant that can produce the high temperatures steam of about 850 to 950°C required to gasify coal and convert natural gas to hydrogen may be achieved only in high-temperature gas-cooled nuclear reactors (HTGR) type reactor. The nuclear reactor coupled to hydrogen production has the potential for higher overall energy use efficiency and better utilization of capital equipment.

Results of calculations by using IAEA HEEP software are presented in Table 3 and in Figures 2 and 3, in terms of levelized cost of hydrogen production and cost breakup, respectively. Two cases were discussed for providing the heat needed for the SMR process from nuclear reactors: (1) two units HTGR (170 MWth/unit); (2) 1unit NPP (600 MWth).

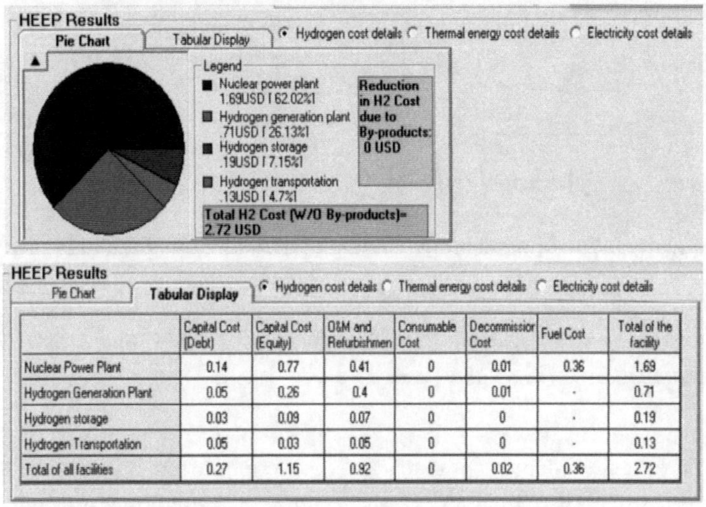


| | Capital Cost (Debt) | Capital Cost (Equity) | O&M and Refurbishmen | Consumable Cost | Decommissior Cost | Fuel Cost | Total of the facility |
|---|---|---|---|---|---|---|---|
| Nuclear Power Plant | 0.14 | 0.77 | 0.41 | 0 | 0.01 | 0.36 | 1.69 |
| Hydrogen Generation Plant | 0.05 | 0.26 | 0.4 | 0 | 0.01 | - | 0.71 |
| Hydrogen storage | 0.03 | 0.09 | 0.07 | 0 | 0 | - | 0.19 |
| Hydrogen Transportation | 0.05 | 0.03 | 0.05 | 0 | 0 | - | 0.13 |
| Total of all facilities | 0.27 | 1.15 | 0.92 | 0 | 0.02 | 0.36 | 2.72 |

**Figure 2.** Results of calculation for case 1

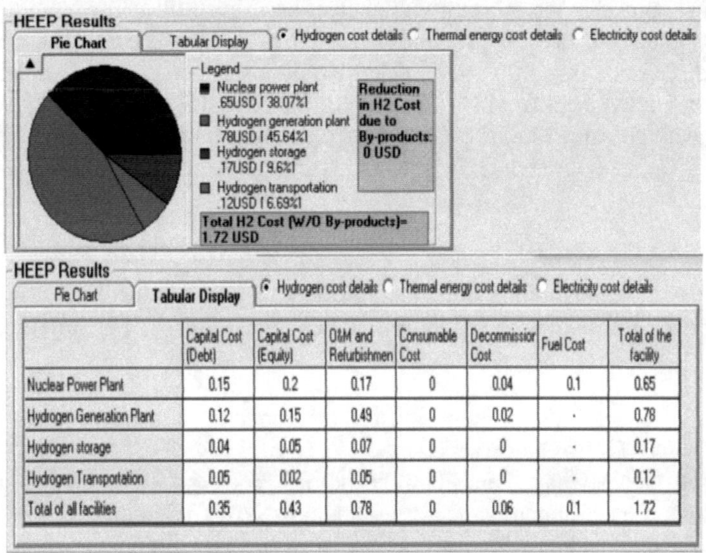


| | Capital Cost (Debt) | Capital Cost (Equity) | O&M and Refurbishmen | Consumable Cost | Decommissior Cost | Fuel Cost | Total of the facility |
|---|---|---|---|---|---|---|---|
| Nuclear Power Plant | 0.15 | 0.2 | 0.17 | 0 | 0.04 | 0.1 | 0.65 |
| Hydrogen Generation Plant | 0.12 | 0.15 | 0.49 | 0 | 0.02 | - | 0.78 |
| Hydrogen storage | 0.04 | 0.05 | 0.07 | 0 | 0 | - | 0.17 |
| Hydrogen Transportation | 0.05 | 0.02 | 0.05 | 0 | 0 | - | 0.12 |
| Total of all facilities | 0.35 | 0.43 | 0.78 | 0 | 0.06 | 0.1 | 1.72 |

**Figure 3.** Results of calculation for case 2

Results as shown in Figure 2 and 3 show cost break up. For case 1, the NPP cost is 1.69 USD (62.02%), hydrogen generation plant cost is 0.71 USD (26.13%), hydrogen storage 0.19 USD (7.15%) and hydrogen transportation 0.13 USD (4.7%). Cost breaks up for case 2 indicated that NPP cost is 0.65 USD (38.07%), hydrogen generation plant cost is 0.78 USD (45.64%), hydrogen storage 0.17 USD (9.6%) and hydrogen transportation 0.12 USD (6.69%). The cost of producing hydrogen depends on the capital, operation, maintenance, feedstock costs, (Kothari et al., 2008).

For instance, from feedstocks viewpoint, cost of hydrogen from fossil fuels is highly dependent on the price of natural gas and other conventional fuels, while the cost of hydrogen produced from renewable energy resources depends on the level of advancement of renewable energy technologies, and whether the system is connected or not to the electric grid.

The cost of hydrogen is highly influenced by the scale of the NPP as energy source for hydrogen production process heat and nuclear hydrogen generation plant. For example, 1 unit of 600 MWth HTGR produces hydrogen at a lower cost of 1.72

**Table 3.** Summary of HEEP calculation for 2 cases NPP

| | Case-1<br>2 HTGRs of<br>170 MWth/unit | Case 2,<br>1 HTGR of<br>600 MWth/unit |
|---|---|---|
| Nuclear Power Plant | 1.69 | 0.65 |
| Hydrogen Generation Plant | 0.71 | 0.78 |
| Hydrogen Storage | 0.19 | 0.17 |
| Hydrogen Transportation | 0.13 | 0.12 |
| Total of all Facilities | 2.72 | 1.72 |

US$/kg$H_2$ (case 2) compared to the 2 HTGR units of 170MWth each for which the hydrogen production cost obtained is 2.72 US$/kg$H_2$ (case 1).

## 5. Conclusion

Coupling hydrogen production plant to a nuclear energy system offers a multitude of advantages. One example is the coupling of HTGR with a SMR process for hydrogen production, capitalizing on the heat generated by the nuclear reactor and contributing to the reduction of the carbon dioxide emissions by replacing the gas fuel needed in the process with nuclear heat. In addition, by coupling the NPP with the hydrogen generation plant the thermal efficiency of NPP increases. The economic evaluation conducted in this study provides a good insight on the breakdown of costs and the results indicated a competitive value obtained when nuclear heat from HTGR is used (2.72$/kg H2 – case 1, 1.72$/kgH2 – case 2), as compared with an average value (2.3$/kgH2) obtained for hydrogen production by SMR method using gas as a fuel, which varies from about 1.25 US$/kg for large systems to about 3.50 US$/kg for small systems.[19]

**Acknowledgements**

The authors are grateful to Dr. Ibrahim Khamis for kindness in reviewing, correcting, and giving some suggestion to this paper and also as coordinator in the IAEA CRP of HEEP Software.

## References

[1] https://hydrogeneurope.eu/hydrogen-industry“Hydrogen in Industry”
[2] afdc.energy.gov>AFDC>Fuels&vehicles>
[3] Siti Alimah, Erlan Dewita,” Pemilihan Teknologi Produksi Hidrogen Dengan Memanfaatkan Energi Nuklir”, Jurnal Pengembangan Energi Nuklir, Vol 10, No 2 (2008)
[4] Pavlos Nikolaidis, Andreas Poullikkas,” A comparative overview of hydrogen production processes”, Renewable and Sustainable Energy Reviews 67 (2017) 597–611
[5] G. F. Naterer, O. Jaber, I. Dincer, Oshawa, Ontario, Canada,” Environmental Impact Comparison of Steam Methane Reformation and Thermochemical Processes of Hydrogen Production”, Proceedings WHEC 2010
[6] G. F. Naterer, O. Jaber, I. Dincer,” Environmental Impact Comparison of Steam Methane Reformation and Thermochemical Processes of Hydrogen Production”, Proceedings WHEC 2010
[7] IAEA Nuclear Energy Series No. NP-T-4.1,” Opportunities For Cogeneration With Nuclear Energy”, International Atomic Energy Agency Vienna, 2017
[8] Xing L. Yan , Hiroyuki Sato , Yukio Tachibana ,Kazuhiko Kunitomi & Ryutaro Hino,” Evaluation of high temperature gas reactor for demanding cogeneration load follow, Journal of Nuclear Science and Technology, volume 49 No.1, Januari (2012) pp.121-131
[9] Erlan Dewita, Siti Alimah,” Analisis Kinerja Bahan Bakar Reaktor Tipe HTGR Sebagai Penghalang Produk Fisi”, Jurnal Pengembangan Energi Nuklir Volume 19, No.1 (2017)
[10] Rachael Elder, Ray Allen,” Nuclear heat for hydrogen production: Coupling a very high/high temperature reactor to a hydrogen production plant”, Progress in Nuclear Energy 51 (2009) 500–525

[11] Olga BIČÁKOVÁ and Pavel STRAKA," The Resources And Methods Of Hydrogen Production", Acta Geodyn. Geomater., Vol. 7, No. 2 (158), 175–188, 2010
[12] Antonia Herzog, Marika Tatsutani," An Economic and Environmental Assessment of Hydrogen Production Pathways", Natural Resources Defense Council issue paper: November 2005
[13] Christos M. Kalamaras and Angelos M. Efstathiou," Hydrogen Production Technologies: Current State and Future Developments", Conference Papers in Energy, Volume 2013, Article ID 690627, 9 pages http://dx.doi.org/10.1155/2013/690627
[14] Roxanne Pinsky, Piyush Sabharwall, Jeremy Hartvigsen, James O'Brien," Comparative review of hydrogen production technologies for nuclear hybrid energy systems", Progress
[15] Erlan Dewita, Dedy Priambodo, Siti Alimah," Sistem Kopling PLTN Tipe HTGR dengan Instalasi Produksi Hidrogen", Prosiding Seminar Nasional Pengembangan Energi Nuklir IV, 2011 in Nuclear Energy 123 (2020) 103317
[16] IAEA TECDOC No. 1859," Examining the Technoeconomics of Nuclear Hydrogen Production and Benchmark Analysis of the IAEA HEEP Software, 2018
[17] Education.jlab.org>itselemental>ele001," It's Elemental-The Element Hydrogen_Jefferson lab"
[18] Roxanne Pinsky, Piyush Sabharwall, Jeremy Hartvigsen, James O'Brien," Comparative review of hydrogen production technologies for nuclear hybrid energy systems", Progress in Nuclear Energy 123 (2020) 103317
[19] DAGDOUGUI, H., SACILE, R., BERSANI, C., OUAMMI, A., Chapter 2 - Hydrogen Production and Current Technologies, in Hydrogen Infrastructure for Energy Applications, Academic Press, (2018).

# Microstructural and Micro-Chemical Evolutions in Irradiated UCO Fuel Kernels of AGR-1 and AGR-2 TRISO Fuel Particles

**Zhenyu Fu, Yong Yang, Isabella J. van Rooyen[1], Subhashish Meher[2], Boopathy Kombaiah[3]**

Nuclear Engineering Program, Department of Materials Science and Engineering, University of Florida, PO Box 116400, 100 Rhines Hall, Gainesville, FL 32611, USA
[1] Fuel Design and Development Department, Idaho National Laboratory, Idaho Falls, ID 83415-6188, USA
[2]Material Science Department, Idaho National Laboratory, Idaho Falls, ID 83415-6188, USA
[3]Advanced Characterization Department, Idaho National Laboratory, Idaho Falls, ID 83415-6188, USA

E-mail: yongyang@ufl.edu

**Abstract** – AGR-1 and AGR-2 tristructural-isotropic (TRISO) fuel particles were fabricated using slightly different fuel kernel chemical compositions, modified fabrication processes, different fuel kernel diameters, and changed $^{235}U$ enrichments. Extensive microstructural and analytical characterizations were conducted to correlate those differences with the fuel kernels' responses to neutron irradiations in terms of irradiated fuel microstructure, fission products' chemical and physical states, and fission gas bubble evolutions. The studies used state-of-the-art transmission electron microscopy (TEM) equipped with energy-dispersive x-ray spectroscopy (EDS) via four silicon solid-state detectors with super sensitivity and rapid speed. The TEM specimens were prepared from selected AGR-1 and AGR-2 irradiated fuel kernels exposed to safety testing after irradiation. The particles were chosen in order to create representative irradiation conditions with fuel burnup in the range of 10.8 to 18.6% fissions per initial metal atom (FIMA) and time-average volume-average temperatures varying from 1070 to 1287°C. The $^{235}U$ enrichment was 19.74 wt.% and 14.03 wt.% for the AGR-1 and AGR-2 fuel kernels, respectively. The TEM results showed significant microstructural reconstructions in the irradiated fuel kernels from both the AGR-1 and AGR-2 fuels. There are four major phases: fuel matrix of $UO_2$ and UC, $U_2RuC_2$, and $UMoC_2$—in the irradiated AGR-2 fuel kernel. Zr and Nd form a solid solution in the UC phase. The $UMoC_2$ phase often features a detectable concentration of Tc. Pd was mainly found to be located in the buffer layer or associated with fission gas bubbles within the $UMoC_2$ phase. EDS maps qualitatively show that rare-earth fission products (Nd et al.) preferentially reside in the $UO_2$ phase. In contrast, in the irradiated AGR-1 fuel kernel, no $U_2RuC_2$ or $UMoC_2$ precipitates were positively identified. Instead, there was a high number of rod-shaped precipitates enriched with Ru, Tc, Rh, and Pd observed in the fuel kernel center and edge zone. The differences in irradiated fuel kernel microstructural and micro-chemical evolution when comparing AGR-1 and AGR-2 TRISO fuel particles may result from a combination of irradiation temperature, fuel geometry, and chemical composition. However, irradiation temperature probably plays a more deterministic role. Limited electron energy-loss spectroscopy (EELS) characterizations of the AGR-2 fuel kernel show almost no carbon in the $UO_2$ phase, but a small fraction of oxygen was detected in the $UC/UMoC_2$ phase.

## 1. Introduction

U.S. Advanced Gas Reactor (AGR) tristructural-isotropic (TRISO) fuel is the culmination of significant efforts to overcome high-temperature performance limitations historically observed in irradiations by using an optimized fuel fabrication process and dedicated accelerated in-pile irradiations [1, 2]. In TRISO-coated fuel particles, a multi-layer system consisting of outer pyrolytic carbon (OPyC), SiC, inner pyrolytic carbon (IPyC), and a porous carbon buffer layer provides the fuel with the thermal-mechanical strength to contain fission products. Based on post-irradiation examination (PIE) results for fuel compacts and individual fuel particles from the first and second AGR experiments (AGR-1 and AGR-2), the overall fuel performance is excellent, with extremely low fuel-failure rates, while the SiC layer exhibits low fission product permeability [3-5].

Achieving high-quality, low-defect TRISO-coated fuels is a key technical milestone in supporting the development, licensing, and operation of high-temperature gas-cooled reactors. Activities in the AGR fuel development and qualification program include fuel fabrication and irradiation, PIE and safety testing, and related fuel performance modeling. PIE and safety tests are conducted to evaluate fission product retention during normal operation and accident scenarios, the microstructural evolution of fuel kernels and coatings, and the causes of coating failures.

Over the past 15 years, irradiation experiments on such fuels as AGR-1, AGR-2, and AGR-3/4 fuels were conducted in the Advanced Test Reactor, with PIE and safety tests on AGR-1/2 fuels completed with final advanced microscopy analysis currently still ongoing. Early lab-scale AGR-1 fuel demonstrated excellent in-pile performance with low fission-product release and very limited in-reactor coating failures. As opposed to AGR-1 fuel particles, AGR-2 fuel particles were produced in a pilot-scale coater. Systematic PIE microstructural and chemical characterization at scales spanning tens of microns to sub-nanometers is needed to fundamentally understand the impact of the fuel fabrication process and as-fabricated fuel properties on fuel performance during normal operation and accident conditions.

This paper presents microstructural characterization details from a safety-tested AGR-2 TRISO fuel kernel, offering a preliminary comparison of the microstructural and micro-chemical evolutions in irradiated fuel kernels of AGR-1 and AGR-2 fuels.

## 2. Experiment, sample description, and characterization methods

The TRISO fuel particle examined in this study was from Compact 2-2-2, irradiated in the AGR-2 experiment. Details of the AGR-2 irradiation experiment were reported by B. P. Collin [6]. After irradiation, Compact 2-2-2 was safety tested using the Core Conduction Cooldown Test Facility (CCCTF). Table 1 lists the irradiation and safety-testing parameters, as well as the $^{110m}$Ag-retention ratio based on both measured and calculated $^{110m}$Ag activity. The absence of detectable Ag indicates that this particle released most of its $^{110m}$Ag inventory during safety testing.

**Table 1.** Irradiated TRISO fuel particle AGR2-222-RS36, compact irradiation conditions, and subsequent safety-testing parameters.

| Parameter | Measurement |
|---|---|
| Burnup (% FIMA) | 12.55 |
| Fast neutron fluence (x $10^{25}$ n/m$^2$), E > 0.18 MeV | 3.39 |
| Time-average volume-average temperature (°C) | 1287 |
| Time-average peak temperature (°C) | 1354 |
| Post-irradiation safety testing | 300 hours at 1600°C |
| $^{110m}$Ag retention | Not detectable |
| Kernel diameter (μm) | 426.7 ± 8.8 |
| Density (g/cm$^3$) | 11.0 ± 0.030 |
| $^{235}$U enrichment (at.%) | 14.03 |
| As-fabricated chemistry, mole% | $UO_2$(71.4)/$UC_{1.86}$(12.3) /UC(16.4) |

Figure 1 shows a scanning electron microscope (SEM) image of the AGR2-222-RS36 particle, illustrating four TEM lamellae locations. These were specifically selected, as the fuel center and half-center have a higher temperature, the kernel edge zone may show the effects of fission fragment recoils, and the fuel kernel/buffer layer interface is of interest in showing fission product migration and the inter-diffusion behavior between the fuel kernel and the carbon-coating buffer layer.

TEM characterizations were conducted using a Talos F200X scanning/transmission electron microscope (STEM/TEM) located at the Irradiated Materials Characterization Laboratory (IMCL) at Idaho National Laboratory. The TEM is equipped with a super-X energy-dispersive x-ray spectroscopy (EDS) system and a Gatan's Enfinium ER (977) spectrometer for electron energy-loss spectroscopy (EELS) analysis. The super-X EDS system provides superior sensitivity and rapid speed for EDS analysis and mapping down to the atomic scale. However, it should be noted that due to the inaccuracy of the absorption correction for light elements (atomic number below 11), quantification of C and O using EDS is inaccurate and unreliable. Microstructural characterizations, elemental analysis, and phase identification were conducted using conventional STEM/TEM imaging, EDS elemental mapping, and selected area electron diffraction. Limited EELS analysis was conducted to quantify the contents of C and O in phases of interest.

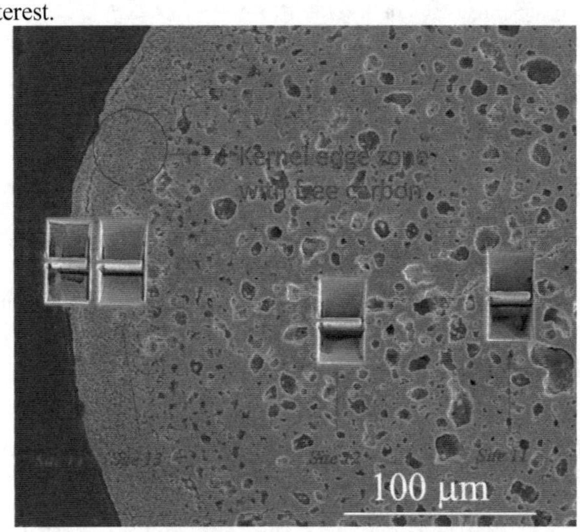


**Figure 1.** SEM image showing four TEM lamellae locations in the fuel particle AGR2-222-RS36: the fuel center, half-center, kernel edge zone with amorphous carbon, and the interface between the fuel kernel and the buffer layer.

## 3. Results

### *3.1. Irradiated AGR-2 Fuel Kernel*

*Fuel kernel center*

Figure 2 shows bright-field (BF) TEM overview images, along with diffraction patterns from fission-product phases of interest. Figure 3 presents elemental maps and line scans across the phases and interfaces of interest. Based on the EDS analysis and SAEDs, there are four primary phases in the irradiated fuel center lamella: (1) the fuel matrix of uranium dioxide in the fluorite structure ($UO_2$ phase), (2) rock-salt structure UC with Zr in the solution, (3) tetragonal-structure (point group 4/mmm) Ru-rich $U_2RuC_2$ phase, and (4) orthorhombic-structure Mo-rich $UMoC_2$ phase. The crystal structures of the $U_2RuC_2$ and $UMoC_2$ phases are confirmed via the diffraction patterns shown in Figure 2 and their chemical compositions (atomic percentages) are shown in the EDS line scans Figure 3. The $U_2RuC_2$ phase was found to consistently precipitate within the Zr-rich UC phase. Our results also show that the UC phase is depleted of Pd and rare-earth elements (Nd, Pr, etc.). These rare-earth elements may form oxides that are in a solid solution in the $UO_2$ phase, similar to what is observed in traditional $UO_2$ fuels. The $U_2MoC_2$ phase shows a slight enrichment of Tc and often resides next to the $UO_2$ phase.

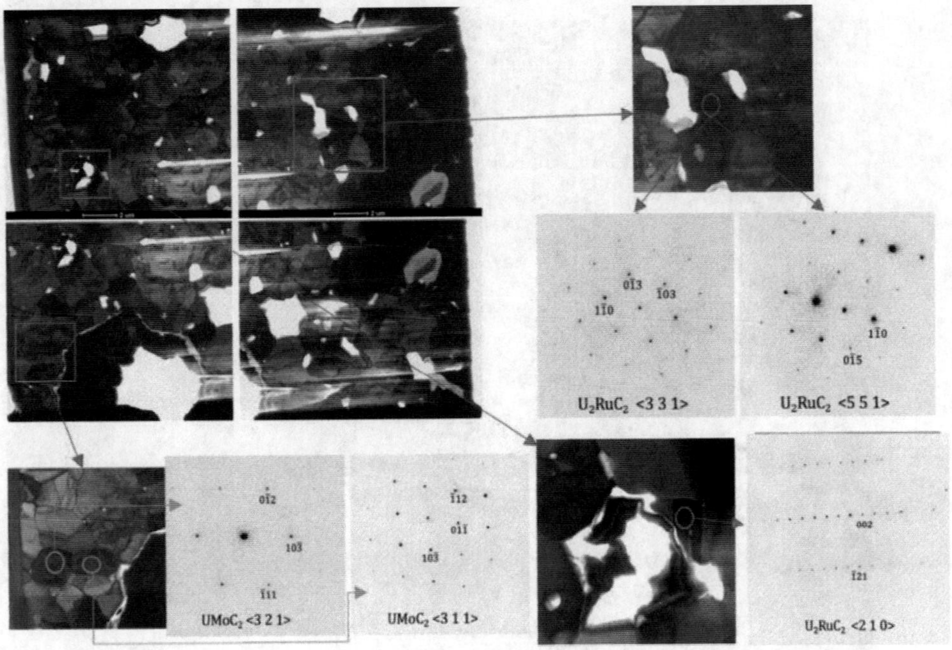


**Figure 2.** Overview of the fuel center lamellae and the diffraction from the fuel center.

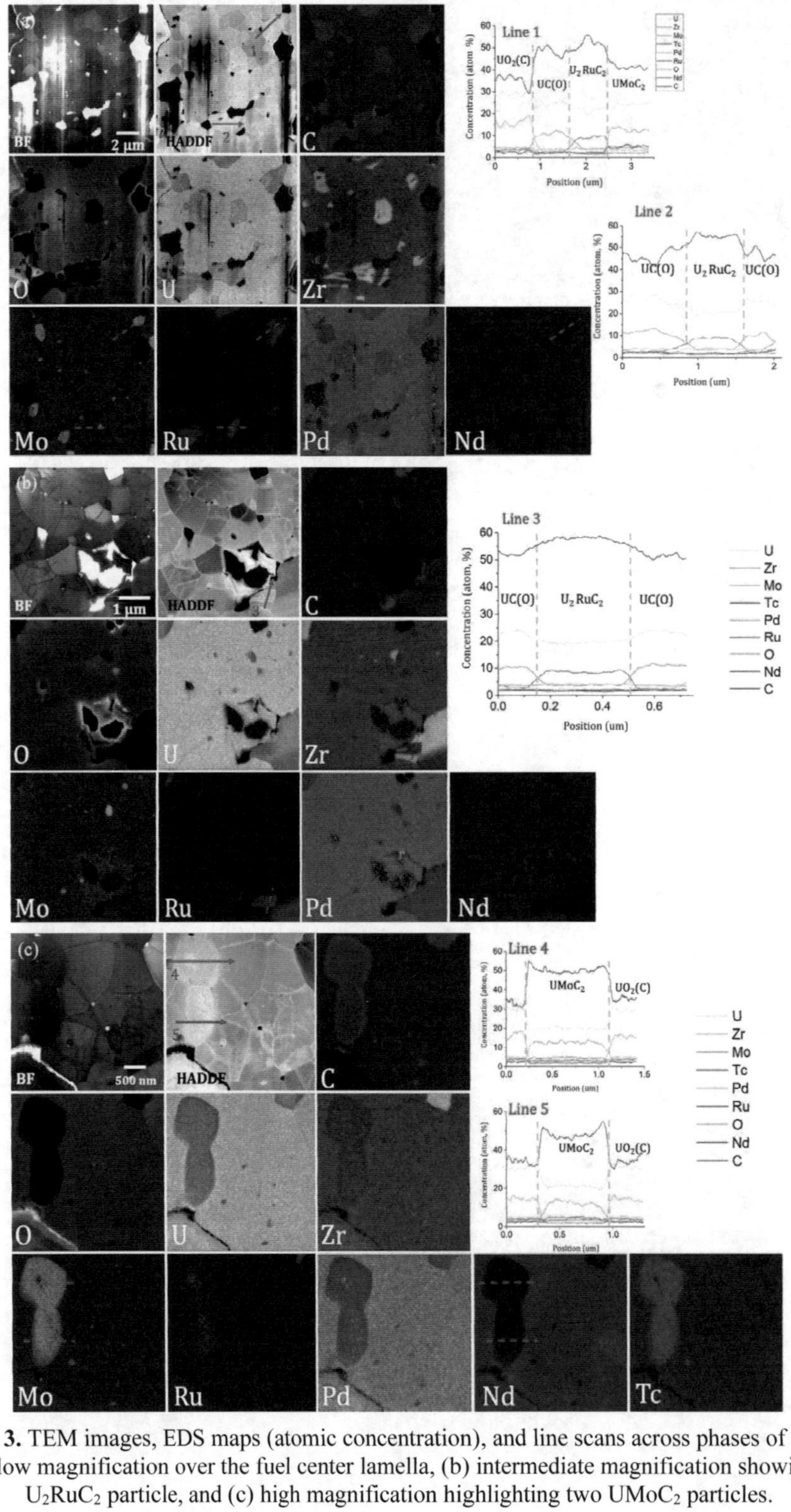


**Figure 3.** TEM images, EDS maps (atomic concentration), and line scans across phases of interest: (a) low magnification over the fuel center lamella, (b) intermediate magnification showing a $U_2RuC_2$ particle, and (c) high magnification highlighting two $UMoC_2$ particles.

*Fuel kernel half-center*

Figure 4 shows the fuel half-center overview BF TEM images along with diffraction patterns, and Figure 5 shows the EDS maps and line scans across the phases of interest. The UC phase is consistently enriched with Zr. As the $^{235}U$ atoms split into light elements, C combines with some fission products (FPs) to form carbides (e.g., ZrC and NdC). The metal-to-carbon bond is known to be significantly stronger than metal-to-metal bonds [7]. The C-Zr bonds are a combination of ionic and covalent bonds. Like most other transition metal carbides, ZrC is polar covalent [8], where the contribution of covalent bonding is significantly higher than that of ionic bonding, despite the considerable charge transfer (~0.42 e/pair) from Zr to the C atom [9]. Yasuo et al. [10] found that zirconium, niobium, and molybdenum monocarbides all have a NaCl-type structure and form a solid solution with UC. Many other studies on UC fuel also confirmed that the UC and ZrC are fully miscible [11-13]. With excess free carbon in the fuel kernels, production of Zr oxide is restrained. Carbothermal reduction of $ZrO_2$ to ZrC is often used by industry to synthesize ZrC. The phases of $U_2RuC_2$ and $UMoC_2$ are consistently identified in this fuel kernel half-center lamella, as well. Besides the fuel kernel, two $UC_2$ grains were identified, then highlighted using blue rectangles. The carbon map in Figure 5 (b) shows they have a relatively higher carbon content compared to neighboring grains.

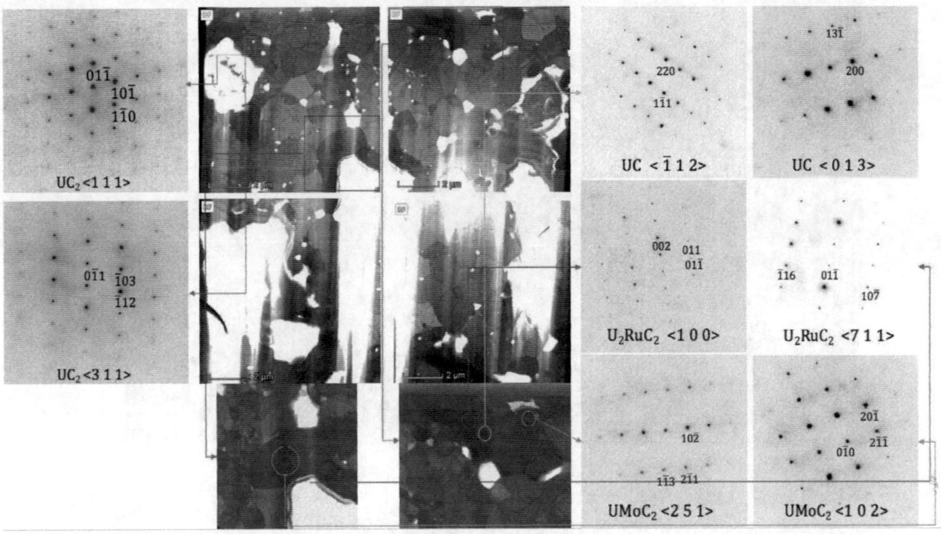


**Figure 4.** Overview TEM images of fuel half-center lamellae and diffraction patterns from selected areas.

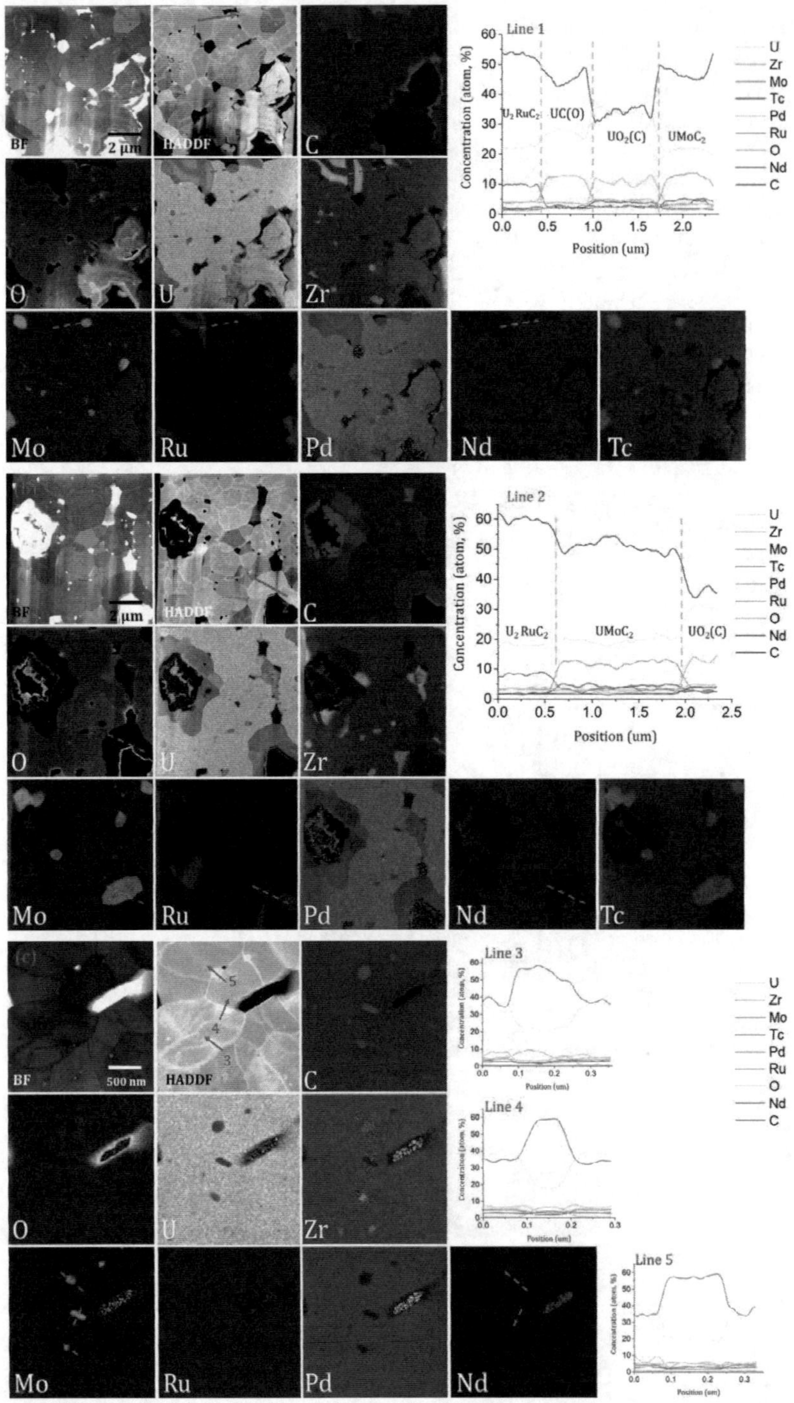


**Figure 5.** EDS maps (atomic concentration) and line scans across the phases of interest in the fuel kernel half-center TEM lamella: (a) top-right quarter, (b) top-left quarter, and (c) high magnification showing the submicron particles at the $UO_2$ grain boundaries.

*Fuel kernel edge*

Figure 6 and Figure **7** show BF TEM overview images, diffraction patterns of phases of interest, and the EDS maps and line scan from the fuel kernel edge zone. In the EDS maps, a high density of free carbon islands, shown in bright, can be clearly seen in the BF images. In contrast, no large pores were observed in this region—which is consistent with observations that the fuel edge has an appearance distinct from the rest of the fuel kernel, as shown in Figure 1. The $U_2RuC_2$ phase was found in the elongated shape shown in Figure 7 (a) of the Ru map.

Furthermore, diffraction patterns from Figure 6 reveal that $U_2RuC_2$ and the UC matrix form a coherent interface. They have an orientation relationship of (001)UC//(110)$U_2RuC_2$. Qualitatively, there is a higher number density of $U_2RuC_2$ precipitates in the fuel edge than in the fuel kernel center and half-center. Consistently, rare-earth elements are depleted in the UC, $U_2RuC_2$, and $UMoC_2$ phases. As shown in Figure 7 (d), very fine fission gas bubbles appear in the Mo-rich phase, accompanied by enrichments of Ru and Pd. Some Widmanstatten-type $UC_2$ plates were expected within the UC matrix, as excessive carbon results from the interdiffusion between the fuel kernel and the carbon buffer layer. However, only Widmanstatten-type $U_2RuC_2$ was found based on our TEM characterizations.

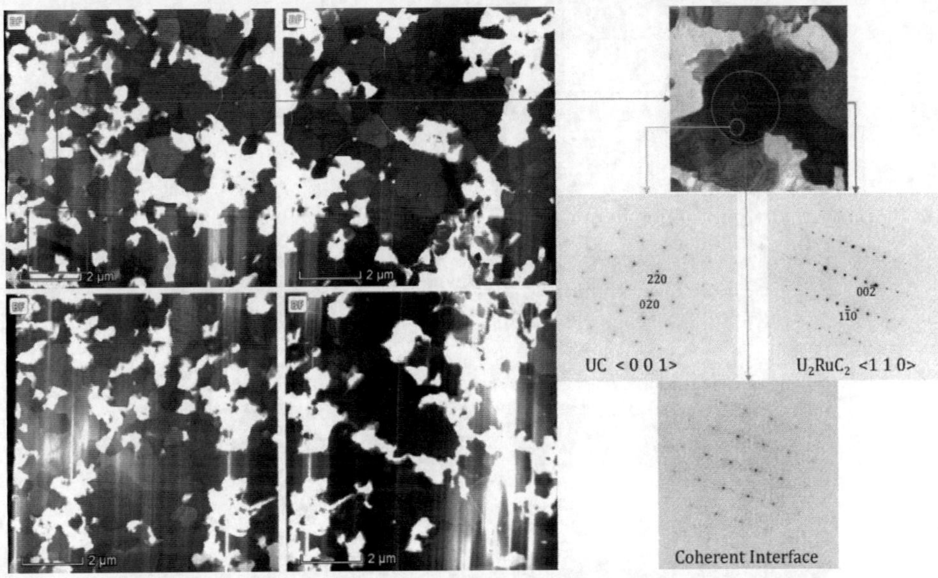


**Figure 6.** Overview of the fuel recoil zone lamellae and diffraction patterns from selected areas.

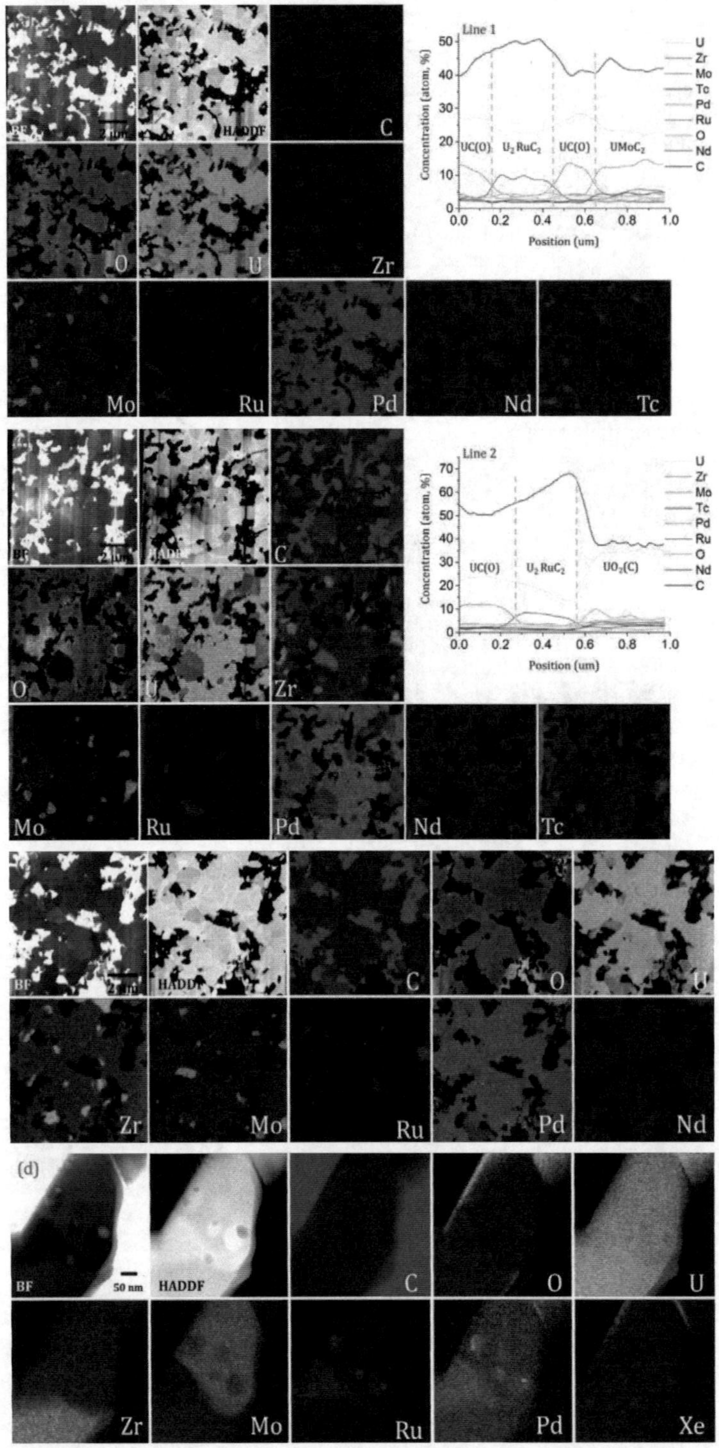


**Figure 7.** EDS elemental maps (atomic concentration) with line scan from (a) the top-left quarter of the kernel edge lamella and (b) the bottom-left quarter, (c) elemental maps from the top-right quarter, and (d) high EDS maps from a selected area containing fission gas bubbles.

*Buffer-kernel interface*

Figure 8 and Figure 9 show the overview BF TEM images, the EDS maps, and the line scans from the interface lamella. Clearly, the interface between the carbon buffer layer and the fuel kernel survived the in-pile irradiation and safety test. The kernel side mainly consists of $UO_2$, free carbon, and Zr-rich phases. Iodine-rich particles are also identified, as shown in Figure 9 (b). One interesting observation is that Pd, Xe, and I are present together at the interface. Particles enriched with Xe and I are highlighted by the dashed circles in Figure 9 (a) and (b) (Note that there are iodine isotopes that are precursors to Xe isotopes). The HFR-EU1bis experiment [14] ($UO_2$ kernel) and limited electron probe micro-analyzer (EPMA) study (AGR-1 particle) [15] both showed that residual I, Xe, and Cs mainly resided within the fuel kernel edge and the buffer layer.

On the carbon buffer layer side (Figure 9 (c)), U along with other fission products such as Zr, Mo, Nd, Xe, Ag, and Pd as small particles dispersed in the buffer layer. The origination of the uranium-rich particles can be from the buffer layer coating process. Additional characterization of the carbon buffer layer region of the as fabricated TRISO fuel particle will provide clarification. However, it shows that Xe, Pd, and Ag might become immobile as they form compounds with other elements even though during the irradiation and safety test, the Ag-self becomes very mobile and majority of it was released from the compact.

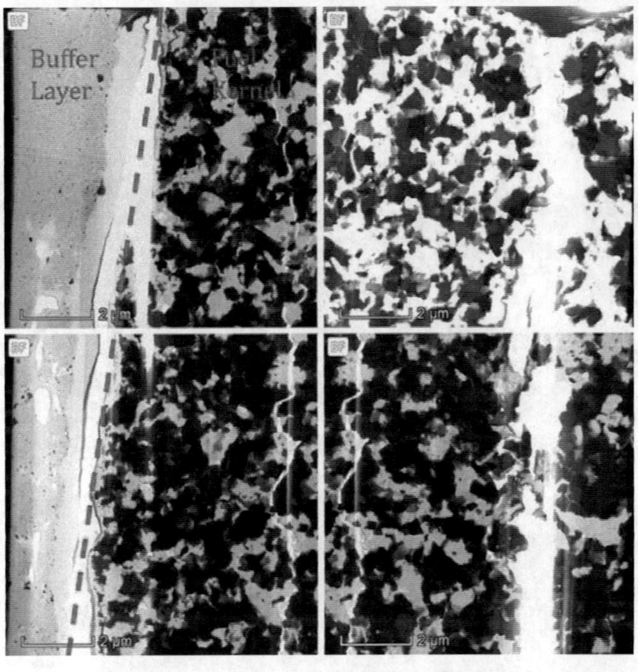


**Figure 8.** Overview TEM images of kernel-buffer interface lamellae.

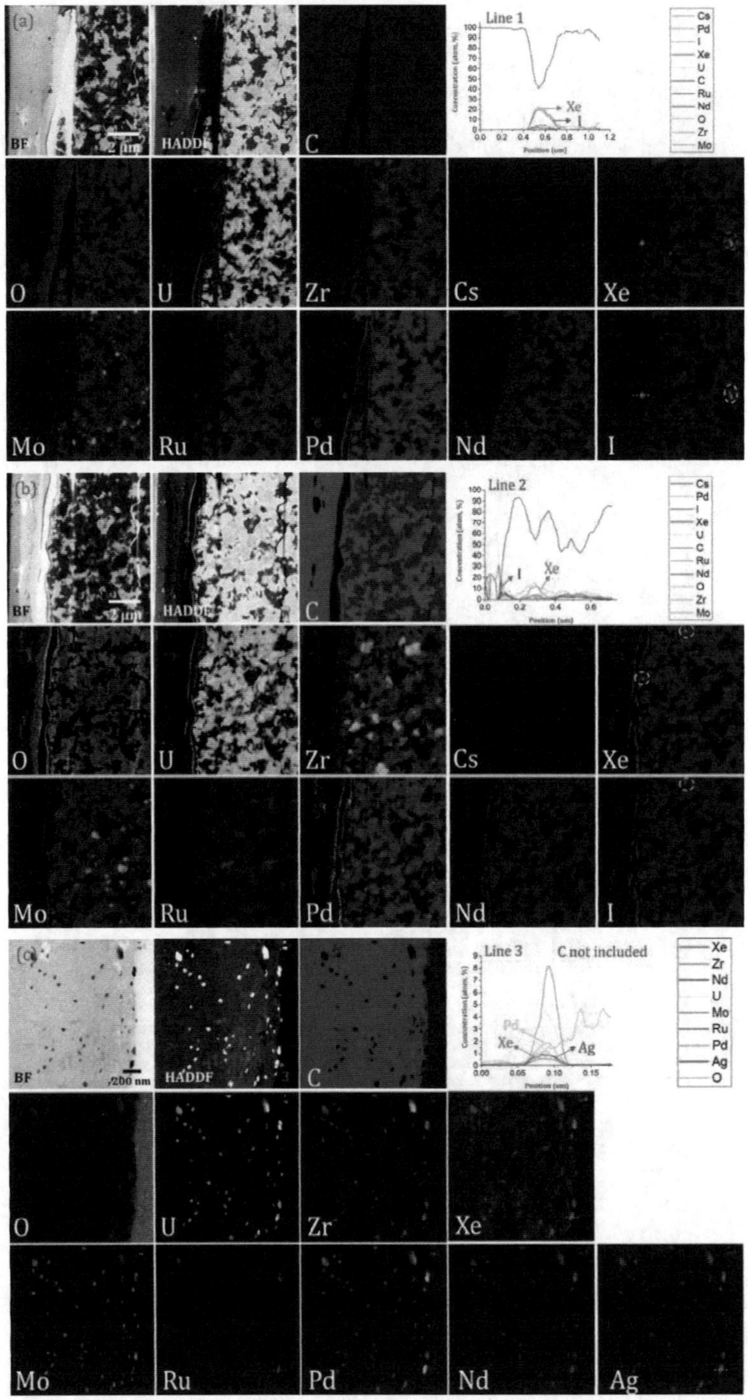


**Figure 9.** EDS elemental maps (atomic concentration) with line scans from the (a) top-left quarter of the buffer-kernel interface lamella, (b) bottom-left quarter of the buffer-kernel interface lamella, and (c) the buffer layer zone that includes dispersed submicron particles (the thin layer on the far right contains both O and C based on the area integrated EDS spectrum and figure (b)).

*3.2. EELS Characterization*

Quantification of carbon and oxygen was attempted using EELS characterization. Figure 10 shows the EELS spectra and carbon/oxygen maps of the areas selected from the fuel kernel center and half-center, respectively. The relative atomic concentrations of C and O are listed in Table 2. In both the fuel center and half-center, the $UO_2$ phase consistently showed almost no carbon, whereas the UC/$UMoC_2$ phase contained a small fraction of oxygen. The presence of oxygen may be attributed to dissolved fission product oxides in the carbides. Unfortunately, the sample size was limited, as a large portion of the TEM lamellae was too thick for EELS characterization, preventing the C and O peaks from being clearly observed. In addition, the selected energy window was made too wide by considering short exposure times, causing accurate peak fitting to be very challenging. These initial EELS examinations provided lessons learned moving forward.

**Table 2.** Relative carbon and oxygen concentrations in the three highlighted areas in the EELS spectra.

| Area | Element | Relative concentration (at.%) |
|---|---|---|
| A1 | C | $0 \pm 6 \times 10^{-6}$ |
| | O | $100.0 \pm 5.0$ |
| A2 | C | $83.0 \pm 4.0$ |
| | O | $16.5 \pm 0.7$ |
| A3 | C | $83.0 \pm 4.0$ |
| | O | $16.5 \pm 0.7$ |

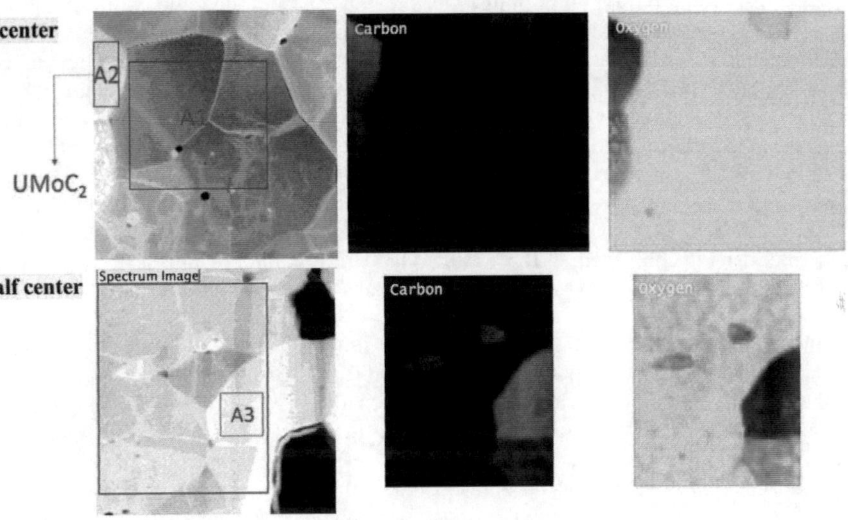


**Figure 10.** EELS spectra and carbon/oxygen maps of selected areas from the fuel kernel center and half center

## 4. Discussion

*4.1. Fission Products' Physical States in Irradiated TRISO Fuel Kernels*

The presence of $U_2RuC_2$ and $UMoC_2$ in the irradiated UCO fuel kernel is consistent with the simulation studies, in that they are two ternary compounds in irradiated uranium carbide fuels [10, 11]. A higher number density of $U_2RuC_2$ precipitates was found in the fuel edge and interface zones than in the fuel kernel center or half-center regions. In the unirradiated UCO fuel kernel, $UC_2$ appears as thin plate within the UC phase [16]. It is suspected that the higher density of $U_2RuC_2$ precipitates is related to excessive $UC_2$ precipitates in the as-fabricated fuel kernel. The $UC_2$ plate may serve as a precursor phase for the $U_2RuC_2$ formation phase. However, this correlation needs to be proven through additional characterizations of the unirradiated fuel kernels. Furthermore, previous thermodynamic studies of the U-C-Ru and U-C-Mo systems indicate that $U_2RuC_2$ and $UMoC_2$ are two primary solid phases in their ternary system [17, 18]. The high-temperature safety test probably promotes formation of $U_2RuC_2$. As there are very little $U_2RuC_2$ observed in the non-safety-tested AGR-2 UCO kernel irradiated to a similar burnup level [19]. Quite often in the $UMoC_2$ phase, a significant concentration of Tc is observed. The Tc probably forms a $UTcC_2$ phase that is soluble in the $UMoC_2$ phase, and they both have an orthorhombic structure with very close lattice parameters [20].

As shown in the previous sections, the UC phase is depleted of Pd and rare-earth elements (e.g., Nd). For the Pd, no ternary compounds are identified in the U-C-Pd system [21]. Pd metal, as well as the Pd-rich phase, was found in high vapor pressure regions and migrates to the colder region [22-25]. An abundance of rich particles only appears in the carbon buffer layer—which is consistent with other studies that show a high number density of Pd particles in the TRISO coating layers [26-28]. Compared with the UC phase, the $UO_2$ phase is slightly enriched with Pd, as shown in the EDS maps. This is consistent with our previous study using atom probe tomography [29]. However, the concentration of Pd in the $UO_2$ phase is too low to be quantified through EDS measurement. Its chemical and physical states are yet to be determined.

In well-studied Light Water Reactor $UO_2$ fuels, Nd and other rare-earth elements form oxide fission products and dissolve in the $UO_2$ fuel matrix [30]. In the UC phase, these rare-earth elements can form carbides , but with very low solubility [10, 12]. It was found that these rare-earth fission product carbides diffused to the colder region and devoid in a carbide fuel matrix at high temperatures (> 1000°C) [12]. These carbide-forming rare-earth elements become oxide ($REC_xO_y$) at a relatively low oxygen potential compared to other carbide FPs (e.g., ZrC and NbC) (from 1000°C to 1600°C). $REC_xO_y$ will diffuse and dissolve in the $UO_2$ phase [31]. Or, some carbides that form rare-earth elements will dissolve in the oxide fuel, depending on solubility limits. Our previous atom probe tomography studies showed that many lanthanide fission products tend to remain in solution of the $UO_2$ phase [29].

A simulation study by Yasuo et al. [10] showed that the principal condensed fuel matrix phases in an irradiated UC fuel should be UC and $U_2C_3$. However, $U_2C_3$ was not positively identified in unirradiated or irradiated UCO fuel kernels [29, 32, 33]. This is probably because of the presence of the $UO_2$ phase in the fuel matrix. It was also reported that $U_2C_3$, is a metastable phase at high temperature (> 1830°C), and decomposes to UC and C during the cooling process [34, 35]. At irradiation peak temperature, UC and $UC_2$ are completely soluble with each other [34]. Some $UC_2$ and/or UC will become oxides to balance the excessive free oxygen liberated from the irradiated $UO_2$ phase. As irradiation ends and the fuel starts to cool down, $U_2RuC_2$ rather than $UC_2$ will form Widmanstatten-type precipitates in the UC matrix. This explains why only few $UC_2$ grains were observed after irradiation at a burnup of 12.55% FIMA.

In this safety-tested irradiated AGR-2 fuel kernel, fission gas bubbles were only observed in the Mo-rich phase and are often accompanied by fine Pd and Ru-rich particles. The presence of Xe associated with the noble metal phase particles was also observed in the $UO_2$ spent fuel Zr cladding liner [36]. The exact chemical mechanisms governing this co-diffusion/co-precipitation behavior are yet to be understood. In the previous non-safety-tested AGR-1 fuel kernel, a large number of fission gas bubbles was found in the Zr-rich UC phase [29]. Most likely, the high-temperature safety testing removed the mobile fission gas bubbles, whereas the fission gas bubbles associated with Pd and Ru-rich particles survived.

### *4.2. Comparison between the Fuel Kernel Irradiation Responses of AGR-1 and AGR-2 TRISO Fuel Particles*

Both the AGR-1 and AGR-2 UCO fuel particle kernels are a mixture of $UO_2$ and UC, but with a different nominal as-fabricated stoichiometry [37]. Table 3 lists the dimensions, $^{235}U$ enrichment, and chemistry of the AGR-1 and AGR-2 UCO particle fuel kernels. AGR-1 UCO kernels have an overall composition of 67.9 mol%$UO_2$-31.7mol%UC with only a trace of $UC_{1.86}$. In contrast, AGR-2 UCO fuel kernels have an overall composition of 71.4mol%$UO_2$-12.3 mol%$UC_{1.86}$-16.4mol%UC. The AGR-2 UCO particles have a larger fuel kernel diameter, but lower $^{235}U$ enrichment compared to AGR-1 fuel particles. The AGR-2 UCO fuel kernels also have a noticeably different appearance, showing a very smooth, reflective surface and a greater homogeneity of chemistry and density [37].

**Table 3.** Dimensions, $^{235}U$ enrichment, and chemistry of AGR-1 and AGR-2 UCO particle fuel kernels [37].

| UCO fuel kernel | | AGR-1 | AGR-2 |
|---|---|---|---|
| Diameter (μm) | | 348.4 ± 8.3 | 426.7 ± 8.8 |
| Density (g/cm$^3$) | | 10.7 ± 0.026 | 11.0 ± 0.030 |
| $^{235}U$ enrichment (at.%) | | 19.74 | 14.03 |
| Chemistry | $UO_2$ | 67.9 | 71.4 |
| (mole%) | $UC_{1.86}$ | 0.4 | 12.3 |
| | UC | 31.7 | 16.4 |

The fuel kernel of the irradiated AGR-1-433-004 TRISO particle was examined in detail, and the microstructural evolution and fission product results were published in a journal article [38]. To better foster a one-to-one comparison, the irradiation conditions and safety testing are explained in [38].

Figure 11 shows a SEM image along with the TEM lamella locations in the irradiated AGR1-433-004 fuel particle. Compared with the AGR2-222-RS36 fuel particle kernel shown in Figure 1 the difference in pore structure is notable. Even though the AGR-1 fuel has a much higher burnup level, the pores are relatively small and evenly distributed. Although it seems that irradiation temperature plays a more pronounced role, as the time-average volume-average temperature for the AGR-2 compact is about 200°C higher than that for the AGR-1 fuel particle, it was found in other studies, that the pore structure can be significantly different from particles from the same compact [39]. High irradiation temperature also promotes a larger temperature gradient, as evidenced by the fact that the irradiated AGR-1 fuel kernel has a relatively homogeneous microstructure compared to the AGR-2 fuel kernel.

**Table 4.** Compact Irradiation and subsequent safety-testing parameters of the AGR1-433-004 fuel particle.

| | |
|---|---|
| Burnup (%FIMA) | 18.63 |
| Fast neutron fluence (x $10^{25}$ n/m$^2$), E > 0.18 MeV | 4.16 |
| Time-average volume-average temperature (°C) | 1094 |
| Time-average peak temperature (°C) | 1179 |
| Post-irradiation safety testing | 300 hours at 1600°C |
| $^{110m}Ag$ retention | 98% |

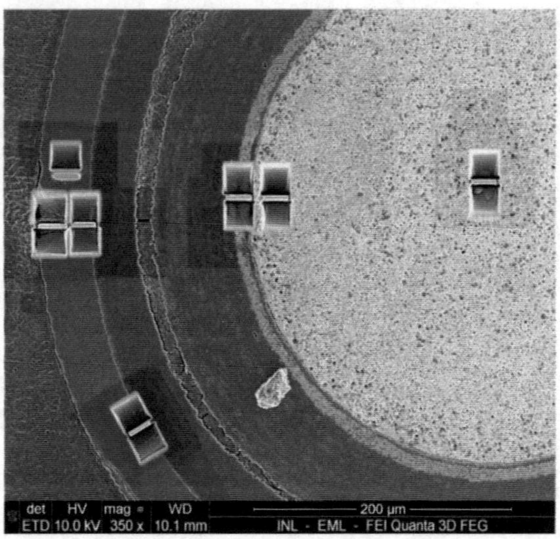


**Figure 11.** SEM image of the AGR1-433-004 fuel kernel, along with TEM lamella locations.

No $U_2RuC_2$ or $UMoC_2$ precipitates were positively identified in the AGR-1 fuel kernels. The absence of those two types of precipitates can be attributed to many possible factors, e.g. irradiation temperature, fuel kernel stoichiometry variation, and irradiation history [38]. As highlighted by dashed red circles in Figure 12, there is a large number of rod-shaped precipitates in the fuel center and edge zone of the AGR-1 fuel kernel. EDS maps showed that the precipitates are enriched with Rh, Ru, Tc, Pd, and/or Mo. However, this rod-like type of precipitate was not identified in the irradiated AGR-2 fuel kernel. In the buffer layer of the AGR-1 fuel kernel, there were large particles consisting of U, Nd, Rh, Zr, Mo, and other fission products.

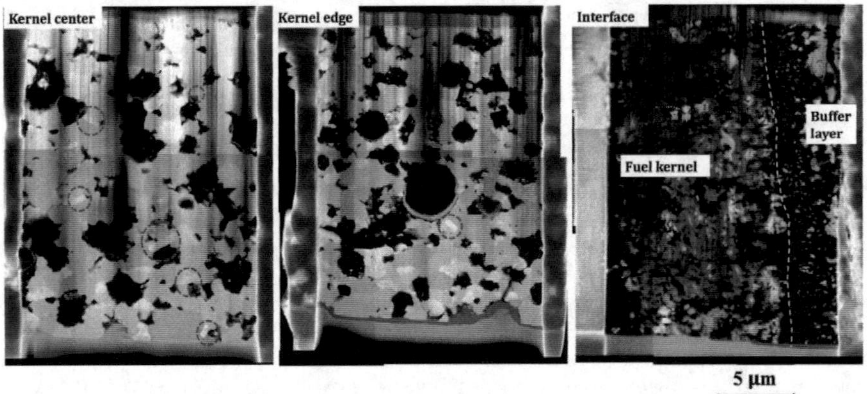


**Figure 12.** High-angle annular dark-field STEM images of the lamellae from the irradiated AGR1-433-004 fuel kernel.

## 5. Conclusions

Systematic TEM characterizations show four primary phases in the safety-tested irradiated AGR-2 particle fuel kernel. They are fuel matrix $UO_2$ and UC, $U_2RuC_2$, and $UMoC_2$. The $UMoC_2$ phase often shows a detectable concentration of Tc. Zr and Nb form a solid solution in the UC phase. Pd was mainly found in the buffer layer or is associated with fission gas bubbles within the $UMoC_2$ phase. Two $UC_2$ grains were identified in the fuel kernel half-center lamella. Limited EELS characterizations show almost no carbon in the $UO_2$ phase, while a small fraction of oxygen was detected in the UC/$UMoC_2$ phase.

A comparison between the irradiated AGR-1 and AGR-2 fuel kernels shows distinguishable differences in their microstructural and micro-chemical evolutions upon irradiation.

These differences may result from a combination of irradiation temperature, fuel geometry and chemical composition. However, irradiation temperature likely plays a more deterministic role.

Possible next activities include the benchmarking of the presence of high yield fission products like Sr vs the predicted fission product inventory generated during irradiation in compacts.

However, by considering the fact that each fuel particle is out of 4000+ in a TRISO fuel compact, and there are considerable differences in irradiation temperature and initial fuel kernel microstructure. The reported results may not explicitly describe the average behavior of the whole TRISO fuel compact.

## Acknowledgements

This work was sponsored by the U.S. Department of Energy, Office of Nuclear Energy, under U.S. Department of Energy Idaho Operations Office Contract DE-AC07-05ID14517, as part of the Advanced Reactor Technology Program and the Nuclear Science User Facilities experiment.

## References

[1] W. Schenk, H. Nabielek, "High temperature reactor fuel fission product release and distribution at 1600 to 1800°C" Nuclear Technology, 96 323-336 1991.
[2] K. Minato, et al., "Release behavior of metallic fission products from HTGR fuel particles at 1600 to 1900°C" Journal of Nuclear Materials, 202 47-53 1993.

[3] J.D. Hunn, et al., "Dection and analysis of particles with failed SiC in AGR-1 fuel compacts" Nuclear Engineering and Design, 306 36-46 2016.
[4] J.D. Hunn, et al., "Initial examination of fuel compacts and TRISO particles from the US AGR-2 irradiation test" Nuclear Engineering and Design, 329 89-101 2018.
[5] R.N. Morris, et al., "Initial results from safety testing of US AGR-2 irradiation test fuel" J. Nucl. Mater., 329 124-133 2018.
[6] B.P. Collin, INL, INL/EXT-14-32277, 2018.
[7] Y. Katoh, et al., "Properties of zirconium carbide for nuclear fuel applications" Journal of Nuclear Materials, 441 718-742 2013.
[8] A. Arya, E.A. Carter, "Structure, bonding, and adhesion at the ZrC(100)/Fe(110) interface from first principles" Surface Science, 560 103-120 2004.
[9] J. Li, et al., "Force-based many-body interatomic potential for ZrC" Journal of Applied Physics, 93 9072-9085 2003.
[10] A. Yasuo, et al., "Chemical state of fission products in irradiated uranium carbide fuel" Journal of Nuclear Materials, 151 63-71 1987.
[11] U. Benedict, et al., "Study of Uranium-Plutonium Carbide-Based Fuel Simulating High Burnup" Nuclear Technology, 35 154-161 2017.
[12] Benedict, U., Commission of the European Communites, EUR 5776 e, 1977.
[13] H. Holleck, H. Kleykamp, "Thermodynamics of multi-component systems containing UC and PuC" Journal of Nuclear Materials, 32 1-19 1969.
[14] M. Barrachin, et al., "Fission-product behaviour in irradiated TRISO-coated particles: Results of the HFR-EU1bis experiment and their interpretation" Journal of Nuclear Materials, 415 104-116 2011.
[15] K.E. Wright, I.J.v. Rooyen, 8th International Topical Meeting on High Temperature Reactor Technology, HTR 2016.
[16] I.J.v. Rooyen, et al., "Micro- and Nano- Characterization of Nuetron Irradiated TRISO Coated Particles" Microsc. Microanal., 25 (Suppl 2) 1612-1613 2019.
[17] K. Korniyenko, "Carbon–Molybdenum–Uranium" Refractory metal systems, 491-515 2010.
[18] K. Korniyenko, Carbon–Ruthenium–Uranium, in: G. Effenberg, S. Ilyenko (Eds.) Landolt-Börnstein - Group IV Physical Chemistry 11C4 Springer, Berlin, Heidelberg, 2007,
[19] Z. Fu, et al., Microstructural and micro-chemical comparisons of AGR-1 and AGR-2 TRISO UCO Fuel Kernels Irradiated in the Advanced Test Reactor TMS 2019 March 10-14, 2019, San Antonio, Texas.
[20] J.D. Farr, M.G. Bowman, LANL, 1963.
[21] V. Ivanchenko, T. Pryadko, Carbon-Palladium-Uranium, in: G. Effenberg, S. Ilyenko (Eds.) Landolt-Börnstein - Group IV Physical Chemistry 11C4 Springer, Berlin, Heidelberg, 2007,
[22] H.F. I. Sato, T. Arima, K. Idemitsu, K. Yamamoto "Behavior of metallic fission products in uranium-plutonium mixed oxide fuel" Journal of Nuclear Materials, 273 239-247 1999.
[23] F.T. Ewart, R.G. Taylor, "The chemical effects of composition changes in irradiated oxide fuel materials II-fission product segregation and chemical equilibria " Journal of Nuclear Materials, 61 254-270 1976.
[24] K. Maeda, T. Asaga, "Change of fuel-to-cladding gap width with the burn-up in FBR MOX fuel irradiated to high burn-up" Journal of Nuclear Materials, 327 1-10 2004.
[25] K. Maeda, et al., "Distributions of volatile fission products in or near the fuel-cladding gap of the FBR MOX fuel pins irradiated to high burn-up" Journal of Nuclear Materials, 344 274-280 2005.
[26] I.J. van Rooyen, et al., "Identification of silver and palladium in irradiated TRISO coated particles of the AGR-1 experiment" Journal of Nuclear Materials, 446 178-186 2014.
[27] S. Meher, et al., "A Novel Dual-Step Nucleation Pathway in Crystalline Solids under Neutron Irradiation" Sci Rep, 8 98 2018.
[28] T.M. Lillo, I.J. van Rooyen, "Associations of Pd, U and Ag in the SiC layer of neutron-irradiated TRISO fuel" Journal of Nuclear Materials, 460 97-106 2015.
[29] I.J. van Rooyen, et al., Microstructure and fission product distribution examination in th UCO kernel of TRISO fuel particles, HTR 2018-3012, HTR 2018, Warsaw, Poland, (2018)
[30] H. Kleykamp, "The chemical state of the fission products in oxide fuels" Journal of Nuclear Materials, 131 221-246 1985.

[31] J.W. McMurray, et al., "Determining the minimum required uranium carbide content for HTGR UCO fuel kernels" Annals of Nuclear Energy, 104 237-242 2017.
[32] J.D. Hunn, et al., Oak Ridge National Laboratory, ORNL/TM-2005/541, 2005.
[33] J.A. Phillips, et al., "Fabrication of uranium oxycarbide kernels and compacts for HTR fuel" Nuclear Engineering and Design, 251 261-281 2012.
[34] Mallett, M. W., et al., "The Uranium-Carbon System" Journal of Electrochemistry Soceity, 99 197-204 1952.
[35] H. HoLleck, H. KLeykamp, Compounds of Uranium with Carbon., in: R. Keim, C. kELLER (Eds.) U Uranium. Gmelin Handbook of Inorganic Chemistry / Gmelin Handbuch der Anorganischen Chemie, Springer, Berlin, Heidelberg, 1986,
[36] R.A. Clark, et al., "Distribution of metallic fission-product particle in the cladding liner of spent nuclear fuel" npj Material Degradation, 4 https://doi.org/10.1038/s41529-41019-40107-41520 2020.
[37] J.A. Phillips, et al., "Fabrication of uranium oxycarbide kernels and compacts for HTR fuel" Nucl. Eng. Des., 251 261-281 2012.
[38] Z. Fu, et al., "Microstructure and Fission Products in the UCO Kernel of an AGR-1 TRISO Fuel Particle after Post Irradiation Safety Testing" Journal of Nuclear Materials, 528 151884-151892 2019.
[39] G. R. Bower, S. A. P;oger, P.A.D. Demkowicz, John. D. Hunn, Measurement of kernel swelling and buffer densification in irradiated UCO-TRISO particles, Journal of Nuclear Materials, 486(2017)339-349

Journal of Physics: Conference Series **2048** (2021) 012007 doi:10.1088/1742-6596/2048/1/012007

# Raman Spectroscopy Studies of TRISO-Particle Fuel

**Zuzanna M Krajewska, and WGudowski**

National Centre for Nuclear Researchul. Andrzeja Sołtana 7 Otwock, Świerk 05-400 Poland

phone: +48 792525066, email: zuzanna.krajewska@ncbj.gov.pl

**Abstract.** Development of High Temperature Gas-cooled Reactors opens new horizons for nuclear power in Poland. Good understanding of the failure-free performance of Tri-structural ISOtropic (TRISO)-particle fuel is a key for the safe and efficient operation of those reactors. It is also essential to avoid potential errors in TRISO fuel production for the HTR program in Poland. In a longer perspective to ensure the highest possible quality of the TRISO fuel fabrication and storage before loading into the reactor core, it is necessary to control the quality of the TRISO-particle fuel in order to understand the aging of fresh fuel. Nevertheless, such a solution requires to determine whether the passage of time affects the occurrence of changes in TRISO fuel layer's structure and at the same time whether it contributes to increasing the probability of damage to the examined fuel material. For this purpose, it is planned to perform an experiment on different types of TRISO fuel, produced in different periods of time. The comparative analysis will be based mainly on the experimental method of Raman spectroscopy.

## 1. Introduction

Poland does not have at present any nuclear power plants in spite of the fact that the development of nuclear technology started already in mid the 50s of the last century. In 1955 the nuclear research institute was established in Świerk, in the outskirts of the capital city Warszawa. The primary mission for this institute was the development of nuclear technology and neutron physics around the first olish research reactor EWA. Today this institute is called the National Centre for Nuclear Research (NCBJ) in Otwock-Świerk and continues its research mission with the MARIA research reactor a successor of reactor EWA.

The first attempt to construct a nuclear power plant in Poland took place in the 1980s with the usage of the technology of the VVER-440 type nuclear reactor at Żarnowiec site, close to the Baltic city Gdańsk. However, the impact of the Chernobyl accident in 1986 and then dramatic political transformations in Poland and other Central European countries caused the construction of the reactor first to stop and then the project to be completely abandoned. Suspended for years, the plan for the construction of the Polish nuclear power plant was reopened in the 2000s. The current program called the Polish Nuclear Power Program (PPEJ) was approved by the government in 2014 and updated in 2020. The objective of the PPEJ program is to construct and commission a Generation III+ nuclear power plants with a pressurized water reactor (PWR) type of a total installed nuclear capacity between 6 and 9 GWe [1].

The PPEJ program envisions also the construction of high-temperature gas cooled (HTGR) research reactor at NCBJ. HTGR research reactor under development at NCBJ is a Generation-IV (Gen-IV) reactor type, with a graphite-moderated, helium-cooled core fueled with uranium TRISO type fuel. Gen-IV is a common name for ongoing research projects of future-oriented different nuclear reactor concepts. The basic features to be met by those reactors are safety, reliability, efficiency, and low production costs. HTGR type of reactor provides several inherent safety advantages due to specific design features, physical laws, and due to reactor materials behavior, such as low-power density in the reactor core, a large heat capacity of the core, and an inert coolant that can mitigate severe accidental consequences during loss-of-coolant accident scenarios. Due to these specific features and due excellent performance of the TRISO based nuclear fuel the high temperature reactor has been recognized as an inherently safe reactor type.

Historically, two concepts of the HTGR have been developed, the pebble-bed (Figure 1) and the prismatic core design (Figure 2):

- The pebble-bed concept is based on spherical fuel elements with 60 mm diameter piled in a reactor vessel. The pebble fuel element consists of an inner 50 mm diameter fuel zone surrounded by a 5 mm thick fuel-free shell of the graphitized fuel matrix material. The fuel zone contains the coated particles, overcoated with the matrix material, and then homogeneously dispersed within the graphitized matrix [2]. The pebble-bed pilot reactor installation was built at Jülich, Germany in the 1960s, and two such reactors are currently in the final stage of commissioning at Shidaowan in China [3,4].

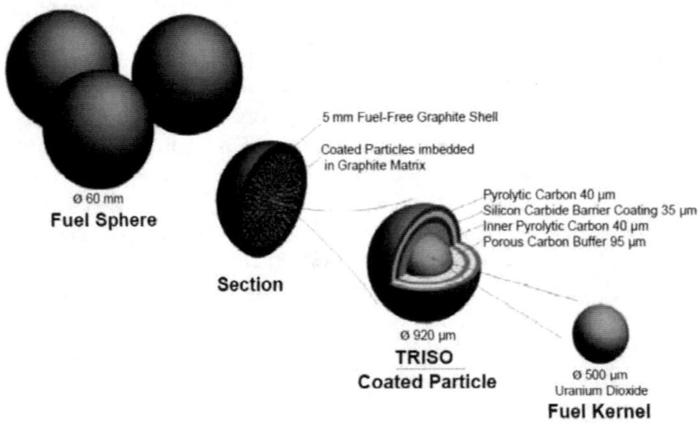


**Figure 1.** Pebble bed design of the HTGR [4].

- The prismatic core includes hexagonal shape blocks with circa 800 mm high and circa 360 mm across flats, fabricated from graphite. In the graphite block, separate fuel and coolant holes are drilled. Cylindrical fuel compacts with circa 12.5 mm of diameter and circa 50 mm long (contain the over-coated fuel particle), are stacked in the fuel channels [5]. The pilot prismatic HTGRs were constructed by General Atomics at Peach Bottom and Fort St. Vrain in the USA [3,4].

Both concepts of the HTGR reactor are based on TRISO particle fuel.

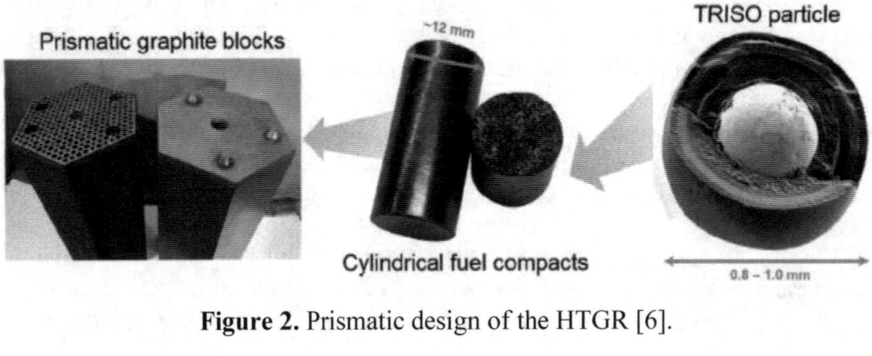


**Figure 2.** Prismatic design of the HTGR [6].

It is assumed that the first industrial HTGR type of reactor will be constructed in Poland around 2040. Until then it is planned to construct an HTGR research reactor at NCBJ. Both for the research reactor project and for the industrial reactor project an important issue is to acquire TRISO- particle fuel. TRISO fuel can be either manufactured in Poland or can be purchased from external suppliers. The second option seems to be today a more advantageous alternative. The TRISO fuel purchase from politically and economically reliable countries will ensure at least at the first stage a secure supply of this fuel for HTGR reactors.

This publication highlights the necessity of quality control of TRISO fuel in order to understand well aging of fresh TRISO fuel and in a longer perspective to ensure the highest possible quality of the fuel fabrication and storage before loading into the reactor core. The rationale for such an action is not only economic but also increasingly stringent climate and environmental requirements. Therefore, it seems necessary to determine whether the passage of time has an impact on the occurrence of the changes in the structure of TRISO fuel layers and at the same time whether it contributes to increasing the probability of damage in the fuel material under investigation.

The research on TRISO-particle fuel would focus on examining the quality of freshly manufactured fuel and degradation processes of the fuel before entering the reactor core. We call this process a front-end investigation of TRISO fuel.

For this purpose, the Raman spectroscopy measurements are planned. The results of these experiments will also help serve as the preliminary stage to establish a laboratory for TRISO fuel quality control and assessments. It would also be a prelude to constructing a TRISO fuel production line in Poland or Europe.

## 2. Experiment

The experiment aims to check the TRISO fuel particle for damage occurrence, through the Raman method of spectroscopy. Moreover, this experiment aims to conduct research on different types of TRISO fuel, produced in different periods of time, and to check the aging effects of the layers in the tested TRISO fuel particles. The experiment includes measurements on TRISO fuel currently produced (e.g., in 2020) by one of the leading companies, e.g., X-energy, and measurements on TRISO fuel produced several decades earlier (e.g., in 2000), e.g., on German fuel which has been stored. In the experiment, both surrogates and TRISO particles with uranium kernel will be measured. The results obtained from the measurements on both types of particles will be compared based on the Raman spectra.

The experiment will be conducted in two stages:

- Stage 1 - analysis of the intact "virgin" sample (front-end);
- Stage 2 - analysis of the sample after ion implantation. Ion implantation will at that stage simulate the processes of irradiation of the TRISO particles in the MARIA reactor.

The ion-beam irradiation technique is used to imitate the neutron irradiation process because it allows investigating the occurrence of damage caused by irradiation without the necessity to deal with radioactive materials and occurs in a relatively short time. The differences between neutron irradiation and ion implantation are energy (ions have smaller energies [keV] than neutrons [~ 2 MeV in fission system]) [7], charge (neutrons have no charge), and size. The size of the colliding particle is much larger compared to the size of the neutron. The disadvantage of ion implantation is that, even if high fluence can be achieved in a short time, the depth of penetration of the sample is shallow. Typically, ion implantation is with noble-gas ions like $Ar^+$, $He^+$, $Xe^+$, $Ne^+$, and $Kr^+$. The irradiation of the sample is performed using different ions and ion energy [8-16]. To perform the experiment on the intact samples, ion irradiation with $He^+$ ions, with a fluence between $10^{12}$ and $10^{17}$ ions/cm$^2$ is assumed.

The preparation of the whole experiment will therefore be based on five parts:

- The preparation of the TRISO sample for examination;
- Verification of the consistency of the original TRISO sample with production data, by using the Raman spectroscopy method;
- Ion implantation on a TRISO sample;

- Revision of the TRISO sample, after ion irradiation, using the Raman spectroscopy method;
- Comparison of the results.

The following factors should be taken into account before starting the experiment:

- TRISO technical data;
- Raman spectroscopy method.

*2.1. TRISO- coated particle*

TRISO fuel production has been developing for more than six decades, during which the fuel has been modified, tested, and improved to achieve the lowest possible degree of damage of the TRISO sample. TRISO fuel consists of uranium kernel, coated with four layers of pyrocarbon and silicon carbide and it confines fission products even at the temperature of 1600 deg C [6].

Each TRISO particle (Figure 3) consists of:

- Kernel - surrounded by four different coating layers of pyrocarbon and silicon carbide;
- Porous pyrocarbon buffer layer (PyC) - first layer surrounded the kernel.
- Highly isotropic inner pyrocarbon layer (IPyC);
- Silicon carbide (SiC) layer;
- Outer pyrocarbon layer (OPyC).

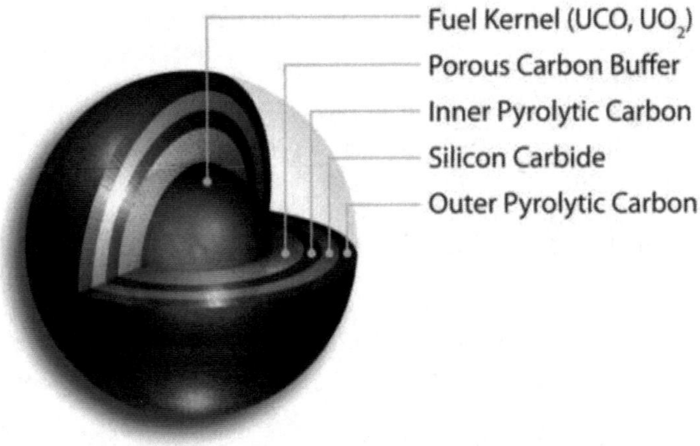


**Figure 3.** TRISO fuel cross-section [17].

The TRISO-coated particles have an overall diameter in the range of 500 to 1000 μm [18].
Each layer has the following dimensions [19]:

- The fuel kernel with the diameter in the range of 350-600 μm. The optimal kernel diameter is a function of enrichment and burn-up limits - with higher enrichment and burn-up designs - smaller diameter;
- Porous pyrocarbon buffer layer thickness is in the range of 90 to 100 μm;
- The IPyC layer thickness is typically in the range of 35 to 40 μm;
- The thickness of the SiC layer is around 35 μm;
- The OPyC layer thickness is typically in the range of 35 to 40 μm.

Many experiences with manufacturing coated-particle fuel have demonstrated the feasibility of producing large quantities of TRISO fuel with simultaneous low defect level which approaching defect fractions of $10^{-5}$ [19]. During irradiation partial or complete failure of the TRISO particle may occur, caused by some failure mechanisms. Fuel failure mechanisms can be categorized. Each author has his own way of dividing the damages, however, the most general division concern mechanical and chemical failures.

The TRISO fuel failure mechanisms have been divided according to two categories:

- Damage location - TRISO fuel failure can be considered in terms of damage location, distinguishing as the external and internal area of the particle. External damage to TRISO structure usually occurs as a result of some physical force and is created mainly during the production process of these particles. The internal damages can be observed on the surface of each layer or at the joint point of these layers. These failures are mainly caused by mechanical or chemical factors;
- Damage factor - There are two types of factors causing damage in TRISO fuel particles, mechanical and chemical. Mechanical failures can appear in each of the structural layers, like in a buffer, IPyC, SiC, and OPyC layer. They arise as a result of the deformation of the layers due to their mutual interactions. A layer may be damaged by the initiation and propagation of a crack or by stress or friction which exceeds the strength criterion of the material. Chemical failures can also exist in each of the TRISO layers. That kind of damage is caused by the interaction of chemical elements and by the presence of fission products that accumulate inside the particle during irradiation.

Our experiment will focus on mechanical failures.

The TRISO fuel can be characterized before and after irradiation to see how the particle has been evolved. It is assumed that two types of TRISO fuel will be used for the experiment, different in terms of year of production as well as place and method of manufacture. Therefore, it seems necessary to determine whether the passage of time has an impact on the occurrence of the changes in the structure of TRISO fuel layers and at the same time whether it contributes to increasing the probability of damage in the fuel material under investigation. Therefore, three stages of the TRISO particle investigation can be defined: front-end (understood as testing the TRISO particle before it is placed in the reactor), irradiation in the reactor core, and post-irradiation examination.

Because the irradiation in the reactor core is a long-term process, to predict the behavior of TRISO fuel particle in a shorter time, ion implantation can be used. This method reflects the irradiation process placed in a reactor. Modeling of irradiation with ion implantation is understood as monitoring the TRISO particle during the irradiation process in the reactor.

### *2.2. Raman spectroscopy method*

The most popular diagnostic methods for the TRISO coated-particle include:

- Scanning electron microscopy (SEM) to observe microstructural features;
- X-ray diffraction (XRD) for crystal structure analysis;
- Nanoindentation for the hardness and modulus Young of each layer;
- Crush test to improve the fracture strength;
- Raman spectroscopy for sample characterization.

In our experiment, Raman spectroscopy was selected as a screening research method for monitoring the changes in spectra, in "virgin" and an ion-irradiated sample of both TRISO fuel particles.

Raman micro-spectroscope is a device for recording Raman scattering spectra. Raman scattering spectra show elements characteristic for substances present in the tested sample, taking the form of bands. These spectra are used to analyze the composition of the test sample or to analyze the chemical components and their location in the sample. Raman spectroscopy makes use of the fact that the Raman scattering spectrum is excited in the visible, near-infrared, or ultraviolet region. This Raman spectrum is an oscillation-rotational spectrum because it provides information about oscillational and rotational energy levels of molecules and it record spectra of the tested molecule. Each molecule is characterized by the number of vibrations, their frequency and amplitude. Raman scattering spectrum showing bands with characteristic contours and position is a reflection of the vibration potential of a given molecule. In this Raman spectrum, one can well observe the symmetrical vibrations of the molecule, vibrations of the carbon skeleton of the molecule, and vibrations between atoms with double and triple bonds [20,21].

The characteristic shape of the Raman spectrum is in the form of the bell curve, which is a feature of the interaction of substances with radiation. The contour of the bell curve band is defined as the dependence of the intensity of the amplitude (I) of absorption, emission, or scattering on the frequency (ν) of radiation interacting with the system. The main parameters characterizing the band is:

- Half-width ($\Delta\nu_{1/2}$) - this is the width of the band contour, determined in the middle of its height,
- Frequency ($\nu_0$) - it is a value corresponding to the maximum height of the contour of the tested band,
- Intensity ($I_{max}$) - this is the height of the band contour measured from the background level,
- Integral intensity ($I_\infty$) - this is the area bounded by the band contour and the background [22,23].

Raman spectroscopy is an efficient, non-destructive, non-contacting, and quick measurement method to characterize the structure of graphitic materials, in particular providing valuable information about defects and in-plane crystallite size. It provides a fingerprint to identify the chemical component, to analyze them, and to better understand their structures.

The use of Raman spectroscopy to analyze the TRISO particle is one of the methods to show the changes in fuel structure as a result of irradiation. Using this method, we can observe, among others, damage appearing in the TRISO particle (layer cracks) and determine the concentration of carbon in each layer. By measuring the particles before and after irradiation, we can compare the changes that have occurred as a result of irradiation in the reactor.

*2.3. TRISO-particle fuel measurement by Raman spectroscopy method*

As was mentioned above the experiment aims to analyze the TRISO fuel particles using the Raman spectroscopy method, in two steps, analysis of virgin sample and sample after ion irradiation. This means that on both stages, each of the TRISO layers will be explored in terms of chemical content. As a result, the Raman spectrum representing the chemical composition of each layer will be resented. Based on the obtained Raman spectra, the results from the measurements will be compared.

The presented TRISO sample analysis process will be carried out for TRISO samples produced at different time periods. The experiment will include the measurements of TRISO fuel currently produced and TRISO fuel produced several decades ago. In both cases, the experiment will start with sample preparation by polishing. The TRISO sample is polished to obtain the cross-section of the sample. The polishing process will use abrasive paper of different grit sizes from 300-2000 12,14,24,25].

The TRISO sample, after polishing, is placed under the Raman spectroscope and subjected to the point, and linear measurements to visualize an average spectrum obtained for each layer of the TRISO sample, and the so-called map surface, which will cover the area from the kernel to the end of the OPyC layer, is measured.

The TRISO particle layers like buffer, IPyC, and OPyC are based on pyrolytic carbon. Pyrolytic carbon is a material similar to graphite. For these reasons, the graphite spectrum is the starting point for TRISO analysis by Raman spectroscopy (Figure 4).

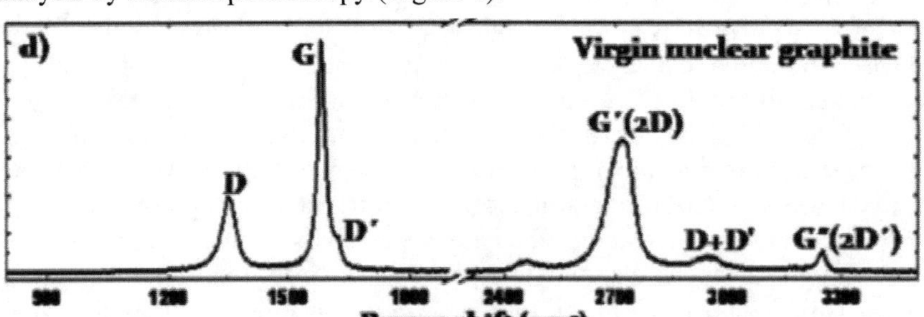


**Figure 4.** Raman spectrum of virgin nuclear graphite [8].

Raman spectra of the carbon materials are constructed with two characteristic bands, G- band mainly at position 1580 $cm^{-1}$ and D- band at position 1355 $cm^{-1}$ [11]. Fully or single crystalline graphite shows only G- band. D- band appears by the introduction of defects in graphite, like disordering of the basal plane. That is why D comes from disorder. The Raman spectra of all carbons show bands in the region of 800-2000 $cm^{-1}$ [26]. The vibrations of two carbon atoms linked by strong double bonds (C=C) find at the position around 1600 $cm^{-1}$ [27]. The first order band, the "G" is due to the bond stretching of all pairs of $sp^2$ atoms in both rings and chains. There are also three bands designed as "D" modes, called: "$D_1$" (1346 $cm^{-1}$), "$D_2$" (1367 $cm^{-1}$) and "$D_0$" (1622 $cm^{-1}$) [7]. These "D" modes are attributed to the disorder in the graphitic structure and due to the breathing modes of $sp^2$ atoms in rings, their positions are not always at the same point.

To the first stage of our experiment the TRISO-particle fuel samples so-called "ZP12" were used. Those surrogate samples were produced by the French Alternative Energies and Atomic Energy Commission (CEA) in 2001 for a research project HTR-F/F1 [28]. Measurements on TRISO samples are taken with a Renishaw Raman spectroscope, and the spectra are collected by focusing a laser $\lambda$ = 785 nm wavelength.

After polishing the samples, the following measurements were performed:

- Point measurements – The point measurement of a sample involves taking a measurement, i.e., collecting a spectrum, at an arbitrarily selected location from the entire cross-section of the sample. Several measurement collection locations are selected for each TRISO layer. The point measurements are intended to illustrate the averaged spectrum obtained for each layer of the sample under investigation. In the case of the TRISO ZP12 sample analyzed, it can be seen that this particle consists of a kernel and only one covering layer. As shown in Figure 5, the ZP12 sample contains a kernel with zirconium dioxide and a covering layer, probably a buffer, consisting of two characteristic bands "D" and "G";

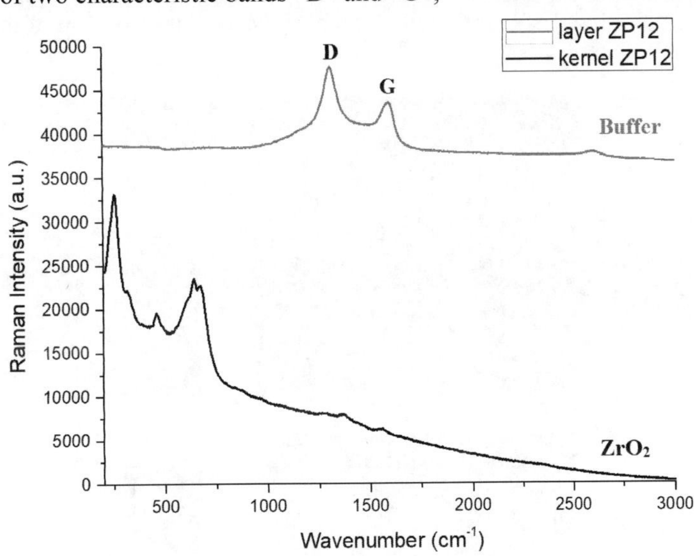


**Figure 5.** The average Raman spectra obtained for the ZP12 sample from point measurements [own data].

- Linear measurement – A linear measurement involves collecting Raman spectra along a single line, starting from the kernel to the end of the last covering layer. This measurement results in information about how the spectra change over successive layers of the TRISO sample. For the TRISO sample ZP12 (Figure 6), Raman spectra were recorded over a length of 100 μm with a step of 2 μm.

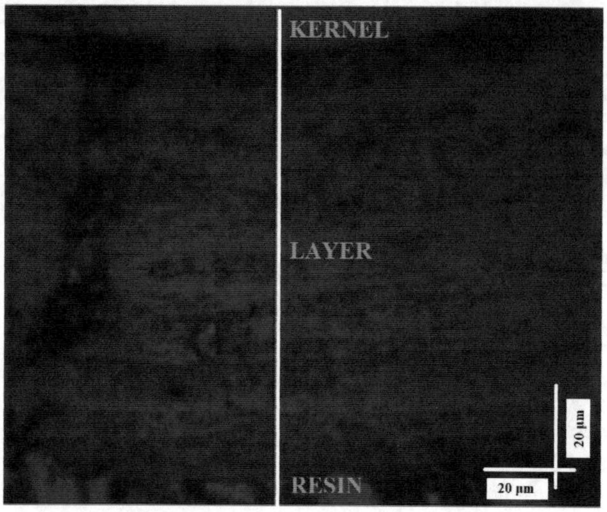


**Figure 6.** Example of the linear measurement through sample ZP12 containing one layer. [own data].

- Surface map – Performing a surface map measurement involves selecting an area of the sample that includes all layers of the TRISO sample. In a given area, Raman spectra are collected. The goal of the measurement is to obtain a large amount of data from the collected spectra, from which parameters such as band position, half-width, and the ratio of the intensity of D- Raman band and G- Raman band (ID/IG) can be described. The intensity of the occurrence of a parameter in the analyzed sample area can then be visualized. As an example of a surface map, the concentration of parameters such as the position of the G and D bands is shown in Figure 7.

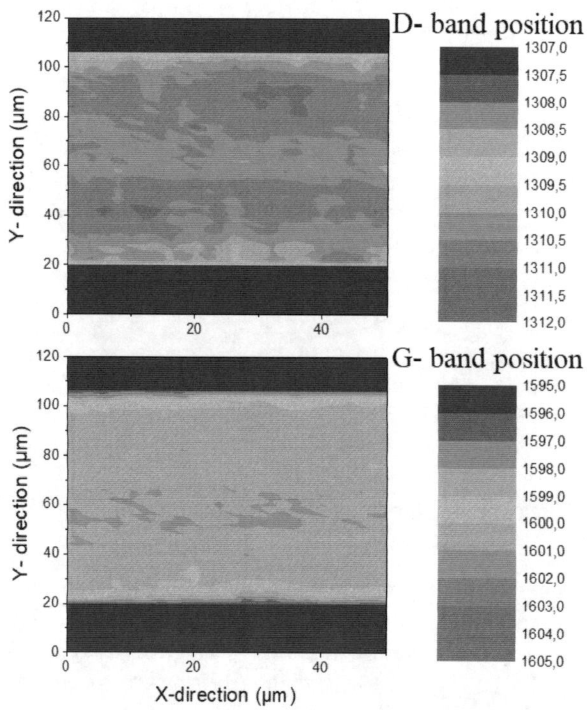


**Figure 7.** Raman surface map of the ZP12 sample with a concentration of the G-band and D-band [own data].

These results were obtained for a TRISO fuel particle consisting of only one layer. For these reasons, further experimental work will not be continued on the ZP12 particle. Currently, we are looking for a TRISO fuel consisting of a kernel and four covering layers for further experiment.

The expected results for the surface map measurements for the TRISO- particle fuel with five layers is shown in Figure 8. Based on the obtained Raman spectra, it is possible to create a map showing the occurrence of a given chemical element in the analyzed structure. In the case of TRISO, the map shows the selected area which has been measured using the Raman spectroscope. The result of the measurement is that TRISO in each layer is based on carbon. To differentiate the TRISO layers, a selection of different colors was used. A given color represents the intensity of a given spectrum, the most similar spectra represent the same layer.

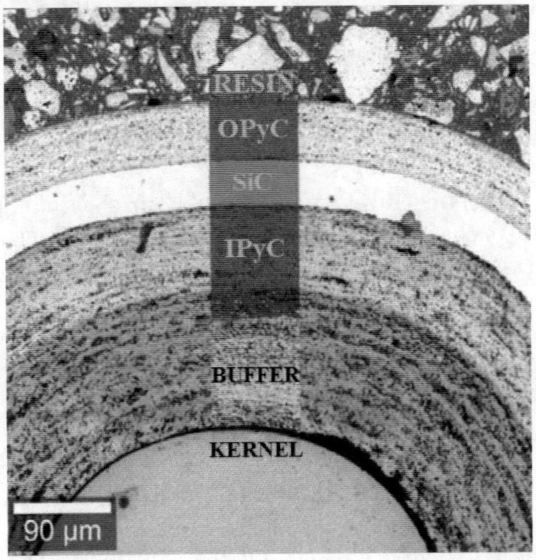


**Figure 8.** The map of TRISO structure made by Raman spectroscopy [29].

After the initial measurement of the TRISO sample by the Raman spectroscopy technique, the sample will be treated with ion irradiation with $He^+$ ions, with a fluence between $10^{12}$ and $10^{17}$ ions/cm$^2$. Afterward, the sample will be placed under the Raman spectroscope again and the measurements will be taken in the same area of the tested sample. Since the ion implantation is to reflect the TRISO fuel irradiation in the reactor, it is expected that after the implantation it will be possible to observe the changes that occurred in each layer of the sample. It is therefore assumed that the analysis of the parameters obtained before and after the ion implantation, will reveal significant changes in the values of the indicated parameters and will be depicted in the shape of the received spectrum. Raman analysis shows that the "D" and "G" bands for implemented samples are broadened. It is assumed that a change in the appearance of the spectrum in the G- and D- band positions will show us the degree of damage to the sample. Figure 9 presents an example of a graph of spectrum changes before and after ion irradiation [9].

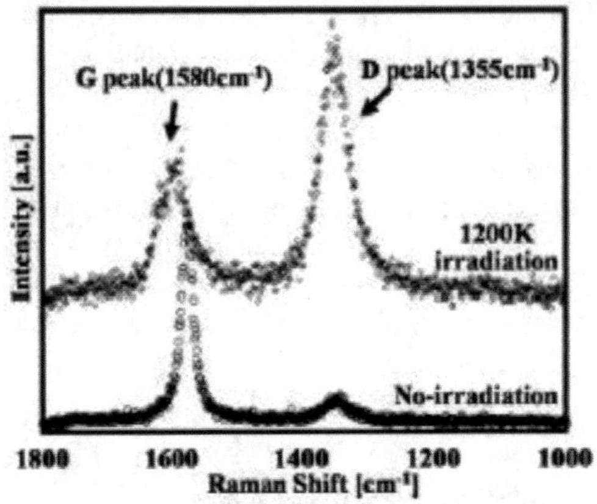


**Figure 9.** Comparison of Raman spectra of the non-irradiated rear surface and the front surface exposed to H plasma [9].

The results will allow observing differences in the Raman spectrum obtained for both types of TRISO fuel particles. Conclusions based on Raman spectrometer measurement will be used to determine whether the passage of time affects the degree of damage that occurred to the analyzed samples.

The results obtained from the experiment are a prerequisite to designing a production line and, above all, to create a laboratory for quality control and preliminary analysis of TRISO fuel, both those currently produced and those that have been or will be stored.

## 3. TRISO Laboratory – Building Up Competence and Excellence for The HTGR Program in Poland

A mission for a TRISO Laboratory at NCBJ would be, at least, three- fold:

- Development of quality control (QC) and quality assessment (QA) methods to prove for the Polish regulatory body that TRISO fuel performance is adequate and complies with safety regulations. This part of the mission will be focused on unirradiated TRISO fuel, i.e., on the front-end of the HTGR nuclear fuel cycle;
- Irradiation of the TRISO fuel under very well controlled conditions in MARIA reactor and then post-irradiation examinations (PIE) of TRISO fuel;
- Investigations of irradiated TRISO fuel with a focus on its performance as a spent fuel/waste for the final disposal. The ultimate objective will be to develop an acceptable – socially and technically, proven and economically viable concept of the final disposal of the HTGR spent fuel.

The front-end research activities will focus on:

- Evaluation of the particles shape and size. 2D inspection using X-ray radiography;
- Properties of unirradiated TRISO compacts. The structural integrity of the TRISO particles. The "leach-burn-leach" test, preceded by fuel compact/pebble deconsolidation. This will be performed after compacting because specifications for particle defects are typically applied on the compact/pebble, not on the loose, as-fabricated particles. The compacting process can introduce coating damage and caused further fuel failures;
- Investigations of PyC layer anisotropy. This is a key coating layer property and is to be measured as part of fuel QC;
- Local properties in unirradiated TRISO coatings:
  - Local thermal conductivity measurement is crucial and high resolution (<1 um) mapping of thermal conductivity techniques are available. This will provide a detailed map of the thermal conductivity in each coated layer. These are very important parameters for quality control and future modeling;

  - Residual stresses must be measured in the coated layers, as they will impact the particle structural integrity as irradiation behavior. High resolution residual stress measurement methods are available: Raman spectroscopy, X-ray diffraction, and Focused Ion Beam based Digital Image Correlation (FIB-DIC). Undesirably high magnitude of residual stresses in the coating layers can then be detected and feedback to processing to optimize the parameters;
  - Interfacial strength between coated layers. This is challenging to measure, but micro-mechanical testing could offer a solution.

The back-end research on TRISO fuel will be focused at:

- Planning irradiation experiments at MARIA reactor, constructing an irradiation sond/rig and then irradiation experiments and all PIE in the existing hot-cell lab;
- The structural integrity of TRISO particle:
  - Non-destructive measurements of coating thickness in order to document the unirradiated particles size and coating thicknesses; the same procedure can then be applied to irradiated particles to evaluate the irradiation induced dimensional changes;
  - Thermal conductivity, residual stresses are both important to measure in irradiated particles for the same reason as for unirradiated ones;
  - In situ irradiation using heavy ions in a transmission electron microscope (e.g., Ag ions) is essential for the understanding of element diffusion mechanism in buffer/ IPyC /SiC. This knowledge can then be a feedback to processing for modifications in materials.
- Fission product diffusion through layers with the use of Secondary Ions Mass Spectroscopy (SIMS).

And finally, for the back-end of the HTGR nuclear fuel cycle, a set of experiments will be designed in order to prepare the strategy for the final disposal of the HTGR fuel. The basic experiments will be focused at:

- Leaching;
- Solubility in different environments and at the different temperature fields;
- Interaction between TRISO and different canister material concepts;
- Addressing the issue of the final disposal of graphite, development of technology to reduce the volume of high/medium radioactive graphite (C-14 transport);
- Experiments in the underground laboratory in cooperation with the Äspö-Hard Rock Laboratory in Sweden.

## 4. Conclusion

Poland has an on-going program to construct a research high-temperature reactor and then consequently deploy an industrial fleet of HTGRs. Operation of HTGR reactors requires high-quality TRISO fuel and it is of the highest priority both for licensing and for the operation of HTGR to develop a reliable supply and quality control chain of this fuel. Quality control should also be directed to investigate the aging process of fresh TRISO fuel to ensure in the long run the highest possible quality of fuel generation and storage before loading into the reactor core.

It should however be concluded that the process of establishing production and quality control lines for TRISO fuel requires time, several years to gather experience, permits, and start construction.

Failure free production of TRISO fuel is a "conditio sine qua non" for a good performance of the HTGRs aiming at minimal risk for release of radioactivity. The planned experiments presented in this paper will allow developing front-end quality control of TRISO particles through visualization and qualification of damages in TRISO. Before the irradiation experiments in the MARIA reactor, will be performed the radiation damages in TRISO fuel, will be simulated by ion irradiation. Then, by comparison, "fresh" and ion irradiated samples, it is possible to conclude the characterization of mechanical damages in individual layers, in both types of TRISO assumed.

## References

[1] Polish Nuclear Power Programme, Uchwała Rady Ministrów z 2/10/2020, Monitor Polski Dziennik Urzędowy Rzeczypospolitej Polskie z 2020 poz. 964.
[2] Performance Analysis Review of Thorium TRISO Coated Particles During Manufacture, Irradiation and Accident Condition Heating Tests, IAEA-TECDOC-1761, 2015.
[3] M.A. Fütterer, L. Fu, C. Sink, S. de Groot, M. Pouchon Y.W. Kim, F. Carre, Y. Tachibana, Status of the very high temperature reactor system, Progress in Nuclear Energy 77, p. 266-281, 2014.
[4] NGNP Fuel Qualification White Paper, INL, INL/EXT-10-17686, 2010.
[5] K. Verfondern, H. Nabielek, M.J. Kania, H.J. Allelein, High-Quality Thorium TRISO Fuel Performance in HTGRs, Forschungszentrum Juelich, 2013.
[6] P.A. Demkowicz, B. Liu, J.D. Hunn, Coated particle fuel: Historical perspectives and current progress, Journal of Nuclear Materials 515, p. 434-450, 2019.
[7] M. Lasithiotakis, B.J. Marsden, T.J. Marrow, Annealing of ion irradiation damage in nuclear graphite, Journal of Nuclear Materials 434, p. 334-346, 2013.
[8] M.R. Ammar, N. Galy, J.N. Rouzaud, N. Toulhoat, C.E. Vaudey, P. Simon, N. Moncoffre, Characterizing various types of defects in nuclear graphite using Raman scattering: Heat treatment, ion irradiation and polishing, Carbon 95, p. 364-373, 2015.
[9] M. Yoshida, T. Tanabe, N. Ohno, M. Yoshimi, S. Takamura, High temperature irradiation damage of carbon materials studies by laser Raman spectroscopy, Journal of Nuclear Materials 386-388, p. 841-843, 2009.
[10] T.D. Burchell, P.J. Pappano, J.P. Strizak, A study of the annealing behavior of neutron irradiated graphite, CARBON 49, p. 3-10, 2011.
[11] H.X. Xu, J. Lin, J.J Li, Z.Y. Zhu, G.L. Zeng, J.D. Liu, B.C. Gu, B. Liu, Characterization the microstructure and defects of matrix graphite irradiated with Xe ions, Nuclear Instruments and Methods in Physics Research B 406, p. 638-642, 2017.
[12] E.S. Kim, Y.W. Kim, Characterization of 3 MeV $H^+$ irradiation induced defects in nuclear grade graphite, Solid State Communications 150, p. 1633-1636, 2010.
[13] H.J. Sarmah, D. Mohanta, Emergence of Raman active D- band and unusually suppressed conductivity mediated by nanoscale defects in pencil-lead graphitic systems under 80 keV $Xe^+$ ion irradiation, Nuclear Inst. and Methods in Physics Research B 463, p. 1-6, 2020.
[14] Q. Huang, Q. Lei, Q. Deng, H. Tang, Y. Wang, J. Li, H. Huang, L. Yan, G. Lei, R. Xie, Raman spectra and modulus measurement on the cross section of proton –irradiated graphite, Nuclear Instruments and Methods in Physics Research B 412, p. 221-226, 2017.
[15] N. Galy, N. Toulhoat, N. Moncoffre, Y. Pipon, N. Bererd, M.R. Ammar, P. Simon, D. Deldicque, P. Sainsot, Ion irradiation to simulate neutron irradiation in model graphites: Consequences for nuclear graphite, Nuclear Instruments and Methods in Physics Research B 409, p. 235-240, 2017.
[16] D.W. Kim, K.W. Lee, D.M. Choi, S.J. Noh, H.S. Kim, Ch.E. Lee, Spectroscopic study of energetic helium –ion irradiation effects on nuclear graphite tiles, Nuclear Instruments and Methods in Physics Research B 368, p. 5-8, 2016.
[17] P. Demkowicz, TRISO Fuel: Design, Manufacturing and Performance, ART INL, NRC HTGR Training July 16-17, 2019.
[18] High Temperature Gas Cooled Reactor Fuels and Materials, IAEA-TECDOC-1645, 2010.
[19] Uranium Oxycarbide (UCO) Tristructural Isotropic (TRISO) Coated Particle Fuel Performance: Topical Report EPRI-AR-1(NP), EPRI, Palo Alto, CA:2019, 3002015750.
[20] J.R. Ferraro, K. Nakamoto, C.W. Brown, Introductory Raman Spectroscopy, Academic Press, 2003.
[21] T. Dieing, O. Hollricher, J. Toporski, Confocal Raman Microscopy, Springer, Berlin Heidelberg, 2010.
[22] M. Drozdowski, Spektroskopia ciała stałego, Wydawnictwo Politechniki Poznańskiej, Poznań,

2001.
[23] Z.M. Krajewska, Metodologia wytwarzania sztucznie próchnicy o danym stopniu zaawansowania w szkliwie ludzkich zębów, Inżynierska Praca Dyplomowa, Poznań, 2017.
[24] X.G. Han, S.M. Miao, X.P. Zhu, M.K. Lei, Phase transformation of graphite irradiated by high –intensity pulsed ion beams, Applied Surface Science 253, p. 5425-5430, 2007.
[25] Q. Huang, J.J. Li, R. Liu, L. Yan, H. Huang, Surface morphology and microstructure evolution of IG-110 graphite after xenon ion irradiation and subsequent annealing, Journal of Nuclear Materials 491, p. 213-220, 2017.
[26] A.C. Ferrari, J. Robertson, Resonant Raman spectroscopy of disordered, amorphous, and diamond like carbon, Physical Review B, Vol. 64, 2001.
[27] https://www.renishaw.com
[28] Private information.
[29] The map of TRISO structure made by Raman spectroscopy in Materials Research Lab at NCBJ, 2020.

# The Release of C-14 of HTR Graphite Spheres during High Temperature Oxidation

**X Chen, B Liu*, T Wang, G Xu, L Zhang, C Mao, H Xiao, Y Shao, H Zhao, L He, and Z Yin***

Institute of Nuclear and New Energy Technology, Collaborative Innovation Center of Advanced Nuclear Energy Technology, Tsinghua University, Beijing 100084, PR China

phone: +86-10-62784394, email: chenxiaotong@tsinghua.edu.cn

**Abstract.** As the key components of the HTGR fuel, the intact TRISO-coated particles contain almost all fission products under the normal and accident conditions in the reactor. On the other hand, the high temperature oxidation of irradiated fuel pebbles is one of feasible processing methods for HTR spent fuel pebbles. The knowledge of the C-14 release from irradiated fuels and the migration behavior during high temperature oxidation is of great importance for the post-irradiation examinations (PIE) and long-term storage and reprocessing of HTR-PM fuel pebbles. In this work, the C-14 release behavior from one irradiated HTR graphite sphere, which was used as a substitute for a irradiated HTR fuel, was determined by out-of-pile examination. The irradiated HTR fuel was oxidized in the hot lab of INET, and the substantial migration of fission products from graphite matrix was adsorbed and systematically studied by $\gamma$-scanning. Specifically, the C-14 release during oxidation was analyzed and illustrated. This work will provide theory and experiment basement for spent fuel disposal of HTGR, as well as a new sample preparation method for C-14 measurement by liquid scintillation counter (LSC).

## 1. Introduction

High temperature oxidation is one of promising methods for head-end of HTR spent fuel processing, through which the graphite matrix was disintegrated and fuel particles were separated [1, 2]. The fuel pebbles of High Temperature Gas-cooled Reactor (HTR) have an overall diameter of 60 mm, composed by 12000 TRISO (Tristructual Isotropic) particles and graphite matrix with more than 90% weight of the fuel [3-5]. For TRISO fuel element, the graphite matrix and outer pyrocarbon layer will oxidized to carbon dioxide during the oxidation, and fuel particles with silicon carbon layer as the outer layer were remained, which can be stored with much smaller volume or further treated. As for irradiated HTR fuel elements, the fabrication break rate as little as $10^{-5}$-$10^{-6}$ of HTR-PM fuel confirms almost all fission products were restrained in the intact TRISO- coated particle contain under the normal and accident conditions in the reactor core [6, 7]. Therefore, carbon-14 (C-14) release with a half-life of 5730 years during HTR spent fuel oxidation is of great concern. C-14 is probably produced through neutron capture by carbon-13 (C-14), nitrogen (N-14), and oxygen-17 (O-17), which has been identified as one of the most important nuclides in irradiated graphite matrix [8].

HTR Graphite spheres, which are also spherical in shape with the same size, raw materials and manufacture process as HTR fuels, are used to balance the core during the first starting period of the reactor, and experience almost the same neutron flux and energy spectrum as the fuel elements.

Therefore, the graphite spheres are ideal alternatives to investigate the properties of graphite matrix of irradiated fuel elements without exposure to high radiation from fuel particles.

In previous studies, C-14 content of one graphite sphere of 10MW high temperature gas-cooled test reactor (HTR-10) was analyzed [9]. The sample was drilled from a selected graphite sphere, ground to graphite powders and then oxidized to $CO_2$ in a combustion vessel with oxygen and NaOH solution. The obtained NaOH absorbent was analyzed with titration to measure the total carbon and liquid scintillation counter (LSC) to measure the activity of $^{14}C$ of each sub-sample. However, the graphite sphere discharged from HTR-10 has a significant radionuclide content arising both from the activation of impurities in the original graphite and from materials transported from other parts of the reactor circuit like steel-oxidation products [10]. As shown in the work of Liu et al., the key nuclides of H-3, C-14, Co-60, Cs-137, Eu-152 and Eu-154 were detected in the irradiated graphite sphere [11]. Thus, there is a possibility that nuclides were carried out by gas flow during the process of high temperature oxidation, absorbed in aqueous absorbent, and disturb the C-14 measurement by LSC.

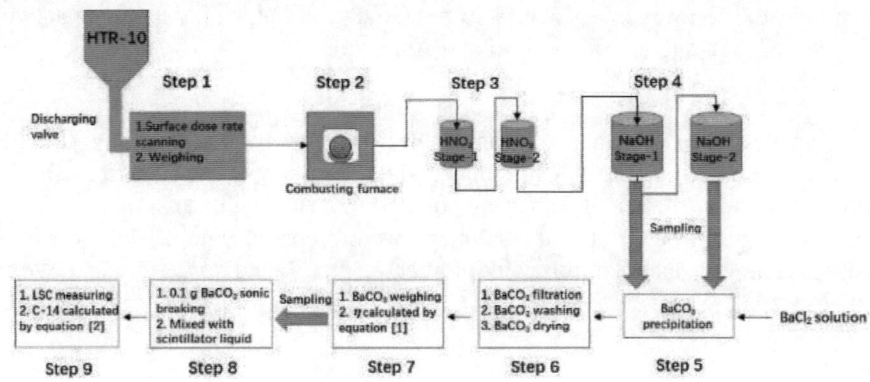


**Figure 1.** The experimental procedure of this work

In this work, a complete graphite sphere with the surface γ dose rate of 21.22 μSv/h was combusted in pure oxygen at temperature range of 750-900 °C to convert the graphite matrix to $CO_2$ form. As C-14 is a $\beta$-ray emitter, radiochemical separation is necessary prior to the measurement procedure, especially for samples with relatively high surface γ dose rate. In the process of $CO_2$ gas sample collection (including $^{12}CO_2$ and $^{14}CO_2$), the oxidized off gas was sequentially absorbed in $HNO_3$ and NaOH washing solutions, by which radioactive metal fission products and metal oxides with low melting point can be absorbed in $HNO_3$ solutions to some extent to decrease the interference on $CO_2$ measuring. In the process of C-14 measurement, $CO^{2-}$ was precipitated by "barium salt method" instead of "calcium salt method" that generally used [12], because the fine $CaCO_3$ particles produced during precipitation is too small to filter in our experiment, and the relative standard deviation (RSD) values were unacceptable for parallel experiments. The larger $BaCO_3$ precipitates facilitated the filtration by common commercial quantitative filter paper with satisfactory RSD values of parallel experiment, and the precipitation could be further ultrasonically broken to the size of smaller than 1 μm and measured by liquid scintillation counting (LSC) technique. This work will provide theory and experiment basement for spent fuel disposal of HTGR, as well as new methods for the treatment of radioactive nuclear graphite waste.

## 2. Experimental Section

The whole analysis procedure includes nine main steps as shown in Fig. 1. In step 1, the graphite sphere was sequentially measured by a surface dose rate scanning machine, and a modular balance with separating controlling and weighing units (WMS404C, Mettler-Toledo, Switzerland) after discharging from the reactor. In step 2, the graphite sphere was combusted in $O_2$ atmosphere (99.9%) at 750-900 °C for 30 h in a furnace special for use in hot-lab. In step 3, the off gas that evolved during the combustion process was successively passed through 5 mol/L $HNO_3$, 1 mol/L $HNO_3$, 1mol/L NaOH and 5mol/L NaOH, to ensure that carbon in $CO_2$ form that evolved during the combustion process could be absorbed in NaOH with a calculable absorption efficiency. In step 5, a "barium-salt method" was used to convert $CO^{2-}$ produced in NaOH absorption process to $BaCO_3$ precipitation. The purpose of two- stage absorption by $HNO_3$ in step 4 and $BaCO_3$ conversion in step 5 is to separate other radiative nuclides from C-14 in the $Ba^{14}CO_3$ form and obtain a minimal γ dose influence on the subsequent β detecting. In step 6, the $BaCO_3$ precipitation was filtered, washed by deionized water and ethanol for 3 times, and dried at 105°C for 4 h. In step 7, the dried $BaCO_3$ was accurately weighed and the $CO_2$ absorption efficiency by NaOH was calculated by equation (1). Afterwards, 0.1 g $BaCO_3$ was sampled by carefully weighing and then placed in 10 mL deionized water. After ultrasonic breaking with high energy, $BaCO_3$ were shattered to particles with submicron size to form a milky emulsion system which could be stable for at least 3 days without sedimentation. γ multichannel spectra (DSA-LX BE3830, Canberra, America) were detected for both absorbent and $BaCO_3$ precipitation. In step 8, the obtained milky emulsion was mixed with Ultima- Gold scintillator liquid and the activity of C-14 was measured by LSC (Tri-carb 5110, PerkinElmer, America).

### *2.1. Sample*
The irradiated graphite sphere was obtained from HTR-10, and the irradiation time is 225 EFPDs. The weight of the graphite sphere is 199.8 g. Unirradiated graphite spheres were used to establish oxidation conditions before thermal treatment. The reagents of $HNO_3$, NaOH and $BaCl_2$ used in this study were Merk, of p.a. (pro analysis) purity, and the solutions were prepared with 18 MΩ water. The liquid scintillator Ultima Gold was obtained from PerkinElmer.

### *2.2. Apparatus and Measurement*
The irradiated graphite sphere was weighed by a modular balance with separating controlling and weighing units (WMS404C, Mettler-Toledo, Switzerland), combusted using a furnace specially used in the hot-lab, with the off gas captured in the accessional trapping apparatus. C-14 content was analyzed by LSC (Tri-carb 5110, PerkinElmer, America). A high-purity germanium detector connected to a multichannel analyzer (Canberra, DSA-LX BE3830) was used to record the γ spectra of the absorbent solution and $BaCO_3$ precipitation.

## 3. Results And Discussion

### *3.1. The measurement of the Irradiated graphite sphere*
The selected irradiated graphite sphere was weighed as 199.8 g. The dose rate at the point of 11 cm away from the sphere center (including 6 cm stainless steel) is 21.2 ± 0.5 μSv/h. According to the multichannel γ spectrum results, Co-60 and Cs-137 were two most distinct nuclides in the graphite sphere.

### *3.2. Combustion of Graphite Spheres*
In order to measure the C-14 by LSC, a combustion process was developed to convert the graphite sphere carbon into $CO_2$ form with can be absorbed in aqueous alkaline solution. The sphere sample was firstly weighed and put into the Pt-Rh (90%-10%) crucible of the combustion furnace. After 750-900 °C oxidation for over 30h under continuous $O_2$ inflation, almost the whole sphere was burned out except for a very small amount of ash residues left on the crucible bottom. The off-gas passed through the escape-pipe of the furnace and then bubbled into $HNO_3$ and NaOH aqueous solutions.

### *3.3. $CO_2$ absorption efficiency in NaOH solutions*
$CO_2$ absorption efficiency in NaOH solutions is important to calculate the total C-14 content for one irradiated graphite sphere. In our study, 5.0 mL NaOH absorbent was sampled from trapping bottles, and put into 30 mL $BaCl_2$ solution (1 mol/L). The white $BaCO_3$ precipitation produced after mixture were

aged for 2 h. As illustrated in Experimental Section, the filter residues obtained from two NaOH absorbent were weighed as $m_{fr1}$ and $m_{fr2}$, respectively. The $CO_2$ absorption efficiency η in NaOH solutions could be calculated according to equation [1]:

$$\eta = \frac{V_0/V_S\cdot(m_{fr1}+m_{fr2})/m_{BaCO3}}{m_{GS}/m_C} \quad (1)$$

Where $V_0$ is the volume of NaOH absorbent, $V_s$ is the volume of the NaOH absorbent sample for precipitating, $M_{BaCO3}$ and $M_C$ are molecular weights for $BaCO_3$ and graphite carbon, respectively, and $m_{GS}$ is the mass of graphite sphere.

Results of LSC analysis of BaCO3 emulsion system confirmed the presence of C-14 in graphite matrix. The calculation equation for C-14 activity in one graphite matrix sphere was as shown in equation [2]:

$$A_{C-14/GMS} = \frac{n_1\times A_1+n_2\times A_2}{\eta} \quad (2)$$

Where $A_{C\text{-}14/GMS}$ is the total C-14 activity in one graphite matrix sphere, $n_1$ and $n_2$ are ratio values of bulk volume of NaOH absorbent to sampling volume for stage-1 and stage 2 NaOH absorbing, respectively, $A_1$ and $A_2$ are C-14 activities of sampling NaOH absorbent measured by LSC, and $\eta$ is $CO_2$ absorption efficiency in NaOH solutions.

**Table 1.** The CO2 absorption efficiency η in NaOH solutions

| $\eta_1$ | $\eta_2$ | $\eta_t$ |
|---|---|---|
| 55.1% | 17.9% | 73.0% |

According to absorption efficiency data shown in Table 1, the absorption efficiency $\eta_1$ for stage-1 NaOH absorbent (55.1%) is larger than that for stage- 2 NaOH absorbent (17.9%), and the total efficiency for $CO_2$ absorption is 73%. This value is larger compared to those obtained from oxygen combustion apparatus (40-45%), indicating that multistage adsorption along with bubbling facilitated $CO_2$ dissolving in and reacting with NaOH solution.

### 3.4. *Nuclide separation of absorbent by Barium Salt Precipitation*

The multichannel γ spectra were measured for $HNO_3$ and NaOH absorbents. The counts of 1000 s for main nuclide peaks were displayed in Table 2, and the results for stage-1 $HNO_3$ absorbent were shown in Figure 2 as examples.

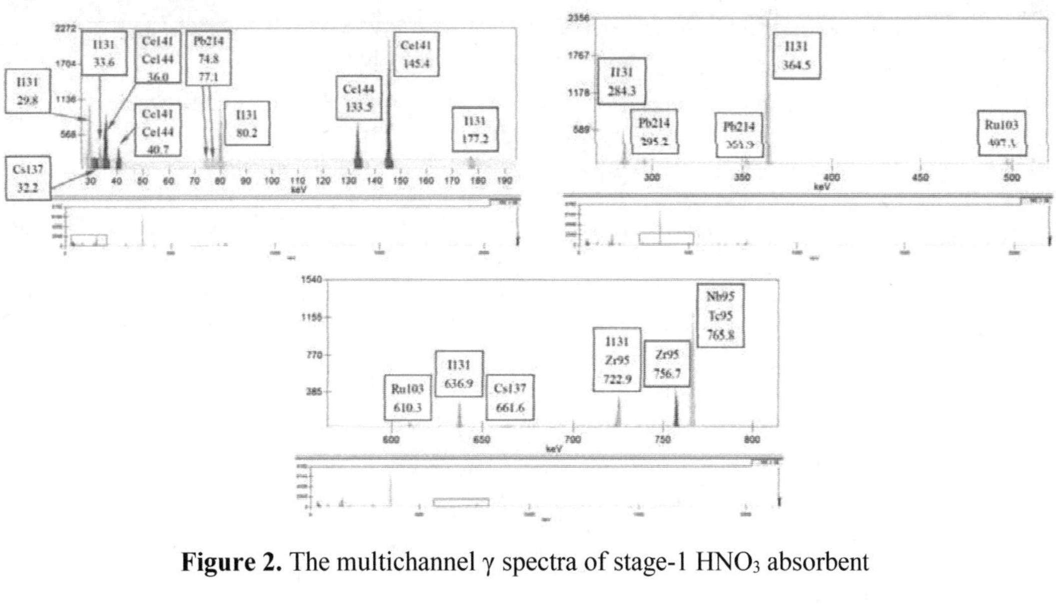


**Figure 2.** The multichannel γ spectra of stage-1 $HNO_3$ absorbent

**Table 2.** The Counts of 1000 s for main nuclide peaks

| Sample | I-131 | Ce-141 | Ru-103 | Cs-137 |
|---|---|---|---|---|
| $HNO_3$-1 | 14800 | 80 | 912 | 195 |
| $HNO_3$-2 | 7382 | 42 | 300 | 82 |
| NaOH-1 | 454 | 18 | 247 | 49 |
| NaOH-2 | 76 | N.A. | 188 | 26 |
| NaOH-1prec. | N.A. | 7 | 12 | N.A. |
| NaOH-2prec. | N.A. | N.A. | 8 | N.A. |

As shown in Fig.2, it clearly displayed species of volatile nuclides under high temperature besides $CO_2$ in off-gas, for instance, I-131, Ce-144, Ru-103, Cs- 137, etc., which were trapped by $HNO_3$ and NaOH solution. According to the $\gamma$ counts (1000 s) results for main nuclides in the absorption solutions (Table 2), there is significant quantities of four main nuclides in gas-collection solutions. Even though an obvious decline of $\gamma$ counts was observed as off-gas passed from $HNO_3$ to NaOH absorbents, there is still a small number of nuclides remaining in NaOH, which would inevitably interfere further C-14 measuring if the NaOH absorbent was directly sampled. Notably, after Barium Salt precipitating treatment, the $\gamma$ counts of $BaCO_3$ precipitation emulsion were nearly close to the background, revealing the interfering nuclides were almost deducted.

Fig.3 presents the typical β spectra of stage-2 NaOH absorbent (0.1 mL, green line) and $BaCO_3$ precipitation emulsion (0.1 g, yellow line). It indicates the existence of $\beta$ emitting-nuclides at lower energy region for NaOH absorbent, which might be originated from interfering nuclides discussed above or H-3. Whereas for $BaCO_3$ precipitation emulsion, the spectrum displayed a typical C-14 radiocarbon emitting curve, indicating a satisfactory separating effect based on precipitating treatment.

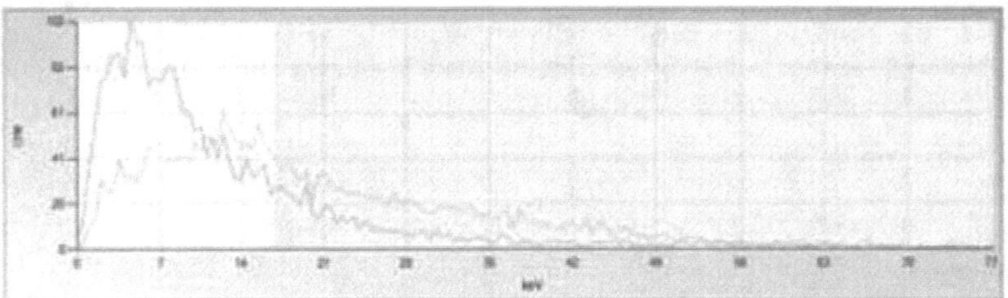

**Figure 3.** Typical β spectra of NaOH absorbent (green line) and $BaCO_3$ precipitation emulsion (yellow line)

According to above discussions, the specific activity of C-14 for one graphite sphere is 6.2 E+6 Bq based on equation [1] and [2], which is accordant with previous studies.

## 4. Conclusions

In this work, the C-14 release from an irradiated HTR-10 graphite sphere was determined by out-of-pile metallographic examination. The graphite sphere was oxidized in the hot lab of INET, and the substantial C-14 from graphite matrix was adsorbed and systematically studied by γ-scanning and LSC measuring. The $CO_2$ absorbing efficiency in NaOH solutions was also analyzed and illustrated. The specific C-14 activity of an irradiated HTR-10 graphite sphere is 6.2 E+6 Bq, which is accordant with previous studies. This work will provide a theory and experiment basement for spent fuel disposal of HTR, as well as a new sample preparation method for C-14 measurement LSC.

**Acknowledgements**
This work was supported by National S&T Major Project (Grant No. ZX06901) and Nuclear Energy Development Project. The authors are also very thankful for Mr. Feng Xiaogui's great help on C-14 measuring and discussion.

**References**
[1] J. Yoo, C. Seo, E. Kim, H. Lee, A conceptual study of pyroprocessing for recovering actinides from spent oxide fuels, Nuclear Engineering and Technology, 40 (2008) 581-590.
[2] J. Li, M. Dunzik-Gouga, J. Wang, Recent advances in the treatment of irradiated graphite: A review, Annals of Nuclear Energy, 110 (2017) 140-147.
[3] B. Wu, Y. Li, H.-s. Zhao, S. Liu, B. Liu, J.-h. Wang, Wear behavior of graphitic matrix of fuel elements used in pebble-bed high-temperature gas-cooled reactors against steel, Nuclear Engineering and Design 328 (2018) 353-358.
[4] C. Tang, Y. Tang, J. Zhu, Y. Zou, J. Li, X. Ni, Design and manufacture of the fuel element for the 10 MW high temperature gas-cooled reactor, Nuclear Engineering and Design 218(1) (2002) 91-102.
[5] Z. Xiangwen, L. Zhenming, Z. Jie, L. Bing, Z. Yanwen, T. Chunhe, T. Yaping, Preparation of spherical fuel elements for HTR-PM in INET, Nuclear Engineering and Design 263 (2013) 456-461.
[6] S. Knol, S. de Groot, R. V. Salama, J. Best, K. Bakker, I. Bobeldijk, J. R. Westlake, M. A. Futterer, M. Laurie, C. H. Tang, R. Z. Liu, B. Liu, H. S. Zhao, HTR-PM fuel pebble irradiation qualification in the high flux reactor in Petten, Nuclear Engineering and Design, 329 (2018) 82-88.
[7] D. Frei, A. El Abjani, D. Coric, R. Nasyrow, J. Somers, C. H. Tang, R. Z. Liu, B. Liu, M. L. Liu, Burn-up determination and accident testing of HTR-PM fuel elements irradiated in the HFR Petten, Nuclear Engineering and Design, 110414. DOI: 10.1016/j.nucengdes.2019.110414.
[8] X. Liu, W. Peng, L. Wei, M. Liu, F. Xie, J. Cao, J. Tong, F. Li, G. Zheng, A comprehensive study of the $^{14}C$ source term in the 10MW high- temperature gas-cooled reactor, Radiocarbon, 61 (2019) 1169-1183.
[9] X. Liu, X. Huang, F. Xie, F. Jia, X. Feng, H. Li, Source term analysis of the irradiated graphite in the core of HTR-10, Science and Technology of Nuclear Installations, (2017) 2614890.
[10] H. Li, X. Liu, F. Xie, F. Jia, Experimental study on the content and distribution of key nuclides in an irradiated graphite sphere of HTR-10, Nuclear Engineering and Design, 323 (2017) 39-45.
[11] F. Xie, H. Li, X. Liu, J. Chen, C. Li, X. Chen, K. Verfondern, A comprehensive study on source terms in irradiated graphite spheres of HTR-10, Annals of Nuclear Energy, 352 (2018) 352-365.
[12] K. Pfeiffer, D. Rank, M. Tschurlovits, Journal of Applied Radiation and Isotopes, 32 (1981) 665- 667.

# Consecutive Heat Treatment of Pre-lathed Pebble Fuel Elements for HTGR

**X Zhou, L Wang, Y Kang, S Zhang, J Li, X Shi, B Liu, J Zhang, and Y Tang**

Institute of Nuclear and New Energy Technology of Tsinghua University, the Key Laboratory of Advanced Reactor Engineering and Safety, Ministry of Education, Beijing, China, 100084

phone: +86-10-89796607,email: xiangwen@mail.tsinghua.edu.cn

**Abstract.** In current manufacture process of pebble fuel elements for HTGR, the green pebbles were first carbonized, then lathed and purified at high temperature. The whole heat treatment process included two cycles of heating and cooling and corresponding two loading and unloading processes, which took approximately 90 hours in total. In order to reduce the time and energy consumed and improve the efficiency during the heat treatment process, a consecutive heat treatment process of pebble fuel elements for HTGR was established. In the newly established consecutive heat treatment process, the pebble fuel elements were carbonized and high temperature purified continuously in a specific furnace. The consecutive heat treatment process took less than 60 hours, which included only one cycle of heating and cooling and corresponding one loading and unloading process. Moreover, in order to recycle the matrix graphite powder after lathing, the green pebbles were machined to a certain size before suffering the heat treatment. However, in order to make the size of pebble fuel elements after the consecutive heat treatment meet the technical requirements, it is necessary to figure out their dimension changes during the heat treatment. As the pebbles were prepared by cold quasi-isostatic molding method, their dimension changes parallel and perpendicular to the molding direction were different. In order to better control the dimension changes of pebbles in the heat treatment process, the effects of physical properties such as apparent density, and particle size distribution of matrix graphite powder on the prepared pebbles were comparatively studied. Finally, the consecutive heat treatment of pre-lathed pebble fuel elements for HTGR was established. The comprehensive properties of pebbles prepared with the newly established consecutive heat treatment process satisfied all the technical requirements.

## 1. Introduction

HTGR fuel element designs commonly include two types: spherical fuel elements and prismatic fuel elements [1]. The former was first developed in Germany and then successfully applied in the AVR and THTR [2]. In China, the spherical fuel elements have been demonstrated in HTR-10 and will be used in HTR-PM soon [3, 4]. As one of the key technologies in the HTR-PM project, the prepared pebble fuel elements have been proved to satisfy the expected performances [5, 6]. In a pebble fuel element for HTR-PM, more than 95% in volume is the A3-3 matrix graphite (MG), which is composed of approximately 71 wt% natural flake graphite, 18 wt% artificial graphite, and 11 wt% phenol resin derived carbon [5, 7]. The fabrication process of pebble fuel elements for HTR-PM mainly includes four steps, namely, preparation of resinated matrix graphite powder, overcoating the TRISO-coated fuel particles, cold quasi-static molding, and carbonization, lathing, and high temperature purification [5].

After molding, the molded green pebbles were first carbonized at a maximum temperature of 800 °C, and significant weight loss and corresponding dimensional shrinkage occurred due to the decomposition of phenol resin [8]. The carbonized pebbles were lathed to diameter of 60 mm, and then subjected to high temperature purification under vacuum at 1900 °C. The whole heat treatment process of pebble fuel elements included two cycles of heating and cooling, and two corresponding loading and unloading processes, which took more than 90 hours in total. Meanwhile, the MG lathed from the carbonized pebbles could not be reused directly due to the decomposition of phenol resin in the carbonized MG during the carbonization. In order to recycle the lathed MG directly, the pebbles were lathed to a certain size and then suffered the heat treatment. Furthermore, in order to reduce the time and energy consumption throughout the heat treatment, a continuous heat treatment equipment and corresponding process were designed and developed. The newly developed consecutive heat treatment process took less than 60 hours and included only one cycle of heating and cooling, and corresponding one loading and unloading process. With careful control of physical properties of A3-3 MG powder such as apparent density and particle size distribution, the dimensions and other comprehensive properties of pebbles prepared with the newly continuous heat treatment process met all the technical specifications.

## 2. Experimental

### *2.1. Raw Materials*

As more than 90% either in volume or in mass of pebble fuel elements for HTR-PM is A3-3 MG, the comprehensive properties of fuel pebbles are commonly investigated with MG or MG pebbles instead of the fuel pebbles. Green pebbles were prepared in INET [5] with qualified raw materials such as natural flake and artificial graphite powders, and phenol resin. The resinated MG consists of 64wt% natural flake graphite powder, 16wt% artificial graphite powder, and 20wt% phenol resin.

### *2.2. Property Measurement*

The measurement of bulk density and tap density of resinated MG strictly complied with Chinese Standards GB/T 16913.3-2008 [9] and GB/T 5162-2006 [10], respectively. The equipment for testing bulk density and tap density is produced by Bettersize Instruments Ltd. Each sample was tested three times and the average was taken as the final result. The particle size distribution of MG was measured using the e200LS air sieve produced by Alpine company. Screens with mesh size of 32μm, 63μm, 160μm, 400μm, and 800μm were selected. In every test of each screen, 10 grams of MG sample were sieved for 5 minutes under the operating negative pressure of 2000 Pa. For instance, the weight of screen with mesh size of 32μm is $W_1$. After sieving under the above conditions, the total weight of the screen and the MG sample left on the screen was $W_2$. The percentage of particle size distribution of less than 32μm ($PSD_{32}$) could be calculated by the following eq. 1.

$$PSD_{32}=100*(1-(W_2-W_1)/10) \tag{1}$$

The comprehensive properties of MG pebbles such as crush strength, thermal conductivity, anisotropy of CTE, corrosion rate and erosion rate were tested in strict compliance with the measurement procedures which were introduced in detail elsewhere [11].

### *2.3. Continuous heat treatment equipment*

The schematic of newly designed continuous heat treatment equipment was shown in Fig. 1. The equipment mainly includes furnace body (1, 13 in Fig. 1), heating and insulation system (2,3,4), loading and unloading system (5, 6), vacuum system (11, 12), exhaust gas exhaust system (8, 9), process gas circuit system (7), cooling water system, exhaust gas combustion system (10) and electrical control system. The furnace body has a horizontal structure, and the front and rear furnace doors are provided with a heat shield layer that can be opened and closed. The heating and insulation system consists of graphite heating element (4), insulation layer (3) and steel furnace liner (2) from the inside to the outside.

The loading and unloading system are inside the heating and insulation system, which is composed of graphite muffle box and loading plates. The loading capacity is around 500 pebbles. The carbonization of pebbles is carried out under argon atmosphere with a slightly positive pressure. In order to prevent the volatile decomposition products from entering the heating and insulation system and allow the decomposition products to be directed through the exhaust system, the process inlet gas is introduced from different directions outside the graphite muffle box, and the exhaust gas is discharged through the only outlet at the bottom of the graphite muffle box, which connects the exhaust pipe (8) and exhaust gas combustion system (10). The macromolecular products in the decomposition products are condensed and collected in the exhaust pipe, while the gaseous products at room temperature go through the valve (9) into the combustion system and are oxidized to water and carbon dioxide. The valve can automatically adjust the degree of opening and closing to ensure a stable slightly positive pressure in the furnace.

The furnace must be evacuated before carrying out the high-temperature purification. The vacuum system mainly consists of two vacuum pumps (12) and vacuum pipe (11) which connects the pumps and the furnace. During the entire high-temperature purification process, the vacuum pump must be kept on to continuously vacuum the furnace.

The equipment can not only perform carbonization or high-temperature purification of pebble fuel elements separately, but also carry out the continuous heat treatment of carbonization and high-temperature purification for pebble fuel elements. After the MG pebbles were placed on the graphite plates in the graphite muffle box, the furnace door was closed and the furnace was evacuated to less than 300 Pa. Subsequently, the furnace was filled with argon gas to a slightly positive pressure and heated up to start the carbonization process. The MG pebbles were slowly heated to 800 °C under argon atmosphere of a slightly positive pressure and kept at 800 °C for 1 hour. It took approximately 28 hours for the total heating and holding during the carbonization process. Unlike the direct cooling down after the holding at 800 °C was completed in traditional carbonization process, the furnace was evacuated and further heated up to at the maximum of 1900 °C to carry out the high-temperature purification under vacuum of less than 50 Pa for the continuous heat treatment. It took around 10 hours to run the high-temperature purification process.

After the high-temperature purification process was completed, the furnace was cooled down and the pumps kept operating until the temperature of furnace was low than 1000 °C. Argon was introduced into the furnace to improve the cooling efficiency. When the furnace temperature was lower than 600 °C, the heat shielding door inside the front and rear doors was opened to further enhance the cooling rate at relatively low temperature of furnace. Through the above measures, it took only about 20 hours for the furnace temperature to drop from 1900 °C to 100 °C, at which it was allowed to open the furnace door. Finally, the MG pebbles treated with the continuous heat treatment were unloaded. The entire continuous heat treatment took less than 60 hours, which was around 30 hours shorter than the common heat treatment process where the carbonization and high-temperature purification was carried out separately.

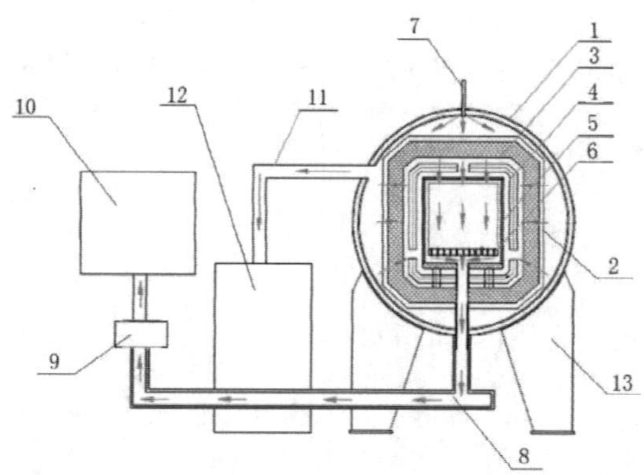


**Figure 1.** Schematic of continuous heat treatment equipment

## 3. RESULTS AND DISCUSSIONS

### *3.1. Characterization of A3-3 MG powder*

The resinated A3-3 MG powder is composed of 64wt% natural flake graphite powder, 16wt% artificial graphite powder, and 20wt% phenol resin. Firstly, the natural graphite powder and artificial graphite powder are mixed in a conical mixer. The mixture is then fed into a kneading machine where phenol resin, dissolved in ethanol, is added and the mixture is homogenized in order to achieve the homogeneous dispersion and adhesion of resin onto the surface of graphitic particles. The homogeneous paste-like mixture is extruded through a punched screen creating strings that are cut into small pieces. These small pieces are then placed in drying trays and heated to ~100 °C under vacuum to remove the ethanol in the mixture. A hammer mill is used to grind the dried mixture into powder with the desired apparent density of 0.51-0.55 g/cm$^3$. Finally, the milled powder is homogenized and the resinated A3-3 MG powder are prepared.

In order to comparatively study the specific characteristics of MG powder on the dimension changes of MG pebbles throughout the heat treatment, two batches of MG powder were prepared. The average apparent density of MG powder 1 and 2 are 0.513 and 0.545g/cm$^3$, respectively. The mean tap density of MG powder 1 and 2 are 0.793 and 0.817g/cm$^3$. The Hausner ratio, i.e., the ratio of tap density to apparent density, of MG powder 1&2 are 1.55 and 1.50, respectively. The ratio of the two MG powders is greater than 1.50, which indicates their poor fluidity. The higher the ratio, the worse the fluidity. Therefore, the fluidity of MG powder 2 is slightly better than that of MG powder 1. The measured particle size distribution (PSD) of MG powder 1&2 is listed in Table 1. It can be seen that nearly half of MG powder 1 has a particle size below 32 μm and more than 95wt% of MG has a particle size of less than 800μm. The particle size of MG powder 2 is larger than that of MG powder 1, which coincides well with the apparent density.

**Table 1.** PSD of resinated A3-3 MG powder

| PSD | MG powder-1 | MG powder-2 |
|---|---|---|
| | wt% | |
| <32μm | 44.37 | 34.78 |
| <63μm | 62.95 | 50.10 |
| <160μm | 73.17 | 62.13 |
| <400μm | 85.20 | 79.23 |
| <800μm | 95.91 | 94.35 |

### *3.2. Shrinkage of MG pebbles*

Using cold quasi-isostatic molding method, green MG pebbles were fabricated with the prepared A3-3 MG powder 1&2, respectively. The green pebbles were lathed to a certain dimension and then suffered the continuous heat treatment of carbonization and high-temperature purification. As shown in Table 2, the dimensions parallel and perpendicular to the molding direction of MG pebbles before and after the continuous heat treatment were measured and calculated to obtain the average dimensional shrinkage rate.

**Table 2.** Dimensional shrinkage of MG pebbles through the continuous heat treatment

| MG powder 1 | Average shrinkage | Deviation |
|---|---|---|
| Parallel | 2.3% | 0.08% |
| Perpendicular | 1.3% | 0.06% |
| MG powder 2 | Average shrinkage | Deviation |
| Parallel | 1.9% | 0.07% |
| Perpendicular | 1.1% | 0.05% |

From Table 2, it can be seen that the shrinkage rate of MG pebbles made of MG powder 1&2 parallel to the molding direction is higher than that perpendicular to the molding direction. The difference in shrinkage between the two orthogonal directions is mainly due to the quasi-isostatic molding brought by the silicon rubber die. During the molding process, the pressure applied on the steel sleeve was transmitted to the pebble through the silicon rubber. Because the silicon rubber is not a complete fluid, the pressure transmission during molding is anisotropic. Namely, the pressure suffered by the pebble parallel to the molding direction is higher than that perpendicular to the molding direction. As a result, the shrinkage rates of MG pebbles made of MG powder 1 either parallel or perpendicular to the molding direction are higher than those made of MG powder 2, which is probably due to the relatively smaller PSD of MG powder 1. From our point of view, the shrinkage of pebbles containing fuel particles should be lower than that of matrix graphite pebbles.

### *3.3. Comprehensive properties of MG pebbles*

In order to further verify the shrinkage rate of MG pebbles throughout the continuous heat treatment, a new batch of MG powder 3 was prepared. The apparent density of MG powder 3 is 0.531g/cm$^3$ and its PSD lies between MG powder 1&2. A batch of 50 MG pebbles were manufactured with MG powder 3. According to the shrinkage rate listed in Table 2, the average shrinkage rate parallel and perpendicular to the molding direction, i.e., 2.1% and 1.2% were used as references. Correspondingly, the dimension parallel and perpendicular to the molding direction of green MG pebbles were machined to 61.3 mm and 60.7 mm, respectively. The expected orthogonal dimensions of MG pebble should be approximately 60.0 mm after the heat treatment. Then these MG ellipsoids were suffered the continuous heat treatment of carbonization and high-temperature purification in the specific furnace mentioned above. The average dimension and its corresponding deviation parallel and perpendicular to the molding direction were 59.96±0.05 mm and 60.03±0.04 mm, respectively. The orthogonal dimensions of all the 50 MG pebbles were in the range of 59.9-60.1 mm, which totally met the technical requirement of 59.6-60.2 mm. The comprehensive properties of MG pebbles were presented in Table 3. It can be seen that the physical, mechanical, thermal, and chemical properties of the MG pebbles manufacture with the continuous heat treatment process totally satisfy the specification requirements.

**Table 3.** Typical properties of MG pebbles

| Item | Specification | Mean value |
|---|---|---|
| Density (g/cm$^3$) | [1.70-1.77] | 1.75 |
| Number of drops [a] | ≥50 | ≥50 |
| Crush strength (kN)[b] | ≥18 | 21.5/26.7 |
| Thermal conductivity (@1000, W/m K) | ≥25.0 | 31.8 |
| CTE anisotropy (20-500°C, $\alpha_{\perp}/\alpha_{//}$) | ≤1.3 | 1.16 |
| Corrosion rate (mg/cm$^2$ h) [c] | ≤1.3 | 0.76 |
| Erosion rate (mg/h) | ≤6.0 | 1.62 |

[a] Number of drops from 4m high onto the pebble bed before break.

[b] Parallel and perpendicular to the molding direction.

[c] @1000°C, 10h, atmosphere is Helium+1vol% $H_2O$.

## 4. Conclusion

Based on the newly developed furnace, a continuous heat treatment process including the carbonization and high-temperature purification was established. With the stringent control of properties such as particle size distribution and apparent density of MG powder, the green pebbles molded by quasi-isostatic molding method were lathed to a certain size before the continuous heat treatment. The dimension and comprehensive properties of MG pebbles treated with the newly established continuous heat treatment process totally satisfied the technical requirements. Comparing with the heat treatment carried out separately, the continuous heat treatment process took less than 60 hours, which significantly improved the efficiency and reduced the energy and time consuming. Moreover, it also provided the potential for the recycling and reusing of the matrix graphite powder produced in the lathing process.

**Acknowledgement**
Supports from the Chinese National S&T Major Project (ZX06901), Chinese National Natural Science Foundation (51420105006), and Key Program for International S&T Cooperation Projects of China (2016YFE0100700) are acknowledged.

**References**

[1] ZHOU Xiang-wen, TANG Ya-ping, LU Zhen-ming, et.al. Nuclear graphite for high temperature gas-cooled reactors, New Carbon Materials, v31, p.193, 2017
[2] H. -J. Allelein, K. Verfondern. Major milestones of HTR development in Germany and still open research issues, Annals of Nuclear Energy, v116, p.114, 2018.
[3] Z.Y. Zhang, Z.X. Wu, D.Z. Wang, Y.H. Xu, Y.L. Sun, F. Li, Y.J. Dong, Current Status and Technical Description of the Chinese 2×250MWth HTR-PM Demonstration Plant, Nuclear Engineering and Design, v239, p.1212, 2009.
[4] Zuoyi Zhang, Yujie Dong, Fu Li, et al, The Shandong Shidao Bay 200 MWe High-Temperature Gas-Cooled Reactor Pebble-Bed Module (HTR-PM) Demonstration Power Plant: An Engineering and Technological Innovation, Engineering, v2, p.112, 2016.
[5] Zhou Xiangwen, Lu Zhenming, Zhang Jie, et al, Preparation of spherical fuel elements for HTR-PM in INET, Nuclear Engineering and Design, v263, p.456, 2013.
[6] S. Knol, S. de Groot, R. V. Salama, et al, HTR-PM fuel pebble irradiation qualification in the high flux reactor in Petten, Proc. HTR-2016, Las Vegas, NV, USA, November 6-10, 2016.
[7] ZHOU Xiang-wen, YANG Yang, SONG Jing, et al, Carbon materials in a high temperature gas-cooled reactor pebble-bed module, New Carbon Materials, v32(2), p.97, 2018.
[8] ZHOU Xiang-wen, ZHANG Jie, LU Zhen-ming, et al. Study on the carbonization process in the fabrication of pebble fuel elements, Nuclear Engineering and Design, v271, p.149, 2014.
[9] GB/T 16913.3-2008. Methods of dust character test – Part 3: Determination of bulk density – Natural bulk method.
[10] GB/T 5162-2006. Metallic powders – Determination of tap density.
[11] Xiangwen Zhou, Zhenming Lu, Jie Zhang, et al. Study on the comprehensive properties and microstructures of A3-3 matrix graphite related to the high temperature purification treatment, v2018, article ID 6084747, 2018.

Journal of Physics: Conference Series **2048** (2021) 012010 doi:10.1088/1742-6596/2048/1/012010

# Release Rates of Short-lived Fission Gases from Modern Spherical Fuel Elements with TRISO-coated Particles

**K Verfondern[1], B Liu[2], H Nabielek[3], T Wang[2], H J Allelein[1], and C H Tang[2]**

[1] Research Center Jülich, 52425 Jülich, Germany
[2] INET, Tsinghua University, Beijing 11, China
[3] Retired from Research Center Jülich, now 1020 Wien, Austria

E-mail: k.verfondern@fz-juelich.de

**Abstract.** Measurement and prediction of fission product release is important in design, licensing and operation of HTRs. Latest development status is near zero particle manufacturing defects and in-pile failures combined with very low matrix contamination levels. In-pile Release over Birth rate measurements will be described and evaluated. Quantitative predictive analyses of short-lived gas release will be provided for MTR irradiation testing with a focus on the most recent experiment with Chinese fuel from HTR-PM production. For irradiation tests with no single particle failure, models describing particle kernel release are not applicable; instead modeling of matrix contamination release is essential. Good agreement between post calculations and in-line R/B measurements has been achieved.

## 1. Introduction

Measurement and prediction of fission product release from the core is important in design, licensing and operation of High Temperature Reactors (HTRs). Both solid fission product release and release rates of short-lived fission gases have come down significantly during the last decades:

(i) Early HTR fuel was uncoated and direct release from the fuel was large. Reactors were built with external fission product trap trains.

(ii) The introduction of dense coating layers around the bare fuel kernel (for better handling) improved the retention significantly, but early fuel elements had high contamination levels in the particle's outer pyrocarbon (oPyC) layer and in the fuel element matrix.

(iii) The systematic introduction of high quality TRISO particles enabled spheres with low contamination levels in the oPyC and in the fuel element matrix. At this stage, releases were dominated by the small number of manufacturing defects, at most one broken particle per three fuel spheres.

(iv) Latest development status is the near zero particle (manufacturing) defects and (in-pile) failures that go hand-in-hand with a further significant reduction of matrix contamination levels.

In-reactor R/B (= Release rate over Birth rate) measurements will be described and evaluated for irradiation tests of spherical fuel elements in the High Flux Reactor (HFR) Petten. Considerations will also be given to historic R/B measurements in operating HTRs AVR, THTR, and Fort St. Vrain. Quantitative predictive analyses of short-lived gas release will be provided for stage (iii) and (iv) irradiation tests in Material Test Reactors (MTRs). Here, the model development from stage (ii) can be fully used although the traces of natural uranium and thorium are now lower by three or four orders of magnitudes.

With no defective and/or failed particles present, releases to be studied are from contamination of the matrix graphite (and the graphite cups in the MTR tests). They have the following components: in-grain diffusion, grain boundary diffusion, recoil from grains into the pores, and transport in the pores the combination of gas-in-gas diffusion and Knudsen diffusion.

The modern intact HTR coated particle retains all fission gases. Therefore, the measured gas releases are, at a first approximation, related to the number of particles with defective coatings from manufacture and the number of coating failures during irradiation. This way, the failed particle fraction is determined experimentally in any fuel assembly from

$$\Phi = \frac{(R/B)_{measured}}{(R/B)_{defective\ particle}} \tag{1}$$

where the defective-particle R/B can be from a model or from a dedicated experiment with designed-to-fail (DTF) particles.

An additional source of fissionable material might be from heavy metal contaminations in the outer pyrocarbon coatings of particles, in the matrix graphite of the fuel body and other graphite components in the irradiation setup.

Iodine is an important fission product in source term predictions [1], but iodine releases are not easily determined in MTR tests and subsequent PIE work:

- During MTR irradiations, the helium purge gas transports continuously released Kr and Xe isotopes to outside measurement stations, but condensable iodine stays within the irradiation capsule.
- Solid fission product release from spherical fuel elements is obtained from measuring the graphite cups that surround the spheres during irradiation and the inner surfaces of the steel capsule. Rig disassembly and transport of components to suitable hot cells equipped with the necessary instrumentation takes usually weeks and months by which time short-lived I-131 is already decayed.

To overcome the iodine detection problem, the MTR post-cycle xenon measurements that are in secular equilibrium with iodine in the rig can be used. In this report, it will be demonstrated how to analyze the data and how to derive quantitative R/B data for I-133 and I-135 from the irradiation tests.

## 2. Release of short-lived noble fission gases from operated HTRs

After the fully releasing HTR fuels in the 1960s, acceptable R/B(Kr-85m) levels were – during 70s and 80s – in the range $1–8\times10^{-6}$ as shown for Fort St. Vrain, THTR, and AVR (Fig. 1). The development of the modern spheres and compacts with clean and strong TRISO particles featuring a SiC interlayer between pyrocarbon coating layers reduced R/Bs down to the range $1\times10^{-10} – 3\times10^{-7}$.

Based on pre-existing particle failure prediction models, on the quality control/quality assurance (QC/QA) results from particle and fuel element manufacture including measured contamination levels in the graphitic components and operational data including breeding of fissile material from natural uranium and thorium, it has been attempted to predict release rates during Fort St. Vrain power operations [1]. While the particle failure models appear somewhat conservative, the level of R/B measurements is well bounded between the two modeling assumptions of release from contamination only and from contamination plus failed particles.

THTR fission gas release predictions worked well during the first 90 days of full power operation. Yet, after forced control rod injection exercises as ordered by the TUEV, many spheres and even coated particles were broken mechanically with subsequent increase of release rates [2]. More significantly, the release mechanisms changed completely from the usual diffusion, decay, and release sequence to knockout from crushed particles as observed by the change of slope from 0.32 down to 0.15 (see Fig. 1), where:

$$slope = \frac{\log(R/B)}{\log(T_{1/2})} \tag{2}$$

is the mean value over all short-lived fission gases and $T_{1/2}$ is the half-life (s) of the respective short-lived fission gases.

Releases in AVR are simple to interpret: most spheres had a $3\times10^{-4}$ heavy metal contamination and with the recommended diffusions coefficients of Kr and Xe in $UO_2$ [3], R/B values for all krypton and xenon isotopes can be easily predicted (green dashed line in Fig. 1).

R/B levels shown in Fig. 1 are typical of HTRs in the 1970s and the 1980s. With modern fuel, release rates of short-lived noble fission gases are by factors ~1000 lower.

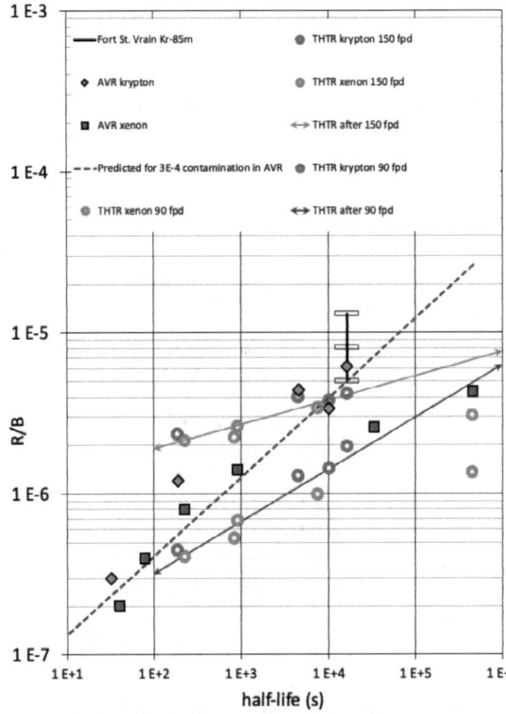


**Figure 1.** Release rates of short-lived noble fission gases from operating reactors AVR, THTR and Fort St. Vrain. THTR 150 efpd (equivalent full power days) refers to the time after forced injection of control rods. The range of half-lives goes from 9 seconds to 5.25 days.

Perfect spheres with perfect TRISO particles were made by HOBEG/NUKEM from December 1978 onwards. These were then used in subsequent AVR reloads 15 and 20 with HEU $(Th,U)O_2$ LTI TRISO and reloads 19, 21, 21-2 with LEU $UO_2$ LTI TRISO. Since AVR still contained 50% dirty old fuel, the massive improvement of fission product releases showed up only to a limited extent.

Examples of modern clean LEU $UO_2$ TRISO fuel from MTR irradiations tests are given in the following Figures 2 and 3.

Two irradiation proof tests, HFR-K5 and HFR-K6, were performed for the qualification of spherical fuel elements for the 200 MW(th) HTR-Modul reactor. In these tests with four spheres each, the temperature cycles characteristic of multi-pass pebble-bed reactors were simulated throughout the irradiation in HFR Petten. Selected results are shown in Fig. 2 for capsule B of HFR-K6, where the top rig A contained one sphere, the mid-rig B the spheres HFR-K6/2 and 3 (no defects, no failures), and the bottom rig C contained one sphere HFR-K6/4 with two initial manufacturing defects, but zero in-reactor failures.

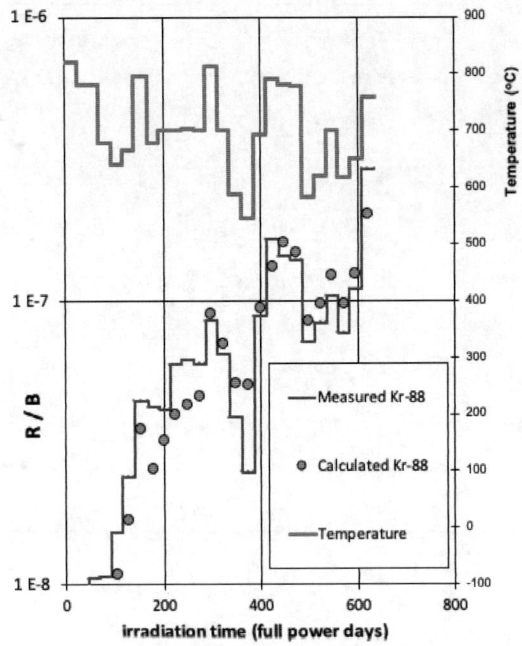


**Figure 2.** Measured and predicted Kr-88 release rates in the temperature-cycled HTR-Modul Proof Test irradiation. The two spherical fuel elements in mid-HFR-K6 capsule B had zero initial defects and zero failed particles throughout irradiation. The predictive calculations used the Röllig 1977 model [4,5,6].

While good models for fission gas release from the various sources of contamination are existing, there are two major problems for a precise numerical prediction:

- Urgently needed are independent measurements of the contamination levels of $U_{nat}$ and Th in the matrix of the spherical fuel elements and in the binderless graphite of the surrounding cups. Even if such measurements are available, they are usually quoted as < 1 ppm and that is not good enough, because from our evaluation we must assume values between 1 ppb and 100 ppb.
- Second problem is that the reactor station makes precise and detailed calculations for the depletion of enriched uranium and the breeding of plutonium for the fuel in the coated particles. Since there are no defects and no failures, this fissile amount is not the real source of fission gas release rates. It is rather the natural uranium and thorium contamination in graphitic materials, for which the reactor station does not provide the necessary nucleonic predictions. An earlier attempt to overcome these problems was made by Alain Marmier [7].

In another MTR test HFR-EU1, the bottom capsule contained three German spheres from AVR reload 21-2 with the best QC/QA data ever in German sphere manufacture. Throughout irradiation, no defects nor failures were observed (Fig. 3) [8]. The top capsule of MTR test HFR-EU1 contained two Chinese spheres from the HTR-10 production demonstrating excellent irradiation behavior much better than earlier HTR-10 fuel tested in experiment VOSTOK-6 in IVV-2M [9].

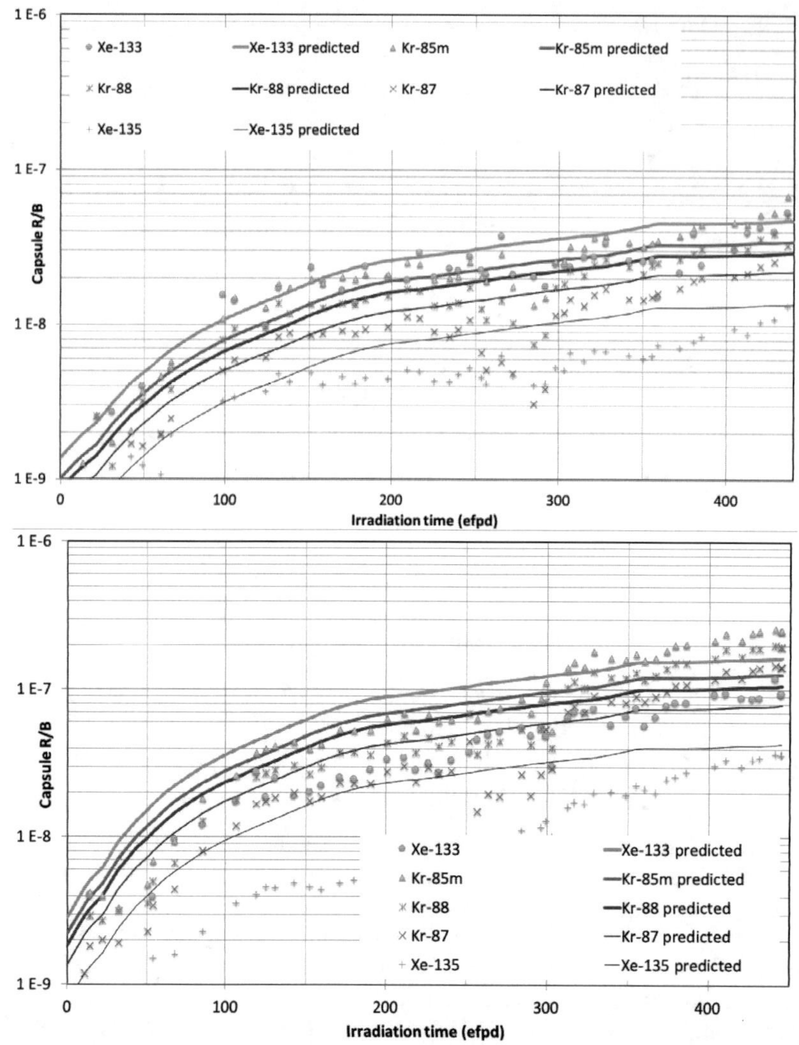


**Figure 3.** Release rates of short-lived fission gases from Petten irradiation tests HFR-EU1 (upper capsule with HTR-10 spheres (top), lower capsule with German spheres (bottom)).

One of the most successful irradiation tests of all times was HFR-PM containing high quality spherical fuel elements from the HTR-PM production. The results from operating this test [10] will be analyzed in great detail.

## 3. Mechanisms of fission gas release from contamination and mathematical modeling

In HTR fuel particles, fission products are retained by the dense coating layers around the fuel kernel. A very small fraction of particles may have coating defects from manufacture or the coating may have failed during irradiation. The pertinent modeling and necessary data are contained in IAEA-TECDOC- 978 [3].

Additionally, we may have heavy metal contaminations, $U_{nat}$ and Th, in the graphite components outside the coated particles that contribute to fission product release.

### *3.1. Release from heavy metal contamination*

The release rate of short-lived fission gases from contamination in graphitic components has been modeled since the early 1970s [4,5,11,12,13,14].

Fissile material that exists or is bred from thorium and (natural) uranium traces outside of coated particles translates into a so-called effective contamination (see later Fig. 9). This contribution to releases has become important with recent irradiation tests of spherical fuel elements having zero defective particles and zero in-reactor failures during irradiation.

The contamination-generated gases escape via three routes into the HTR coolant stream:

1. Diffusion in A3-matrix graphite grains;
2. Diffusion in the amorphous component of the A3-matrix;
3. Direct recoil into pores of the A3-matrix or the graphite components;

This is shown in Fig. 4.

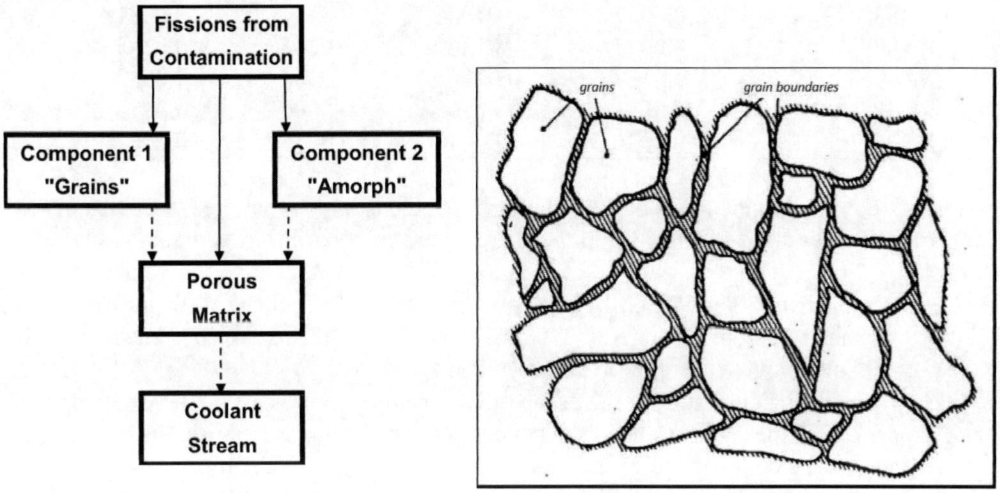


**Figure 4.** Modeling release paths of short-lived noble fission gases from heavy metal contaminations in graphitic components [4,5].

Diffusion in and from grains and the amorphous binder is mathematically described by the Equivalent Sphere Model predicting the ratio of steady state release rate to birth rate by

$$\frac{R}{B} = \frac{3}{x}\left(\coth x - \frac{1}{x}\right) \quad x = \sqrt{\frac{\lambda}{D'}} \tag{3}$$

where λ – decay constant [$s^{-1}$], D' – reduced diffusion coefficient [$s^{-1}$], Q – activation energy [J/mol], R=8.3145 J/(mol·K) gas constant, and T – temperature [K].

Early work on heavily contaminated THTR spherical fuel elements with HEU $(Th,U)O_2$ HTI BISO particles had established the values as given in Table 1 [12].

**Table 1.** Parameters for the prediction of gas release rates from contamination in A3.

| Parameter | Krypton | Xenon |
|---|---|---|
| Frequency factor $D'_o$ [$s^{-1}$] | | |
| Grain fraction | $3.04\times10^{-5}$ | $1.67\times10^{-7}$ |
| Amorphous fraction | $1.7\times10^{-2}$ | $1.7\times10^{-2}$ |
| Activation energy Q [kJ/mol] | | |
| Grain fraction | 106 | 78.6 |
| Amorphous fraction | 54 | 54 |
| | | |
| Amorphous fraction in A3 | 0.005 | |
| Recoil fraction into pores | 0.0002 | |

Journal of Physics: Conference Series **2048** (2021) 012010 doi:10.1088/1742-6596/2048/1/012010

With the amorphous fraction and recoil fraction into pores given in Table 1, the R/B ratios of the noble gas isotopes released from the heavy metal contaminations in the A3 matrix can be finally calculated with their corresponding decay constants as a function of irradiation temperature. They are given in Table 2 for some temperature values.

**Table 2.** Effective total R/B values from contamination in A3 matrix according to the Röllig model [4].

| Temperature (°C)<br>Isotope | 700 | 900 | 1100 | 1300 |
|---|---|---|---|---|
| Kr-85m | 0.0082 | 0.0159 | 0.0291 | 0.0482 |
| Kr-87 | 0.0057 | 0.0104 | 0.0177 | 0.0281 |
| Kr-88 | 0.0072 | 0.0136 | 0.0242 | 0.0395 |
| Xe-133 | 0.0128 | 0.0226 | 0.0364 | 0.0533 |
| Xe-135 | 0.0051 | 0.0070 | 0.0090 | 0.0113 |
| Xe-135m | 0.0026 | 0.0041 | 0.0055 | 0.0067 |

Fission gas transport in the pores of the A3 matrix proceeds by two parallel processes: (i) Knudsen diffusion, and (ii) gas-in-gas diffusion, and these are determined by different material and operational parameters:

- Knudsen diffusion is predicted by temperature, molar mass of the diffusing species and the pore diameter (assumption here: 270 nm); the Kr-88 diffusion coefficient at 1000°C is $3.32\times10^{-6}$ $m^2/s$, independent of pressure.
- Gas-in-gas diffusion describes the competition between the released Kr, Xe atoms and He in the pores. This makes the transport dependent on temperature, pressure, the respective atomic weights and the collision integrals.

Here, transport between the 0.1 MPa in an MTR test and the, e.g., 7 MPa in an operating HTR can make a significant difference. The combination of Knudsen and gas-to-gas diffusion processes (modeled by taking the harmonic mean of the respective diffusion coefficients much like two parallel electrical circuits) at 1000°C, for example, results in a Kr-88 diffusion coefficient of $2.33\times10^{-6}$ $m^2/s$ in an MTR at atmospheric pressure and $0.11\times10^{-6}$ $m^2/s$ in the operating HTR.

Finally, transport is further hindered by porosity and tortuosity. The A3 matrix has a total 20% porosity and a tortuosity factor of 3 is assumed.

*3.2. Release of short-lived iodine derived from post irradiation measurements of xenon*

Fuel performance is demonstrated by two dedicated measurement technologies:

- Continuous in-reactor on-line measurements of short-lived noble (rare) fission gases and relating these to a computed birth-rate resulting in "R/B" values;
- Post irradiation measurements of longer-lived solid fission product deposited in graphite cups and capsule walls.

Neither of these technologies cover iodine isotopes, because during irradiation iodine remains within the capsule and the iodine isotopes are too short-lived for post-test measurements.

There is, however, a practical possibility for experimental iodine release determination that had been applied already in ORR fuel irradiations tests in the years 1964 to 1969 and in Oak Ridge HFIR tests in the 70s [15]: when fission gas measurements are continued after irradiation cycle reactor shutdown, Xe-135 and Xe-135m releases of Xe-135 and Xe-135m can still be measured while the krypton releases stop immediately. Now these two xenon isotopes decay – because in secular equilibrium with the precursor – with the I-135 half-life (Fig. 5). And this works similarly for I-133.

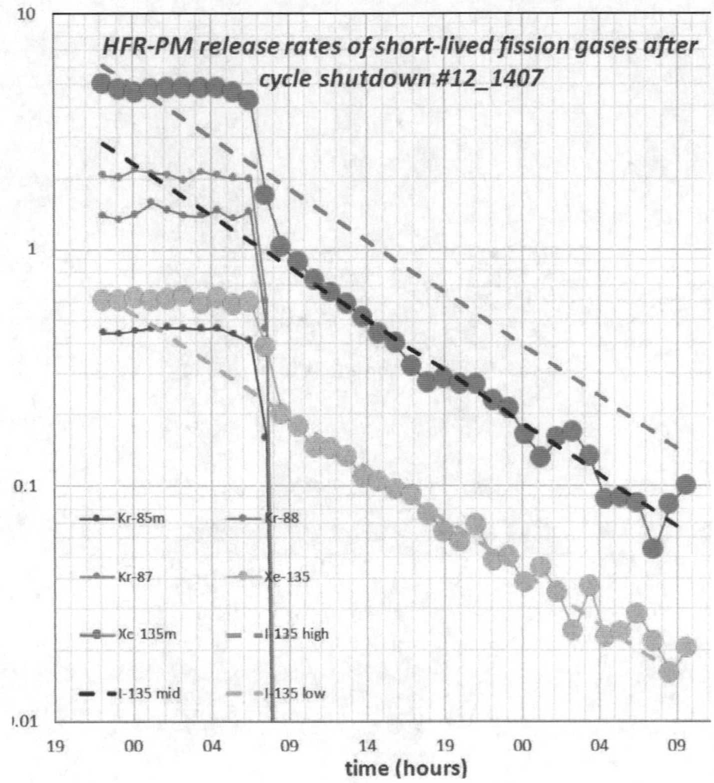


**Figure 5.** Post-cycle measurements of Xe-135m (blue) and Xe-135 (yellow) demonstrating I-135 half-life. Results from HFR-Petten measurements after cycle #12 of the thirteen HFR-PM irradiation cycles.

The procedure is as follows: the iodine precursor of xenon is emitted from fissile sources and, as a condensable, deposits on the interior surfaces of the capsule. Upon decaying into xenon, this isobar enters the sweep gas instantaneously. This way, the amount of iodine deposited is measured be the residual xenon in the sweep gas with krypton dropping to zero at the end of the irradiation cycle and xenon isotopes Xe-133, Xe-135m, and Xe-135 decaying with the corresponding iodine half-life. Then the analysis of the xenon activities is used to derive a quantitative measure of I-133 and I-135 release rates at the end of the prior irradiation cycle.

## 4. Analysis of fission gas and iodine release from HTR-PM fuel irradiation testing

The HFR-PM irradiation test [10] was conducted with five HTR-PM spherical fuel elements in the High Flux Reactor in Petten. The irradiation of 13 cycles took place from August 2012 until December 2014. The rig consisted of one single capsule with five spheres, each surrounded by graphite cups (Fig. 6).

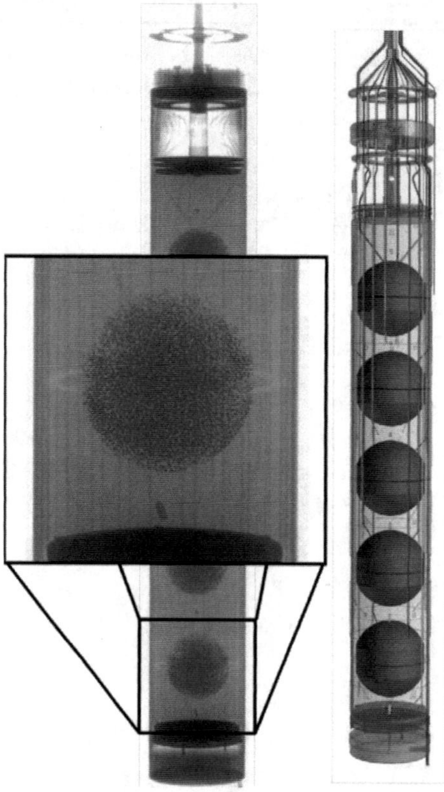

**Figure 6.** Arrangement of five spherical fuel elements of HTR-PM fuel production irradiated in the High Flux Reactor Petten.

The spheres were irradiated at a temperature of 1050°C up to 12% FIMA and accumulated a fast neutron fluence near $5\times10^{25}$ n/m$^2$ (E>16fJ). All five spherical fuel elements had zero manufacturing defects and zero in-reactor failures as can be seen from the R/B measurements (see later Fig. 9).

Throughout, the HFR-PM irradiation experiment has been closely monitored with release rate measurements recorded every hour, also through the down-cycles between active irradiation cycles. In the absence of defective and failed particles, the release modeling has concentrated on fissile isotope breeding in the heavy metal contamination, even if this is only at the ppb level.

Starting with natural uranium, the fissile contribution is – due to build-up of Pu isotopes – linearly increasing from 3 to $5\times10^{-9}$ of the complete fissile content of the whole rig with 5 spheres (blue curve in Fig. 7).

Thorium contribution to fissile starts – of course – with zero, but is steeply rising to the $7\times10^{-9}$ fraction of total (red curve in Fig. 7). 1050°C predicted contamination based R/Bs for the Kr and Xe releases are shown in Fig. 8 as function of the isotope half-life computed with the 1978 Röllig model [4]. Notice different release mechanisms for krypton and xenon.

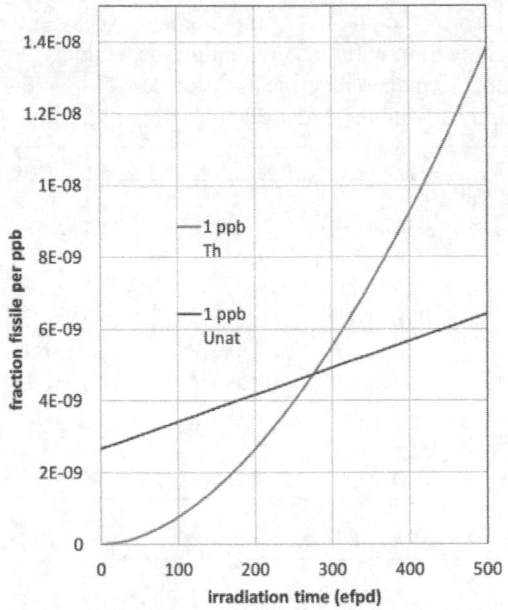


**Figure 7.** Fissile source contribution per 1 ppb $U_{nat}$ or Th: the actual source term of the measured gas releases is the contamination in spheres and capsule components.

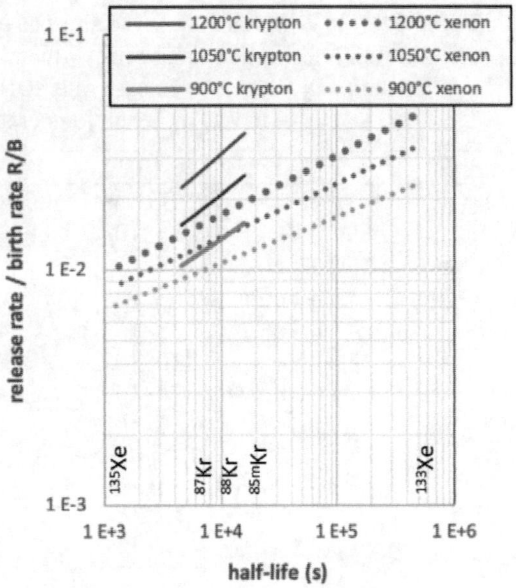


**Figure 8.** Röllig model [4] predicted release rates of short-lived fission gases from matrix graphite grains.

The applicable 1050°C numerical R/B-values are also listed in top row of Table 3. These have to be multiplied by the respective contamination levels, namely

- in the A3-matrix: 0.5 ppb $U_{nat}$ and 0.5 ppb Th, and
- in the graphite cups: 12 ppb $U_{nat}$ and 14 ppb Th,

to reproduce measured R/Bs. Figure 9 shows the superb agreement with the huge numbers of measurement data from the HFR Petten reactor station.

Two minor deviations are noticeable:

- Early R/B measurements are much smaller than predicted and we postulate that possibly the assumed A3-matrix pore structure has not yet fully opened during the early phases of the irradiation.
- Excess Kr-85m can be observed around day 190 and day 270: this was caused by a krypton contamination in the neon gas supply at the time as indicated in the Petten cycle reports.

In any case, reported HFR-PM R/Bs are unbelievably low at $5\times10^{-11}$ to $5\times10^{-9}$ (compared to $1\times10^{-7}$ to $1\times10^{-5}$ in the earlier diagrams): the sheer steady stable measurement technology at these extremely low levels is already admirable.

The dashed lines at the top of Fig. 9 show hypothetical R/B predictions to be expected from a single defect or failed particle in any of the five spherical fuel elements with 12,000 particles each. This comparison demonstrates that we are very far away indeed from any fuel failure.

The red-yellow circles at the bottom of Fig. 9 are the results of the derivation of I-135 R/B-values from the inter-cycle activity measurements of Xe 135 and Xe-135m with the error bars indicating the difference in derived values from between the two xenon isotopes. This demonstrates that xenon releases are a safe upper limit for iodine release predictions by a far distance. Interestingly, the I-135 R/B seems to remain constant throughout irradiation while all the other noble gas isotopes are increasing due to the increase of fissile content in the test, but we have no explanation for this so far.

**Table 3.** HFR-PM predicted R/B-values as computed by the product of the momentary fissile contribution from the existing heavy metal contamination with the temperature dependent contamination specific release rate. R/B-values from one defective of failed particle have a different temperature and half-life dependence.

| Isotope | | Xe-133 | Kr-85m | Kr-88 | Kr-87 | Xe-135 |
|---|---|---|---|---|---|---|
| | | R/B (from contamination at 1050°C) | | | | |
| | | $3.26\times10^{-2}$ | $2.52\times10^{-2}$ | $2.11\times10^{-2}$ | $1.56\times10^{-2}$ | $8.51\times10^{-3}$ |
| Irradiation time (efpd) | Fissile contribution | | | | | |
| 50 | $4.12\times10^{-8}$ | $1.35\times10^{-9}$ | $1.04\times10^{-9}$ | $8.70\times10^{-10}$ | $6.44\times10^{-10}$ | $3.51\times10^{-10}$ |
| 150 | $7.04\times10^{-8}$ | $2.30\times10^{-9}$ | $1.78\times10^{-9}$ | $1.49\times10^{-9}$ | $1.10\times10^{-9}$ | $5.99\times10^{-10}$ |
| 250 | $1.15\times10^{-7}$ | $3.74\times10^{-9}$ | $2.89\times10^{-9}$ | $2.42\times10^{-9}$ | $1.79\times10^{-9}$ | $9.74\times10^{-10}$ |
| 350 | $1.72\times10^{-7}$ | $5.61\times10^{-9}$ | $4.34\times10^{-9}$ | $3.63\times10^{-9}$ | $2.68\times10^{-9}$ | $1.46\times10^{-9}$ |
| | | R/B from one defective or failed particle | | | | |
| | | $6.34\times10^{-6}$ | $1.21\times10^{-6}$ | $9.59\times10^{-7}$ | $6.47\times10^{-7}$ | $4.45\times10^{-7}$ |

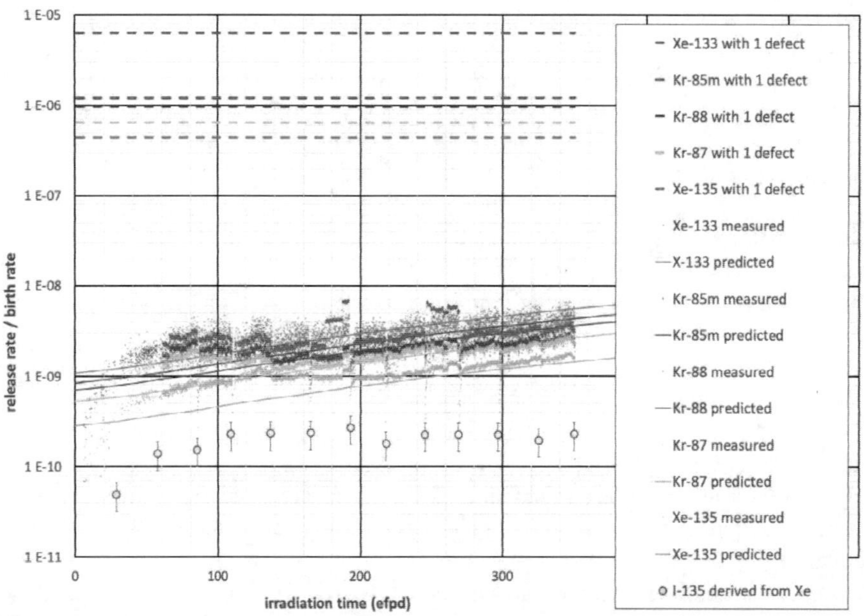


**Figure 9.** Measured release rates of short-lived noble fission gases during the operation of the HFR-PM irradiation test in comparison to release predictions from 0.5 ppb $U_{nat}$ and 0.5 ppb Th in the fuel element matrix and from 12 ppb $U_{nat}$ and 14 ppb Th in the graphite cups surrounding the five spherical fuel elements. Also shown hypothetical release rates for the case of one (out of 60,000) defective or failed particle with a noticeable different half-life behavior. I-135 releases have been derived from post-cycle measurements of Xe-135 and Xe-135m.

## 5. Summary and conclusions

Modern HTR fuels are by factors ~1000 cleaner than those of the 1970-80 power stations, because manufacturing, quality control, test irradiation and post-irradiation technology have advanced massively during the last decades.

All the recent irradiations have shown spherical fuel elements with zero manufacturing defects and zero irradiation-induced particle failures featuring – at the same time – extremely low contamination levels, ppb rather than ppm.

Models and data exist for the comprehensive prediction of in-reactor release of short-lived fission gases also using the full set of irradiation data provided by the reactor station. There are two problems though:

(i) we need better precision $U_{nat}$/Th trace contamination measurements in the graphitic components of the irradiation rig; and
(ii) we need the reactor station to predict the precise fissile contribution arising from the breeding of $U_{nat}$/Th. In both cases, we had to use circumstantial evidence to provide the necessary data.

A 1964 method has been used to derive iodine release rates from measured post-cycle xenon activities. Thc rcsults show that our long-term conservative assumption - those noble gases provide an upper limit to iodine release - is fully correct. Furthermore, the newly determined iodine releases are actually factoring 2 to 5 lower than the corresponding measured xenon releases.

Future work should include independent measurements of $U_{nat}$/Th contamination levels in spherical fuel elements and in the graphite cups that are used in irradiation experiments. In addition, isotope analyses of the uranium and thorium obtained in the burn-leach tests of spherical fuel elements with TRISO particles are needed. While, wide-ranging studies are performed and reported in the preparation of irradiation experiments, full scale post-test analyses that account for measured monitors and measured burnups are missing and should be more forcefully requested in future tests. This must also include post-test depletion code computations including the breeding of U-233 from the thorium contamination in matrix material and in graphite cups. Studies so far have neglected the Röllig proposed modeling of Knudsen and molecular diffusion in the pores of the A3. This model aspect has the potential to predict lower gas release rates at the higher pressures of operational HTRs, but is negligible in the evaluation of irradiation tests.

In conclusion, release rate measurements from fuel elements in MTR tests and in operating HTRs are the important indicator both for initial fuel quality and for performance during operation.

**References**

[1] Hanson D L 2004 *A Review of Radionuclide Release from HTGR Cores during Normal Operation* (Palo Alto: EPRI)
[2] Röllig K 1990 *Auswertung von Inbetriebnahmeergebnissen am THTR-300 für HTR-Nachfolge-anlagen* (Mannheim: HRB)
[3] IAEA 1997 *Fuel Performance and Fission Product Behavior in Gas Cooled Reactors* (Vienna IAEA-TECDOC-978)
[4] Röllig K 1977 Release of Rare Fission Gases from Spherical Fuel Elements with Coated Fuel Particles *(Nuclear Technology vol 32)* p 516
[5] Van der Merwe H and Venter J H 2009 A Method to Evaluate Fission Gas Release during Irradiation Testing of Spherical Fuel *(J. Eng. Gas Turbines Power vol 131)*
[6] Gontard R and Nabielek H 1993 *Quantitative Evaluation of the Performance of German HTR Fuel under Normal Operating and under Accident Conditions* (Jülich: Research Center Jülich)
[7] Marmier A 2012 *Sustainability and Efficiency Improvements of Gas-Cooled High Temperature Reactors* (Delft: PhD Thesis Technische Universiteit)
[8] Laurie M Marmier A Berg G Lapetite J-M Fuetterer M A and Tang C H 2010 *Proc. HTR 2010 (Prague)*
[9] Tang C H 2004 *Proc. HTR2004 (Beijing)*
[10] Knol S et al. 2018 *Proc. HTR2018 (Warsaw)*
[11] Thiel J 1983 *Transiente Gasfreisetzung aus der Brennelementkontamination* (Mannheim: HRB)
[12] Röllig K 1993 *Transiente Edelgasfreisetzung* (Mannheim: HRB)
[13] Richards M 2018 *Proc. HTR2018 (Warsaw)*
[14] Verfondern K and Nabielek H 2020 *TRISO Fuel Performance Modeling and Simulation* (Amsterdam: North-Holland/American Elsevier)
[15] Carroll R M and Sisman O 1970 *Evaluating Fuel Behavior during Irradiation by Fission-Gas Release* (Oak Ridge: ORNL)

Journal of Physics: Conference Series **2048** (2021) 012011 doi:10.1088/1742-6596/2048/1/012011

# R&D on Surrogate Kernel Fabrication in Support of Reaktor Daya Eksperimental (RDE) Project

**Sarjono, S Riyanto, E Mutiara, E Yusnitha, T Yulianto, R Langenati, and A Sumaryanto**

Center for Nuclear Fuel Technology – BATAN, Kawasan Puspiptek Gd 65, Setu, Tangerang Selatan, Banten, Indonesia

phone: +62-21-7560915, email: sjono@batan.go.id

**Abstract.** R&D program on HTGR fuel to support the RDE project has been outlined and is aimed to develop national capabilities on nuclear fuel technology. The external sol-gel technology has been adopted for the fabrication of kernels. Laboratory scale work has been ongoing at the Center for Nuclear Fuel Technology (PTBBN) BATAN to study various parameters involved in the process of kernel fabrication including tuning of parameters related to droplet formation (feed flow rate, vibrator frequency, NH3 gas flow rate), optimizing chemical formulation in broth preparation, various treatments in aging, washing, drying process, and thermal treatment for densification of kernels. In this early stage, zirconium precursors were used to manufacture surrogate kernels of ytrria-stabilized zirconia. The steps for kernel fabrication include chemical formulation of broth and droplet casting, aging-washing-drying of gel microspheres, calcination and sintering, and characterization of sintered kernels (surface morphology, density, diameter/sphericity, solid phase). Stable cast of droplets from 1 mm nozzle diameter was optimized by adjusting feed flowrate at 30 ml/min, viscosity at 45-60 cP, and vibrating frequency at 100 Hz. Presolidification of gel skin was optimized at a working NH3 flow rate of 3.5 - 4 L/min. Addition of urea with mole ratio urea/metal 2.5/1.0 gave the most preferable results based on SEM examination for crack and morphological structure. Control the opaqueness of the sol can be done by portioning addition of urea, where a portion of urea was added at decomposing temperature around 85°C, while another portion was added at a lower temperature. Addition of urea has a desirable effect on crack reduction during heat treatment of gel microspheres. Increase in metal concentration results in an increase in kernel diameter when other sol-to-gel conversion parameters were kept unvaried. Phase determination by X-Ray Diffractometer indicates that solid phase for ceria-stabilized zirconia prepared with precursor composition of 16% yttrium in zirconium-yttrium sol results in yttria-stabilized zirconia 8YSZ with cubic phase.

## 1. Introduction

The National Nuclear Energy Agency of Indonesia (BATAN) has established a plan to construct an Experimental Power Reactor of pebble bed HTGR type with a thermal output of 10 MWth as a demonstration purpose for the introduction of larger nuclear power plants of similar type in the country [1]. HTGR fuel R&D program for national capacity building has been outlined, where BATAN, national universities and related ministries are involved in the task of R&Ds on HTGR fuels under the coordination of the Ministry of Research, Technology and Higher Education. This HTGR fuel R&D

program is aimed to develop national capabilities on nuclear fuel research to support HTGR fuels for RDE operation [2].

The RDE fuel R&D program at this early step includes research in fuel kernel fabrication and designs of laboratory scale coater and pebble compaction facilities. The fuel manufacture technology employs the German Nukem external gelation process. The external gelation process (also known as the "gel-precipitation" process) is adopted for the fabrication of UO2 kernel for the HTR-10 (China), HTTR (Japan) and PBMR (South Africa) reactors.

Laboratory scale work is ongoing at the Center for Nuclear Fuel Technology (PTBBN) BATAN to study the chemical processes of surrogate (uranium-free) kernels fabrication. The surrogate kernels are necessary for utilization in the TRISO coating process development.

Tuning of parameters involved in gel casting process (such as viscosity of the feed solution, metal concentration, flowrate, nozzle frequency, and $NH_3$ flowrate) requires repeated experiments of gel casting. For this purpose, surrogate materials are preferable to avoid the radiological hazards and the complexity of radioactive material handling. In this work, zirconia has been selected for the analogue material considering that nitrate precursors of zirconium are capable of being converted from a sol into a gel microsphere by the external gelation technique upon their reaction with ammonia solution. Further, stabilizing zirconia with yttria is also of interest to closely resemble urania in terms of crystallography and microstructure, i.e., fluorite crystal structure (face centered cubic, space group Fm-3m). Phase stabilizing of zirconia is needed because three crystal structures of zirconia exist at different temperatures: cubic (c) (from 2680°C to 2370°C); tetragonal (t) (from 2370°C to 1170°C); monoclinic (m) (from 1170°C to room temperature) [3]. The monoclinic (m) phase is a more stable phase, but the cubic phase is preferred. Incorporation of cubic oxides like MgO, CaO, $Y_2O_3$ and $CeO_2$ to zirconia can delay creation of the transformation phase to maintain the stability of the zirconia crystals in their tetragonal or cubic phase at room temperature [4]. These materials are referred to as stabilizers.

Presolidification of the surface of gel microsphere is required in the external gelation method in order to avoid spherical shape deformation during contact of droplets with the $NH_4OH$ column bath [5]. For this purpose, the metal solution needs to be preneutralized or be made acid deficient for rapid hardening of the droplets before reaching the $NH_4OH$ bath surface. In this way the spherical shape of gel microspheres can be maintained during gel casting process. Preneutralization can be performed by precipitation-redispersion upon dropwise addition of $HN_4OH$ to the metal solution. Another technique of preneutralization is by allowing urea to decompose in the metal solution. Raising the temperature of the solution above about 70°C will allow urea to slowly decompose in the aqueous system solutions. This will result in a homogeneous generation of hydroxyls in the solution and homogenous precipitation in the whole volume to convert the solution into sol. Some previous works have adopted this method in the preparation of sol for the fabrication of zirconia kernels [6, 7].

Unlike hydrous uranium oxide gel spheres that can be highly porous, Zr based gel spheres are amorphous, and cracking is a common problem with amorphous microspheres. The porosity of the amorphous microspheres is typically not sufficient to permit the gases that are formed during heat treatments to escape. The microspheres will crack if the internal pressure becomes too great [8]. The potential for microspheres fabricated through external gelation process to crack during thermal treatment exists because the gel spheres will contain ammonium nitrate ($NH_4NO_3$), organic additives such as PVA (polyvinyl alcohol) and THFA (tetra-hydrofurfuryl alcohol. PVA is used to control viscosity of the solution and serves as an organic frame to improve strength of the gelled microsphere. THFA is a kind of complexing agent for adjusting the performance of solution with PVA.

Decomposition of non-oxides components during thermal treatment, i.e., drying and calcining, will release various gases that add to the risk of defects in the final oxide microspheres. In view of the heat treatment process, higher porosity will facilitate the evaporation of water and the release of degradation products of additive components.

Readily decomposable additive materials, such as urea, are found to notably improve the surface area and porosity. Nohman, A.K.H. and H.M. Ismail [9] have examined the marked effect of the presence of decomposable urea on the structure and surface texture of $ZrO_2$. They believed that decomposition of urea would lead to pore widening and/or pore creation.

It has been observed that serious cracking or damage would also occur in microspheres during heating steps if the gel microspheres are not washed clean enough. Attempts to overcome the heat treatment damages resulted from washing process include the use of propylene glycol monomethyl ether (PGME) as the washing alcohol [6, 7, 10, 11], instead of the commonly used isopropyl alcohol (IPA), to remove moisture and any remaining ammonium nitrate.

This work aims to study the influence of chemical preparation routes on the morphological properties of the sintered yttria-stabilized kernels. The chemical preparation routes involve two parameters, i.e., preneutralization treatment and the use of urea as pore promoter. Pore widening and/or pore creation effects of urea on the structure and $ZrO_2$ has been reported by [9] through thermal analysis, X-ray diffraction and measurements of nitrogen adsorption. Preneutralization were done both by precipitation-redispersion upon dropwise addition of $NH_4OH$ and by decomposition of urea. It is assumed that rapidness of gelation reaction can be controlled by the extent of acid deficiency caused by preneutralization treatment, and urea that will serve as pore promoter upon its subsequent decomposition during thermal treatment is expected to have a significant influence on the properties and structure of the resulting oxide kernels. Isopropyl alcohol as washing agent was used in this work considering that it is more affordable and widely available in Indonesian market.

## 2. Materials and Method

The schematic diagram for the fabrication of zirconia kernels is presented in Figure 1.

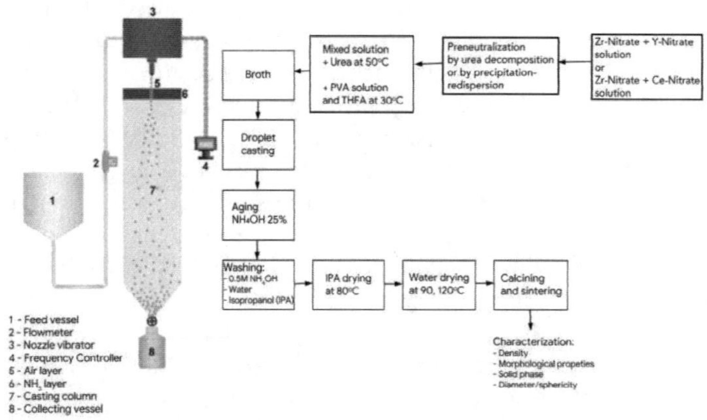


**Figure 1.** Schematic diagram for zirconia kernel fabrication

### 2.1. *Materials*

Zirconium The starting materials used were zirconium oxynitrate $ZrO(NO_3)_2{\cdot}6H_2O$, Yttrium(III) nitrate hexahydrate ($Y(NO_3)_3{\cdot}6H_2O$) 99.9 %, tetrahydrofurfuryl alcohol 98%, poly(vinyl alcohol) - Mowiol® 56-98, ammonia solution 25%, isopropyl alcohol ≥99.5%, demineralized water, and urea EMD Millipore.

### 2.2. *Chemical formulation of broth and droplet casting*

Zirconium and yttrium precursors were used as metal precursors. For preparation of zirconium-yttrium sol was prepared with 16% yttrium content. A certain amount of urea was decomposed to prepare sol. PVA solution (8%) was prepared as a viscosity modifier. Broth for casting feed was a mixture of sol, PVA solution, and THFA stirred for a certain time for homogeneity and finally stored in the feed tank overnight to release micro bubbles. The presence of micro bubbles in the feed flow, if not removed, may interfere with droplet sphericity during casting. Casting process of broth was carried out at adjusted feed flowrate, vibrating frequency and the amount of $NH_3$ gas flow.

*2.3. Aging, washing and drying of gel microspheres*

Processes of aging of gel in ammonia solution, washing sequentially with diluted ammonia solution, demineralized water, fresh isopropanol as well as recycled isopropanol and isopropanol drying at 80°C were carried out in a rotary flask. Water in gel, which is not chemically bonded, was removed by drying the gels in an oven at 90°C and 120°C for 4 hours each.

*2.4. Calcination and sintering*

Thermal treatment was aimed to decompose and remove additives, convert hydroxides to oxides and remove by process byproducts, and for densification of oxide kernels. The temperature profile for calcination and sintering process was set at 200°C, 400°C, 600°C and 1350°C for 4 hours each as can be seen in Fig. 2.

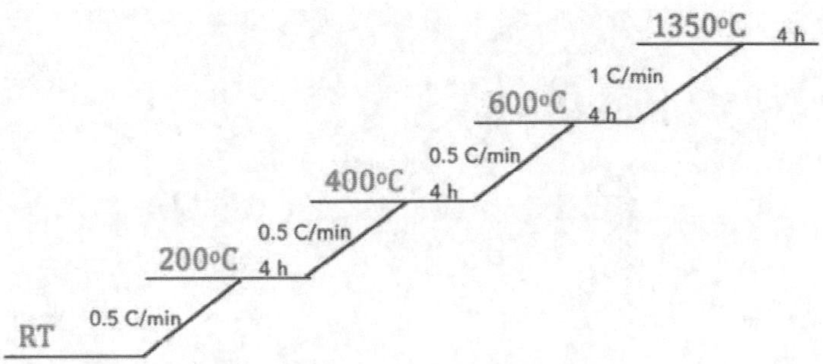


**Figure 2.** The temperature profile for calcination and sintering process

*2.5. Characterization of sintered kernels*

The sintered kernels were characterized for their diameter and sphericity, density, surface morphology (SEM) and oxide solid phase (XRD).

## 3. Result and Discussion

The gelation mechanism of mixed zirconium and yttrium or cerium sol is based on the precipitation of metal hydroxides by polymerization of hydrolysis species. In external gelation method, rapid presolidification of spherical droplets is a prerequisite to maintain spherical shape of gelled microspheres intact. Dropping of the casting sol through a nozzle will cause impact between the spherical droplets with the surface of the ammonia solution bath as gelation agent. The absence of presolidification of the sol droplets may cause will lead to droplet deformation. Although rapid gelation is preferable, however, it is anticipated to result in amorphous structure of the gel, which leads to the potential for cracked microspheres during subsequent heat treatment, i.e., drying, calcining and sintering. In this work, urea was used as an attempt to retard the occurrence of cracking of the crack-prone Zr based gel spheres.

In the fabrication of such multicomponent oxide microspheres, the preneutralization step poses a challenge because it involves metal aqueous solutions with different chemical properties. In this work the preneutralization was by the addition urea and allow it to decompose upon heating. In our preliminary experiment some difficulties were encountered, however, when this method was adopted. We found it difficult to control the precipitation, i.e., agglomeration took place readily in a few minutes, that such re-work of sample preparation was unavoidable to obtain visually clearer sols without precipitates. Attempts to preneutralize zirconium nitrate solution by urea decomposition with mole ratio urea/metal 2.5:1 were mostly unsuccessful, where we found that adding urea at that amount at 80-85°C resulted in visually murky suspension even in relatively short time of 10-15 minutes, resulting in a sol solution containing recoverable precipitates. The desirable casting solution should be a colloidal suspension or sol, namely a solution containing dispersed fine particles but possessing a slow (often negligible) settlement rate under normal gravity.

A workaround to overcome rapid sol settlement was by portioning the amount of urea used in the broth preparation. During preneutralization process the ammount of urea was reduced to 1:1 and the other portion was added after sol preparation at lower temperature below the decomposition temperature of urea in water. This portioning method of urea decomposition exhibited change in opaqueness of the sol into murky solution in around 50 minutes at 85°C.

In the casting process, tuning of casting parameters showed that stable cast of droplets from 1 mm nozzle diameter was optimized by adjusting feed flowrate at 30 ml/min, viscosity at 45-60 cP, and vibrating frequency at 100 Hz. Presolidification of gel skin was optimized at a working $NH_3$ flow rate of 3.5 - 4 L/min at room temperature.

The morphological images of yttria stabilized zirconia (YSZ) sintered kernels prepared with varied mole ratio of urea/metal are presented in Fig. 3.

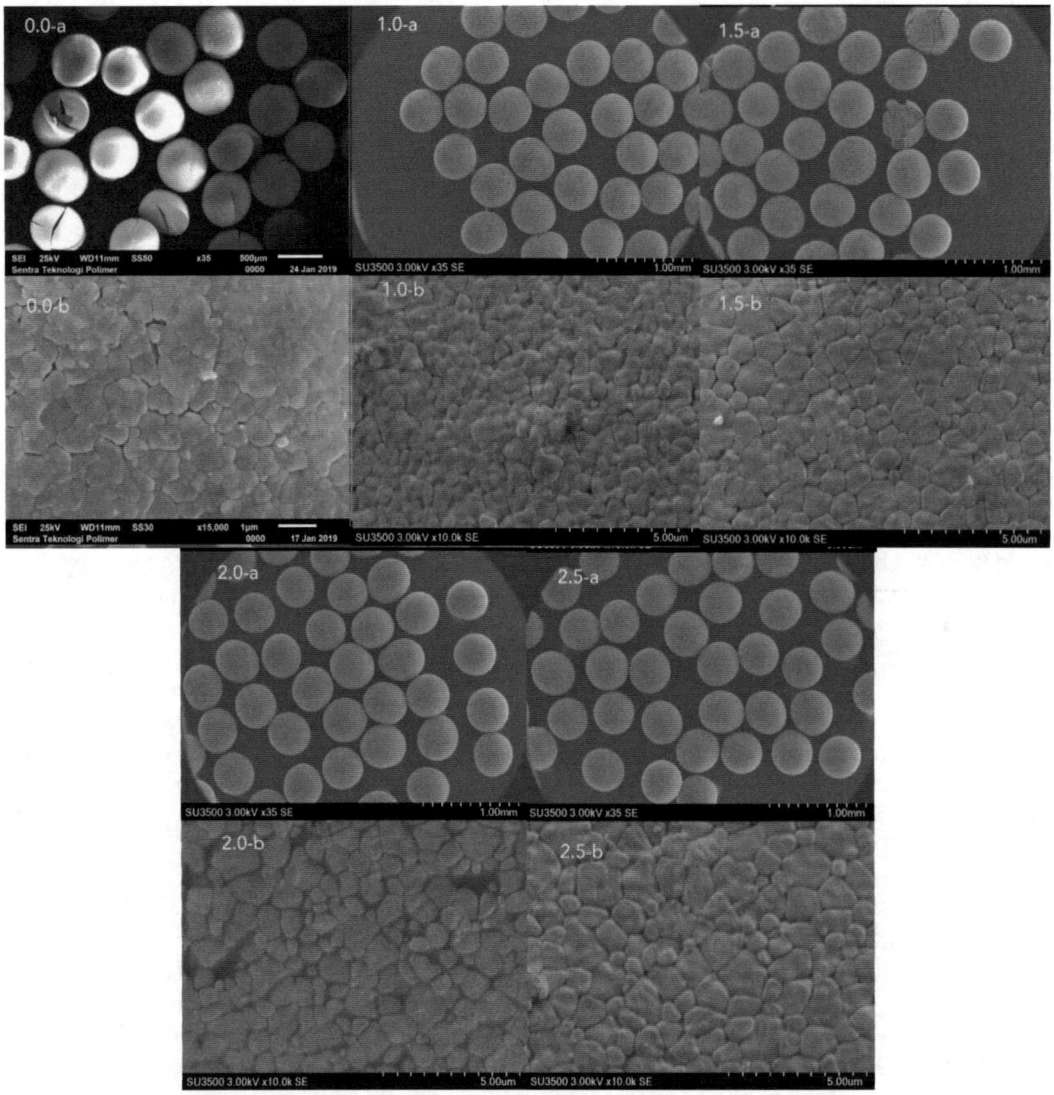


**Figure 3.** Morphological images of YSZ sintered kernel prepared with a mole ratio of urea/metal 0.0/1.0 (0.0-a and 0.0-b), 1.0/1.0 (1.0-a and 1.0-b), 1.5/1.0 (1.5-a and 1.5-b), 2.0/1.0 (2.0-a and 2.0-b), and 2.5/1.0 (2.5-a and 2.5-b)

We performed SEM image observation to study the most desirable characteristic of the sintered kernels in term of crack issue and morphological pore that relates to the resulting density, and we found that the mole ratio of urea/metal 2.5/1.0 to be the most desirable, i.e., less crack and morphologically less pores. To further study the effects of other parameters on the resulting kernels, the broth was then prepared with mole ratio of urea/metal 2.5/1.0, where 1.0 mole ratio was used at 85°C for preneutralization and the other remainder of the urea was added at lower temperature.

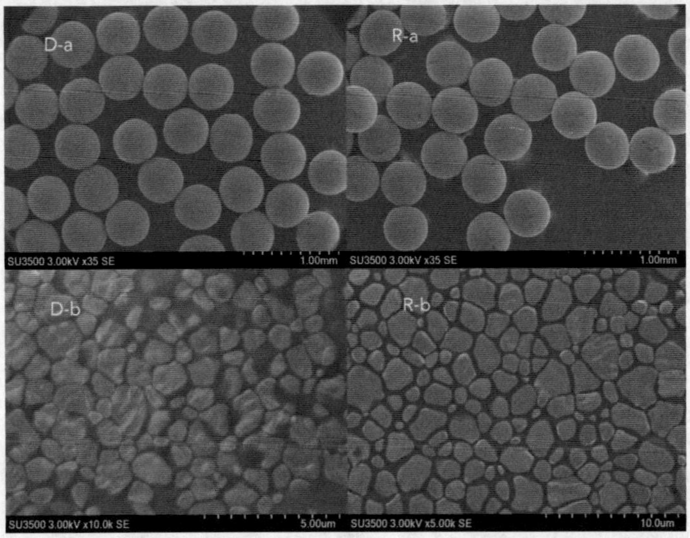


**Figure 4.** Morphological images of sintered YSZ kernel prepared with preneutralization process by urea decomposition method (D-a and D-b) and by precipitation-redispersion (R-a and R-b)

We observed that both techniques of preneutralization (i.e., precipitation-redispersion and urea decomposition) gave satisfactory kernel product based on the morphological images of kernels prepared by both techniques, as shown in Fig. 4. However, we anticipated that the preneutralization by dropwise addition of $NH_4OH$ in precipitation-redispersion technique may pose issues of repeatability since manual dropwise addition of $NH_4OH$ may cause some portion of the $NH_4OH$ to evaporate before reaction with the metal nitrates precursors. Therefore, the preneutralization by urea decomposition was preferable.

Diameter of the sintered kernels were controlled by metal concentration in broth. Figure 5 shows the correlation between concentration of metal and the resulted sintered dimeter. Higher metal content tends to increase the resulted kernels.

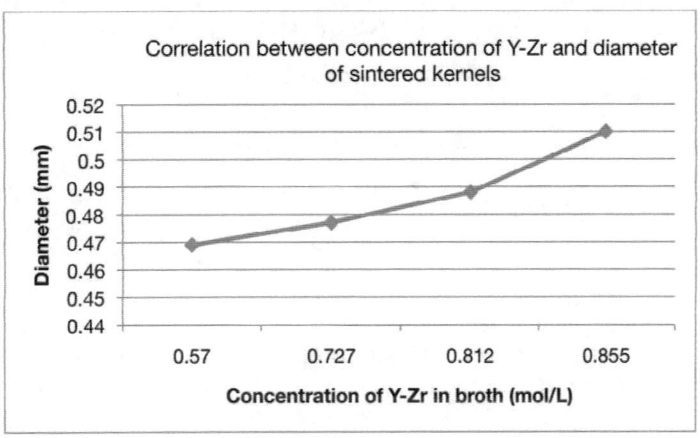


**Figure 5.** Correlation between concentration of metal (mol/L) and the resulted sintered diameter (mm)

Figure 6 shows photo of sintered YSZ kernel, and the sphericity of the sintered kernel typically prepared with 0.812 mole metal/L broth is showed in Fig. 6. It is shown that the sphericity value (Dmax/Dmin) of the sintered kernels are below 1.1. It is well known that for gel casting by the external gelation method, higher concentrations may result in poorer sphericity.

**Figure 6.** Photo of sintered YSZ kernel

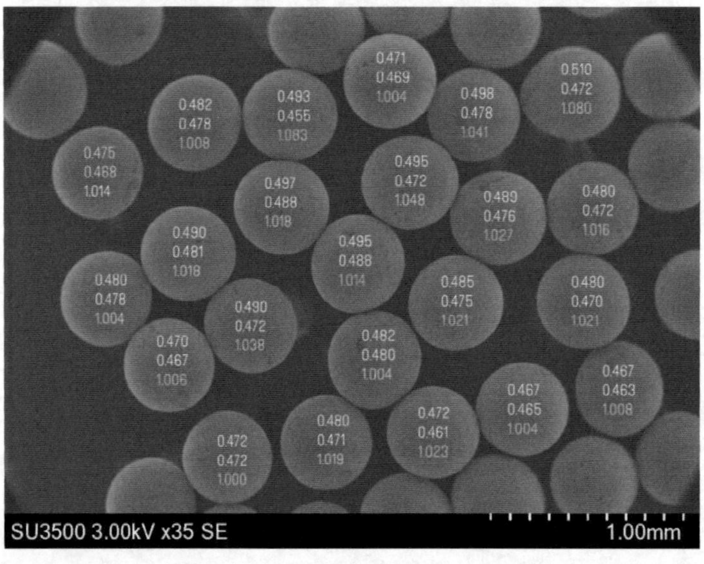


**Figure 7.** Sphericity of the sintered kernel typically prepared with 0.812 mole metal/L broth

The density measurement of sintered YSZ kernel prepared by different preneutralization routes is presented in Table 1.

**Table 1.** Density of sintered YSZ kernel

| Sol Preparation Route | Kernel Density (gram/cc) | % Theoretical density |
|---|---|---|
| Precipitation-Redispersion | 5.85 | 98.15 |
| Urea Decomposition | 5,56 | 93.34 |

Analysis of the XRD pattern of this composition shows that the resulted solid solution of yttria-zirconia with cubic structure. in compliance with ICDD database no. 00-030-1468 with chemical formula of $Y_{0,15}Zr_{0,85}O_{1,93}$ or $92ZrO_2.8Y_2O_3$ (Fig. 8). According to literature, when 16 mol% of yttrium nitrate is added to a zirconium sol, a thermal treatment of this mixed solution will cause diffusion of $Y_2O_3$ into the $ZrO_2$ resulting in 8YSZ [12].

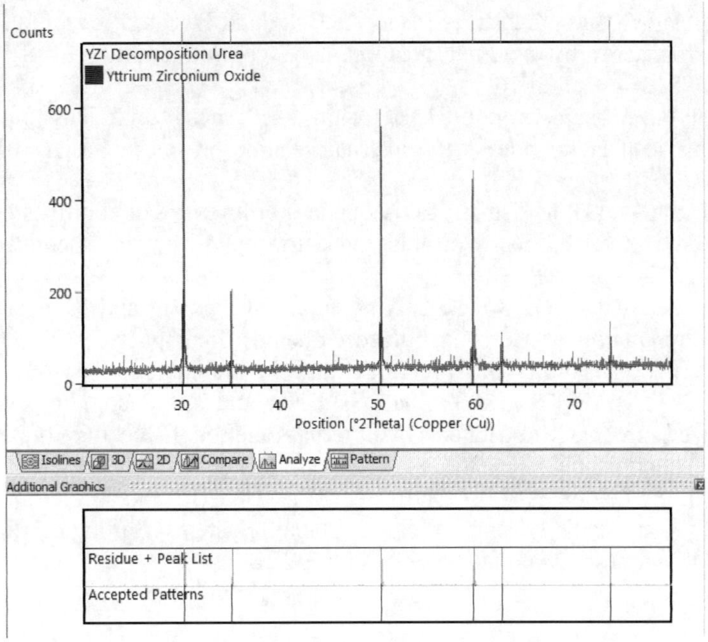


**Figure 8.** XRD pattern of YSZ sintered kernels with *cubic* phase in compliance with ICDD database no. 00-030-1468 with chemical formulation of $Y_{0,15}Zr_{0,85}O_{1,93}$ or $92ZrO_2.8Y_2O_3$

## 4. Conclusion

Rapid gelation of zirconium nitrate solution will result in amorphous zirconia gel microspheres, and this structure may increase the risk of cracking during heat treatment of the gel microspheres. Urea can be used to serve both as agent for preneutralization process for preparing homogenous sol and as pore promoter for suppressing the occurrences of crack of the sintered kernels. Addition of urea with mole ratio urea/metal 2.5/1.0 gave the most preferable results based on SEM examination for crack and morphological structure. Portioning addition of urea can be employed to control the opacity of the sol by mole ratio of urea/metal 1.1, where opacity change occurred in about 50 minutes at 85°C, while the other remainder of the urea can be added at lower temperature. Both techniques of preneutralization (i.e., precipitation-redispersion and urea decomposition) gave satisfactory kernel product in term of morphological structure of the sintered kernels. Broth composition of 84% mole zirconium nitrate dan 16% mole yttrium nitrate precursors can be applied to produce solid-solution of $92ZrO_2.8Y_2O_3$ or also known as 8YSZ, which has cubic structure and is stable up to its melting point. Increase in metal concentration will result in kernels with greater diameter.

## References

[1] BATAN, User Requirement Document – Reaktor Daya Eksperimental, BATAN, 2014.
[2] IAEA-TECDOC-1450, Thorium fuel cycle — Potential benefits and challenges, Nuclear Fuel Cycle and Materials Section, International Atomic Energy Agency, Austria, 2005.
[3] V. Lughi and V. Sergo, Low temperature degradation -aging- of zirconia: A critical review of the relevant aspects in dentistry, Dental Materials, 26, 807-820, 2010.
[4] I. Dion, L. Bordenave, F. Lefebvre, R. Bareille, C. Baquey, J. R. Monties and P. Havlik, Physico-chemistry and cytotoxicity of ceramics, Journal of Materials Science: Materials in Medicine, 5, 18-24, 1994.
[5] E. Brandau, Microspheres of UO2, ThO2 and PuO2 for the high temperature reactor, NL, 2002.
[6] G. Wang, J. Ma, Y. Gao, X. Zhao, S. Hao, C. Deng and B. Liu, A comparative study of small-size ceria–zirconia microspheres fabricated by external and internal gelation, Journal of Sol-Gel Science and Technology, 78, 673–681, 2016.

[7] G. Wang, J. Ma, Y. Gao, X. Zhao, S. Hao, C. Deng and B. Liu, Preparation of ceria-stabilized zirconia microspheres by external gelation: size control, Journal of Sol-Gel Science and Technology, 78, 514–522, 2016.
[8] R. D. Hunt, F. C. Montgomery and J. L. Collins, Treatment techniques to prevent cracking of amorphous microspheres made by the internal gelation process, Journal of Nuclear Materials, 405, 160-164, 2010.
[9] A. K. H. Nohman and H. M. Ismail, Consequences of foreign salt additives on the structure and texture of some metal oxides, Colloids and Surfaces A: Physicochemical and Engineering Aspects, 136, 237-243, 1998.
[10] W. Guogao, M. Jingtao, G. Yong, Z. Xingyu, H. Shaochang and D. Changsheng, Precisely Controlling Preparation of Ceria-Stabilized Zirconia Microspheres of ~100 μm by External Gelation, International Journal of Applied Ceramic Technology, 13, 831-837, 2016.
[11] G. G. Wang, J. T. Ma, Y. Gao, X. Y. Zhao, S. C. Hao and C. S. Deng, Preparation of Small Size Ceria Stabilized Zirconia Microspheres by External Gelation: Effect of Vibration Frequency, Key Engineering Materials, 697, 364-367, 2016.
[12] K. Vernieuwe, P. Lommens, J. C. Martins, F. Van Den Broeck, I. Van Driessche and K. De Buysser, Aqueous ZrO(2) and YSZ Colloidal Systems through Microwave Assisted Hydrothermal Synthesis, Materials, 6, 4082-4095, 2013.

# TRISO Fuel Performance Modelling with BISON

**B Collin*, W Jiang[1], K Gamble[1], R Gardner[2], J Hales[1], B Haugh[2], S Novascone[1], J Roche[2], B Spencer[1], and A Toptan[1]**

(*) Kairos Power LLC 707 W Tower Avenue, Alameda, CA 94501, USA
phone: +1-510-808-5265 (ext. 1303), collin@kairospower.com
[1]Idaho National Laboratory, 1955 N. Fremont Avenue, Idaho Falls, ID 83415, USA
[2]Kairos Power LLC, 707 W Tower Avenue, Alameda, CA 94501, USA

**Abstract.** Modeling of tristructural isotropic (TRISO)-coated particle fuel is being refined in the fuel performance code BISON. New developments include the implementation of an updated set of material properties, TRISO failure mechanisms, fission product diffusion parameters, and the design of a Monte Carlo scheme that allows BISON to calculate the probability of fuel failure within a population of TRISO particles and the subsequent fractional release of key fission products.

## 1. Introduction

BISON is an engineering-scale multidimensional finite-element based nuclear fuel performance code that has been under development at Idaho National Laboratory (INL) since 2008 [1]. The code can be applied to a variety of fuel forms including LWR pellets and fuel rods, TRISO-coated fuel particles, and metallic fuel in both rod and plate geometries. Modeling of these fuels is available in 1D-spherical, 2D-axisymmetric, or 3D geometries for both steady-state and transient fuel behavior and reactor operations.

BISON is built on the Multiphysics Object Oriented Simulation Environment (MOOSE [2]), a massively parallel, finite-element based framework that solves systems of coupled nonlinear partial differential equations using the Jacobian-free Newton-Krylov method [3]. This enables investigation of computationally large problems, as often encountered in nuclear fuel calculations. It also avoids the need for generating and inverting the Jacobian matrix, which is typically not analytically attainable and whose numerical approximation via finite-difference methods is not easily invertible.

In addition, MOOSE supports the use of complex two- and three-dimensional meshes and uses implicit time integration, which is important for the widely varied time scales in nuclear fuel simulation.

Although BISON has previously been used to demonstrate its capability to model TRISO fuel [4], a complete analysis requires a statistical treatment of a large population of particles to account for the particle-to-particle statistical variations in physical dimensions and fuel properties (layer thickness, density, etc.) that arise from the fuel fabrication process. It is well established that particles with properties that fall in the tail of their statistical distributions are more prone to failure and these cases must be captured to accurately compute the overall failure probability of the entire population of particles.

To this end, BISON has been updated with an enhanced TRISO model. The new model includes a comprehensive set of thermal and mechanical material properties, TRISO fuel failure mechanisms, and fission product diffusivities. BISON also includes an implementation of a Monte Carlo scheme that allows the calculation of the probability of failure of a population of TRISO particles and of the subsequent release of fission products.

This paper provides a brief summary of TRISO fuel behavior that justifies the TRISO developments made in BISON. These developments are then detailed for the TRISO particle. Although BISON can also model the fuel element (compact or pebble), the focus here is on the demonstration of the failure probability capability, which is unaffected by the surrounding fuel form. Consequently, the developments associated to the fuel element are not discussed here.

The methodology to conduct failure probability and fission product release calculations is laid out and used on a benchmark case.

## 2. TRISO Fuel Behavior

### *2.1. TRISO Fuel Description*

The TRISO-coated fuel particle is composed of a fissile fuel kernel surrounded by successive coating layers consisting of a porous carbon buffer layer, a dense inner pyrolytic carbon (IPyC) layer, a silicon carbon (SiC) layer, and a dense outer pyrolytic carbon (OPyC) layer (Fig. 1). Historically, the kernel has been in an oxide or carbide form, but current developments in the USA favor the use of uranium oxycarbide (UCO - a mixture of $UO_2$, UC, and $UC_2$) which has shown superior performance [5]. The buffer accommodates the irradiation-induced swelling of the kernel, acts as a reservoir for fission gases to limit the internal pressure buildup in the TRISO particle, and protects the IPyC layer by absorbing fission product recoil. The IPyC protects the kernel from chlorine attack during chemical deposition of the SiC and, conversely, protects the SiC from the attack of fission products migrating from the kernel; it also serves as secondary structural layer to alleviate tensile pressure on the SiC and acts as a fission gas barrier. The SiC is both the primary structural layer and primary fission product barrier. It is protected by the OPyC layer during fuel handling; like the IPyC, the OPyC is a secondary structural layer and a fission gas barrier; it also provides a bonding surface to the overcoating matrix material. The TRISO particles are overcoated with resinated graphite powder before being pressed into the fuel element. The resinated graphite powder transforms into "so-called" matrix material upon pressing and subsequent heat treatments.

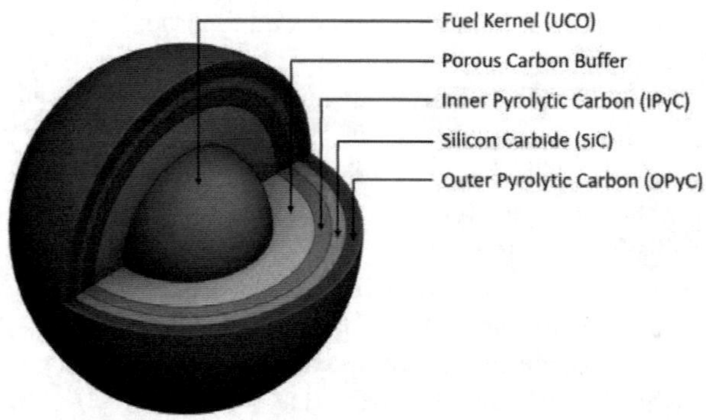


**Figure 1.** Graphical description of a TRISO-coated particle.

### *2.2. UCO TRISO Fuel Performance*

In $UO_2$ TRISO fuel, excess oxygen generated by fission reacts with surrounding carbon from the buffer to form carbon monoxide [6]. CO is responsible for kernel migration [6], chemical degradation of the SiC layer [6], and increase of the internal pressure in the TRISO particle [6], which all increase the risk of fuel failure during irradiation. To mitigate these effects, UCO fuel has been developed by the Department of Energy Advanced Gas Reactor (AGR) Fuel Development and Qualification Program [7]. UCO TRISO fuel is planned to be used by current designers of small modular reactors such as Kairos Power.

In a TRISO particle, the primary function of the three outer coating layers (IPyC, SiC, and OPyC) is to contain the fission products produced in the kernel. The loss of structural integrity and leak-tightness to fission products of a coating layer constitutes a failure of this coating layer. Such failures can occur when TRISO-coated fuel particles undergo neutron irradiation. Under neutron flux, the accumulation of fission products in the kernel results in outward swelling. At the same time, the porous buffer shrinks as its porosity collapses. Both PyC layers also shrink early during irradiation but this reverts to swelling at longer irradiation times. As the buffer pulls away from the IPyC, a "buffer-IPyC" gap forms between the two layers. This gap fills with fission gases and provides the largest thermal resistance in the TRISO particle.

In the early phase of irradiation, the PyC layers are put into tension by shrinkage, which creates compressive forces on the more rigid SiC layer. However, if the tensile stress in the IPyC reaches its fracture strength, the layer can crack and concentrate a high localized tensile stress on the SiC layer. At longer irradiation times, the irradiation-induced creep of the PyC layers offsets their shrinkage, which relieves their tensile stress but also some of the compressive stress in the SiC. Concomitantly, fission gas pressure builds up in the free volume of the particle, reducing compressive stress in the SiC layer even more. As internal gas pressure increases, the tangential stress in the SiC layer can eventually become tensile. Failure of the SiC layer is then expected if the tensile stress reaches its fracture strength.

Historically, the following failure mechanisms of TRISO-coated fuel particles have been identified [6]:

- Pressure vessel failure of spherical or aspherical particles resulting in the failure of all three coating layers.
- Cracking of the IPyC layer leading to SiC failure.
- Partial debonding of the IPyC from the SiC leading to SiC failure.
- Kernel migration towards the SiC layer and its subsequent failure.
- Chemical attack of the SiC layer by fission products or CO leading to its failure.
- Thermal decomposition of the SiC layer at high temperatures.
- Buffer fracture leading to cracking of partially debonded IPyC.

As CO production is limited in UCO fuel, kernel migration and CO contribution to internal pressure and SiC corrosion are not considered in this UCO TRISO BISON model. Furthermore, thermal decomposition of the SiC is only expected at temperatures > 2100°C [8], far exceeding expected TRISO fuel operating or accident temperatures, and is also not modeled. Additionally, TRISO fuel manufactured to the German process requirements, including AGR fuel, has not exhibited IPyC-SiC debonding leading to SiC failure. Finally, there is currently no existing model for the cracking of a partially debonded IPyC layer because of lack of experimental data (e.g., buffer-IPyC bond strength).

### 2.3. *Fission Product Transport*

Several mechanisms might be involved in the transport of mobile fission products through the kernel and coating layers of TRISO particles. Such mechanisms could include lattice diffusion, grain boundary diffusion, pore diffusion, nano-cracking, or vapor transport [9]. Furthermore, effects like irradiation-induced trapping and adsorption, thermal decomposition of the coating layers, or chemical attack of the coating layers by other fission products, such as palladium or rare earth elements, could potentially impact these transport mechanisms.

To get by the lack of adequate models to conceptualize the fundamental knowledge of all possible transport mechanisms, Fick's laws of diffusion are used with "effective" diffusivities to model fission product transport through a TRISO particles. "Effective" implies that the diffusivities describe the overall fission product transport using classical Fickian diffusion [6]. The application of these "effective" diffusion coefficients will result in the same fractional release of fission products from the TRISO particle as was observed in the integral release measurements from which they were derived.

## 3. UCO TRISO Fuel Modeling

### *3.1. Material Properties*

TRISO fuel material properties include mechanical and thermal properties for the kernel and coating layers. BISON has the capability of modeling the fuel element in which TRISO particles are embedded, but the material properties of the matrix are not discussed here.

#### *3.1.1. Kernel*

Legacy TRISO fuel development programs have predominantly focused on $UO_2$ fuel and, consequently, most kernel properties are based on $UO_2$ experimental data.

Kernel swelling occurs throughout irradiation as solid and gaseous atoms released by fission accumulate in the kernel, resulting in a volume increase of the kernel. The volumetric change in kernel volume, or swelling S (-), is given by [10]:

$$S = \frac{\Delta V}{V_0} = 0.8\% \times \Delta B_u \tag{1}$$

where $V_0$ ($m^3$) is the initial volume of the kernel, $\Delta V$ ($m^3$) is the kernel volume increase, and $\Delta B_u$ (%FIMA) is the burnup increment.

The Young's modulus of the kernel, E (GPa), is given by [11]:

$$E = 219 \times f(T) \times g(\rho) \tag{2}$$

$$f(T) = 1 - 1.07 \times 10^{-4} \times T - 2.16 \times 10^{-7} \times T^2 + 3.10 \times 10^{-10} \times T^3 - 1.54 \times 10^{-13} \times T^4 \tag{3}$$

$$g(\rho) = \frac{1.92 \times \rho - 0.92 \times \rho_{th}}{\rho_{th}} \tag{4}$$

where T (°C) is the temperature of the kernel, $\rho$ ($g/cm^3$) is the density of the kernel, and $\rho_{th}$ ($g/cm^3$) is the theoretical density of UCO.

The Poisson's ratio of the kernel, $\mu$ (-), is derived from its Young's modulus (see above) and its shear modulus [11]:

$$\mu = 1.35 \times \frac{1.92 \times \rho - 0.92 \times \rho_{th}}{1.66 \times \rho - 0.66 \times \rho_{th}} - 1 \tag{5}$$

The thermal conductivity of the kernel, k (W/m-K), is given by [10]:

$$\begin{aligned} k(T) &= 0.0132 \times e^{0.00188 \times T} + \frac{4040}{464 + T} \quad \text{if } T < 1650°C \\ k(T) &= 0.0132 \times e^{0.00188 \times T} + 1.9 \quad \text{if } T \geq 1650°C \end{aligned} \tag{6}$$

where T (°C) is the temperature of the kernel.

The heat capacity of the kernel, $c_p$ (J/mol-K), is given by [12]:

$$c_p = 52.1743 + 87.951 \times \frac{T}{1000} - 84.2411 \times \left(\frac{T}{1000}\right)^2 + 31.542 \times \left(\frac{T}{1000}\right)^3 - 2.6334 \times \left(\frac{T}{1000}\right)^4 - 0.71391 \times \left(\frac{T}{1000}\right)^{-2} \tag{7}$$

where T (K) is the temperature of the kernel.

#### *3.1.2. Buffer*

The Young's modulus of the buffer, E (GPa), is given by [10]:

$$E = 25.5 \times (0.384 + 0.324 \times \rho) \times (1 + 0.23 \times \phi) \times \left(1 + 1.5 \times 10^{-4} \times (T - 20)\right) \tag{8}$$

where $\rho$ ($g/cm^3$) is the density of the buffer, $\phi$ ($\times 10^{25}$ $n/m^2$, $E > 0.18$ MeV) is the fast neutron fluence, and T (°C) is the temperature of the buffer.

The Poisson's ratio of the buffer, $\mu$ (-), is given by [10]:

$$\mu = 0.33 \tag{9}$$

The irradiation creep of the buffer, that leads to its gradual deformation in response to irradiation-induced damage, is directly proportional to fast neutron fluence. The proportionality factor, i.e., the irradiation-induced creep coefficient of the buffer, $K_S$ ($\times 10^{-25}$ (MPa-n/m$^2$)$^{-1}$), is given by [10]:

$$K_S = 2 \times [1 + 2.38 \times (1.9 - \rho)] \times (2.193 \times 10^{-4} - 4.85 \times 10^{-7} \times T + 4.0147 \times 10^{-10} \times T^2) \tag{10}$$

where $\rho$ (g/cm$^3$) is the density of the buffer and T (°C) is the temperature of the buffer.

The Poisson's ratio in creep of the buffer, $\nu$ (-), is given by [10]:

$$\nu = 0.5 \tag{11}$$

The irradiation-induced dimensional change (strain) of the buffer, $\varepsilon$ (-), is given by [10]:

$$\varepsilon = a_1 \times \phi + a_2 \times \phi^2 + a_3 \times \phi^3 + a_4 \times \phi^4 \tag{12}$$

where the $a_i$ coefficients depend on density and temperature and $\phi$ ($\times 10^{25}$ n/m$^2$, E > 0.18 MeV) is the fast neutron fluence. The $a_i$ coefficients are detailed in reference [10] and in the online BISON documentation.

The thermal conductivity of the buffer, k (W/m-K), is given by [10]:

$$k = \frac{k_0 \times k_{th} \times \rho_{th} \times (\rho_{th} - \rho_0)}{k_{th} \times \rho_{th} \times (\rho_{th} - \rho) + k_0 \times \rho \times (\rho - \rho_0)} \tag{13}$$

The thermal conductivity of the buffer depends on its initial and theoretical densities ($\rho_0$ and $\rho_{th}$ = 2.25 g/cm$^3$) and on the thermal conductivities at these two densities ($k_0$ = 0.5 W/m-K and $k_{th}$ = 4 W/m-K).

The specific heat capacity of the buffer, $c_p$ (J/kg-K), is given by [13]:

$$c_p = 720 \tag{14}$$

The coefficient of thermal expansion of the buffer, $\alpha$ ($\times 10^{-6}$/°C), is given by [10]:

$$\alpha = 5 \times \left(1 + 0.11 \times \frac{T - 400}{700}\right) \tag{15}$$

where T (°C) is the temperature of the buffer.

### *3.1.3. PyC*

The Young's moduli (GPa) of the PyC in the tangential ($E_t$) and radial ($E_r$) directions are given by [10]:

$$E_t = 25.5 \times (0.384 + 0.324 \times \rho) \times (1 + 0.23 \times \phi) \times \left(1 + 1.5 \times 10^{-4} \times (T - 20) \times (0.481 + 0.519 \times BAF_0)\right) \tag{16}$$

$$E_r = 25.5 \times (0.384 + 0.324 \times \rho) \times (1 + 0.23 \times \phi) \times \left(1 + 1.5 \times 10^{-4} \times (T - 20) \times (1.463 - 0.463 \times BAF_0)\right) \tag{17}$$

where $\rho$ (g/cm$^3$) is the density of the PyC, $\phi$ ($\times 10^{25}$ n/m$^2$, E > 0.18 MeV) is the fast neutron fluence, T (°C) is the temperature of the PyC, and $BAF_0$ (-) is the initial anisotropy of the PyC measured by its Bacon Anisotropy Factor.

The Poisson's ratio of the PyC, $\mu$ (-), is given by [10]:

$$\mu = 0.33 \tag{18}$$

The irradiation-induced creep coefficient of the PyC, $K_S$ ($\times 10^{-25}$ (MPa-n/m$^2$)$^{-1}$), is given by [10]:

$$K_S = 2 \times [1 + 2.38 \times (1.9 - \rho)] \times (2.193 \times 10^{-4} - 4.85 \times 10^{-7} \times T + 4.0147 \times 10^{-10} \times T^2) \tag{19}$$

where $\rho$ (g/cm$^3$) is the density of the PyC and T (°C) is the temperature of the PyC.

The Poisson's ratio in creep of the PyC, $\nu$ (-), is given by [10]:

$$\nu = 0.5 \tag{20}$$

The irradiation-induced dimensional change (strain) of the PyC, ε (-), is given by [10]:

$$\varepsilon = a_1 \times \phi + a_2 \times \phi^2 + a_3 \times \phi^3 + a_4 \times \phi^4 \quad (21)$$

where the $a_i$ coefficients depend on BAF, density, temperature, and the direction (radial or tangential) of the strain and $\phi$ ($\times 10^{25}$ n/m$^2$, E > 0.18 MeV) is the fast neutron fluence. The $a_i$ coefficients are detailed in Ref. [10] and in the online BISON documentation.

The thermal conductivity of the PyC, k (W/m-K), is given by [10]:

$$k = 4.0 \quad (22)$$

The specific heat capacity of the PyC, $c_p$ (J/kg-K), is given by [13]:

$$c_p = 720 \quad (23)$$

The coefficients of thermal expansion of the PyC ($\times 10^{-6}$/°C) in the radial ($\alpha_r$) and tangential ($\alpha_t$) directions are given by [10]:

$$\alpha_r = \left(30 - 37.5 \times \frac{2}{2+BAF}\right) \times f(T) \quad (24)$$

$$\alpha_t = \left(1 + 36 \times \frac{1}{(2+BAF)^2}\right) \times f(T) \quad (25)$$

$$f(T) = 1 + 0.11 \times \frac{T-400}{700} \quad (26)$$

where BAF (-) is the Bacon Anisotropy Factor of the PyC and T (°C) is the temperature of the PyC.

Pyrocarbon is a brittle material and, as such, its probability of failure is calculated using Weibull statistics. The Weibull characteristic strength, $\sigma_0$ (MPa-m$^{3/m}$), and modulus, m (-), of the PyC are given by [10]:

$$\sigma_0 = 16.8 \times \sqrt{f(\phi) \times g(T)} \quad (27)$$

$$f(\phi) = 1 + 0.23 \times \phi \quad (28)$$

$$g(T) = 1 + 1.5 \times 10^{-4} \times (T - 20) \quad (29)$$

$$m = 9.5 \quad (30)$$

where $\phi$ ($\times 10^{25}$ n/m$^2$, E > 0.18 MeV) is the fast neutron fluence and T (°C) is the temperature of the PyC.

### *3.1.4. Buffer-IPyC Gap*

Heat produced in the kernel is transferred to the outer coating layers through the buffer-IPyC gap via a gap conductance model using the width of the gap and the conductivity of the gas mixture (Kr and Xe) in the gap. Radiation (limited temperature difference between the buffer and IPyC) and convection (small gap width) are not included in the model.

The thermal conductivity of the Kr-Xe gas mixture, $k_{gas}$ (W/m-K), is given by [14]:

$$k_{gas} = \frac{f_{Kr} \times k_{Kr}}{f_{Kr} + f_{Xe} \times \Psi_{KrXe}} + \frac{f_{Xe} \times k_{Xe}}{f_{Xe} + f_{Kr} \times \Psi_{XeKr}} \quad (31)$$

where $f_{Kr}$ (-) and $f_{Xe}$ (-) are the molar fractions of Kr and Xe, respectively, and $k_{Kr}$ (W/m-K) and $k_{Xe}$ (W/m-K) are their thermal conductivities. The thermal conductivities depend on the average temperature of the gap, T (K), and are given by:

$$k_{Kr} = 8.247 \times 10^{-5} \times T^{0.8363} \quad (32)$$

$$k_{Xe} = 4.351 \times 10^{-5} \times T^{0.8616} \quad (33)$$

and the "Ψ" functions are given by:

$$\Psi_{KrXe} = \left(1 + 2.41 \times \frac{(M_{Kr} - M_{Xe}) \times (M_{Kr} - 0.142 \times M_{Xe})}{(M_{Kr} + M_{Xe})^2}\right) \times \Phi_{KrXe} \quad (34)$$

$$\Psi_{XeKr} = \left(1 + 2.41 \times \frac{(M_{Xe}-M_{Kr})\times(M_{Xe}-0.142\times M_{Kr})}{(M_{Xe}+M_{Kr})^2}\right) \times \Phi_{XeKr} \quad (35)$$

$M_{Kr}$ (83.8 g/mol) and $M_{Xe}$ (131.3 g/mol) are the molecular weights of the gas mixture components and the "Φ" functions are given by:

$$\Phi_{KrXe} = \frac{\left(1+\sqrt{\frac{k_{Kr}}{k_{Xe}}}\times\sqrt[4]{\frac{M_{Kr}}{M_{Xe}}}\right)^2}{2^{1.5}\times\sqrt{1+\frac{M_{Kr}}{M_{Xe}}}} \quad (36)$$

$$\Phi_{XeKr} = \frac{\left(1+\sqrt{\frac{k_{Xe}}{k_{Kr}}}\times\sqrt[4]{\frac{M_{Xe}}{M_{Kr}}}\right)^2}{2^{1.5}\times\sqrt{1+\frac{M_{Xe}}{M_{Kr}}}} \quad (37)$$

*3.1.5. SiC*

The Young's modulus of the SiC, E (GPa), is given in Table 1 [10] as a function of its temperature, T (°C). Values in-between table entries are linearly interpolated.

**Table 1.** SiC Young's Modulus.

| T (°C) | E (GPa) | T (°C) | E (GPa) |
|---|---|---|---|
| ≤ 25 | 428 | 1215 | 340 |
| 940 | 375 | ≥ 1600 | 198 |

The Poisson's ratio of the SiC, μ (-), is given by [10]:

$$\mu = 0.13 \quad (38)$$

The thermal conductivity of the SiC, k (W/m-K), is given by [10]:

$$k = \frac{17885}{T+273} + 2 \quad (39)$$

where T (°C) is the temperature of the SiC.

The specific heat capacity of the SiC, $c_p$ (J/kg-K), is given by [15]:

$$c_p = 925.65 + 0.3772 \times T - 7.9259 \times 10^{-5} \times T^2 - 3.1946 \times 10^7 \times T^{-2} \quad (40)$$

where T (K) is the temperature of the SiC.

The coefficient of thermal expansion of the SiC, α ($\times10^{-6}$/°C), is given by [10]:

$$\alpha = 4.9 \quad (41)$$

SiC is a brittle material and, as such, its probability of failure is calculated using Weibull statistics. The Weibull characteristic strength, $\sigma_0$ (MPa-m$^{3/m}$), and modulus, m (-), of the SiC are given by [10]:

$$\sigma_0 = 9.64 \quad (42)$$

$$m = 6 \quad (43)$$

*3.2. Physical Models*

*3.2.1. Strain-Displacement and Stress-Strain Constitutive Relationships*

In BISON, displacements can be calculated by application of either small strain or finite strain [16] theories. For TRISO fuel calculations, the small strain theory is used and the strain-displacement constitutive equations in any coating layer of a spherical TRISO particle are given by:

$$\varepsilon_r = \frac{\partial u}{\partial r} \quad (44)$$

$$\varepsilon_t = \frac{u}{r} \quad (45)$$

where $\varepsilon_r$ (-) and $\varepsilon_t$ (-) are the radial and tangential components of the strain, respectively, and u (m) is the radial displacement. In the absence of shear strains in axisymmetric solids, all the other components of the strain tensor are zero. The total strain tensor, $\{\varepsilon\}$, and stress tensor, $\{\sigma\}$, are related by the constitutive relationship:

$$\sigma\{\sigma\} = [E] \times \{\varepsilon_E\} = [E] \times (\{\varepsilon\} - \{\varepsilon_C\} - \{\varepsilon_{IIDC}\} - \{\varepsilon_{TE}\}) \quad (46)$$

where [E] is the elastic matrix and $\{\varepsilon_E\}$ is the elactic strain tensor consisting of creep strain, $\{\varepsilon_C\}$, irradiation-induced shrinkage/swelling strain, $\{\varepsilon_{IIDC}\}$, and thermal expansion strain, $\{\varepsilon_{TE}\}$.

Stress equilibrium is enforced by solving the so-called weak form of the following partial differential equation:

$$\nabla\sigma = 0 \quad (47)$$

In BISON, the displacement is the field variable being solved for by the mechanics models. It is iteratively updated, along with other field variables, until convergence is achieved. During each iteration, the strains are computed from the displacements (eq. 44 and eq. 45), after which the stresses are obtained from the strains (eq. 46). The stresses are then integrated over the finite elements to get the nodal forces, which must be in equilibrium (eq. 47) for the solution to be considered converged.

### *3.2.2. Failure probability*

Pyrocarbon and silicon carbide are brittle materials. The fracture strength of a brittle material is typically represented by a statistical distribution expressed in terms of Weibull parameters (characteristic strength $\sigma_0$ (MPa-m$^{3/m}$) and modulus m (-)) that are indicative of the flaw distribution in a given volume of the material. When a maximum stress, $\sigma_{max}$ (MPa), is applied to the material, its failure probability, Pf (-), is given by [10]:

$$P_f = 1 - e^{-(\sigma_{max}/\sigma_{ms})^m} \quad (48)$$

where the mean strength, $\sigma_{ms}$ (MPa), is related to the characteristic strength and to the normalized integration of the tensile stress distribution over the volume of the material, I (m$^3$):

$$\sigma_{ms} = {}^{\sigma_0}/_{I^{1/m}} \quad (49)$$

### *3.2.3. Heat Equation*

The general heat conduction equation is given by:

$$\rho \times c_p \times \frac{\partial T}{\partial t} - k \times \nabla^2 T - E_f \times \dot{F} = 0 \quad (50)$$

where $\rho$ (g/cm$^3$) is the density, $c_p$ (J/kg-K) is the specific heat capacity, T (K) is the temperature, k (W/m-K) is the thermal conductivity, $E_f$ ($3.204\times10^{-11}$ J = 200 MeV) is the average energy released per fission, and $\dot{F}$ (fission/cm$^3$-s) is the volumetric fission rate.

### *3.2.4. Fission Yields*

The numbers of fission product atoms created per fission, or fission yields, depend on the neutron spectrum in each core using TRISO fuel. Default values, $\gamma$(-), are included in BISON for Ag, Cs, Sr, and noble gases (Kr + Xe) [10]:

For $^{235}$U enrichment lower than 17.5%:

$$\gamma_{Ag} = 1.31625 \times 10^{-3} \times (B_u \vee 1)^{0.55734} \quad (51)$$

$$\gamma(Cs) = 0.14 \quad (52)$$

$$\gamma(Sr) = 0.11754 \times (B_u \vee 0.6)^{-0.21762} \quad (53)$$

$$\gamma(Kr + Xe) = 0.297 \quad (54)$$

For $I^{235}U$ enrichment higher or equal to 17.5%:

$$ply_{Ag} = 8.24492 \times 10^{-4} \times (B_u \vee 1)^{0.53853} \tag{55}$$

$$\gamma(Cs) = 0.16 \tag{56}$$

$$\gamma(Sr) = 0.11819 \times (B_u \vee 0.6)^{-0.15778} \tag{57}$$

$$\gamma(Kr + Xe) = 0.297 \tag{58}$$

where $B_u$ (%FIMA) is the burnup and $\vee$ is the "max" function.

### 3.2.5. *Fission Gas Release of Long-Lives Isotopes*

The release of long-lived fission gases from the kernel is modeled as a two-step process: first, the gas atoms are driven through the grain towards the grain boundary; second, the gas atoms migrate from the grain boundary to the free surface of the fuel where they are instantaneously released into the free volume of the TRISO particle. The model includes both direct recoil and diffusion to grain boundaries. The release fraction, RF (-), which corresponds to the fraction of the gas generated by fission that is released by the kernel is given by:

$$RF = (RF)_R + (1 - (RF)_R) \times (RF)_B \tag{59}$$

where $(RF)_R$ is the fraction of fission gas released by recoil and $(RF)_B$ is the fraction of the remaining fission gas released by diffusion.

Direct recoil is accounted for by geometrical considerations using the respective molar fractions of Kr and Xe, $f_{Kr}$ (-) and $f_{Xe}$ (-):

$$(RF)_R = f_{Kr} \times (RF)_{R,Kr} + f_{Xe} \times (RF)_{R,Xe} \tag{60}$$

$$(RF)_{R,i} = 0.25 \times \frac{r_k{}^3 - (r_k - r_i)^3}{r_k{}^3} \tag{61}$$

$$r_i = 10 \times \frac{r_{i,U} + \frac{O}{U} \times r_{i,O} + \frac{C}{U} \times r_{i,C}}{\rho_k \times \left(1 + \frac{O}{U} + \frac{C}{U}\right)} \tag{62}$$

where $r_k$ (μm) is the radius of the kernel, $\rho_k$ (g/cm$^3$) is the density of the kernel, $r_{i,U}$, $r_{i,O}$, and $r_{i,C}$ are the mean ranges (mg/cm$^2$) of Kr and Xe in uranium, oxygen, and carbon, respectively ($r_{Kr,U}$ = 11.7 mg/cm$^2$, $r_{Kr,O}$ = 3.3 mg/cm$^2$, $r_{Kr,C}$ = 3.1 mg/cm$^2$, $r_{Xe,U}$ = 8.3 mg/cm$^2$, $r_{Xe,O}$ = 2.3 mg/cm$^2$, $r_{Xe,C}$ = 2.2 mg/cm$^2$) [17] , and O/U (-) and C/U (-) are the oxygen to uranium and carbon to uranium atomic ratios.

Diffusive release to the grain boundaries is estimated by the Booth equivalent sphere diffusion model [18]:

$$(RF)_B = 1 - \frac{6}{\frac{D}{a^2} \times t} \times \sum_{n=1}^{\infty} \left( \frac{1 - e^{-n^2 \times \pi^2 \times \frac{D}{a^2} \times t}}{n^4 \times \pi^4} \right) \tag{63}$$

which corresponds to the fraction diffused out of a sphere of radius a (m) with diffusivity D (m$^2$/s) during time t (s). In the case of a fuel kernel, the effective radius for diffusion is taken equal to the average radius of a kernel grain (~10 μm). The diffusivity is an effective diffusion coefficient which accounts for intrinsic, radiation-enhanced, and thermal diffusion [19]:

$$D = 7.6 \times 10^{-10} \times e^{-\frac{35225}{T}} + s^2 \times j_v \times \sqrt{\frac{K'}{j_v \times Z}} + 2 \times 10^{-40} \times R_f \tag{64}$$

$$j_v = 10^{13} \times e^{-\frac{27778}{T}} \tag{65}$$

$$K' = \frac{K \times B_u}{t} \tag{66}$$

where T (K) is the temperature of the kernel, s (=$3\times10^{-10}$ m) is the atomic jump distance, $j_v$ (s$^{-1}$) is the cation vacancy jump rate, K' is the rate of defect production per atom and is obtained from the damage rate K (=$10^4$ defects/fission) and the burnup $B_u$ (FIMA), Z (=2) is the number of sites around a point defect where recombination is inevitable, and $R_f$ (fission/m$^3$-s) is the fission rate density.

*3.2.6. Internal Gas Pressure*

Fission gas released from the kernel accumulates in the void volume of the particle (porosities in the kernel and buffer plus the volume of the buffer-IPyC gap) where it builds up the internal pressure. The pressure, P (Pa), is calculated using the ideal gas law whose equation of state is given by:

$$P = \frac{n_{fg} \times R \times T}{V} \tag{67}$$

where $n_{fg}$ (mol) is the inventory of fission gas (Kr+Xe) occupying the void volume V (m$^3$) at temperature T (K) and R (8.3145 J/K-mol) is the ideal gas constant. The inventory of krypton and xenon is obtained from fission gas release, while the void volume is obtained by calculating the variation in density of the kernel, buffer, and IPyC, which determines the porosities and volume of the buffer-IPyC gap. The temperature is averaged over the void volume.

*3.2.7. Palladium Penetration*

The fission product palladium is known to attack SiC at localized reaction sites. Based on the international historical database, the penetration rate of palladium into SiC, $\dot{P}_{Pd}$ (μm/day), has been found to have an Arrhenius temperature dependence given by [20]:

$$\dot{P}_{Pd} = 38.232 \times e^{-11342.3/T} \tag{68}$$

where T (K) is the temperature of the SiC. The SiC layer is conservatively considered failed when the penetration reaches 50% of its thickness.

*3.2.8. Fission Product Transport*

The transport of mobile fission products through a TRISO particle is modeled by Fick's laws of diffusion using effective diffusion coefficients:

$$\frac{\partial C}{\partial t} + \nabla J - S = 0 \tag{69}$$

$$J = -D \times \nabla C \tag{70}$$

where C (atom/m$^3$) is the concentration of the diffusing species, t (s) is the diffusing time, J (atom/m$^2$-s) is the diffusive flux, S (atom/m$^3$-s) is the production rate of the diffusing species (fission products), and D (m$^2$/s) is the diffusivity of the diffusing species in the diffusing medium.

An international database has been assembled by the International Atomic Energy Agency (IAEA) and serves as a reference for fission product transport in TRISO modeling codes [21]. The diffusivities are available for Ag, Cs, Sr, and Kr and are expressed as temperature-dependent Arrhenius functions:

$$D = D_1 \times e^{-Q_1/RT} + D_2 \times e^{-Q_2/RT} \tag{71}$$

where R (8.3145 J/K-mol) is the ideal gas constant and the pre-exponent coefficients, D (m$^2$/s), and activation energies, Q (kJ/mol), are provided by the IAEA [21]. Diffusion coefficients for the kernel are values derived from experimental data with $UO_2$ fuel. These values are used due to lack of data for UCO kernels.

## 4. UCO TRISO Fuel Performance Methodology

The purpose of the BISON TRISO model is to assess the structural integrity and leak-tightness to fission products of TRISO-coated UCO fuel particles under neutron irradiation. The calculation flow chart is shown in Figure 2 and summarized below:

- The fission rate density (code input) is used to calculate the heat generation rate in the TRISO particle and the fission product inventory (including fission gas that contributes to internal pressure); combined with the boundary temperature, the fission rate is used to solve the heat equation in the TRISO particle and determine its temperature profile.
- The temperature in a TRISO particle is used to calculate the internal gas pressure corresponding to its fission gas inventory; combined with the input fast neutron fluence, the temperature also drives the material properties used to compute the stress levels in the coating layers and the diffusivities used in fission product diffusion calculations.
- Using Weibull statistics, the stress levels determine the failure probability of the TRISO particles.
- Combined with diffusivities, obtained from the thermal analysis, the failure probability is used to calculate the diffusion and release of fission products from the intact and potentially failed TRISO particles.

Figure 3 depicts the methodology used to calculate the failure probability of a population of TRISO particles. The methodology relies on a Monte Carlo approach where each particle corresponds to a set of statistically sampled parameters from the distributions of as-fabricated fuel characteristics (e.g., dimensions, densities, etc.) that can be found amongst the particles in a pebble. For each sample, BISON runs a 1D model of the particle over the required time steps of the simulation. The 1D approach allows a fast determination of the stress distributions in the coating layers if the particle is spherical. For particles with localized flaws (i.e., aspherical particles and particles with cracked IPyC), an adjustment of the stress distributions is necessary to account for increased stress caused by these flaws. This adjustment is provided through so-called "2D stress factors". The 2D stress factors are obtained by running 2D simulations aimed at developing correlation functions that maps the stress in an aspherical particle or a particle with cracked IPyC as a function of its dimensions, aspect ratio, and irradiation conditions. The 1D simulation then uses these correlations to calculate the required correction factors for asphericity or IPyC cracking and determine whether or not the flawed particle fails.

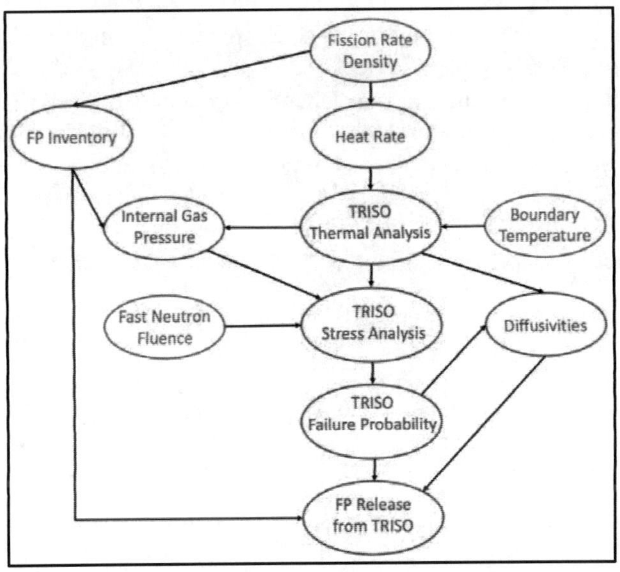


**Figure 2.** BISON flow chart for calculation of TRISO performance.

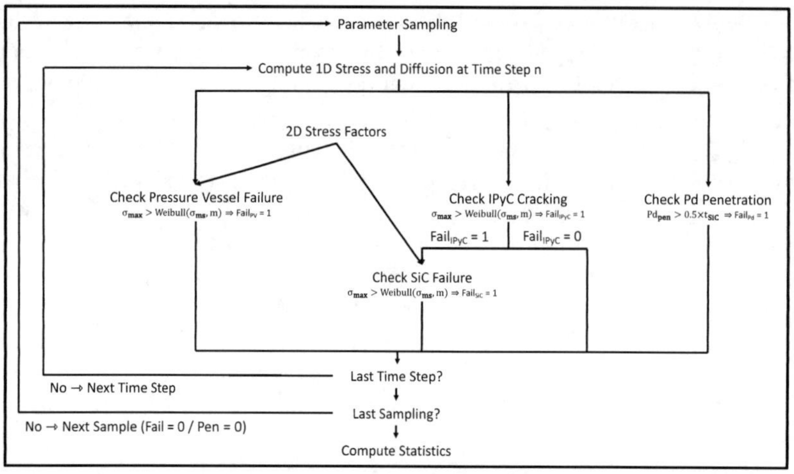


**Figure 3.** BISON scheme for calculation of failure probability of TRISO particles.

At each time step, the following failure mechanisms are checked:

- Pressure vessel failure of a spherical or aspherical particle – Failure is assumed when the maximum tangential tensile stress induced in the SiC layer by internal gas pressure is greater than the fracture strength of the SiC.
- IPyC cracking – Cracking of the IPyC is assumed when the maximum tangential tensile stress in the PyC layer is greater than its fracture strength. A cracked IPyC induces additional stress in the SiC layer.
- SiC failure is assumed when the maximum tangential tensile stress induced in the SiC layer by the cracked IPyC is greater than its fracture strength.
- Pd penetration – Failure is assumed when Pd penetration exceeds half the thickness of the SiC layer. In this case, the SiC layer loses its structural integrity and leak-tightness to fission products and is assigned a non-retentive diffusivity. Pd penetration is still to be implemented in the failure probability calculation scheme.

In all cases, the maximum stress ($\sigma_{max}$) is compared to a strength that is sampled from a Weibull distribution (mean strength $\sigma_{ms}$ and modulus m) to determine whether or not failure (i.e., IPyC cracking, SiC failure) occurs.

The methodology laid out in Figure 3 also includes the simulation of fission product diffusion, which is also evaluated at each time step for each Monte Carlo sample. The fission product diffusion calculations combine the release fractions (release normalized to calculated inventory) of all TRISO particles in the Monte Carlo sample. Coating layers that have been determined failed by stress analysis are assigned a large diffusivity (e.g., $10^{-6}$ $m^2/s$) to model the loss of retention power of that layer. Release is calculated by Fickian diffusion, while inventory is obtained from fission rate density and fission yields.

## 5. Preliminary Results

BISON was compared to the Particle Fuel Model (PARFUME [10]) code that has been developed at INL since the early 2000's to support the AGR program. A benchmark was developed using existing PARFUME results [22]. Both codes were used to predict the performance of a UCO TRISO particle with characteristics detailed in Table 2.

**Table 2.** Fuel parameters used in modeling.

| Category | Parameter | Nominal Values ± Standard Deviation |
|---|---|---|
| Fuel Characteristics | $^{235}U$ enrichment (wt%) | 15.5 |
| | C/U (atomic ratio) | 0.4 |
| | O/U (atomic ratio) | 1.5 |
| Particle geometry | Kernel diameter ($\mu$m) | 425±10 |
| | Buffer thickness ($\mu$m) | 100±10 |
| | PyC thickness ($\mu$m) | 40±3 |
| | SiC thickness ($\mu$m) | 35±2 |
| Fuel properties | Kernel density (g/cm$^3$) | 11.0 |
| | Kernel theoretical density(g/cm$^3$) | 11.4 |
| | Buffer density(g/cm$^3$) | 1.05 |
| | Buffer theoretical density(g/cm$^3$) | 2.25 |
| | PyC density(g/cm$^3$) | 1.9±0.02 |
| | IPyC/OPyC BAF | 1.9±0.02 |

The UCO fuel was modeled under three different sets of irradiation conditions, as shown in Table 3.

**Table 3.** Irradiation conditions.

| Case | EFPD | Burnup (%FIMA) | Fast fluence ($10^{25}$ n/m$^2$, E > 0.18 MeV) | Irradiation Temperature (°C) |
|---|---|---|---|---|
| 1 | 500 | 13.5 | 5 | 700 |
| 2 | 500 | 13.5 | 5 | 1000 |
| 3 | 500 | 13.5 | 5 | 1300 |

For each of the three cases of Table 3, the tangential stress in the SiC layer is plotted in Figure 4. Preliminary results show a good agreement between BISON and PARFUME. The slight under-prediction by BISON on the maximum compressive stress (negative stress values in Figure 4) early in irradiation seems to be partially compensated at higher fluence by the higher fission gas inventory calculated by PARFUME (see Figure 5) as release of these fission gases builds up internal pressure that results in increasing tensile stress in the SiC layer. Nevertheless, the discrepancies between both codes are still under investigation.

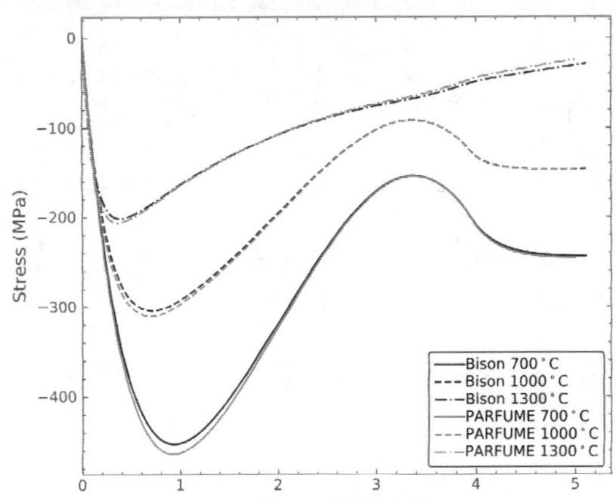


**Figure 4.** Tangential stress in SiC layer.

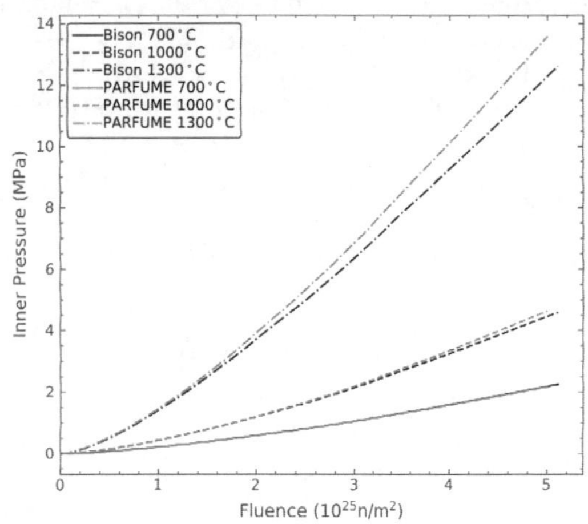


**Figure 5.** Internal gas pressure

Finally, both codes were used to compute the probability of cracking of the IPyC layer. Results are reported in Table 4 and show decent agreement with BISON over-predicting PARFUME by 2% at 700°C and by 30% at 1000°C but under-predicting by 30% at 1300°C. Analysis is ongoing to explain these differences.

**Table 4.** Probability of IPyC cracking.

| Condition | PARFUME | BISON |
|---|---|---|
| 1 | $8.94 \times 10^{-1}$ | $9.11 \times 10^{-1}$ |
| 2 | $5.48 \times 10^{-2}$ | $7.10 \times 10^{-2}$ |
| 3 | $1.16 \times 10^{-3}$ | $0.80 \times 10^{-3}$ |

## 6. Conclusion

A new TRISO model has been implemented in BISON to expand the code's ability to model the fuel performance of TRISO particles, including its probability of failure.

Updated material properties were added to the code and a methodology was developed to allow Monte Carlo sampling of a population of TRISO particles to account for the particle-to-particle statistical variations in physical dimensions and fuel (e.g., density) and material (e.g., strength) properties that arise from the fuel fabrication process. The Monte Carlo sampling allows to properly capture the probability of failure of the fuel within that population of TRISO particles.

A benchmark was developed to compare BISON and AGR's code PARFUME. Preliminary results show a decent agreement in stress level and failure probability, but BISON results are still being analyzed to find out the origin of the discrepancies.

Future work will involve developing the tables of 2D stress factors to allow 1D calculation of aspherical particles and particles with cracked IPyC layers and combine all stress analysis results into fission product release calculations. Additional developments will include accounting for pre-existing defects from fuel fabrication that contribute to increasing fission product release. Finally, Pd penetration will be implemented as part of the failure probability calculation scheme.

## References

[1] R. Williamson, J. Hales, S. Novascone, M. Tonks, D. Gaston, C. Permann, D. Andrs, R. Martineau, Multidimensional multiphysics simulation of nuclear fuel behavior, Journal of Nuclear Materials, v423, p.149, 2012.

[2] D. Gaston, C. Newman, G. Hansen, D. Lebrun-Grandié, MOOSE: A parallel computational framework for coupled systems of nonlinear equations, Nuclear Engineering and Design, v239, p.1768, 2009.

[3] D. Knoll, D. Keyes, Jacobian-free Newton–Krylov methods: a survey of approaches and applications, Journal of Computational Physics, v193, p.357, 2004.

[4] J.D. Hales, R.L. Williamson, S.R. Novascone, D.M. Perez, B.W. Spencer, G. Pastore, Multidimensional multiphysics simulation of TRISO particle fuel, Journal of Nuclear Materials v443, p.531, 2013.

[5] EPRI, Uranium Oxycarbide (UCO) Tristructural Isotropic (TRISO) Coated Particle Fuel Performance: Topical Report EPRI-AR-1(NP), Electrical Power Research Institute, Report 3002019978, 2020.

[6] K. Verfondern, TRISO Fuel Performance Modeling and Simulation, Comprehensive Nuclear Materials, p.755, Elsevier Ltd, 2012.

[7] D. Petti, J. Maki, J. Hunn, P. Pappano, C. Barnes, J. Saurwein, S. Nagley, J. Kendall, R. Hobbins, The DOE Advanced Gas Reactor Fuel Development and Qualification Program, JOM, v62, no9, p.62, 2010.

[8] N. Rohbeck, P. Xiao, Evaluation of the mechanical performance of silicon carbide in TRISO fuel at high temperatures, Nuclear Engineering and Design, v306, p.52, 2016.

[9] I v.Rooyen, M. Dunzik-Gougar, P. v.Rooyen, Silver (Ag) transport mechanisms in TRISO coated

particles: A critical review, Nuclear Engineering and Design, v271, p.180, 2014.
[10] G.K. Miller, D.A. Petti, J.T. Maki, D.L. Knudson, W.F. Skerjanc, PARFUME Theory and Model Basis Report, Idaho National Laboratory, Report INL/EXT-08-14497 Rev. 1, 2018.
[11] D.R. Olander, Fundamentals Aspects of Nuclear Reactor Fuel Elements, Technical Information Center - Energy Research and Development Administration, 1976.
[12] J. Fink, Thermophysical properties of uranium dioxide, Journal of Nuclear Materials , v279, p. 1, 2000.
[13] V. Barabash, I. Mazul, R. Latypov, A. Pokrovsky, C. Wu, The effect of low temperature neutron irradiation and annealing on the thermal conductivity of advanced carbon-based materials, Journal of Nuclear Materials, v307-311, p.1300, 2002.
[14] L.J. Siefken, E.W. Coryell, E.A. Harvego, J.K. Hohorst, MATPRO - A Library of Material Properties for Light-Water-Reactor Accident Analysis, Idaho National Laboratory for the U.S. Nuclear Regulatory Commission, NUREG/CR-6150 Vol. 4 Rev. 2, 2001.
[15] L.L. Snead, T. Nozawa, Y. Katoh, T.-S. Byun, S. Kondo, D.A. Petti, Handbook of SiC properties for fuel performance modeling, Journal of Nuclear Materials, v371, p.329, 2007.
[16] M.M. Rashid, Incremental kinematics for finite element applications, International Journal for Numerical Methods in Engineering, v36, no23, p.3937, 1993.
[17] U. Littmark and J.F. Ziegler, Handbook of Range Distributions for Energetic Ions in All Elements, Pergamon Press, 1980.
[18] A.H. Booth, A Method of Calculating Fission Gas Release from UO2 Fuel and Its Implication to the X-2-f Loop Test, Atomic Energy of Canada Limited, Report AECL 496, 1957.
[19] J.A. Turnbull and C.A. Friskney, The Diffusion Coefficient of Gaseous and Volatile Species During the Irradiation of Uranium Dioxide, Journal of Nuclear Materials, v107, p.168, 1982.
[20] INERI, Development Of Improved Models And Designs For Coated-Particle Gas Reactor Fuels, International Nuclear Energy Research Initiative, INEEL/EXT-05-02615, 2004.
[21] IAEA, Fuel performance and fission product behaviour in gas cooled reactors, International Atomic Energy Agency, TECDOC-978, 1997.
[22] W.F. Skerjanc, B.P. Collin, Assessment of Material Properties for TRISO Fuel Particles used in PARFUME, Idaho National Laboratory, Report INL/EXT/18-44631, 2018.

# Hyphenated SEM-Raman Characterization for Matrix Graphite of HTGR Spherical Fuels

**Z Jiao, X Chen*, C Zhang, G Xu, B Liu, and Z Yin***

Institute of Nuclear and New Energy Technology, Collaborative Innovation Center of Advanced Nuclear Energy Technology, Tsinghua University, Beijing 100084, PR China,

phone: +86-10-62784394, e-mail: jzt19@mails.tsinghua.edu.cn

**Abstract** – Matrix graphite (MG) is an important material for the spherical fuel elements of high temperature gas-cooled reactors (HTGR). After carbonization, the matrix material is composed of three isomers of natural graphite, artificial graphite, and carbon derived from phenolic resin (resin carbon) with the same element but different structure. According to previous study, the three components have different effect on the fission products diffusion and adhesion in the irradiated fuel. However, the characterizing methods to discriminate natural graphite, artificial graphite and resin carbon are rare. In this study, Raman Imaging and Scanning Electron (RISE) microscopy was used to study the structure and distribution of natural graphite, artificial graphite, resin carbon and graphite oxides produced from electrochemical deconsolidation of MG in post-irradiation examination (PIE). Natural graphite and artificial graphite have only a couple of Raman-active bands visible in the spectra between 1100-2400 $cm^{-1}$, including the strong G band at ~1580 $cm^{-1}$ and the weak Dband at ~1350 $cm^{-1}$. The D band is activated once the defects are introduced into sp2 hybridized carbon networks, and the intensity of D band is proportional to the defect concentration. Resin carbon has a strong D band, which can be easily distinguished from natural graphite and artificial graphite. The results show that the resin carbon is evenly coated on the surface of the natural and artificial graphite particles, and the network frame is formed during the pressing process to fix the graphite particles. This work also revealed that the changes of surface morphologies of MG after electrochemical deconsolidation by In-situ SEM analysis, of which a lot of cracks and holes on the surface of MG. Meanwhile, Raman spectra suggest that crystalline graphite and resin carbon have different oxidation behaviors. This work will provide a new method for MG components discriminating.

## 1. Introduction

The utilization of spherical fuel elements is one of the unique characteristics of pebble-bed high-temperature gas-cooled reactors (HTGR), which effectively enhances the retention capability for fission products and the inherent safety of the reactor especially at high temperature [1]. Spherical fuel element is manufactured by mixing TRISO (triple isotropic coating materials) coated fuel particles with MG which is composed of approximately 71 wt% natural graphite, 18 wt% artificial graphite and 11 wt% carbon derived from phenolic resin (resin carbon) [2, 3]. Spherical fuel elements consist of a 50 mm diameter inner fuel zone and 5 mm thick shell of fuel free zone that is made of pure MG. The mass of MG component accounts for more than 90% of total spherical fuel element. MG in spherical fuel element acts as neutron moderator and thermal conductor with high mechanical strength, good corrosion resistance, and high dimensional stability. The microstructure characteristics of MG largely determine the final properties of MG. Therefore, studying the microstructure of MG, such as phase composition, morphology, and distribution, has important guiding significance for optimizing the fabrication process of MG.

An understanding of the microstructure and performance of MG is of immense interest, and a great many techniques have been used to investigate this system. Lee et al. [4] studied the microstructure evaluation of MG powder samples with two different binder materials during compaction and carbonization by scanning electron microscope (SEM). Some grains growth and closed pores in MG with phenolic resin binder were observed after carbonization at 1073 K whereas no apparent pores in MG with polyvinyl butyral binder. Yeo et al. [5] studied the orientation of graphite grains in MG fabricated by conventional Uniaxial Pressing (UP) and Cold Isostatic Pressing (CIP). The observation revealed the alignment of graphite grains with the axial section of UP MG was not observed in CIP MG. Although graphite grain orientation and pore distribution can be observed from SEM images, different MG components, i.e., natural graphite, artificial graphite and resin carbon, are difficult to distinguish due to the similar chemical composition to that of graphite. So, it is necessary to find an effective technology to distinguish different MG components.

Micro-Raman spectroscopy is a widely used hyphenated techniques in materials sciences that combines an optical microscopy to locate features of interest and Raman spectroscopy to identify these features. Raman spectroscopy extracts information on chemical bonds, molecular structure and crystallinity. It has been an important tool in characterization of graphitic carbon materials, because the Raman spectrum is particularly sensitive to the double carbon-carbon bonds [6, 7]. However, Micro-Raman spectroscopy is not able to provide high precision information on morphology and texture of carbon materials due to its relatively low resolution for optical microscopy. In recent years, the combination of Raman Imaging and Scanning Electron microscopy (RISE) is a promising technique that adds chemical information to the high-resolution imaging capabilities of electron microscopy [8-10]. Here the SEM/EDX and Raman data are obtained separately by precisely moving sample stage between the electron beam vacuum cavity and the Raman optics located outside the electron beam axis, as shown in Fig. 1. It means that SEM and Raman systems are “off-axis”, allowing Raman molecular imaging can be performed without compromising SEM performance [10]. In this work, RISE technique was used to study the microstructure and distribution of natural graphite, artificial graphite, resin carbon and graphite oxides produced from electrochemical deconsolidation of MG in post-irradiation examination (PIE).

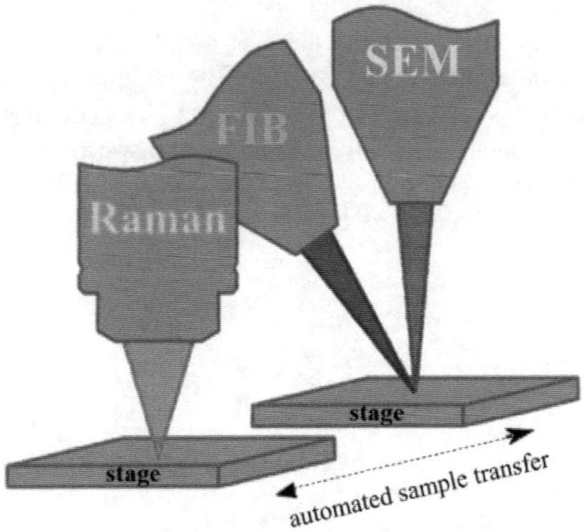


**Figure 1.** Schematic of Raman Imaging and Scanning Electron (RISE) Microscopy system showing SEM and Raman data are obtained sequentially after a precisely movement of the sample stage (courtesy of TESCAN).

## 2. Experiment

All MG samples discussed in this work were manufactured by the Institute of Nuclear and New Energy Technology (INET), Tsinghua University. It should be mentioned that in order to simplify the experiment, coated fuel particles were not included, and only MG powders were used as raw materials. The fabrication procedure of MG pebbles is the same as that of the HTR-PM spherical fuel element in INET, which mainly consists of manufacture of the MG powder, cold quasi-isostatic molding and heat treatment [3, 11].

### *2.1. Preparation of MG Powder Samples*

The resinated MG powder was composed of natural graphite powder, artificial graphite powder and phenolic resin binder. Natural graphite powder and artificial graphite powder were premixed in the ratio of 4:1. Phenolic resin binder dissolved in alcohol was then added to the graphite powder mixture with different mass ratio of 5%, 20% and 50%, and thoroughly blended in order to achieve the homogeneous dispersion [12]. The mixture was dried under vacuum at approximately 100 °C. After drying, the mixture was heated up to 800 °C in an argon atmosphere in order to carbonize the phenolic resin binder. The final MG powders had different amounts of resin carbon, named MG pewder-5% resin carbon, MG powder-20% resin carbon, and MGpowder-30% resin carbon, separately.

### *2.2. Preparation of MG pebbles*

MG pebbles were manufactured by pressing MG powder with cold quasi-isostatic molding, which is consistent with that of HTGR spherical fuel element [2]. Afterwards, resinated MG pebbles were heated up to 800 °C under argon atmosphere for carbonization, and further to 1950 °C under vacuum for purification. Similar to the MG powders, the MG pebbles containing different amounts of resin carbon are named MG pebble-5% resin carbon, MG pebble- 20% resin carbon and MG pebble-50% resin carbon. In particular, we performed electrochemical deconsolidation and RISE characterization of the MG pebble-20% resin carbon sample.

### *2.3. Electrochemical Deconsolidation of MG Pebble-20% resin carbon*

The electrochemical deconsolidation method is usually used for post-irradiation examination (PIE) of fuel elements, and is considered to be a promising method for spent fuel reprocessing of HTGR [13, 14]. The electrochemical deconsolidation method for the preparation of electrolytic graphite oxide was derived from the method used in our previous studies [12, 14]. Fig. 2 shows a schematic diagram of the electrochemical deconsolidation apparatus in this work. The MG pebble was inserted as anode into the 65%~68% HNO3 solution, with a cylindrical Pt mesh around it as counter-electrode. Constant current of 4.0 A was applied to the two electrodes using a DC electrolytic power supply and control system. The deconsolidated MG powders were separated by filter and washed with water and ethanol until the pH was neutral, and then dried at 80 °C for future characterization.

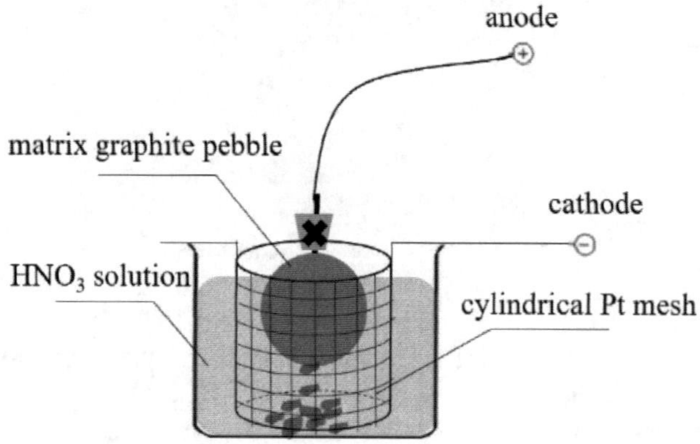


**Figure 2.** Schematic diagram of the electrochemical deconsolidation apparatus.

### 2.4. Characterization Methods

The microstructural observation of MG powder with different proportion of resin carbon, MG pebble and deconsolidated MG powders were carried out by ZEISS Gemini-300 SEM (ZEISS, Germany). Focused Ion beam (FIB) and mechanical polishing were carried out to investigate the formation of pores and the direction of graphite grains. Raman spectra (spectral images) were measured with a Raman Imaging and Scanning Electron (RISE) microscopy (TESCAN, Czech Republic) at an excitation wavelength of 532 nm (75 mW). The X-ray diffraction (XRD) spectra were characterized by a D8 X-ray diffractometer (Bruker, Germany) with the 2- theta range of 10-80°. The X-ray photoelectron spectrometry (XPS) properties were carried out with a 250XI XPS instrument (Thermo, USA).

## 3. Results and Discussion

### 3.1. Microscopic Observation

Fig. 3 shows SEM images of natural graphite, artificial graphite and resin carbon powder separately. Natural graphite powder is a kind of irregular plate- like particle with sharp edges, as shown in Fig. 3(a). Artificial graphite powder is a columnar crystalline aggregate with lots of pits and cracks on the surface, as shown in Fig. 3(c). Although the base surface is quite different, their end faces have clearly layered structure, as shown in Fig. 3(b) and 3(d). Resin carbon shows a smooth, featureless, conchoidal fracture surface similar to that of glass, as shown in Fig. 3(e) and 3(f).

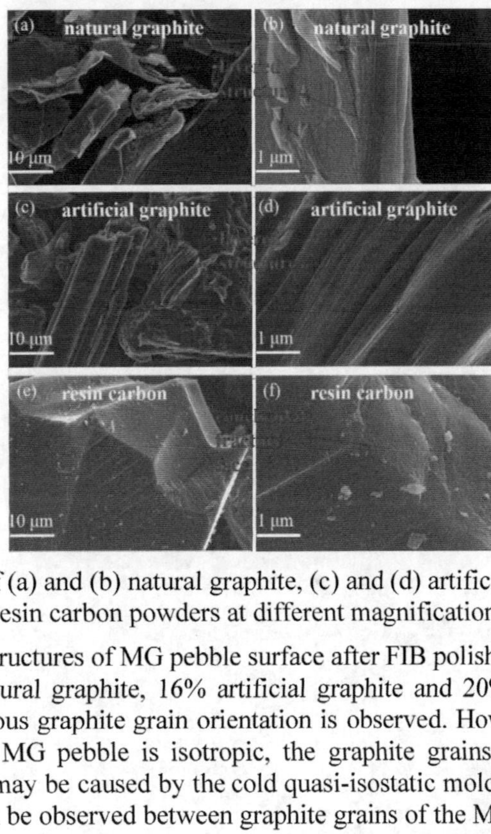


**Figure 3.** SEM images of (a) and (b) natural graphite, (c) and (d) artificial graphite, and (e) and (f) resin carbon powders at different magnifications.

Fig. 4 shows the microstructures of MG pebble surface after FIB polishing 5 hours at 6 kV. The MG pebble containing 64% natural graphite, 16% artificial graphite and 20% resin binder has isotropic property, in which no obvious graphite grain orientation is observed. However, it is worth noting that although the total area of MG pebble is isotropic, the graphite grains are divergent locally. This microscopic characteristic may be caused by the cold quasi-isostatic molding method. A large number of isolated closed pores can be observed between graphite grains of the MG pebble. The size of closed pores is < 10 μm. These closed pores may be caused by the gas escaping from the carbonization of phenolic resin. In addition to closed pores, cracks with a length of about 100 μm were also observed in the MG pebble. Graphite grains and resin carbon were not distinguishable in MG pebble through SEM characterizing method, while their original morphology and composition were different. It is necessary to distinguish the graphite grain and resin carbon in order to further investigate the PIE of irradiated fuel pebbles in detail.

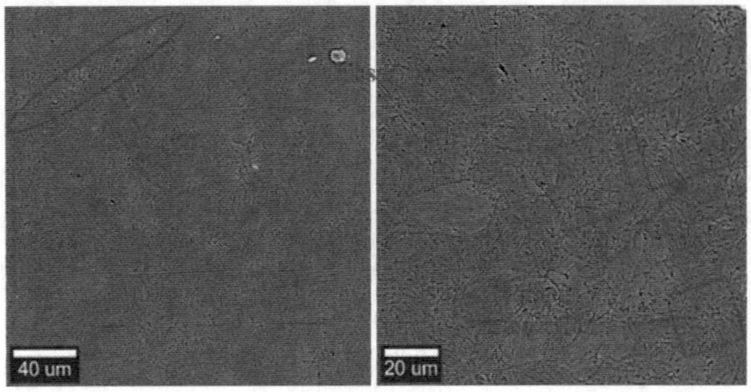


**Figure 4.** SEM image of MG pebble surface after FIB polishing.

Fig. 5 shows the SEM images of carbonized MG powders with different mass ratios of phenolic resin. It can be seen that with the increase of phenolic resin carbon content, the surface of natural graphite and artificial graphite powders gradually becomes smoother, and the pits and cracks gradually disappear. Compared with Fig. 5(b), the interface between the graphite layers in Fig. 5(d) and 5(f) is more blurred. Some extra resin carbon agglomeration formed on the surface of natural graphite and artificial graphite can even be observed in Fig. 5(f). These changes indicate that the surface of graphite particles has been coated by a layer of dense resin carbon, and with the increasing of phenolic resin concentration, the formed carbon layers on the surface of graphite become thicker. Fig. 6 shows the cross-section of MG pebbles containing 5%, 20%, and 50% resin carbon. The MG pebbles containing 5% resin carbon is very loose and has a rough surface as shown in Fig. 6(a). As the resin carbon content increases, the surface of the MG pebbles become flatter and more integrated, but the pores increase as shown in Fig. 6(b) and 6(c). This indicates that the density of the MG pebbles gradually decreases with increasing resin carbon content, but the strength gradually increases. The thermal conductivity at 293 K of MG pebble-5% resin carbon, MG pebble-20% resin carbon and MG pebble-50% resin carbon was measured to be 3.3, 4.0, and 3.5 W/ (m K), separately. Considering that the MG must have sufficient density, strength, thermal conductivity and other physical property indexes, the MG material made with 64% natural graphite, 16% artificial graphite and 20% resin binder can well meet the requirements of HTGR spherical fuel elements. Therefore, the following experiments focus on the further SEM-Raman characterization of the MG pebbles with 20% resin carbon.

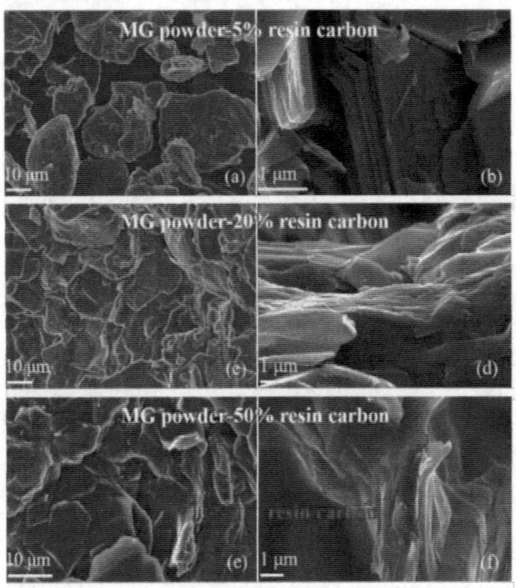


**Figure 5.** SEM images of carbonized MG powders with different mass ratios of phenolic resin: (a) and (b) 5%; (c) and (d) 20%; (e) and (f) 50%.

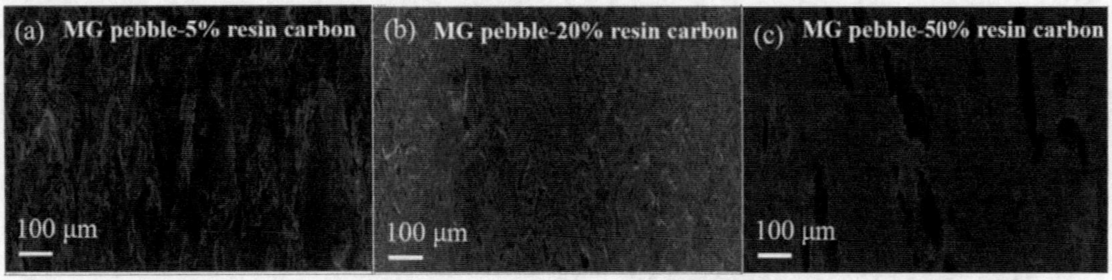


**Figure 6.** SEM images of cross-section of MG pebbles containing (a) 5%, (b) 20%, and (c) 50% resin carbon.

*3.2. Raman Spectroscopy*

In this work, Raman imaging has been performed on the pristine MG pebble and deconsolidated MG produced from electrochemical deconsolidation of MG pebble. Fig. 7 shows the Raman spectrum of three different compositions in the MG pebble, i.e., natural graphite, artificial graphite and resin carbon after carbonization at 800°C. Natural graphite and artificial graphite have only a couple of Raman-active bands visible in the spectra between 1100-2400 $cm^{-1}$, the strong G band at ~1580 $cm^{-1}$ from the $E2g$ vibrational mode of graphitic structure and the weak D band at ~1350 $cm^{-1}$ [6]. The D band is activated once the defects are introduced into sp2 hybridized carbon networks, and the intensity of D band is proportional to the defect concentration [15, 16]. The Raman spectra of natural graphite and artificial graphite are nearly the same, which indicates that they have the same degree of graphitization. Resin carbon has a strong D band, which can be easily distinguished from natural graphite and artificial graphite. Therefore, natural graphite and artificial graphite were seen as a whole, crystalline graphite to distinguish from resin carbon in this study.

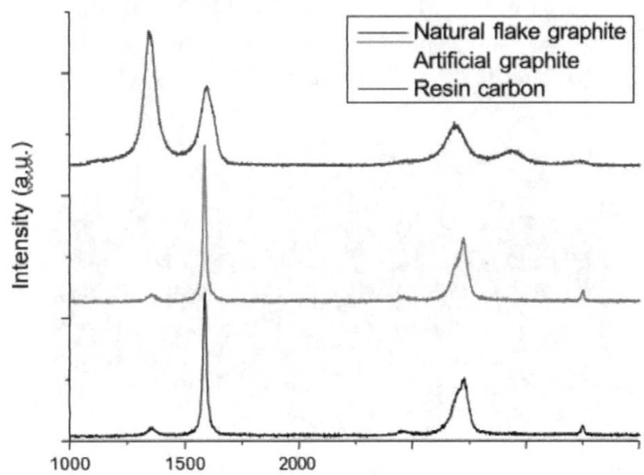


**Figure 7.** The Raman spectra of natural graphite, artificial graphite and phenolic resin carbon powders.

Fig. 8 shows SEM-Raman imaging of MG pebble after carbonization at 800°C and purification at 1950°C, as well as two typical Raman spectra. In Raman imaging, the blue color represents crystalline graphite and the red color represents resin carbon. Their corresponding spectra are also shown in Fig. 7. It can be seen that resin carbon is evenly coated on the outside of the crystalline graphite. In MG, resin carbon forms a three-dimensional network structure after pressing and heat treatment, and crystalline graphite is embedded in network structure. This result is also consistent with the SEM results in *III.A*.

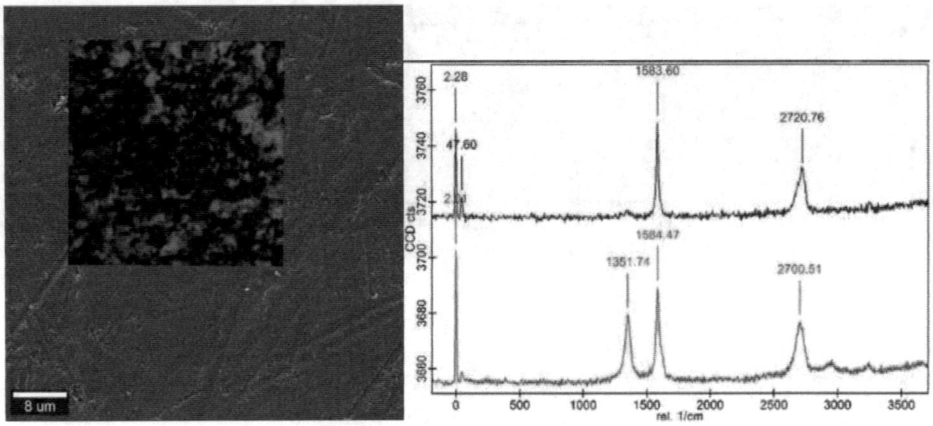


**Figure 8.** SEM-Raman imaging of pristine MG after mechanical polishing, and two typical Raman spectra (Blue spectrum: crystalline graphite; Red spectrum: resin carbon).

*3.3. Structural Transformation of MG during the electrolytic process*

Fig. 9 shows the SEM-Raman imaging of deconsolidated MG, and three typical Raman spectra. It can be seen that the morphology and composition of the pristine MG pebble have changed significantly after electrolysis. Fig. 10 shows that the edge of MG curls after electrochemical oxidation, indicating the production of graphite oxide. On the surface of the deconsolidated MG, crystalline graphite and resin carbon are oxidized in varying degrees. There are a large number of cracks and holes on the surface of MG, which may be due to the electrochemical oxidation etching of resin carbon, because of the higher surface energy compared with crystalline graphite [12, 17]. The peak intensity and peak position of the Raman spectrum in the green area in Fig. 9(a) have changed to a large extent compared to the pristine crystalline graphite, indicating a greater degree of electrochemical oxidation. It is worth noting that although there are a lot of cracks in the blue area, the degree of graphitization is higher than that of the green area.

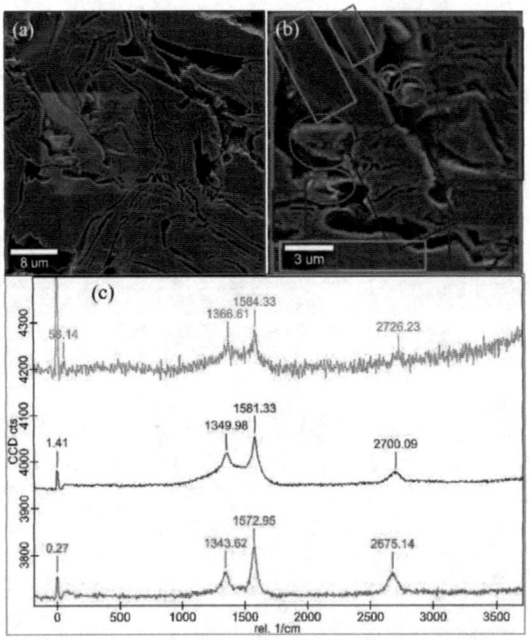


**Figure 9.** (a) SEM-Raman imaging of deconsolidated MG, (b) enlarged SEM image corresponding to the Raman imaging in (a), and (c) Raman spectrum corresponding to the color in (a).

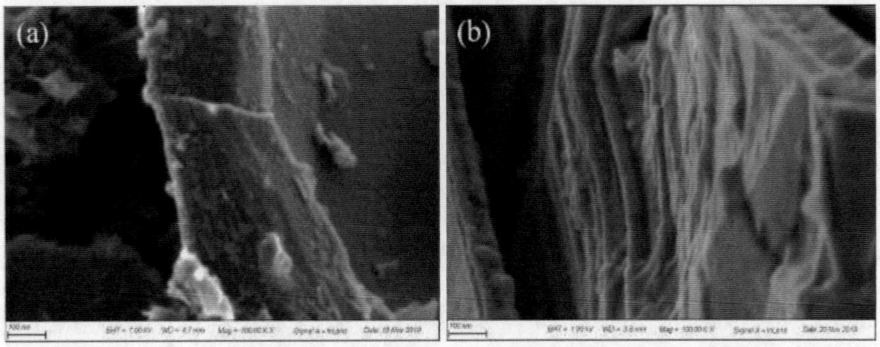


**Figure 10.** SEM images of (a) pristine MG and (b) deconsolidated MG.

In order to further determine the composition of deconsolidated MG, XRD patterns and XPS data were analyzed. Fig. 11 presents the XRD patterns of pristine MG and deconsolidated MG. (002) and (004) peaks are observed for them corresponding to typical graphite structures, indicating that electrochemical oxidation did not destroy the basic layered structure of graphite. As for deconsolidated MG, the intensity of (002) and (004) peaks decrease after electrochemical oxidation which is caused by the decrease of crystallinity of graphite due to the formation of graphite oxide. Fig. 12(a) shows a predominant graphitic C 1s peak at 285 eV and an O 1s peak at 533 eV for both pristine MG and deconsolidated MG. The higher O 1s peak seen for the deconsolidated MG suggested that oxidation reaction took place during the electrolytic process. Fig. 12(b) shows the presence the wider C 1s peak of deconsolidated MG associated with the oxygen containing groups. It confirmed the presence of C=C (284.5 eV), C-C (285.0 eV), C=O (286.9), and $C_2O_4/CO_3$ (290.1 eV) bonds, which is consistent with the results of our previous study [12]. This indicates the deconsolidated MG was rich in carbonyl, hydroxyl and carboxylic acid groups on the surfaces.

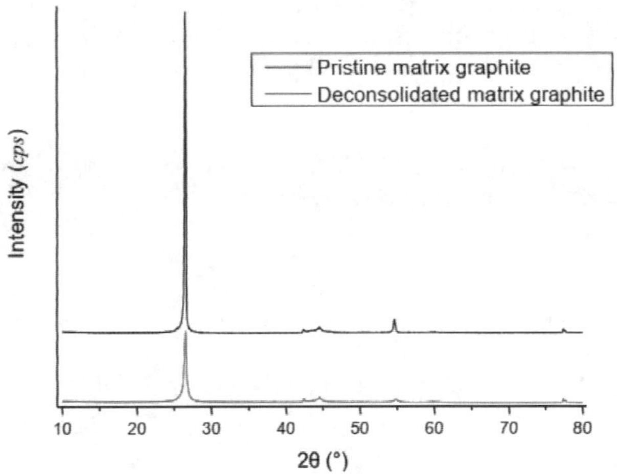


**Figure 11.** XRD patterns of pristine graphite matrix and

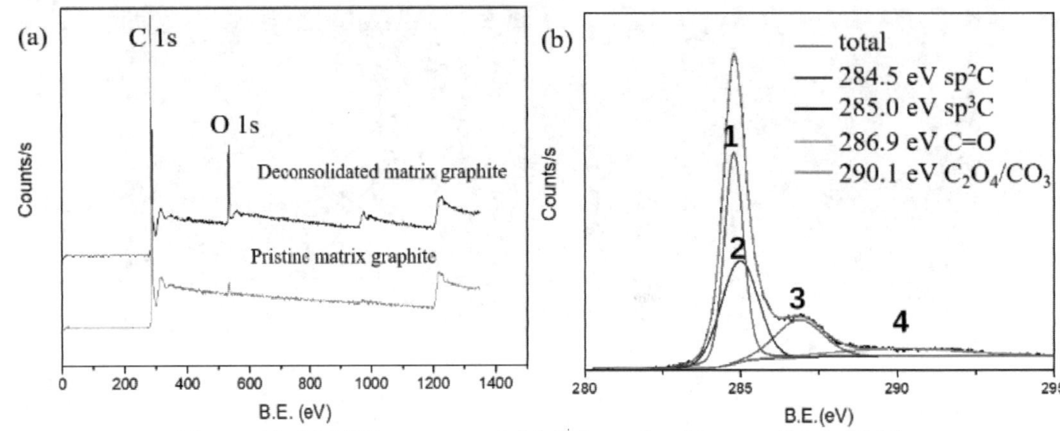


**Figure 12.** (a) XPS spectra and (b) C 1s peak of deconsolidated MG.

## 4. Summary

In this work, microscopic morphology and pores of MG pebbles containing 5%, 20% and 50% resin carbon were characterized by SEM. The results show that MG pebble containing 20% resin carbon exhibit better physical properties such as density, strength, and thermal conductivity compared to MG pebbles containing 5% and 50% resin carbon. MG pebble-20% resin carbon has isotropic property, in which no obvious graphite grain orientation is observed. A large number of isolated closed pores and a few cracks caused by the gas escaping from the carbonization of phenolic resin were observed between graphite grains of the MG pebble after pressing and heat treatment. The distribution of resin carbon in MG was studied by SEM, Raman, and RISE methods. The surface of natural and artificial graphite particles was coated by a layer of dense resin carbon. In the MG, resin carbon forms a three-dimensional network framework after pressing and heat treatment, and crystalline graphite is embedded in network framework. Besides, a larger number of cracks and holes were observed on the surface of deconsolidated MG during electrolysis compared with pristine samples. XPS results show that the deconsolidated MG was rich in carbonyl, hydroxyl and carboxylic acid groups on the surfaces.

**Acknowledgement**

This work is supported by National S&T Major Project (Grant No. ZX06901), Nuclear Energy Development Project and the Young Talents of CNNC Project.

**References**

[1] B. Wu, Y. Li, H.-s. Zhao, S. Liu, B. Liu, J.-h. Wang, Wear behavior of graphitic matrix of fuel elements used in pebble-bed high-temperature gas- cooled reactors against steel, Nuclear Engineering and Design 328 (2018) 353-358.

[2] C. Tang, Y.Tang, J. Zhu, Y.Zou, J. Li, X. Ni, Design and manufacture of the fuel element for the 10 MW high temperature gas-cooled reactor, Nuclear Engineering and Design 218(1) (2002) 91-102.

[3] Z. Xiangwen, L. Zhenming, Z. Jie, L. Bing, Z. Yanwen, T. Chunhe, T. Yaping, Preparation of spherical fuel elements for HTR-PM in INET, Nuclear Engineering and Design 263 (2013) 456-461.

[4] Y.-W. Lee, J.H. Kim, J.H. Kim, M.-S. Cho, Microstructural modification and porosity evolution during carbonization of fuel element compact for HTGR, Nuclear Engineering and Design 271 (2014) 244-249.

[5] S. Yeo, Y.-W. Lee, Reduced anisotropic properties of Cold Isostatic Pressed graphite matrix compacts, Journal of Nuclear Materials 515 (2019) 245-256.

[6] Y. Wang, D.C. Alsmeyer, R.L. McCreery, RAMAN-SPECTROSCOPY OF CARBON MATERIALS - STRUCTURAL BASIS OF OBSERVED SPECTRA, Chem. Mat. 2(5) (1990)

557-563.
[7] K.N. Kudin, B. Ozbas, H.C. Schniepp, R.K. Prud'homme, I.A. Aksay, R. Car, Raman spectra of graphite oxide and functionalized graphene sheets, Nano Lett. 8(1) (2008) 36-41.
[8] C. Cardell, I. Guerra, An overview of emerging hyphenated SEM-EDX and Raman spectroscopy systems: Applications in life, environmental and materials sciences, Trac-Trends Anal. Chem. 77 (2016) 156-166.
[9] G. Armstrong, L. Kailas, Hyphenated analytical techniques for materials characterisation, Eur. J. Phys. 38(5) (2017) 54.
[10] G. Wille, U. Schmidt, O. Hollricher, RISE: Correlative Confocal Raman and Scanning Electron Microscopy, in: J. Toporski, T. Dieing, O. Hollricher (Eds.), Confocal Raman Microscopy, 2nd Edition, Springer-Verlag Berlin, Berlin, 2018, pp. 559-580.
[11] H. Zhao, T. Liang, J. Zhang, J. He, Y. Zou, C. Tang, Manufacture and characteristics of spherical fuel elements for the HTR-10, Nuclear Engineering and Design 236(5) (2006) 643-647.
[12] C. Zhang, X.T. Chen, B. Liu, Z.T. Jiao, L.H. Fan, G. Xu, T.W. Wang, L.F. He, M.L. Qi, Z.M. Lu, H.S. Zhao, Z.Z. Yin, Y.P. Tang, The electrochemical deconsolidation mechanism of graphite matrix in HTGR spherical fuel elements, Journal of Nuclear Materials 525 (2019) 1-6.
[13] G.Y. Zhang, M.F. Wen, S.W. Wang, J. Chen, J.C. Wang, Insights into electrochemical behavior and anodic oxidation processing of graphite matrix in aqueous solutions of sodium nitrate, J. Appl. Electrochem. 46(12) (2016) 1163-1176.
[14] X.T. Chen, Z.M. Lu, H.S. Zhao, B. Liu, J.G. Zhu, C.H. Tang, The Electric Current Effect on Electrochemical Deconsolidation of Spherical Fuel Elements, Sci. Technol. Nucl. Install. 2017 (2017) 6.
[15] C. Thomsen, S. Reich, Doable resonant Raman scattering in graphite, Phys. Rev. Lett. 85(24) (2000) 5214-5217.
[16] L.G. Cancado, A. Jorio, E.H.M. Ferreira, F. Stavale, C.A. Achete, R.B. Capaz, M.V.O. Moutinho, A. Lombardo, T.S. Kulmala, A.C. Ferrari, Quantifying Defects in Graphene via Raman Spectroscopy at Different Excitation Energies, Nano Lett. 11(8) (2011) 3190-3196.
[17] S. Yeo, J. Yun, S. Kim, M.S. Cho, Y.-W. Lee, Fabrication methods and anisotropic properties of graphite matrix compacts for use in HTGR, Journal of Nuclear Materials 499 (2018) 383-393.

Journal of Physics: Conference Series **2048** (2021) 012014 doi:10.1088/1742-6596/2048/1/012014

# $Ti_3SiC_2$-TiC-Si Antioxidant Coating Prepared on SiC coated MG Spheres of HTR Fuel Element by Molten Salt Technique

**H Yang, H Zhao[1], X Liu, K Zhang, T Wang, Z Li, Y Gao, and Bing Liu**

Institute of Nuclear and New Energy Technology, Tsinghua University, Beijing, 100084, PR China

[1]Corresponding author. E-mail address: hshzhao@tsinghua.edu.cn (H.S. Zhao)

**Abstract.** A $Ti_3SiC_2$-TiC-Si composite coating was prepared by molten salt technique on the surface of SiC coated matrix graphite (MG) spheres of HTR fuel element with different Ti content. The coating is composed of a transition layer, a SiC layer and an outer Ti- rich layer. When the content of Ti is 0.6g, the coating consists of $Ti_3SiC_2$, SiC, and TiC; when Ti content are 1.2g and 2.4g, the coating is composed of $Ti_3SiC_2$, SiC, TiC, and Si. Oxidation tests show that the kinetics of oxidation is parabolic at the beginning of oxidation; then it becomes linear after oxidation for 5h. The coating prepared with 0.6g Ti shows the best oxidation resistance, and the weight reduction of the coated MG spheres is only 0.33% after oxidation in static air at 1773K for 50h. These results show that Ti-based composites coating a kind of anti-oxidation coating system worth studying.

## 1. Introduction

Graphite exhibits several advantages, including its low neutron absorption cross-section, prominent thermal shock resistance, low thermal expansion coefficient (CTE), as well as high thermal conductivity. As impacted by the mentioned characteristics, it has extensively acted as the matrix material of thermal barrier, the absorbing elements and the fuel elements for the high-temperature gas-cooled reactor (HTR) [1-3]. However, the poor anti-oxidation performance exhibited by graphite in the oxidation environment above 773 K significantly limits its high-temperature application. If high purity helium (He) gas acts as the coolant in the HTR, the excellent properties of graphite could be maximally exploited. However, under extreme accident conditions, air or water will enter the reactor core to varying degrees. As a result, the graphite applied in the fuel element will be exposed to the oxidizing environment directly, thereby adversely affecting the safety of the HTR [4, 5]. Accordingly, enhancing the oxidation resistance of matrix graphite of nuclear fuel elements can ensure the safety and development of the HTR.

Thus far, the coating method acts as a common method to improve the anti-oxidation performance exhibited by graphite or C/C composites. As indicated from existing studies, the anti-oxidation property exhibited by single coating is limited [6-8]. Thus, multilayer coatings have been extensively studied to improve the oxidation resistance exhibited by graphite or C/C composites. SiC is widely applied as the inner transition layer of multilayer coating for its high physical and chemical compatibility with graphite[9-11]. Apart from the stability at high temperatures and low neutron absorption cross-section of SiC, it will be oxidized into the $SiO_2$ glass phase at high temperatures. $SiO_2$ has a low oxygen diffusion coefficient and high fluidity at high temperatures, so it can fill the pores, cracks and other defects in the coating. Fu et al. [12] prepared a $SiO_2$/SiC coating by employing the vapor reaction diffusion combined with slurry techniques to improve the anti-oxidation performance exhibited by matrix graphite. After heated in high purity He for 100 h at 1273 K, the $SiO_2$/SiC could still maintain its stability and effectively prevent the oxidation of matrix graphite. In addition, the $SiO_2$/SiC-coated sample exhibited an excellent thermal shock performance. Huang et al. [13] fabricated a $ZrO_2$-$SiO_2$ layer on the surface of SiC-coated C/C composites. After the oxidation for 10 h at 1773 K in air, the composite coating could prevent the graphite from being oxidized with the weight reducing by 1.97%. The internal SiC coating could effectively release the CTE mismatch between the external coating and the graphite substate. The mentioned SiC-based multilayer coatings were found to be capable of greatly improving the anti-oxidation performance exhibited by graphite and C/C composites.

Specific to multilayer coatings, numerous materials can act as the outer coatings, (e.g., $MoSi_2$ [14-16], ZrC [17, 18] and HfC [19, 20]). As impacted by the ceramic and metallic properties, the fracture energy absorption, the chemical stability, and the irradiation resistance, MAX phases are recognized as the potential materials for the nuclear application [21-23]. Wang et al. [24] investigated the oxidation behavior exhibited by $Ti_3AlC_2$. The bulk $Ti_3AlC_2$ was found to exhibit a prominent oxidation resistance in air, and the oxide scale included an $Al_2O_3$ inner layer and a $TiO_2$ outer layer. As reported by Ko et al. [25], the oxide scale of $Ti_3SiC_2$ (TSC) also covered an inner layer composed of amorphous $SiO_2$ and $TiO_2$, as well as an outer layer formed by $TiO_2$. According to Fan et al. [26], cracks could be filled by $TiO_2$ and $SiO_2$, which was suggested as the oxidation production of TSC. For the mentioned reason, the anti-oxidation property exhibited by the material can be enhanced. Thus far, MAX phases coating has been rarely used to improve the anti-oxidation properties of graphite or C/C composites.

In this study, a $Ti_3SiC_2$-TiC-Si composite coating was prepared on the surface of the SiC-coated graphite spheres with the molten salt technique. The microstructure, the composition and the mechanical properties were characterized, and an investigation was conducted on the anti-oxidation property exhibited by the mentioned coatings at 1773 K in air.

## 2. Experiment

The substrates applied here the graphite spheres. The diameter of the sphere is 15 mm. Table 1 lists the properties of the graphite substrates. After being polished, cleaned and dried, the pack cementation was performed for the graphite spheres with mixed powers in the graphite crucibles, and then the spheres were placed in an electrical furnace. The mixed powers are composed of graphite (8-12 wt%), SiC (18-22 wt%), $Al_2O_3$ (2-12 wt%), and Si (58-68 wt%). The heat treatment was performed at 1973-2023 K for 2-3 h in Ar atmosphere. After the first pack cementation, the mentioned spheres were immersed in a molten salt of $Al_2O_3$ crucibles. The mixture for the molten salt technique was mixed with NaCl, KCl, and Ti. In addition, the mass of Ti was 0.6 g, 1.2 g, and 2.4 g. The coatings prepared with different Ti contents (i.e., 0.6 g, 1.2 g, and 2.4 g) were termed as T1, T2, and T3, respectively. The molten salt technique was used at 1373 K for 2-3 h in Ar atmosphere. The pack cementation and the molten salt technique for preparing composite coatings are illustrated in Fig. 1. For an in-depth characterization, when cooled to ambient temperatures, the mentioned coated graphite spheres were repeatedly washed with distilled water to remove residual salt. Finally, these coated samples were dried in an oven at 373K.

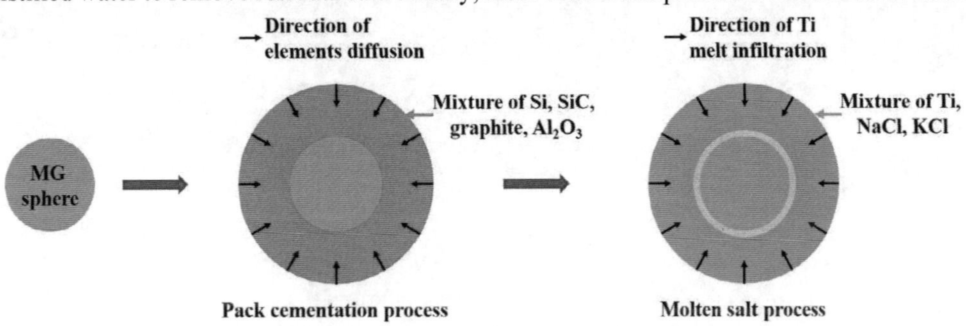


**Figure 1.** The preparation process of the composite coating by pack cementation and molten salt techniques.

**Table 1.** Properties of the MG spheres used in this paper [1, 27]

| Properties | Parameter Value |
|---|---|
| Density | 1.72~1.73g/cm$^3$ |
| Ash content | 130-190μg/g |
| Li content | 7-23μg/kg |
| Boron equivalent | ≤0.15μg/g |
| Thermal conductivity | 30W·(m·K)$^{-1}$, at 1273K |
| Anisotropy of thermal expansion α⊥/α∥ | 1.10 |

The morphology and fracture cross-sections exhibited by the coatings were characterized under a Quanta 200 FEG field-emission scanning electron microscope (SEM, FEI, the Netherlands). In addition, the composition and phases of the mentioned coatings were examined with a Genesis Energy-dispersive X-ray spectroscopy (EDAX, Mahwah, NJ) and a D/Max IIIA X-ray diffractometer (XRD, Rigaku, Tokyo, Japan), respectively. To prepare the XRD samples, the graphite spheres coated were crushed, so the graphite within the spheres could be exposed. Subsequently, the crushed spheres were heated in air for 10 h at 1073 K to remove the overall graphite. The powder obtained after the coating shells were fully ground in the mortar was examined by using the XRD. The compressive strength exhibited by the coated graphite spheres was tested by employing the general electromechanical test system (CMT5105, MTS, USA). Then, the precise weighing sensor was calibrated with a force of 1/3000 kN, at and a displacement rate of 0.5 mm/min. Each experiment was repeated three times to ensure the repeatability of the experiment.

The anti-oxidation properties of the mentioned coated graphite spheres were characterized in static air at 1773 K. Next, the coated spheres were placed into the muffle furnace for a certain period and then taken out. When the spheres cooled to ambient temperatures, the weight of the sample was recorded. In order to ensure sufficient air during oxidation process, a hole was drilled in the muffle furnace. The oxidation weight loss percentage of the coated graphite spheres $\Delta m_t$ was calculated determined by using Eq. 1.

$$\Delta m_t = \frac{m_t - m_o}{m_0} x\ 100\% \quad (1)$$

where $m_t$ and $m_0$ denote the weight of the coated graphite spheres after the oxidation for t h and the original weight of the coated sample, respectively.

## 3. Results and discussion

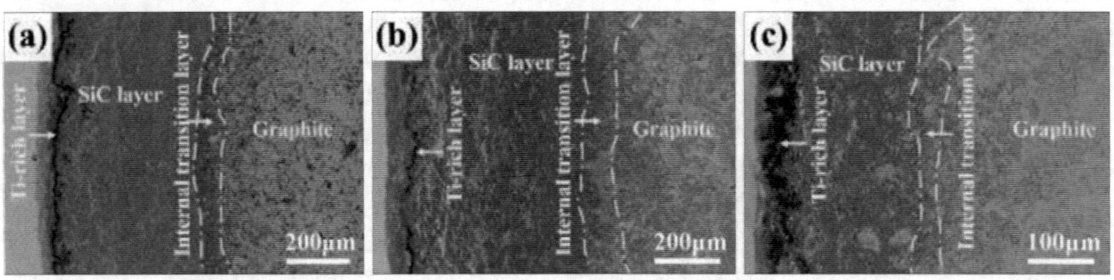


**Figure 2.** The fracture cross of the composite coating prepared with different Ti contents (a) 0.6 g, (b) 1.2 g, (c) 2.4 g.

Fig. 2 presents the cross-section morphologies of the mentioned composites coating. The thickness of the mentioned coatings is around 500~600 μm. Regardless of the amount of Ti was added, the coating consists of three parts, the transition layer, the SiC layer and the Ti-rich layer. When the amount of Ti added was 0.6 g, the Ti-rich layer is significantly uniform with the thickness almost unchanged; when 1.2 g Ti was added, the thickness of the whole coating increased, the internal transition layer thickened, and the Ti-rich layer is discontinuous; the Ti-rich layer thickened, and the thickness was not uniform when 2.4 g Ti was added, and an obvious contrast was identified on this layer. The XRD patterns of different coatings are presented in Fig.3. The coating composition includes TSC, SiC and TiC when 0.6 g Ti was added. However, the coating composition included TSC, SiC, TiC, and Si when the content of Ti reached 1.2 g and 2.4 g. Thus, the Ti-rich layer in Fig. 2 is largely composed of TSC and TiC.

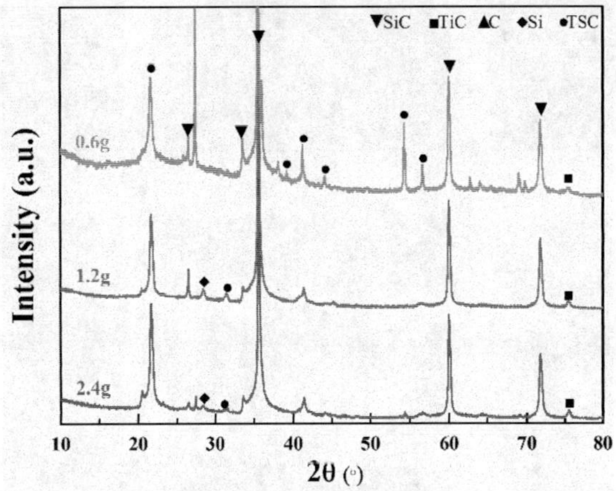


**Figure 3.** XRD patterns of the Ti-based composite coating.

The bonding strengths of the mentioned coatings and graphite were determined by performing the crushing test. The crushing strength of each the respective sample is illustrated in Fig. 4. TT1, T2 and T3 had the crushing strength of 1100.3 N, 1305.6 N, and 1247.3 N, respectively. In significant difference was reported in the crushing strength of the mentioned graphite spheres coated with different coatings. Accordingly, the Ti content was found to insignificantly affect the bonding strength of the mentioned coatings and graphite.

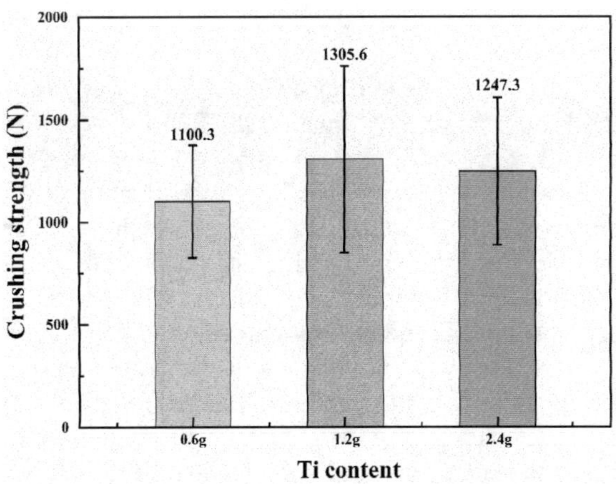


**Figure 4.** Crushing strength of these coatings prepared with different Ti content.

Fig. 5 presents the typical crushing mode and the breaking models of the mentioned coated graphite spheres. According to Fig. 5 (a), the T1-coated graphite spheres were broken in the middle during the crushing. The crack penetrated the graphite spheres via the Ti-rich layer, the SiC layer and the inner transition layer. No obvious crack was reported between different layers. After the crushing, the coating remained tightly bonded to the graphite spheres, which demonstrated a strong binding force between the coating and the graphite sphere. The crack passed through the entire coating area to the graphite sphere coated with T2. Subsequently, the mentioned cracks stretched in different directions over the graphite sphere till the whole graphite spheres failed. However, when T3-coated graphite spheres were being crushed, the cracks spread along the interface between the Ti-rich layer and the SiC layer, as well as the area close to the coating in graphite sphere. It was therefore suggested that the adhesion between different layers and that between the whole coating and the graphite sphere were very weak.

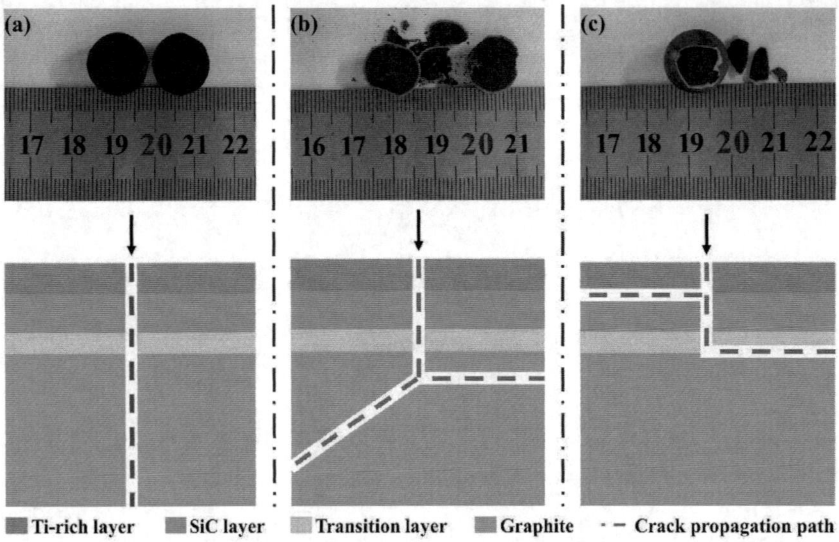


**Figure 5.** Typical crushing mode and fracture models of these coatings prepared with different Ti content: (a) 0.6g, (b) 1.2g, (c) 2.4g.

Given the oxidation experimental results at different times, Fig. 6 presents the weight change curve of different coated graphite spheres over time. After the mentioned spheres were oxidized for 50 h in air at 1773 K, the weight reduction of the graphite spheres coated with T1, T2, and T3 reached 0.33%, 0.35% and 0.42%, respectively. The oxidation of the mentioned coated graphite spheres could fall to three stages in line with the different oxidation rates. At the first stage, the weight reduction of the coated graphite spheres increased in a parabolic pattern in the first 4 h. The T2-coated graphite spheres achieved the fastest oxidation rate, the T1-coated graphite spheres had the slowest rate, and the T3-coated graphite spheres achieved the medium rate. After the oxidation at 1773 K for 4 h, the weight reduction of the graphite spheres coated with T1, T2, and T3 reached 0.067%, 0.099% and 0.073%, respectively.

In the second stage of the oxidation process, the weight change trend of the coated graphite sphere changes significantly. Compared with the parabolic behavior at the early phase of the oxidation, the linear oxidation behavior was identified after 4 h, which demonstrated that the oxidation mechanism of the coated graphite spheres was transformed. The oxidation rate of the T2 coated graphite spheres continued to be the fastest, and the T3 coated graphite spheres had the slowest rate. Moreover, the oxidation rate of all coated graphite spheres at this stage is the slowest during the whole oxidation.

At the third stage, the weight of the coated graphite spheres reduced sharply, which suggested that cracks might be generated in the coating. The weight of the T3-coated spheres decreased most rapidly. The weight variation curves of the coated graphite spheres first exhibited a parabolic dependence, while the curve displayed a linear correlation over time, which is consistent with the results of other studies [28, 29].

During the oxidation, the following reactions might occur:

$$Ti_3SiC_2 + 6O_2(g) \rightarrow 3TiO_2 + SiO_2 + 2CO_2(g) \quad (2)$$

$$TiC + 2O_2(g) \rightarrow SiO_2 + CO_2(g) \quad (3)$$

$$2Ti_3SiC_2+3TiC+18O_2(g) \rightarrow 9TiO_2+2SiO_2+7CO_2(g) \quad (4)$$

$$SiC+2O_2(g) \rightarrow SiO_2+CO_2(g) \quad (5)$$

$$Si+O_2(g) \rightarrow SiO_2 \quad (6)$$

As indicated from the calculation results, the oxidation of graphite caused the weight to decrease, while the oxidation of TSC, TiC, Si, and SiC caused the weight of the coated spheres to increase. The oxidation rates of TSC and TiC were higher than those of SiC, thereby showing a worse oxidation resistance [26]. During the oxidation, the mentioned reactions could occur spontaneously. The content of the respective phase is different in different coatings, thereby leading to different weight variations of the coated graphite spheres.

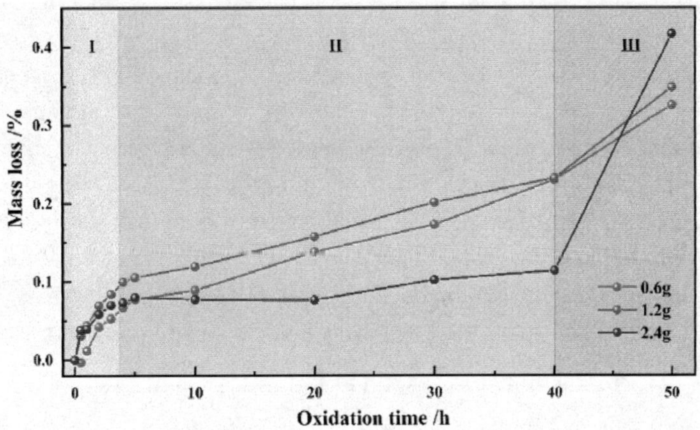


**Figure 6.** Weight gain curves of the isothermal oxidation tests at 1773 K in static air for Ti-based composite coated samples.

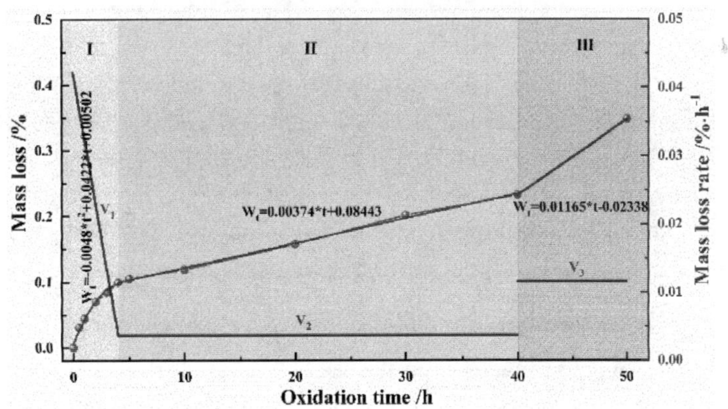


**Figure 7.** The mass change curve and the data fitting of the T2-coated graphite spheres.

Though Eq. 2-6 could result in an increase in the mass of the coated sample, the weight of the coated graphite spheres decreased during the oxidation. Since the mass lose curve of the $SiC/Si-TiC-Ti_3SiC_2$ composite coating samples prepared with different Ti additions displayed the identical trend, the coating prepared with 1.2 g Ti added is 1.2 g is selected in the study. The mass change curve of the graphite sphere covered by the $SiC/Si-TiC-Ti_3SiC_2$ composite coating is fitted in Origin, and the mass loss rate and mass loss rate of the sample are determined. The dynamic curve is plotted in Fig.7. As more clearly indicated from the fitting curve of T2 in the oxidation in Fig.7, the coating-coated sample exhibited a parabolic oxidation model at stage I and showed a linear oxidation model at stage II and III.

At stage I, the mass loss rate $W_t$ of the graphite sphere covered with T2 is defined as:

$$W_t = -0.0048 \cdot t^2 + 0.0422 \cdot t + 0.00502(0 \le t \le 4\text{ h}) \tag{7}$$

The mass loss rate $V_I$ of the sample is expressed as:

$$V_I(\% \cdot h^{-1}) = -0.0096 \cdot t + 0.0422 \tag{8}$$

At stage I (0 ~ 4 h), the mass of the sample decreased in a parabolic trend over the oxidation time, and the mass loss rate of the sample is the fastest such a period. There is a layer of white substance on the surface of the sample after the oxidation, which is attributed to the escape of residual salt in the coating during the oxidation. Though the coating quickly reacted with the oxidizing gas at the beginning of the oxidation reaction, the mass increase rate of the sample is significantly high. However, the oxidizing gas could easily diffuse via the original pores and cracks in the coating to the graphite sphere within the coating.

Due to the oxidation mass loss of graphite sphere and the escape of residual salt, the mass of the sample would decrease. Since there is insignificant cracking on the coating surface, the mass loss caused by the oxidation of the internal graphite sphere is limited. On the whole, the mass loss of the coated graphite sphere is mainly attributed to the volatilization of salt. Thus, the weight loss of the sample at this stage resulted from the oxidation, and the volatilization of residual NaCl and KCl in the coating would cause the weight of the coated sample to decrease. Over time, the weight loss rate of the sample decreased linearly, from 0.0422%·$h^{-1}$ at the beginning to 0.0038%·$h^{-1}$.

At stage II, the mass loss rate $W_t$ of the graphite sphere covered by T2 is expressed as:

$$W_t = 0.00374 \cdot t + 0.08443\ (4 \le t \le 40\text{ h}) \tag{9}$$

The mass loss rate $V_{II}$ of the sample is defined as:

$$V_{II}(\% \cdot h^{-1}) = 0.00374 \tag{10}$$

At stage II (4~40 h), the oxidation weight loss rate of the sample remained unchanged at 0.00374%·$h^{-1}$, which was an order of magnitude lower than the oxidation rate at stage I. At this stage, there are two reasons for the decrease in the mass loss rate of the sample: the residual salt in the coating was basically volatilized at the first stage, and there is no sample weight loss caused by salt escape; at stage I, the oxide layer formed by the oxidation of Si, SiC, TiC and TSC aimed to isolate the oxidizing gas. The diffusion of the oxidizing gas into the coating is limited, and the oxidation loss of the internal graphite sphere is reduced, thereby reducing reduces the oxidation rate of the sample.

At stage III, the mass loss rate $W_t$ of the coated graphite sphere is defined as:

$$W_t = 0.01165 \cdot t - 0.02338(40 \le t \le 50\text{ h}) \tag{11}$$

The mass loss rate $V_{III}$ of the sample is expressed as:

$$V_{III}(\% \cdot h^{-1}) = 0.01165 \tag{12}$$

However, at stage III (40~50 h), the oxidation mass loss rate of the sample increased again, and the mass of the sample further dropped significantly. The mass loss rate of the sample reached over 0.01%·$h^{-1}$. After 40 h of the oxidation, the residual salt in the coating is basically volatilized. Accordingly, the degradation of the T2 coated graphite spheres at stage III is largely attributed to the oxidation of the graphite spheres within the coating. It was therefore suggested that during this process, a certain number of cracks are produced in the coating and its surface oxide layer, and the graphite sphere within the coating would be rapidly oxidized. Besides the difference in CTE between the oxide layer and the coating, the escape of residual salt at stage I could be another vital factor in the formation of cracks on the coating surface. At this stage, the coating would quickly fail, and the coating would lose its oxidation resistance.

During the oxidation, the oxidation of TSC, TiC, Si and SiC would increase the weight of the coated samples, while it failed to offset the decrease in the weight of the samples. There are two reasons for the deterioration of the sample weight, one is the volatilization of residual salt in the coating. Though the coating was repeatedly cleaned after the preparation, a certain amount of residual salt remained in the coating. Since the oxidation is performed at a high temperature of 1500°C, higher than the melting point of the salt, the salt gradually evaporated, thereby reducing the weight of the sample. The other is that the coating prepared in the study is not dense, and there are a certain number of defects in the coating, so the oxidizing gas could diffuse to the inner graphite spheres, thereby causing the weight of the sample to decrease. The reasons for the defects in the coating are presented below. First, the molten salt technique was adopted in Ar atmosphere, and the presence of the atmosphere caused the prepared coating to be relatively loose and porous. The second is the intrinsic defect of the molten salt technique. When the coating was being formed, the Ti element should diffuse into the loose SiC layer under the action of the molten salt, so the salt took up considerable space in the coating. In the cleaning process after the coating preparation, the salt in the coating was gradually dissolved in the water. After the salt is dissolved, numerous holes would be generated in the coating, and the volatilization of the residual salt at the early stage of the oxidation would produce more defects in the coating. Thus, the coating prepared by the molten salt technique is not dense. In addition, due to the difference in CTE between different phases in the coating, more cracks are generated in the coating. Accordingly, the oxidizing gas could enter the coating through the mentioned cracks and holes, and oxidize with the graphite sphere.

Thus, the mass loss of SiC/Si-TiC-$Ti_3SiC_2$ composite coating coated graphite spheres at the early stage of the oxidation is mainly caused by the volatilization of residual salts. During the oxidation, TSC, TiC, Si and SiC phases are gradually oxidized to generate $TiO_2$ and $SiO_2$, which remedied some defects in the coating, so the intrusion of oxidizing gas could be effectively blocked, and the weight of the coated samples could increase. Accordingly, at the second stage of the oxidation, the mass loss rate of the coating-coated graphite sphere gradually decreased. The difference in CTE between the oxide layer and the coating, as well as the volatilization of the residual salt in the early stage of the oxidation, led to the generation of increasing cracks and pores in the coating, and the oxidizing gas is more easily diffused into the coating until the coating completely failed. Thus, in the third stage of the oxidation, after 40 h of the oxidation at 1500°C, the mass loss of the coated graphite spheres increased sharply and the coating failed.

## 4. Conclusions

A $Ti_3SiC_2$-TiC-Si composite coating was synthesized with the molten salt technique on the surface of SiC-coated graphite spheres of the HTR fuel element with different Ti contents. The microstructure, composition, and anti-oxidation properties of the mentioned composite coatings were investigated. The composite coating consisted of an internal transition layer, an intermediate layer of SiC and a Ti-rich outermost layer. The coating composition comprised TSC, SiC, and TiC when the addition of Ti is 0.6 g during the coating preparation; while when the content of Ti are 1.2 g and 2.4 g, the coating consists of TSC, SiC, TiC, and Si. The oxidation tests revealed that the T1 coated graphite spheres showed the optimal oxidation resistance, and the weight reduction of the coated graphite spheres is only 0.33% after the oxidation in static air at 1773 K for 50 h. The T3-coated graphite spheres exhibited the worst anti-oxidation property, and the anti-oxidation property exhibited by T2 coated graphite spheres is in the middle. The weight variation curves of all the coated graphite sphere displayed a parabolic dependence initially, while the curve exhibited a linear correlation at longer times. The mentioned results suggested Ti-based composites coating as a type of anti-oxidation coating system worth studying.

**Acknowledgments**

This paper supported by the National S&T Major Project of China (ZX06901) and the National Natural Science Foundation of China (21671116).

**References**

[1] H.S. Zhao, T.X. Liang, J. Zhang, J. He, Y.W. Zou, C.H. Tang, Manufacture and characteristics of spherical fuel elements for the HTR-10, Nuclear Engineering and Design, 236, 643, 2006.

[2] K. Shen, Z.H. Huang, K.X. Hu, W.C. Shen, S.Y. Yu, J.H. Yang, G.Z. Yang, F.Y. Kang, Advantages of natural microcrystalline graphite filler over petroleum coke in isotropic graphite preparation, Carbon, 90, 197, 2015.

[3] X.L. Yu, L. Brissonneau, C. Bourdeloie, S.Y. Yu, The modeling of graphite oxidation behavior for HTGR fuel coolant channels under normal operating conditions, Nuclear Engineering and Design, 238, 2230, 2008.

[4] W.H. Huang, S.C. Tsai, I.C. Chiu, C.H. Chen, J.J. Kai, The oxidation effects of nuclear graphite during air-ingress accidents in HTGR, Nuclear Engineering and Design, 271, 270, 2014.

[5] Z.Q. Fu, T.X. Liang, J.C. Robin, C.H. Tang, The stability of SiC coating and $SiO_2$/SiC multilayer on the surface of graphite for HTGRs at normal service condition, Applied Surface Science, 240, 349, 2005.

[6] C. Sun, H.J. Li, Q.G. Fu, J.P. Zhang, H. Peng, Double SiC coating on carbon/carbon composites against oxidation by a two-step method, Transactions of Nonferrous Metals Society of China, 23, 2107, 2013.

[7] D.J. Y, H.J. Li, H. Wu, Q.G. Fu, X.F. Qiang, Ablation resistance of ZrC/SiC gradient coating for SiC-coated carbon/carbon composites prepared by supersonic plasma spraying, Journal of the European Ceramic Society, 36, 3739, 2016.

[8] X. Yang, Q.Z. Huang, Y.H. Zou, X. Chang, Z.A. Su, M.Y. Zhang, Z.Y. Xie, Anti-oxidation behavior of chemical vapor reaction SiC coatings on different carbon materials at high temperatures, Transactions of Nonferrous Metals Society of China, 19, 1044, 2009.

[9] B. Zhang, J.F. Huang, H.B. Ouyang, L.Y. Cao, C.Y. Li, A mullite oxidation protective coating on SiC coated carbon/carbon composites by hot dipping, Ceramics International, 42, 17932, 2016.

[10] X.Y. Yao, H.J. Li, Y.L. Zhang, H. Wu, X.F. Qiang, A SiC-Si-$ZrB_2$ multiphase oxidation protective ceramic coating for SiC-coated carbon/carbon composites, Ceramics International, 38, 2095, 2012.

[11] Q.G. Fu, H.J. Li, X.H. Shi, K.Z. Li, J. Wei, M. Huang, Oxidation protective glass coating for SiC coated carbon/carbon composites for application at 1773 K, Materials Letters, 60, 431, 2006.

[12] Z.Q. Fu, C.B. Wang, C.H. Tang, H.S. Zhao, J.C. Robin, Oxidation behaviors of $SiO_2$/SiC coated matrix graphite of high temperature gas-cooled reactor fuel element, Nuclear Engineering and Design, 265, 867, 2013.

[13] J.F. Huang, X.R. Zeng, H.J. Li, X.B. Xiong, G.L. Sun, $ZrO_2$-$SiO_2$ gradient multilayer oxidation protective coating for SiC coated carbon/carbon composites, Surface & Coatings Technology, 190, 255, 2005.

[14] T. Feng, H.J. Li, Q.G. Fu, X.T. Shen, H. Wu, Microstructure and oxidation of multi-layer $MoSi_2$-$CrSi_2$-Si coatings for SiC coated carbon/carbon composites, Corrosion Science, 52, 3011, 2010.

[15] H.J. Li, H. Xue, Y.J. Wang, Q.G. Fu, D.J. Yao, A $MoSi_2$-SiC-Si oxidation protective coating for carbon/carbon composites, Surface & Coatings Technology, 201, 9444, 2007.

[16] Q.G. Fu, J.P. Zhang, Z.Z. Zhang, H.J. Li, C. Sun, SiC-$MoSi_2$/$ZrO_2$-$MoSi_2$ coating to protect C/C composites against oxidation, Transactions of Nonferrous Metals Society of China, 23, 2113, 2013.

[17] Y. Long, A. Javed, J. Chen, Z.K. Chen, X. Xiong, Phase composition, microstructure and mechanical properties of ZrC coatings produced by chemical vapor deposition, Ceramics International, 40, 707, 2014.

[18] L. Li, H.J. Li, Y.Y. Li, X.M. Yin, Q.L. Shen, Q.G. Fu, A SiC-$ZrB_2$-ZrC coating toughened by electrophoretically-deposited SiC nanowires to protect C/C composites against thermal shock and oxidation, Applied Surface Science, 349, 465, 2015.

[19] Y.J. Wang, H.J. Li, Q.G. Fu, H. Wu, D.J. Yao, H.L. Li, SiC/HfC/SiC ablation resistant coating

for carbon/carbon composites, Surface & Coatings Technology, 206, 3883, 2012.
[20] J.C. Ren, Y.L. Zhang, Y.Q. Fu, J. Zhang, Influence of HfC nanowires on the growth behavior, microstructure and ablation resistance of CVD-HfC coating, Ceramics International, 45, 5321, 2019.
[21] D.J. Tallman, L.F. He, B.L. Garcia-Diaz, E.N. Hoffman, G. Kohse, R.L. Sindelar, M.W. Barsoum, Effect of neutron irradiation on defect evolution in $Ti_3SiC_2$ and $Ti_2AlC$, Journal of Nuclear Materials, 468, 194, 2016.
[22] D.J. Tallman, E.N. Hoffman, E.N. Caspi, B.L. Garcia-Diaz, G. Kohse, R.L. Sindelar, M.W. Barsoum, Effect of neutron irradiation on select MAX phases, Acta Materialia, 85, 132, 2015.
[23] Z.M. Sun, Progress in research and development on MAX phases: a family of layered ternary compounds, International Materials Reviews, 56, 143, 2013.
[24] X.H. Wang, Y.C. Zhou, Oxidation behavior of $Ti_3AlC_2$ at 1000-1400°C in air, Corrosion Science, 45, 891, 2003.
[25] J.H. Ko, S.S. Hwang, S.W. Park, D.B. Lee, High temperature oxidation behavior of $Ti_3SiC_2$ in air, Materials Science Forum, 486-487, 97, 2005.
[26] X.M. Fan, X.W. Yin, Y.Z. Ma, L.T. Zhang, L.F. Cheng, Oxidation behavior of C/SiC-$Ti_3SiC_2$ at 800-1300°C in air, Journal of the European Ceramic Society, 36, 2427, 2016.
[27] Q.S. Zhu, X.L. Qiu, C.W. Ma, The oxidation resistance improvement of matrix graphite of spherical fuel elements by slip-gelation process, Journal of Nuclear Materials, 254, 221, 1998.
[28] R. Radhakrishnan, J.J. Williams, M. Akinc, Synthesis and high-temperature stability of $Ti_3SiC_2$, Journal of Alloys and Compounds, 285, 85, 1999.
[29] M.W. Barsoum, L.H.H. Duc, M. Radovic, T.E. Raghy, Long time oxidation study of $Ti_3SiC_2$, $Ti_3SiC_2$/SiC, and $Ti_3SiC_2$/TiC composites in air, Journal of The Electrochemical Society, 150, B166, 2003.

# Capability of Indonesian Hot cell Towards Pebble Bed Post Irradiation Examination

**J Setiawan[1,2], S Ismarwanti[1], A Paid[1], H F Rahmatullah[1], R Sigit[1] and M K Ajiriyanto[1]**

[1] Center for Nuclear Fuel Technology, BATAN, Kawasan PUSPIPTEK Building 20, Tangerang Selatan, Banten, Indonesia
[2] Electrical Engineering, Pamulang University, Jl. Surya Kencana No.1, Pamulang, Tangerang Selatan, Banten, Indonesia.

E-mail: jansetiawan@batan.go.id

**Abstract.** Post irradiation examination is one of the requirements to obtain licensing of nuclear fuel, and the purpose of this activity is to represent the performance of nuclear fuel itself. Currently, Indonesia is developing the 10 MWth high-temperature reactor type with its fuel in the form of pebble bed. Indonesia has a hot cell installation that has a function to do post-irradiated examinations. This hot cell mainly used for plate and rod type fuel. This paper wants to show this installation capability to perform the post-irradiation examinations based on its documents and current status. We also show the future possibility of performing pebble bed post-irradiation examinations. The hot cell installation in Indonesia, mainly divided into two areas. First areas are to perform the examinations in the intact form of fuel and second areas are to perform in the small specimen of fuel. For the future pebble bed examinations, Indonesian hot cell structure is possible to perform these examinations. These examinations are possible with limiting amount and stay time of fuel inside the hot cell. The current status gap with requirements for pebble bed tests such as handling tool, deconsolidation apparatus, simulation accident test apparatus also is described.

## 1. Introduction

Indonesia is developing an Experimental Power Reactor (RDE) 10 MWth, which is a type of high-temperature reactor (HTR) [1]. This reactor should generate equal to 3 MWe [2]. Design of this reactor will be operated at 700 °C [3], higher than commercial reactor that operated at 320 °C. Research on coated particle already starts since the 1950s in the United States and Europe for High-Temperature Gas-cooled Reactor (HTGR) program [4]. The reactor designs for HTR based on their fuel are the pebble bed reactor and prismatic-block gas-cooled reactor. Indonesian RDE's design will use pebble bed fuel. The pebble bed fuel consists of the coated particles that disperse in the graphite pebble. For future self-sustainability of RDE's fuel, a research program in Indonesia, in this case, is BATAN massively started since 2014. This research program, necessary to irradiation program and post-irradiation examination (PIE), also arises. Indonesia has a facility to do PIE, that takes place on Radio-metallurgy Installation (RMI). The RMI facility contains hot cell to perform the PIE on nuclear fuel and its structural components. In this paper, the RMI hot cell's readiness and the gap will describe.

## 2. RMI hot cell facility overview

RMI is one facility under the Center for Nuclear Fuel Technology (CNFT/PTBBN) management in BATAN. This facility was built in 1991 and commissioning in 1992 from German Consortium Nuclear Facility (GCNF). The layout of the RMI laboratory showed in Figure 1.

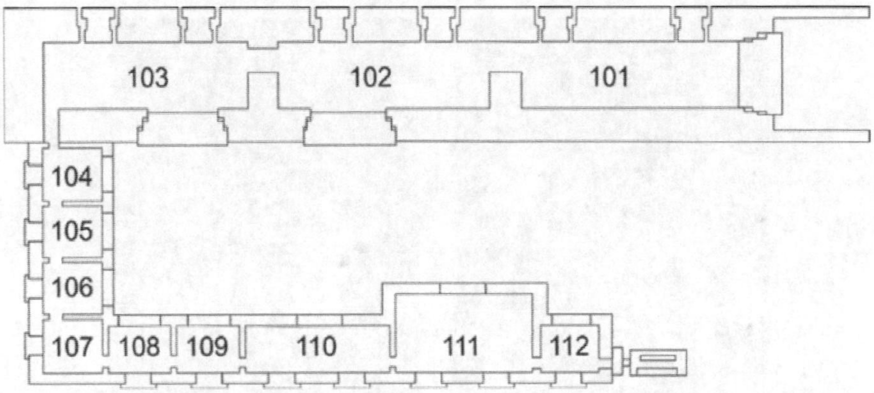


**Figure 1**. Layout of Hot cell in RMI laboratory (+0.00 m).

Figure 1 showed the layout of the laboratory and the hot cell in RMI. The hot cell itself denoted by number 101, 102, 103 through 112. Each cell consists of two manipulators and Pb glass window/s. Equipment's and task to be done in a cell is very specific. Mainly, the hot cell structure type distinguishes into two sections. The first section is the structure of the cells made by high-density concrete. These cells denote by 101, 102 and 103. The concrete density is 3.6 g/cm3, with a thickness of 110 cm. The second section is the structure of the cells made by steel, and these cells denote by 104 through 112. The steel cells density is 7.8 g/cm3 with thickness 70 cm. Each cell capability describes as follows:

*2.1. Hot cell 101*

Design of the cell 101 structure is high-density concrete that purposes for radiation shielding. This cell meant to be receiving cell for irradiated fuel, in the cell equipped by fuel element rack for plate type and welding machine. Inside of this hot cell showed in Figure 2.

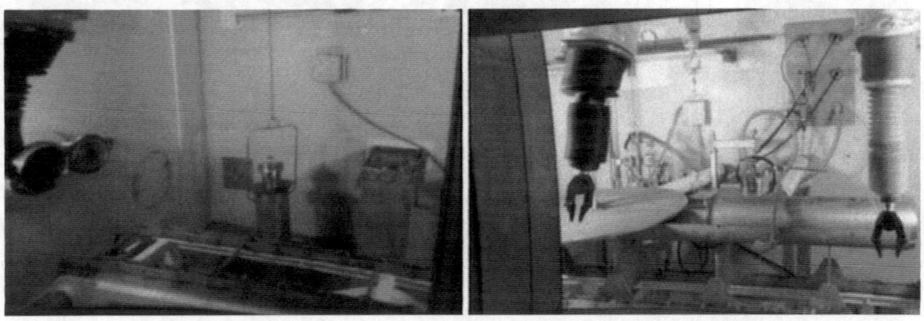

(a) (b)

**Figure 2.** (a) Receiving cell 101 and (b) It is the supporting system.

*2.2. Hot cell 102*

Cell 102 as showed in Figure 3, designed for dismantling and a visual inspection of the fuel element. Beside two manipulators, also equipped by power manipulator in order to handling material with high load. This power manipulator can move to cell 103 vice versa. Equipment in this cell is dismantling machine fuel element for plate type and cutting machine for fuel rod. Outside the hot cell, there is a periscope to enlarge the view inside the cell. At present, equipment for dismantling machine is changed into cutting machine for single fuel plate. Another task in this cell is waste extracting to the outside of the hot cell through Drum Lifting Device (DLD) to ZG 001 at -5.50 m. This DLD system recently repaired.

Journal of Physics: Conference Series **2048** (2021) 012015 doi:10.1088/1742-6596/2048/1/012015

(a) (b)

**Figure 3.** (a) Cell 102 and (b) ZG 001 Drum Lifting Device system.

*2.3. Hot cell 103*

Cell 103 designed for physical test for fuel plate or fuel rod. This cell showed in Figure 4. In this cell, physical tests are Gamma spectrometer, X-ray radiography, leak test device, laser puncturing for gas sampling, fuel rod welding, and measurement bench. Inside the cell 103 as shown in Figure 4, the ultrasonic test (UT), and X-Ray radiography are available.

(a) (b) (c)

**Figure 4.** Equipment's in cell 103 (a) Gamma spectrometer; (b) Ultrasonic test; and (c) X-ray radiography.

*2.4. Hot cell 104 through 107*

Cell 104 through Cell 107 designed to conduct the metallography process until observation in the optical microscope. The cell 104 equipped with a small cutting machine, grinder, ultrasonic cleaner and vacuum impregnation. Inside the cell 105 equipped with grinder and polisher. For, the cell 106 equipped with by the polisher, ultrasonic cleaner, electrolytic etching and desiccator. Each of these cells also is equipped by storage rack for the specimen. At present, these cells are well operated. Cell 107 equipped with by optical microscope and also designed for microhardness. At present this microhardness still in the under repair.

*2.5. Hot cell 108 and 109*

Cell 108 and cell 109 are showed in Figure 6. These cells are designed for chemistry analysis. Cell 108 designed for physical chemistry equipped with analytical balance, desiccator, thermography metric furnace, and deposition plate. For cell 109 designed for wet chemistry analysis, it equipped with support plate thermostat, rabbit station, and laboratory balance. The rabbit station is designed for transfers sample into a glove box in the laboratory area R.135.

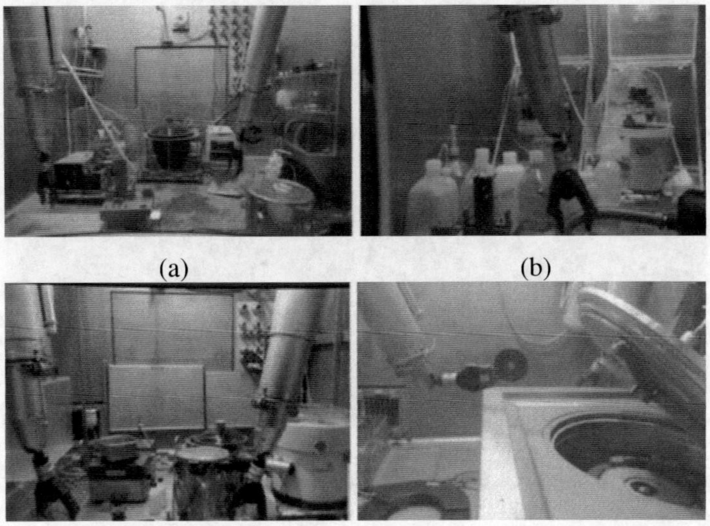

(a) (b)

(c) (d)

**Figure 5.** Ceramography and metallography cell, started by (a) cutting process in cell 104; (b) grinding and polishing in cell 105; (c) interim storage for microstructure testing specimen in cell 106 and (d) microstructure observation by optical microscope in cell 107.

(a) (b)

**Figure 6.** (a) thermogravimetry apparatus in cell 108 and (b) wet chemistry analysis apparatus in cell 109.

*2.6. Hot cell 110 and 111*

The mechanical test carried out inside the cell 110 and cell 110 as showed in Figure 7. Cell 110 equipped with Low Cycle Fatigue (LCF) machine, tensile creep machine, burst test machine and annealing furnace. At present, cell 110 not fully used. The cell 111 are equipped with the tensile machine, impact test machine, macrohardness tester and blister test equipment. At present, the macrohardness and tensile test are actively for aluminum cladding testing irradiated in G.A Siwabessy Reactor.

*2.7. Hot cell 112*

Cell 112 designed for SEM/TEM Specimen preparation showed in Figure 8. This cell equipped with microhardness Vickers test machine, sputtering device, ultrasonic cleaner and storage rack.

Fuel element inside the hot cell is transferred from cell 101 to 102 using transport carriage (rolled conveyor) and from 102 to 103 using transport trolley vice versa. For specimen transfer to the steel-cell is using conveyor line. Conveyor line II (two) serve the specimen transfer from cell 103 through cell 107. For specimen transfer from cell 107 through cell 112 is using conveyor line I (one).

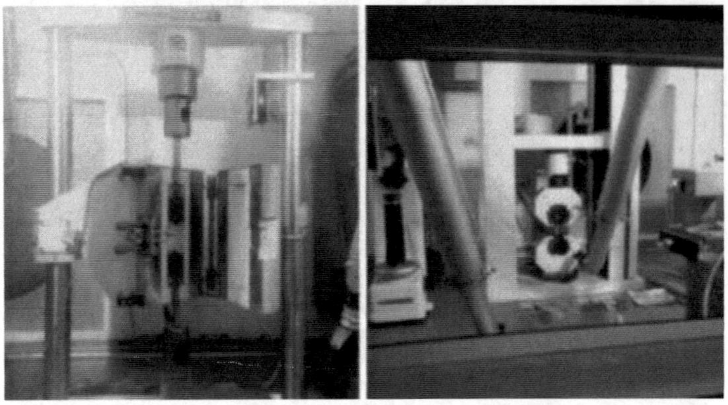

(a) (b)

**Figure 7.** (a) One of the test equipment in cell 110, creep test apparatus, and (b) macrohardness, tensile test and blister test apparatus in cell 111.

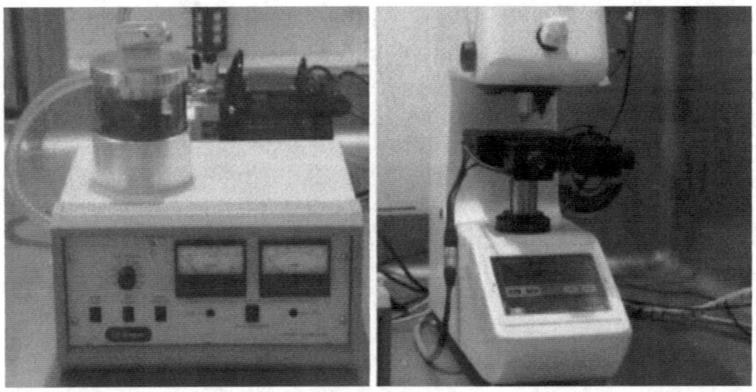

(a) (b)

**Figure 8.** (a) Sputtering device, and (b) microhardness test machine, inside cell 112.

## 3. RMI post irradiation examination program

During all this time, IRM hot cells' activities were conduct PIE of U3O8-Al, U3Si2-Al fuel plate type and pin dummy of PWR fuel. Another activity was the development of LEU foil target for Molybdenum-99 production during the period 1995 until 2009. Activity for PIE fuel plate in RMI showed as follows in Figure 9.

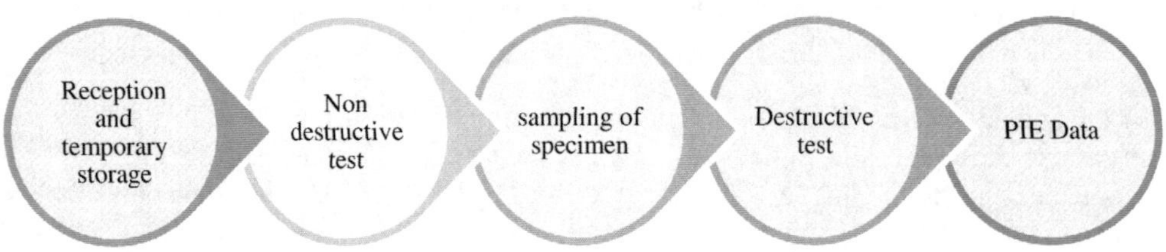


**Figure 9.** Flows of PIE activity for fuel plate in RMI.

The irradiated fuel plate received at cell 101. The irradiated fuel plate could be transferred from the reactor using transfer cask/container or through transfer channel connected to the G.A Siwabessy reactor. The first step of the examination is the non-destructive test. This test is about visual inspection, dimension measurement and the gamma scanning. A sampling of specimens was chosen based on the standard position of sampling at the top, middle and bottom positions. It is also chosen at the place where the anomalies occurred. The specimen's destructive test then continued to start from metallography and ceramography, O/U ratio, fissile product analysis, burn-up analysis, and fissile product into cladding analysis. All of this data, collected as PIE data of nuclear fuel plate, was analyzed as feedback for quality improvement in the production process and used for feasibility analysis of nuclear fuel for use in the reactor. All of the radioactive waste produced in RMI was not stored permanently in RMI. These radioactive wastes sent to the Center for Radioactive Waste Technology (CRWT/PTLR).

## 4. Pebble bed post irradiation examination in RMI

The pebble bed fuel to do the examination shows several differences in examination process due to different dimension and material characteristic of fuel. Learn from the US, Europe (especially Germany), Japan and China. There are several examinations which should be done as follows [5,6].

Dimension measurement is needed to examine the dimensional comparison changes before and after irradiation such as measurement for diameter fuel sphere and measurement sphericity of pebble bed. From these two measurements can get supporting data about quality control for the fabrication process [7]. This measurement was chosen based on the structure of the hot cell own by RMI. The dimension measurement tools will be placed in hot cell 102, as hot cell after the reception so only large-scale measurement can be performed.

The visual inspection is the standard of inspection with the non-destructive testing method. It is the process of looking over a piece of equipment using the naked eye or with help from an optical tool to look for flaws. Visual inspection for pebble bed will be conducted in hot cell 102, and the operator takes a look from the operating area through glass lead hot cell.

Weighting measurement used to weight the sample in this case pebble bed. The results of this weighing will be useful for calculating burn-up from fuel. It can be done both at hot cell 102 after dismantling the fuel for a destructive test or being done at metallographic and physicochemical.

X-ray radiography test is useful for examining the material's structure and quality with a non-destructive test using x-rays radiographic sources. Examination on structure and quality material of pebble bed is to determine whether there is an effect of radiation in the reactor for determining the reliability of pebble bed. The most important observation on pebble beds using x-ray radiography is to determine the thickness consistency of each layer of pebble bed and irradiation behavior the pebble bed, and it is Tristructural Isotropic (TRISO) particle [8-10].

Gamma analyzer used to analyze radioactive substances that emit gamma radiation. One of the tools that can be used is gamma spectroscopy to analyze it. Reactor fuel, in this case, is the pebble bed that has been irradiated in the reactor will experience a chain fission reaction, after being irradiated there is a split product from fission reaction which is then analyzed by gamma analyzer for being scanning to an obtained indicator of burn-up distribution.

Deconsolidation is the process of separating loose particle from pebble bed, in other words, to separate the kernel from the graphite matrix. This process is needed in post-irradiation testing. Graphite particles separated from the kernel can be tested for analysis of burn-up factors and kernel can be moved for further testing after non-destructive testing.

Ceramography is the science of ceramics microstructure preparation, examination and evaluation. This technique is one of the methods used in destructive testing after going through non-destructive testing in the previous tests, where when the non-destructive test is carried out to determine the location of the sample points indicates as defect then it will be further proven by ceramography testing. Ceramography testing is an observation of microstructures such as grain size, secondary phase, grain boundaries, pores, micro-cracks, and microhardness. Ceramography is usually reserved for high-performance ceramic materials, so selecting ceramography techniques for testing damaging pebble beds can be used more optimally.

Microstructure analysis is carried out to compare the pebble bed's microstructure from the irradiation with the pre-irradiation. Using a microstructure lens with bigger magnification to analyze it by comparing the microstructure results from pre-irradiation to post-irradiation material [11]. From this microstructure, analysis treatment can later be known if defects occur due to the irradiation process and can be known phases formed from the irradiation process.

The accident simulation test is a series of simulation tests to determine the condition of pebble bed when it is on abnormal condition. An abnormal condition referred to here is by conducting high temperature to pebble bed. After pebble bed is irradiated up to 7th phase, then an accident test will be conducted to determine the effect on the pebble bed when given a high temperature.

These nine examinations are seeming mandatory to obtain minimum PIE data. Not limited to these examinations, many tests should be done in order to obtain comprehensive PIE data. For the future PIE program in RMI based on the existing facility, we do the conceptual design for its needed. The examinations for pebble bed fuel based on existing facility described in Figure 10.

The gap on equipment that should be conducted for PIE on pebble bed with currently existing equipment's described as follows,

Capsule for irradiating the pebble bed in the reactor serves as a fuel test container to be irradiated in the reactor. Making a new capsule as a container for pebble bed samples must be done to be irradiated in the reactor. The capsule itself is designed according to the character and dimensions of the sample pebble bed. The new design may be required to make changes to the existing capsule, which is the pin's fuel test capsule. It can use the same material that ever existed because it was proven to accommodate the fuel test type pin when irradiation takes place. The new design has to be done because the reactor itself has provided a Power Ramp Test Facility (PRFT). PRTF is an experimental facility outside the reactor core used for testing fuel power reactor.

The transfer cask for pebble bed and waste container are different from current existing. The existing transfer cask and waste container are used for fuel power reactor and MTR type. Transfer cask serves to move pebble bed that has been irradiated at the reactor to the RMI for post-irradiation testing. Removal of pebble bed from the reactor through transfer channel underground connected to hot cell 101 from RSG-GAS. New transfer cask needs to be made according to the pebble bed capsule and easy to handle using manipulators and handling during transfer through transfer channel.

The waste container is used for storage of spent fuel pebble bed or after sampling. The waste container must be made comfortable in handling by manipulator from the operating area. It can be made according to the dimension of the pebble bed. The waste container must be made so that it can reduce radiation exposure so that the remaining sample pebble bed from the test can be stored in temporary waste storage.

Manipulator clamp should be modified to suitable with pebble bed fuel, where the physical shape of pebble bed resembles a ball with diameter 6 cm, so suitable handling tools are needed. The existing manipulator clamps not suitable for it, because the clamp is flat. Therefore, it should be modified into a suitable clamp for handling the pebble bed. The clamp itself must be modified into concave shape so it can grip pebble bed tightly.

The handling tool for pebble bed fuel and coated particle should be specially designed. To handle pebble bed, especially for a coated particle, the dimension much smaller than the pebble bed and it is really hard to handle with manipulator clamp. Modification is done by adding a new tool that looks like a needle and its function to gather the coated particle using a pneumatic system. Tools that look like a needle used because it has a tiny hole in the edge. Furthermore, when the pneumatic system is on, it can suck the coated particle to stick in the edge of the needle to move easily.

Transfer container for pebble bed and coated particle should be specially designed. Transfer container for pebble bed and coated particle is needed to accommodate transfer between hot cells. The design should be unique, which means it must efficiently operate using a manipulator from the operating area. Including the cover can easily be opened-closed and there is a handgrip so a manipulator can easily move it.

Design of an apparatus for deconsolidation pebble bed is to obtain loose particle from pebble bed for further analysis and determine the distribution of solid fission and activation products in the matrix graphite. In other words, it can separate the kernel from the matrix graphite, and then the kernel can be moved to another test while the matrix graphite can be used to analyze fission and activation product from irradiation process. An apparatus for deconsolidation will be placed in the hot cell 102, dismantling the fuel cells. Therefore, it must be designed according to the dimension of space in hot cell 102.

Design an apparatus for accident simulation test used to analyze when pebble bed simulated under abnormal conditions. This tool will be placed in hot cell 103, which is used for non-destructive testing. The accident simulation test is non-destructive because pebble bed, which has been irradiated until the seventh order, will be taken and transferred to RMI and put in this device. Accident simulation test that will be to conduct, such as high-temperature effect, aims to get data about the effect of a pebble bed under operated in the abnormal situation. Nevertheless, because it will place inside the hot cell 103, it needs to be designed to fit the space.

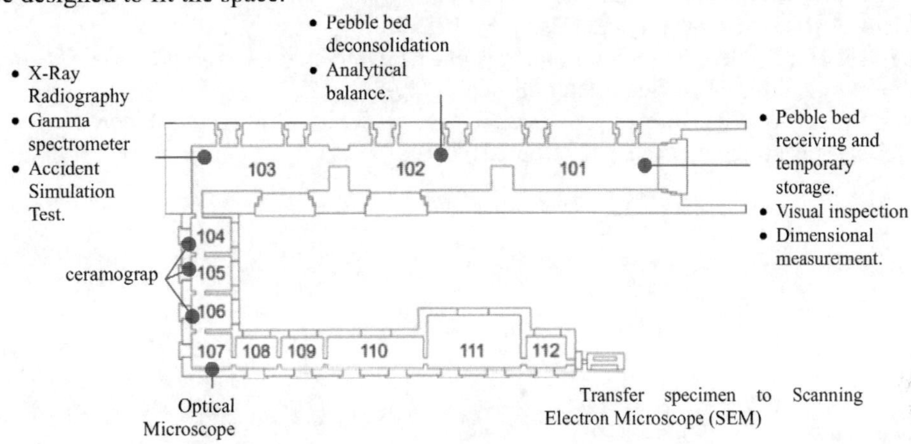


**Figure 10.** PIE route for pebble bed fuel PIE in RMI.

## 5. Final remarks

PIE for pebble bed is a big challenge for RMI. Preliminary information for the hot cell structure as primary radioactive shielding has met the criterion to confine and containment the pebble bed fuel. There is so much equipment to fulfil minimum PIE data used as feedback to nuclear fuel fabricator. In 2018 and 2019, RMI has been designing an additional apparatus for gripping TRISO and pebble bed, the container for transfer and used the existing X-ray radiograph to simulate non-destructive test for pebble bed fuel.

## Acknowledgments

Authors would like to thank the Ministry of Research, Technology and Higher Education of Indonesia for funding through INSINAS-Flagship program with contract number 04/INS-2/PPK/E4/2018. Thanks to the Head of Radiometallurgy Installation and the Head of Center for Nuclear Fuel Technology to support this research.

## References

[1] Taswanda T Ridwan Geni R S Meniek R 2018 *The Strategy to Support HTGR fuels for the 10 MW Indonesia's Experimental Power Reactor (RDE).* Urania Jurnal Ilmiah Daur bahan bakar Nuklir 24(1) pp 1-16.
[2] Helmi F R et al 2018 *Analysis of Irradiated Pebble Bed Fuel Transfer System in Hot Cell 101 Radiometallurgy Installation.* SENTEN 2018 Palembang
[3] Maman K A et al 2018 *Analisis Kesiapan Sistem Handling Fasilitas Hotcell 104 – 107 Instalasi Radiometalurgi Untuk Uji Pasca Iradiasi Bahan Bakar Reaktor Daya Eksperimental.* SENTEN 2018 Palembang
[4] Konings R 2011 *Comprehensive nuclear materials.* Elsevier
[5] Sawa K et al 2001 *Integrity confirmation tests and post-irradiation test plan of the HTTR first-loading fuel.* Journal of nuclear science and technology 38(6) pp 403-410

[6] Taowei Wang, H.Z., Gang Xu, Xiaotong Chen, Bing Liu, Chunhe Tang. *New Hot Cell Laboratory and Post Irradiation Examination Research Project on HTR Spherical Fuel Element in INET*. in Hot Lab Conference. 2016. Karlsruhe, Germany.

[7] Maurits C R H Sander G Jan A V 2017 *Comparison of Irradiation Behaviour of HTR Graphite Grades*. Journal of Nuclear Materials. 492: p. 148-156. 2017.

[8] Sri Ismarwanti et al 2020 *Performance Analysis of Digital X-Ray Radiography System in Radiometallurgy Installations for Pebble Bed Fuel Imaging* IOP Conf. Series: Journal of Physics 1436 012131

[9] Dong L Steven K Jon E Harold B Mark D Jan A V Robert O 2020 R, *X-ray Tomography Study on The Crushing Strength and Irradiation Behavior of Dedicated Tristructural Isotropic Nuclear Fuel Particles At 1000 °C* Material and Design 87 108382

[10] Lowe T et al 2015 *Microstructural analysis of TRISO particles using multi-scale X-ray computed tomography* Journal of Nuclear Materials 461 pp 29-36

[11] Ploger S A et al 2004 *Microscopic analysis of irradiated AGR-1 coated particle fuel compacts* Nuclear Engineering and Design, 271 pp 221-230

# Intensive Study of Ceria Microsphere Stabilized with Zirconia by The External Gelatin Method

**Ridwan, A Insani, Mujamilah, A Patriati, G T Sulungbudi, M Rifai, and Sarjono[1]**

National Atomic Energy Agency Center for Science and Advanced Material Technology, BATAN, Serpong, Indonesia,
[1] Center for Nuclear Fuel Technology, BATAN, Serpong, Indonesia
phone: +62-21-7562860, pstbm@batan.go.id

E-mail: ridwan@batan.go.id

**Abstract.** One of the keys to success in the process of fuel synthesis for pebble type high temperature nuclear reactors is mastery in kernel synthesis technology which is the core of the fuel itself. In this paper, the results of a comprehensive study of the preparation of a kernel microsphere from ceria stabilized zirconia (CSZ) using the external gelatin method in BATAN will be discussed. Important parameters obtained from this experiment will be the basis for the actual manufacturing of nuclear fuel kernels. Analysis based on measurement data using the Small Angle Neutron Spectrometer (SANS) provides a deep understanding of the mechanism of CSZ microsphere formation, so that at the end it can provide an understanding of how to avoid possible cracks during heat treatment.
Keywords: Kernel, Ceria stabilized Zirconia, Small Angle Neutron Scattering

## 1. Introduction

Fuel for gas-cooled high temperature nuclear reactors (HTGR) was researched and developed to support the operation of HTGR in the UK in 1956 and the simultaneous but independent operation of the 'pebble bed reactor' in Germany in 1967 [1]. The fuel consists of three layers of carbon and one ceramic based layer as a containment layer of fission products with a kernel core in the form of uranium oxide, or later known as TRISO. The initial challenge in the TRISO fuel manufacturing process is how to obtain a kernel with a uniform size, high density and free from cracks.

Based on various considerations, BATAN as a research institution in the field of nuclear technology in Indonesia has adopted a policy to explore the potential implementation of high temperature power reactors with helium gas coolers (Gas Cooled High Temperature Reactors, HTGR). The choice of HTGR was based on various considerations, apart from the main factors related to safety, and also efficiency in terms of heat exchange which was ultimately expected to support various aspects of industrial activities in Indonesia. The HTGR type chosen is the 'pebble bed' type with a TRISO-based fuel. The TRISO type fuel is the most advanced type of nuclear fuel at this time. The choice of TRISO-coated particles could reduce fission product release, extended burnup and higher fuel temperature applications [1].

Considering that in the future, Indonesia is expected to be able to meet HTGR fuel needs independently from within the country, so one of the activities in preparation for the first HTGR implementation in Indonesia is to prepare facilities to carry out research in the field of pebble fuel manufacturing processes. The research began with preparing the kernel using NUKEM technology-based facilities, Germany. The method used is an external gelation system. The mastery of manufacturing technology is carried out through intensive collaboration of several research centers within BATAN, namely the Center for Nuclear Fuel Technology (PTBBN) and the Center for Science and Technology of Advanced Materials (PSTBM).

Although research on Ceria stabilized Zirconia (CSZ) has been widely carried out, both aiming at developing biocompatible materials [2], as well as relating to the study of the development of high temperature nuclear fuel reactors. Systematic research to obtain uniform CSZ particle sizes with small deviations has been carried out by varying the broth flow velocity according to the nozzle size used in the dropping process. It was also found that microspheres with low Zr content were more oblique compared to high Zr concentrations, apart from that the measurement results also showed that the density increased with increasing Zr concentrations [3]. Another challenge in the synthesis of microspheres with the external gelatin method is size uniformity. Uniformity in size and shape is also an important parameter in obtaining high-quality nuclear fuel. The results showed that the uniformity of shapes of a certain size was greatly influenced by the large vibration vibrational frequencies that functioned for liquid jet breaking up into uniform droplets with a certain nozzle size. The optimal frequency is found to follow Raleigh's theory [4]. The microsphere formed is composed of crystallites with a size of about 200 micrometers.

As discussed in previous research, it has succeeded in providing a clear picture on the micrometer scale about the microsphere, however it has not yet discussed what happened from the early stage of the crystallization process. It has also been explained about several parameters that must be controlled to get the kernel (microsphere) with the external gelatin method as desired. However, by understanding the process of forming the microsphere from the formation of the crystallite core, it is hoped that the possibility of failure in the manufacturing process of nuclear fuel will be reduced. One method that can be used for characterization is the small angle scattering technique, both using x-rays or neutrons as probes. These two facilities, Small Angle X-ray Scattering (SAXS) and Small Angle Neutron Scattering (SANS) complement each other. SAXS can be used to see crystallite sizes in the range 0.1-0.2 nm, while SANS can see sizes up to micrometers [5,6]. Actually, with this facility it is very possible to follow the dynamics of phase growth related to changes in temperature or caused by other external influences both chemically and physically.

In this paper, intensive studies of the crystallization process of Ce-Zr surrogate-based kernels have been carried out using small-angle neutron scattering facilities located at the Center for Advanced Materials Technology, BATAN and also small-angle X-ray scattering installed in BL.3 in. SLRI, Thailand. The research is focused on understanding the mechanism of kernel formation, especially with regard to the phase transformation from the polymeric system to the ceramic system through the heat treatment process. The heat treatment in the formation of the kernel plays an important role, because with the right heat treatment can avoid cracking in the kernel. The neutron scattering technique can be used to understand how the agglomeration patterns of the polymer metal molecules are deformed by the heating process and then followed by the formation of the kernel crystallite core.

## 2. Experimental

### *2.1. Sample Preparation*

CSZ synthesis process with the external gelatin method, as has been discussed in many papers, starts with making broth which is the result of mixing a salt of $Z(NO_3)_4$ and a salt of $Ce(NO_3)_3$ which is dissolved in 250 ml of demineralized water and then while stirring heated at 80°C, so that a homogeneous solution is obtained. After part of the salt is completely dissolved, 8% PVA (Polyvinyl alcohol) and 50 ml THFA (Tetra Hydro Furfuryl Alcohol) are added to form the sol. The solution is stirred continuously until it reaches a pH of 2.67 and the viscosity is close to 60 mPa.s. The soles that have been formed are left in place for one night, so that the gas bubbles formed can come out perfectly. The preparation of the sol solution is in line with what has been done by Guogao W et.al [7].

The sol liquid that has been obtained is placed in a container that is ready to be dispersed with a nozzle inner diameter 1.0 mm and in this experiment the vibration frequency was setting follow Haas

[8], by regulating using a frequency generating facility [4]. To check whether the sol liquid dispersion rate through the nozzle is stable, a frequency-adjusted strobe light is used so that the sol is distributed in the form of a stable sphere. Schematically, it can be seen in Figure 1 a and 1 b. Like a gelatin external process, the liquid that comes out of the nozzle has passed through the passage of air flow, ammonia gas flow before falling into the gelatin column containing ammonia solution [9]. Gel that has been hardened on the outer skin in ammonia solution with a concentration of 3mol/l and allowed to stand for 2 hours, then separated with a sieve and then washed using 0.5 M $NH_4OH$ solution 2 times with an interval of aging 30 minutes, followed by washing using demineralized water six times and followed by washing using propylene glycol monomethyl ether (PGME) four times with an interval of soaking for 30 minutes.

After the systematic washing process is completed, the microsphere gel granules are then dried at 60°C for 12 hours using a Rotary Vacuum Evaporator. To ensure the kernel is free from water content, the drying process is continued at 120°C for 4 hours.

*2.2. Heat Treatment*

As explained earlier, the heat treatment process plays an important role in the formation of the kernel. Basically, it can be said that the formation of metallic kernels occurs through the deformation process of gelatin and is followed by the formation of crystallites of Ce and Zr oxides. The deformation process of the gelatin system can be clearly seen from the thermal analysis data using DTA, see Figure 1.

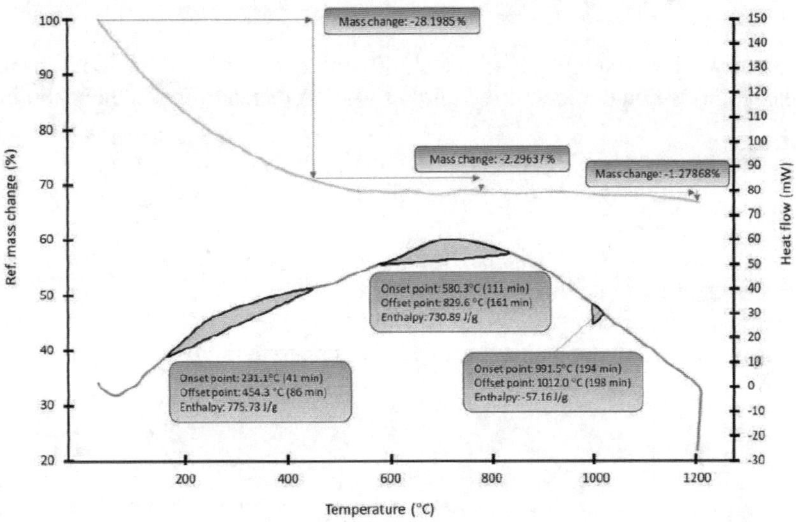


**Figure 1.** Thermal analysis data measured by DTA [10].

The thermal data measured by DTA is very important, as shown in Figure (above), there is a change in enthalpy and mass at 231°C due to the decomposition of organic materials that function as a matrix of the gelatin system, namely PVA (Poly vinyl alcohol) and THFA (tetra hydro furfuril alcohol). Therefore, from the effect of this decomposition, there was a significant reduction in the relative mass of 28.2%. The mass change in the second stage is very important, because at this stage the calcination process occurs. However, it must be admitted that the measured DTA data are not very detailed, because at around 400°C-500°C the-$Zr_2O_3$ [9] phase formation should be detected which is very much influenced by pH. To complete the thermal data, a series of measurements using FTIR has been carried out for a range of temperatures of 60, 120, 200, 400, 600, and 1200 °C, as shown in Figure 2. Based on this FTIR data, the decomposition mechanism of chemical compounds the gelatin process can be analyzed. As shown in Figure 2, at a temperature of 60-200 °C, the water evaporation process occurs and the OH group associated with the alcohol compound used in the gelatin synthesis also disappears, according to the wave numbers 1099 $cm^{-1}$, 2941 $cm^{-1}$ and 3258 $cm^{-1}$. Meanwhile, at a temperature of 400 °C, FTIR data.

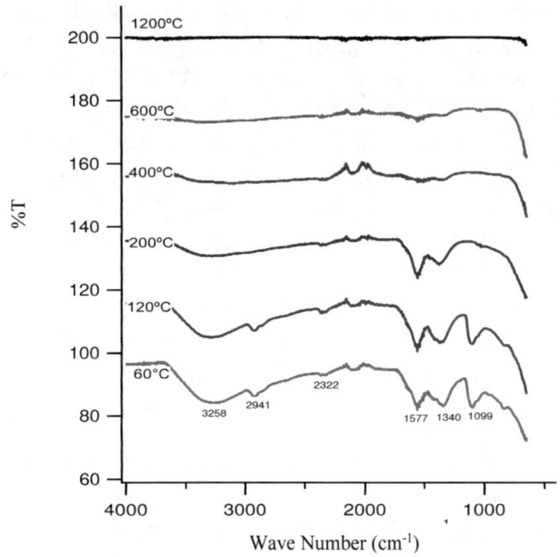


**Figure 2.** FTIR measurement data.

shows that the absorption wave numbers around 1340 $cm^{-1}$ and 1577 $cm^{-1}$ have not been detected, this is related to the decomposition process of the nitro (NO) group, according to the reaction:

$$(NH_4)_2ZrO_3\ (s) \dashrightarrow ZrO_2\ (s) + NO\ (g) + H_2O\ (g) \quad (1)$$
$$(NH_4)_2CeO_3\ (s) \dashrightarrow CeO_2\ (s) + NO\ (g) + H_2O\ (g) \quad (2)$$

So that at a temperature of 400 °C, the $\alpha$-$Zr_2O_3$ oxide compound began to form in accordance with the observations of very fine crystallites [2].

Based on the results of measurements with DTA and also analysis using FTIR, the CSZ system phase formation process is carried out according to the heating pattern as shown in Figure 3.

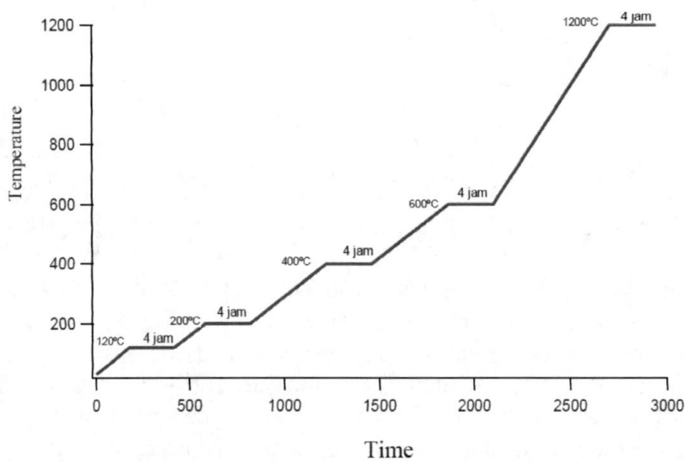


**Figure 3.** Diagram of heat treatment of CSZ

The heating process is carried out with a heating speed of 0.5°C/minute, by holding the temperature stable at 120, 200, 400, 600, and 1200 °C for 4 hours, with the aim of providing sufficient time for the decomposition process to occur perfectly.

## 3. Results and Discussion

Based on the heat treatment process, qualitatively the metal oxide formation phase system from the gelatin process by an external method can be evaluated. In Figure 4, it can be seen clearly the results of the heat treatment process of the microsphere according to the X-ray diffraction measurement data.

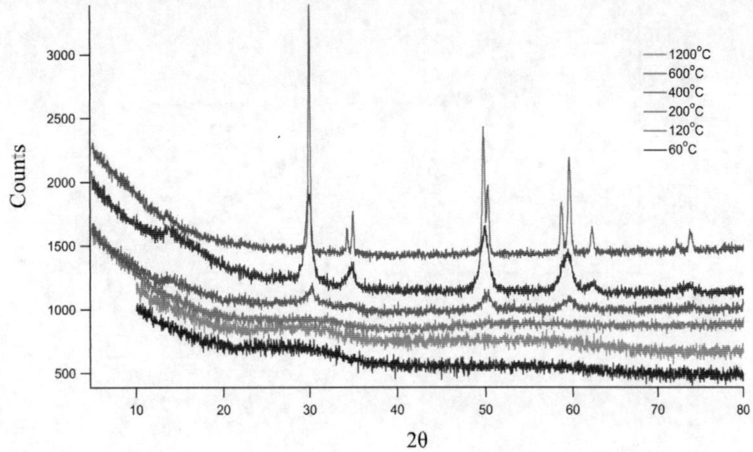


**Figure 4.** X-ray diffraction patterns for each heat treatment performed on CSZ [10]

Based on X-ray diffraction data, it can be seen that at temperatures below 400°C, no diffraction peaks are formed according to FTIR data. The main process that occurs is in the form of decomposition of organic groups as part of the formation of sol-gel. After the polymer matrix has completely decomposed, at 400°C it begins to enter a very fine crystallization phase of the oxide system, such as $\alpha$-$Zr_2O_3$. This is shown from the diffraction peaks that are still wide with low diffraction intensity. Apart from the crystallization process, it is also hoped that a microsphere will be formed without cracks. So the decomposition mechanism followed by crystallization must run simultaneously. Using a small angle scattering technique using X-ray beams and neutrons, the assembly process can be observed in stages.

The scattering pattern of X-rays and neutrons is generally described as the intensity versus the amplitude of the scattering vector or momentum transfer, which is expressed by:

$$q = \frac{4\,\pi \sin\theta}{\lambda} \tag{3}$$

where $\lambda$ represents the wavelength of the radiation beam hitting the sample, and $\theta$ is the angle formed between the incident beam and the normal scattering plane. Remembering as long as the measurement $\lambda$ is fixed, and assuming the scattering occurs in a small angle, the relationship between intensity and the angle of scattering can be stated

$$I(q) = \langle \left| \int [(\rho(\vec{r}) - \overrightarrow{\rho_s}) e^{i\vec{q}\cdot\vec{r}} d\vec{r} \right|^2 \rangle \tag{4}$$

here $\langle\,\rangle$ represents the rotatrional average and $(\rho(\vec{r}) - \overrightarrow{\rho_s})$is the difference in scattering density between a particle volume at the position indicated by the vector $\vec{r}$ in the solvent which contributes to the background count. So that with the small angle scattering method, we can distinguish the scattering originating from particles (solids) and the media from the system in the form of a liquid, or what is known as $\Delta q$[11] contrast. As seen in the wide-angle X-ray diffraction data in Fig.4, we cannot see any diffraction peaks (high irregularity effect), but based on SAXS measurement data, see Fig.5, the results showed that there was regularity on a very small scale with an average particle size of 3.2 nm. This regularity is of course related to the distribution of CSZ in the very initial phase, namely after the drying process at 60°C. What is very interesting about the measured SAXS data, it appears that the intensity of the scattering continues to decrease as q (0.002) increases. Measurements of samples that have been aged at 200°C, polydipersity of about 3.6 nm, see Fig. 6. Based on these data, it will be possible to combine small particle clusters so that they are measured as particles with a larger size. This gives an indication that in addition to the distribution of fine particles, there are also larger particles.

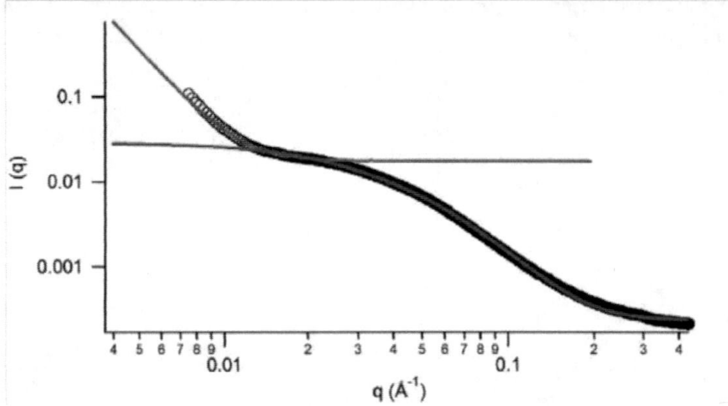


**Figure 5.** SAXS scattering profile of the kernel after drying at 60°C

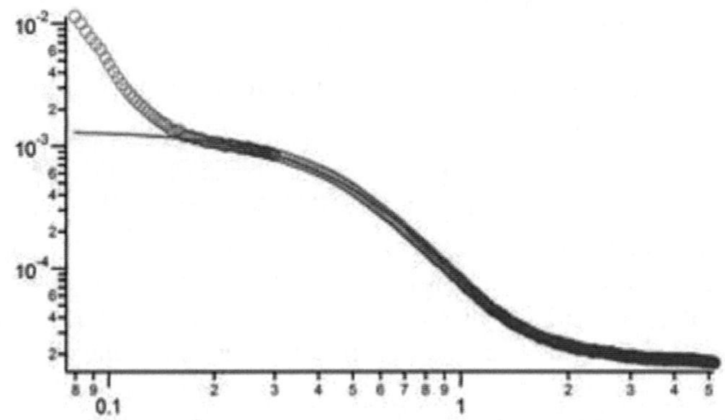


**Figure 6.** SAXS scattering profile of the kernel after drying at 200°C [12]

However, considering that the measurement range with SAXS is very limited, to identify larger particle sizes, the Small Angle Neutron Scattering (SANS) facility available at the Center for Advanced Materials Science and Technology (PSTBM) -BATAN has been used, see Figure 7.

**Figure 7.** Small Angle Neutron Scattering (SANS) at Center for Science and Advanced Material Technology.

Using SANS, the observed particle size is up to 12 nm. The measurement parameters are used by selecting a wavelength (λ) of 3.9 nm using the velocity selector, while the distance between the detector to the sample varies from 3, 6, 13 and 18 m, the measurement time is 24 hours per detector position. Data of measurement results for samples heated at 400 °C can be seen in Figure 8.

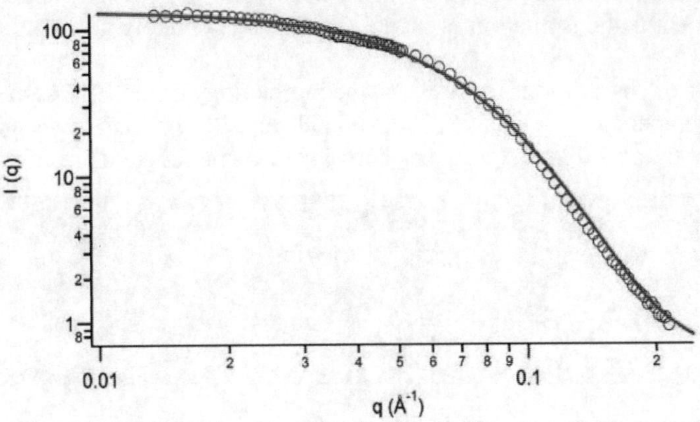


**Figure 8.** Small-Angle Neutron Scattering (SANS) intensity profile corresponding to kernel heated at 400°C

As shown in the measurement data using the X-ray diffraction method at 400°C, the crystallization process has begun to form. Based on the results of the analysis, it shows that in addition to the diameter of about 3.5 nm, it is also spherical with a uniformity level of 0.3 as shown in Figure 9.

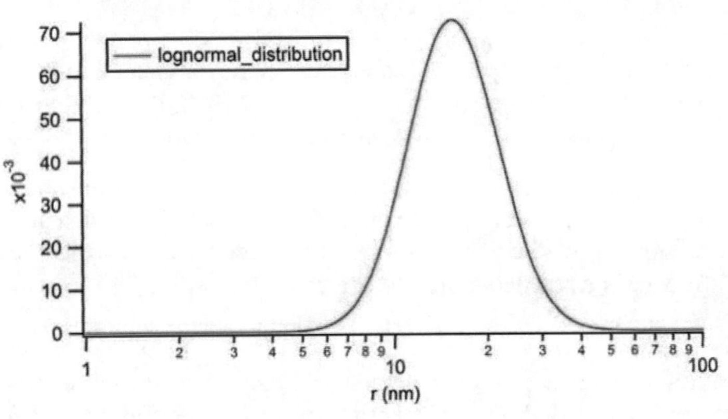


**Figure 9.** Profile log normal of uniformity of kernel after heating at 400°C

Based on the results of the analysis using both SAXS and SANS, the stages of crystallite phase formation in the Zirconia kernel stabilized system by Ceria can be illustrated as follows:

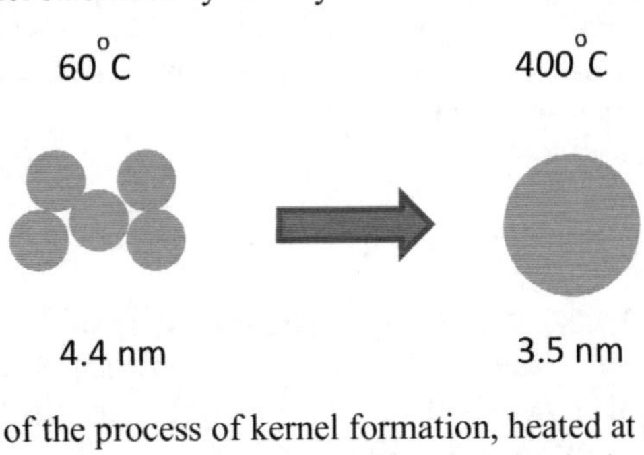


**Figure 10.** An illustration of the process of kernel formation, heated at 60 °C to 400 °C based on the results of SAXS and SANS data analysis.

What is seen from SAXS is the presence of a cluster of tiny crystals scattered in the polymeric system, which after heating to a higher temperature the clusters then coalesce to form particles with higher density but with smaller size. Therefore, in the early stages of handling the CSZ gelatin system it will be very sensitive to changes in temperature. It is estimated that a very fast temperature increase can cause the crystallite phase formation process in the kernel system to not run properly. The irregularity of the fractal arrangement in the formation of kernel crystals is very likely to trigger micro cracks from the kernel system.

Based on the results of observations using SEM, the morphology of the CSZ kernel as a result of the heating process from temperatures of 60, 120, 200, 400, 600 and 1200 °C can be seen in Figure 11. SEM observations show that the CSZ-based kernel has been formed without have a crack.

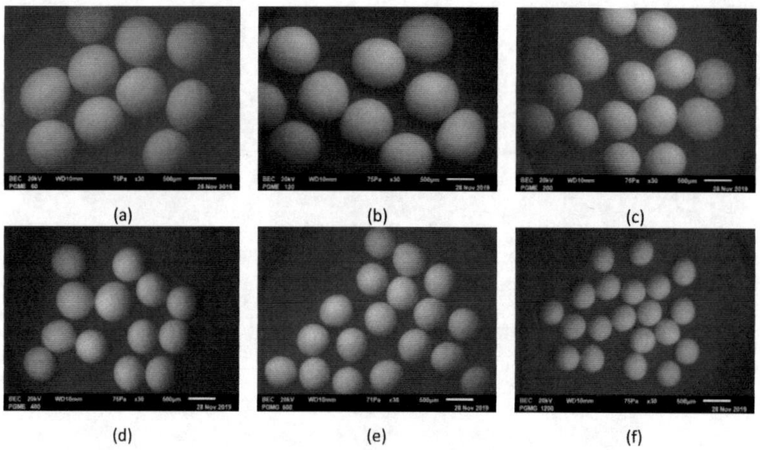


**Figure 11.** SEM photos of surrogate kernel samples after various heat treatments, at the stage (a) Drying 60°C, (b) Heating 120°C, (c) Heating 200°C, (d) Heating 400°C, (e) Heating 600 °C and (f) 1200 °C heating.

It can be seen that the higher the heating temperature, the smaller the kernel and without any cracks, thus the higher the calcination temperature. It can be estimated that the density of the kernel will increase. Just as a note, in terms of the density of $UO_2$ as a nuclear fuel the theoretical one is 10.96 g/ $cm^3$ and experimentally it can be reached up to 10.59 $g/cm^3$.

## 4. Conclusions

A study on the synthesis of ceria stabilized zirconia (CSZ) as a nuclear fuel surrogate for high temperature reactors has been carried out. CSZ kernels were synthesized by external gelatin method. The fractal form of crystallite growth process from the outset can be identified using SAXS in the size range below 2nm and distributed polydipersity in the organic matrix system as a solvent. At higher calcination temperatures, deformation of the organic matrix is accompanied by fractal agglomeration to form a perfect kernel without cracks. The proper heat treatment process allows the fractal arrangement of CSZ crystallites in the formation of the kernel to not develop defects which are thought to be the main cause of kernel cracking since the calcination process.

## References

[1] High Temperature Gas Cooled Reactor Fuels and Materials, IAEA-TECDOC-1645-CD, IAEA, Vienne, 2010

[2] Damian S. Nakonieczny , Zbigniew K. Paszenda, Marcin Basiaga, Tomasz Radko, Sabina Drewniak, Jacek Podworny, Wojciech Bogacz, Phase composition and morphology characteristics of ceria-stabilized zirconia powders obtained via sol-gel method with various pH conditions, Acta of Bioengineering and Biomechanics, v19,p.21, 2017

[3] Guogao W, Jingtao M, Yong G, Xingyu Z, Shaochang H, and Changsheng D, Precisely Controlling Preparation of Ceria-Stabilized Zirconia Microspheres of ~100 μm by External Gelation, Int. J. Appl. Ceram. Technol., p.1-7, 2016

[4] Guogao W, Jingtao M, Yong G, Xingyu Z, Shaochang H, and Changsheng D, Preparation of Small Size Ceria Stabilized Zirconia Microspheres by External Gelation: Effect of Vibration Frequency, Key Engineering Materials, p.364,v.697,2016

[5] Benjamin Chu1,2 and Tianbo Liu1, Characterization of nanoparticles by scattering techniques, Journal of Nanoparticle Research v.2, p.29–41, 2000

[6] S. Kotaro, Y. Masao , H. Hideitsu, S. Tetsuya, A. Akinori, M. Hidekazu, M. Chiharu, K. Joachim & O. Kanta, Accelerating small-angle scattering experiments on anisotropic samples using kernel density estimation, Scientific Reports, v.9, p.1526, 2019 https://doi.org10.1038

[7] Guogao W, Jingtao M, Yong G, Xingyu Z, Shaochang H, and Changsheng D, "Precisely Controlling Preparation of Ceria-Stabilized Zirconia Microspheres of ~100 μm by External Gelation," Int. J. Appl. Ceram. Technol., vol. 13, no. 5, pp. 831–837, 2016

[8] Haas PA, Formation of uniform liquid drops by application of vibration to laminar jets. Ind Eng Chem Res 31: p. 959–967,1992

[9] Guogao W, Jingtao M, Yong G, Xingyu Z, Shaochang H, Changsheng D, Bin L, A comparative study of small-size ceria-zirconia microspheres fabricated by external and internal gelation, J Sol-Gel Sci Technol, v. 78, p. 673-681, 2016

[10] Insani A, Mujamilah, Rifai M, Prastya A D, and Sarjono, XRD study of ceria stabilized zirconia (CSZ) microsphere synthesized by external gelation, to be published at 10$^{th}$ ICOPIA .

[11] Jacques D, and Trewhella J, "Small-angle scattering for structural biology - Expanding the frontier while avoiding the pitfalls," *Protein Sci.*, v. 19, no. 4, p. 642–657, 2010.

[12] Patriati A, Insani A, Suparno N, Hutamaningtyas E, Soontaranoon S, Mujamilah, Study of Dried and Calcinated Ceria Stabilized Zirconia Microspheres Morphology by Small-Angle X-Ray Scattering and Optical Microscopy, to be published.

# The Effect of Catalysts Addition to Silicone Rubber as Pressure Transmitting Medium in the Pebble Fuel Production Process

**D Sutarya, I R Pamungkas[1], H Sukma[1], A Sartono DS[2]**

Centre for Nuclear Fuel Technology, BATAN Kawasan Puspiptek Serpong 15314, Indonesia
phone: +62-21-7560915, dedes@batan.go.id
[1]Mechanical Engineering Department, Pancasila University, Jakarta 12640, Indonesia
[2]Centre for Nuclear Fuel Technology, BATAN, Kawasan Puspiptek Serpong 15314, Indonesia

**Abstract.** Pebble Fuel is a spherical fuel for high temperature gas-cooled reactors (HTGR). This fuel must have a homogeneous density distribution. Hyperelastic material is used as a pressure transmitting medium (PTM) material in making Pebble fuel using the cold quasi-isostatic pressing method. PTM material properties and characteristics were predicted using the finite element analysis method. The problem is the type of material used and its suitable composition to make a pressure-transmitting medium that has the properties and characteristics of the material as predicted. This research discusses the manufacture of tensile specimens for pressure-emitting media using RTV-586 silicone rubber. The composition comprises three different variants with two major ingredients, namely RTV-586 silicone rubber and catalyst. The test results are then analyzed using the finite element method to determine the material composition that is appropriate or close to the predicted properties and characteristics of the PTM material. This initial study used the Mooney-Rivlin hyperelastic model. The Mooney-Rivlin model shows good similarity to the test result data. In future studies, it will make comparisons with other hyperelastic models to get a suitable PTM material constant.

## 1. Introduction

The design of HTGR fuel elements is usually divided into two categories: prismatic fuel elements or spherical fuel elements [1]. The fabrication process of spherical fuel element is mainly composed of four steps, i.e., preparation of resinated matrix graphite powders, overcoating the Tristructural Isotropic (TRISO) coated fuel particle, cold quasi-isostatic pressing or molding, and lathing and subsequent heat treatments [2]. Cold quasi-isostatic pressing (QIP) is a pressing technique developed from the hydrostatic pressing technique. The QIP technique is efficient and simple but has the advantage of being able to provide a triaxial volumetric suppression effect on pressed material (powder), to produce a final product with a uniform density and good physical and mechanical properties [3]. The QIP method in addition to providing volumetric (triaxial) compression of the pressed material also combines the advantages of biaxial hydrostatic suppression and uniaxial static suppression [4, 5].

At present, the QIP technique in powder has gained wide acceptance in the production of ceramic, graphite, metal and abrasive components [6] as well as the fabrication process of spherical fuel elements for high-temperature gas-cooled reactors (HTGR). The fabrication process consists of two stages: pre-molding and final molding, where both stages use the QIP technique to reduce the anisotropic properties [7,8].

Quasi-isostatic pressing is a pressing technology for materials in powder form that allows uniform density to be obtained in all parts [9]. This process is carried out using hydraulic equipment or standard compression mechanisms. The equipment design, installation, and operational conditions for QIP are not much different from conventional compression techniques. The principle of quasi-isostatic pressing is based on the use of hyperelastic material as a medium (pressure transmitting medium) to transmit uniform static pressure in all directions. The quasi-isostatic pressing process is shown in Figure 1.

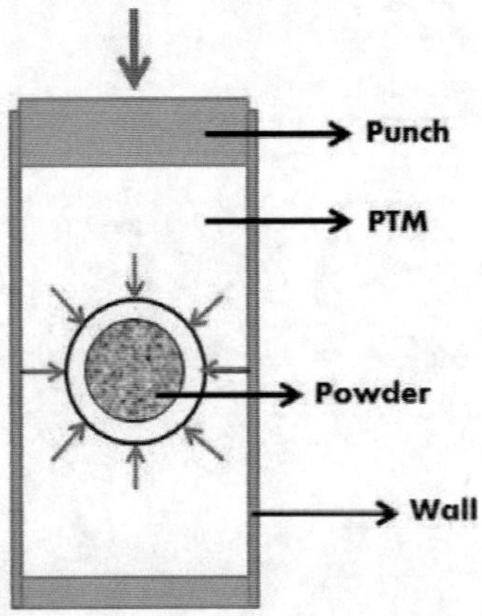


**Figure 1.** Quasi-isostatic pressing (QIP).

As shown in Figure 1, the process begins with the punch moving downward pressing the pressure transmitting medium (PTM) which will then transfer the pressure received to the powder to be processed. The final result that is processed depends on the nature of the PTM. If the PTM can transfer the pressure received uniformly in all directions, then the pressed powder will have a uniform density.

The PTM selection is the most important part in the compacting process with the QIP technique. PTM functions as a medium that continues isostatic pressure uniformly in all directions during the compacting process. PTM material is an elastomer which simultaneously forms part of the mold that forms the result of the compression process, providing internal and external pressure to the material being pressed [10]. Therefore, this research focuses on determining the material properties of PTM by using Finite Element Analysis (FEA) and hyperelastic models especially Mooney-Rivlin. The results obtained will be a reference in determining the material properties of PTM that will be made.

## 2. Material and Methods

In this section, analytic methods are presented to determine the parameters of hyperelastic materials and two types of experimental tests for hyperelastic materials, namely the uniaxial tensile test and the uniaxial compression test. For each type of test, three specimens were taken from the same RTV586 silicone rubber product with a difference in additional catalyst percentage. This is intended to investigate the composition that best suits the material characteristics needed as a PTM for the quasi-isostatic pressing process.

RTV586 silicone rubber consists of two parts, part A and part B. Where part B is the catalyst. For each catalyst composition three specimens were made for tensile and compression tests, so that there were nine test specimens. This is intended to investigate the uniformity of product compositions and to ensure that products provide representative test data.

The variation of the catalyst addition is based on the conventional RTV catalyst composition which is about 30 – 40 ml/kg (addsil RTV586 technical information). The catalyst composition of each specimen is shown in Table 1, while Figure 2 shows the entire RTV586 test specimen for tensile and compression test.

**Table 1.** Catalyst composition

| Specimen | RTV586 composition | |
|---|---|---|
| | Part A (%) | Part B (%) |
| H1-1 | | |
| H1-2 | 99 | 1 |
| H1-3 | | |
| H2-1 | | |
| H2-2 | 98 | 2 |
| H2-3 | | |
| H3-1 | | |
| H3-2 | 97 | 3 |
| H3-3 | | |

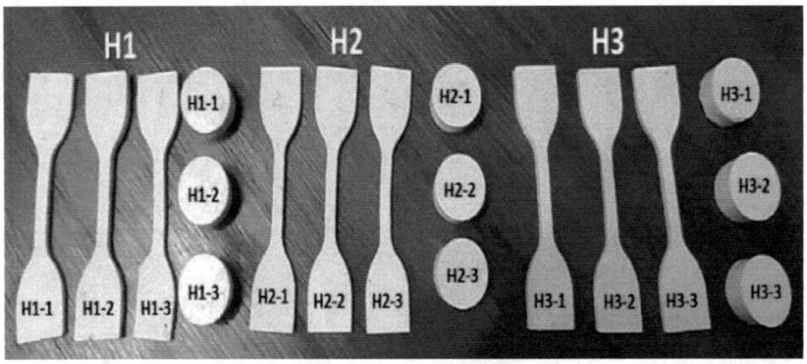


**Figure 2.** Tensile and compression test specimen.

The test data is used for the curve fitting process to get the RTV586 material constant and to choose the appropriate constitutive model. The requirement for the curve fitting process is a simple stress-strain function that is able to represent every expected load condition in the experiment.

In experimental testing, a Gotech AI-7000S universal servo control system and laser extensometer is used.

*2.1. Uniaxial Tensile Test*

In the tensile test the specimen is tested for its tensile strength by being given a tensile load to find out the maximum stress before the specimen is broken. The standard used is ASTM D412 (see fig. 3), using a universal testing machine (UTM Al-7000S Gotech) as shown in fig.4.

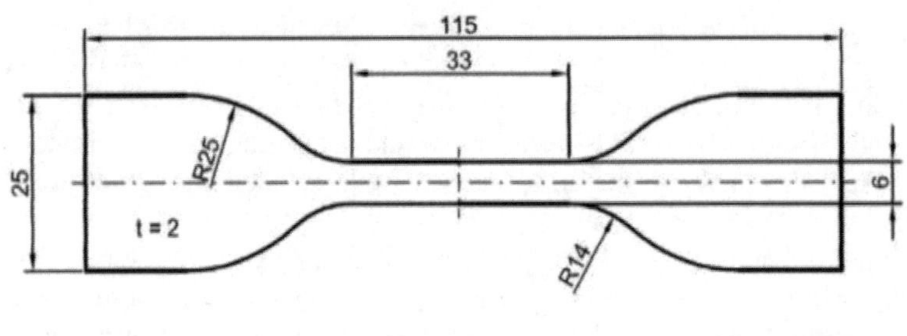


**Figure 3.** Dimensions of the tensile test specimen according to ASTM D412 [11].

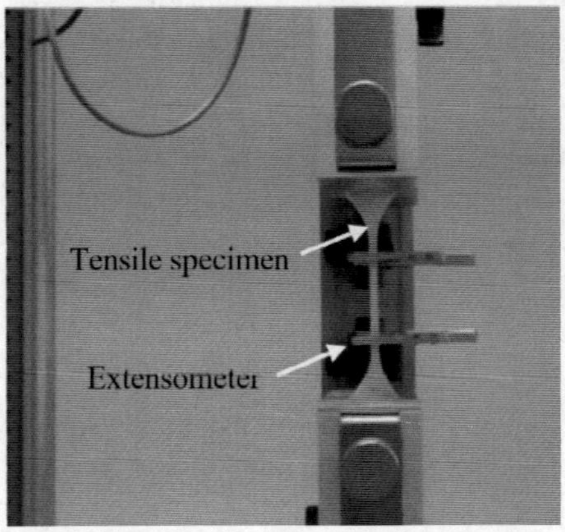


**Figure 4.** Uniaxial tensile specimen mounted on UTM Al-7000S Gotech

### *2.2. Uniaxial Compression Test*

In this test the specimen is tested by giving a load that presses the specimen to determine the stress and strain values that occur during loading as well as the maximum load that the specimen is able to accept. The standard used is ASTM D575-91.

Compression testing is usually done because the rubber is often applied to pressure or force when used. Compression testing is done by applying uniaxial pressure to the rubber to determine the rubber's elasticity ability when pressed.

The shape of the test specimen in the form of a cylinder refers to the ASTM standard D575-91 with the dimensions of the test specimen that is diameter 28.6 ± 0.1 mm and thickness 12.5 ± 0.5 mm (see Fig.5).

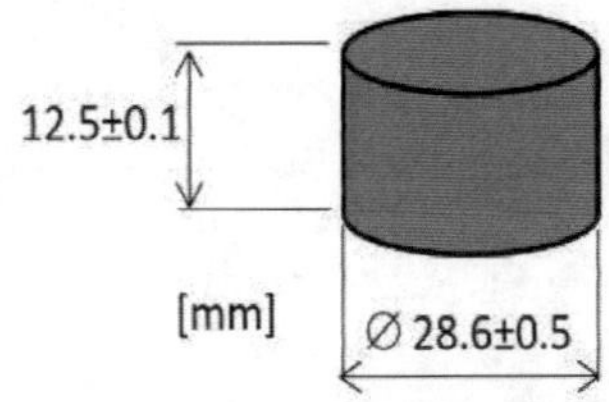


**Figure 5.** Dimensions of the compression test specimen.

### *2.3. Hyperelastic Material Model*

To study the behavior of an elastic material with a non-linear, which experienced a large strain with little emphasis given, used non-linear version of the classical elasticity theory which has been developed by Ogden [12]. The theory of non-linear elasticity, is a theoretical basis for the study of hyperelastic materials, such as silicon rubber using the strain energy function (W) to describe in the form of energy the mechanical behavior of the material.

To capture the non-linear mechanical properties of silicone rubber material in this study, a Mooney-Rivlin model will be used with three parameters of the material. It can be assumed that silicone rubber behaves like an isotropic, hyper-elastic and non-linear material [13]. The strain energy function (W) can then be described as a function of the following invariant strain:

$$W = W(I_1, I_2, I_3) \tag{1}$$

where:

$$\begin{aligned} I_1 &= \lambda_1^2 + \lambda_2^2 + \lambda_3^2 \\ I_2 &= \lambda_1^2\lambda_2^2 + \lambda_2^2\lambda_3^2 + \lambda_1^2\lambda_3^2 \\ I_3 &= \lambda_1^2\lambda_2^2\lambda_3^2 \end{aligned} \tag{2}$$

where $\lambda_1$, $\lambda_2$ and $\lambda_3$ are stretching principles. Assuming that the material is incompressible (I3 = 1), Equation (1) becomes:

$$W = W(I_1, I_2) \tag{3}$$

The Cauchy stress principle can be stated as a stretching function as follows:

$$\sigma_i = \lambda_i \frac{\delta W}{\delta \lambda_i} + p \quad i = 1, 2, 3 \tag{4}$$

where p is the hydrostatic pressure which can be determined from the boundary conditions [9]. Martins et al. [9] conducted a comparative study of several material models for the prediction of hyper-elastic properties, with applications for silicone rubber and soft tissue, using data obtained from a uniaxial tensile test.

Mooney-Rivlin was one of the first hyper-elastic models developed in 1940. Currently it is still widely used, because it has high accuracy when predicting non-linear behavior of isotropic, rubber-like material [14].

Two parameters of the Mooney-Rivlin material model in the form of a strain energy equation can be seen in the following equation:

$$W = C_{10}(I_1 - 3) + C_{01}(I_2 - 3) \tag{5}$$

where $C_{10}$ and $C_{01}$ are empirically determined material constants, and $I_1$ and $I_2$ are the first and second invariant unimodular components of the Cauchy-Green deformation tensor, respectively.

Whereas, for the three parameters of the Mooney-Rivlin material model in terms of strain energy can be described as follows:

$$W = C_{10}(I_1 - 3) + C_{01}(I_2 - 3) + C_{20}(I_1 - 3)^2 \tag{6}$$

where $C_{10}$, $C_{01}$ and $C_{20}$ are an empirically determined material constant.

## 3. RESULTS AND DISCUSSIONS

### *3.1. Uniaxial Tension*

Figure 6 shows the stress versus strain data for specimens with catalyst composition of 1%, 2% and 3% tested in stress. Nine silicon rubber specimens with three different catalyst compositions exhibit various behaviors under stress, highlighting their different mechanical properties (Table 3.1). The H1 specimen (H1-1 through H1-3) had the largest strain on failure (439.9%) of the three specimens. Then decrease sequentially on H2 and H3 specimens with increasing catalyst addition to the specimen.

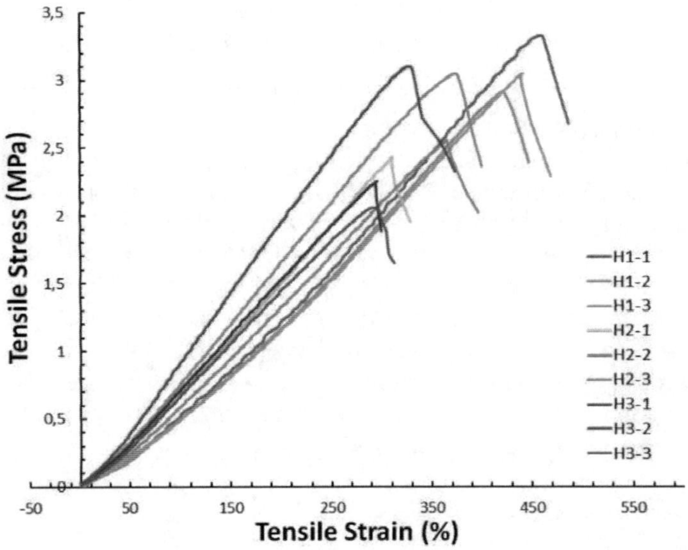


**Figure 6.** Tensile stress versus strain data as measured for 9 specimen silicone rubber RTV586 with 3 catalyst composition.

**Table 2.** Tensile stress vs. strain experimental data

| No | Sample | Max Stress (Mpa) | Max Strain (%) |
|---|---|---|---|
| 1 | H1-1 | 3,3273 | 458,3738 |
| 2 | H1-2 | 2,9089 | 421,1922 |
| 3 | H1-3 | 3,0436 | 440,1828 |
| 4 | H2-1 | 2,4271 | 309,6972 |
| 5 | H2-2 | 2,5508 | 365,0698 |
| 6 | H2-3 | 3,0463 | 373,3158 |
| 7 | H3-1 | 2,2527 | 294,8545 |
| 8 | H3-2 | 3,0999 | 327,6383 |
| 9 | H3-3 | 2,0601 | 293,4552 |

### *3.2. Uniaxial Compression*

The stress-strain behavior of the silicon rubber sample under compression is shown in Figure 7. Displacement that occurs during the test is very small. The basic assumption of rubber behavior during this test is similar to that of fluid regarding the same reaction force in all directions. Very small volume changes during testing under hydrostatic pressure (p) characterize rubber material as a material that is virtually incompressible.

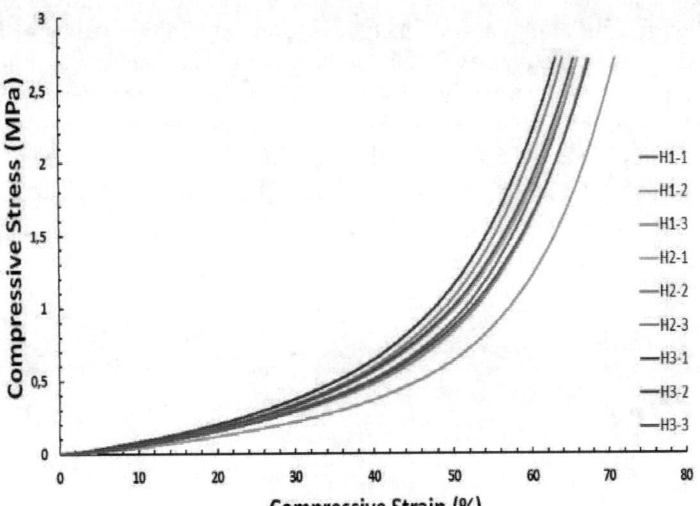


**Figure 7.** Compressive stress versus strain data as measured for 9 specimen silicone rubber RTV586 with 3 catalyst composition.

The deformation of nine silicon rubber samples with three different catalyst compositions, and the mechanical properties calculated under compression indicate that the compressive strain of the whole sample did not show a significant difference as shown in Table 3.

**Table 3.** Compressive stress vs. strain experimental data

| No | Sample | Max Stress (MPa) | Ultimate Elongation (%) |
|---|---|---|---|
| 1 | H1-1 | 2,7092 | 65,9359 |
| 2 | H1-2 | 2,7089 | 67,2692 |
| 3 | H1-3 | 2,7099 | 70,8322 |
| 4 | H2-1 | 2,7099 | 65,9055 |
| 5 | H2-2 | 2,7098 | 63,9522 |
| 6 | H2-3 | 2,7097 | 65,4105 |
| 7 | H3-1 | 2,7097 | 63,0613 |
| 8 | H3-2 | 2,7090 | 65,4162 |
| 9 | H3-3 | 2,7090 | 67,4757 |

### *3.3. Curve Fitting*

To choose the most suitable hyperelastic model, ANSYS provides a curve fitting feature. This feature simplifies the user's effort by comparing some available models with experimental data so we can decide on the most suitable model. Experimental stress-strain data is need to determine the exact strain energy function coefficient during the curve-fitting process. Test data needed for the installation process of the curve is a uniaxial tensile test, planar shear, equibiaxial, and volumetric (compression test) which produces an equation for the strain energy function in terms of strain invariant or hyperlastic material strain. In this research paper, the data available are only the uniaxial tensile and uniaxial compression (volumetric) test data. Therefore, curve fitting will perform by using the two data test.

The hyperelastic model used is Mooney-Rivlin with three parameters. The experimental stress-strain data was evaluation using Equation 5 to match the experimental data as shown in Figures 8 to 10. The most stable experimental data of all cycles for each test were selected for the curve fitting process [15].

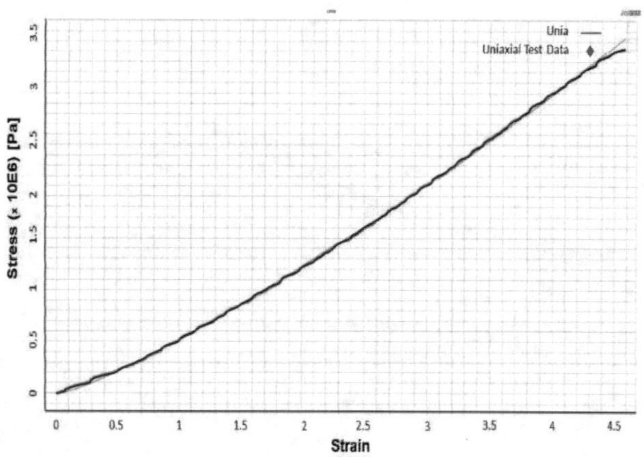


**Figure 8.** Curve fitting of Mooney-Rivlin model with uniaxial test data H1-1 sample.

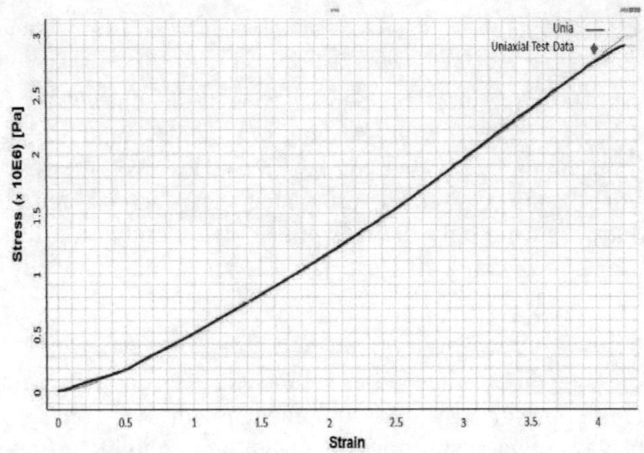


**Figure 9.** Curve fitting of Mooney-Rivlin model with uniaxial test data H1-2 sample.

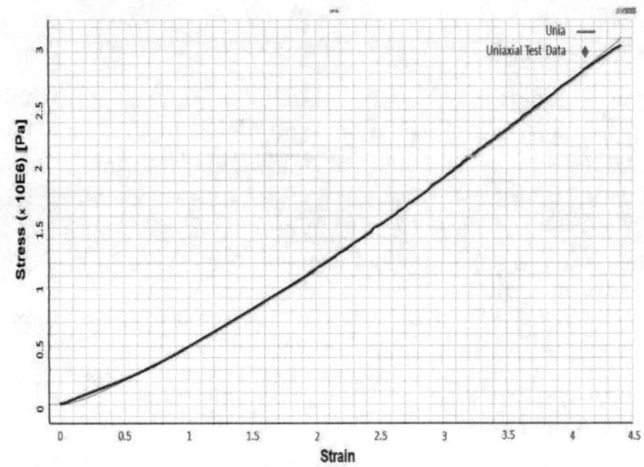


**Figure 10.** Curve fitting of Mooney-Rivlin model with uniaxial test data H1-3 sample.

From the results of the curve fitting of the hyperelastic Mooney-Rivlin 3 model parameters, we get the PTM material constants using silicone rubber as shown in Table 3.3.

**Table 4.** Mooney-Rivlin coefficient

| Coef. | Value (MPa) | | | |
|---|---|---|---|---|
| | H1-1 | H1-2 | H1-3 | Average |
| $C_{10}$ | 0,2518 | 0,2394 | 0,2287 | 0,2400 |
| $C_{01}$ | -0,2417 | -0,2321 | -0,2076 | -0,2271 |
| $C_{11}$ | 0,0076 | 0,0077 | 0,0077 | 0,0077 |

After determining the properties of the PTM material, the next step is to simulate the quasi-isostatic pressing (QIP) process using the material properties of the hyperelastic modeling results. The QIP simulation will be carried out in future studies.

## 4. Conclusion and Future Works

### *4.1. Conclusion*

The addition of a catalyst affects the mechanical properties of silicone rubber. From the experimental results, we found that the H1 sample with the addition of 1% catalyst had the best tensile and compressive stress vs strain compared to other compositions. However, the actual test data required for the curve fitting process are the uniaxial tensile test, planar shear, biaxial, and volumetric (compression test). Whereas in this study we used only the tensile test and compression test, however at least two experimental data that have been conducted can provide an initial picture in the selection of PTM materials.

### *4.2. Future Works*

Some of the test and experimental data needed to get the exact strain energy function coefficient have not been carried out. This is because the test equipment is not available in our laboratory, so it is necessary to collaborate with other institutions. In the future, a joint testing will be carried out to complete the data so that it is possible to compare several hyperleastic models and obtain the desired PTM material coefficient.

## References

[1] Petti, David Andrew, Buongiorno, Jacopo, Maki, John Thomas, and Hobbins, Richard Redfield, Key differences in the fabrication, irradiation and high temperature accident testing of US and German TRISO-coated particle fuel, and their implications on fuel performance., Nucl. Eng, 222, p. 281-297, 2003.

[2] Zhou, Xiangwen & Zhenming, Lu & Jie, Zhang & Bing, Liu & Yanwen, Zou & Chunhe, Tang & Yaping, Tang, Preparation of spherical fuel elements for HTR-PM in INET. Nuclear Engineering and Design. 263, p.456-461, 2013.

[3] M. I. Timokhova, "Design Specifics of Quasi-Isostatic Molds," Refractories and Industrial Ceramics, 47(6), pp.344 – 347, 2006.

[4] M. I. Timokhova, "Quasi-isostatic pressing of ceramic products," VNIIESM, Moscow, Series 5. Keramicheskaya Promyshlennost', No. 1, pp.1 – 68, 1990.

[5] M. I. Timokhova, "Physical foundations of the quasi-isostatic pressing of powdered materials," Novye Ogneupory, No. 12, pp.12 – 17, 2009.

[6] M. I. Timokhova, "Quasi-Isostatic Technique for Powder Materials," Novye Ogneupory, No. 11, pp. 31 – 34, 2003.

[7] C. Tang et al.," Design and manufacture of the fuel element for the 10 MW high temperature gas-cooled reactor," Nuclear Engineering and Design, 218 , pp. 91– 102, 2002.

[8] H. Zhao et al.," Manufacture and characteristics of spherical fuel elements for the HTR-10," Nuclear Engineering and Design, 236, pp.643–647, 2006.

[9] M. I. Timokhova, "Industrial Technology for the Automated Production of Grinding Balls by Quasi-Isostatic Pressing," Refractories and Industrial Ceramics, No. 12, pp. 7 – 10, 2012.

[10] M. I. Timokhova, "Advantages of Quasi-Isostatic Pressing for Powder Materials," Refractories and Industrial Ceramics, Vol. 53(3), Springer Science, pp.147–150, 2012.

[11] ASTM D412. Standard test methods for vulcanized rubber and thermoplastic elastomers- tension. ASTM International; 2013.

[12] Ogden, R.W.," Non-linear Elastic Deformations," Dover Publications Inc., Mineola, NY, USA, 1984.

[13] Martins, et al," A Comparative Study of Several Material Models for Prediction of Hyperelastic Properties: Application to Silicone-Rubber and Soft Tissues," Strain, 42(3), pp. 135–147, 2006.

[14] Mooney, M.,"A theory of large elastic deformation," Journal of Applied Physics,vol. 11, 1940.

[15] Miller, K. "Testing Elastomer for Hyperelastic Material Models in Finite Element Analysis." Axel Products Testing and Analysis Report, 2000.

# Corrosion Phenomena of High Temperature Alloys by Helium Impurities in the Primary Coolant of HTGR

**Q Wang, W Zheng, H Yin, S Li, X He, and T Ma**

Institute of Nuclear and New Energy Technology, Collaborative Innovation Center of Advanced Nuclear Energy Technology, Key Laboratory of Advanced Reactor Engineering and Safety of Ministry of Education, Tsinghua University, Beijing 100084, China

phone: +86-010-80194012, yinhuaqiang@tsinghua.edu.cn

**Abstract.** The primary coolant circuit of the high temperature gas-cooled reactor (HTGR) contains trace impurities. A nickel base alloy would corrode when exposed to an atmosphere at a high temperature and for a long time. The protective oxide scale formed by chromium is an important factor to prevent severe corrosion of high temperature alloys. Corrosion tests were conducted on Inconel 617, Incoloy 800H, Hastelloy X, and T-22, which are commonly used in the steam generator of HTGR. The alloys were exposed to helium with trace impurities for 48 hours at 950℃. The corrosion results were analyzed by weighing, scanning electron microscopy (SEM) and electron probe microanalyzer (EPMA). All the four alloys formed oxide scales in this atmosphere, but they differ in the capacity to resist corrosion. Therefore, the carbon transfer phenomenon observed in this experiment varies for the different alloys. In addition, for Cr in Inconel617, the expected depletion phenomenon near the corrosion layer occurred, which is consistent with the results from theoretical analysis.

## 1. Introduction

The high temperature gas-cooled reactor (HTGR) is characterized by the high outlet temperature, which is up to 950°C. Meanwhile, there are trace impurities in the primary coolant circuit, such as CO, $CH_4$, $H_2O$ and $H_2$ in the 0.1–10 Pa range [1]. The impure helium atmosphere puts forward new challenges to the material performance. Nickel-based alloys have been used in high temperature applications since long time due to their superior corrosion resistance, especially, they have been widely utilized in the heating surface tubes of the HTGR steam generator in recent decades.

Decarburization, carburization and internal oxidation are three main corrosion phenomena for the Nickel based alloy. According to a large number of previous experimental data [2-4], it is shown that the decarburization leads to a decrease in the creep performance, the severe carburization leads to the low temperature embrittlement of materials, and the internal oxidation leads to surface embrittlement. Therefore, this corrosion should be prevented. Generally speaking, Ni based Cr rich alloys can form the dense oxide scale, which effectively improves the corrosion resistance. The protective oxide scale can prevent the further rapid corrosion such as decarburization and carburization. Inconel 617 and Hastelloy X alloys were mainly used in the prototype plant for nuclear process heat (PNP) project in Germany and HTTR in Japan [5-6]. In Shandong province of China, the Pebble-bed Modular High-Temperature Gas-cooled Reactor (HTR-PM) has been designed and constructed by INET of Tsinghua University. In the heating surface tubes of the steam generator, the evaporation and overheat segment are made of Incoloy

800H and T-22 alloy [7-8]. At present, there are few engineering application examples of these two alloys in the HTGR field, so a lot of experiments should be conducted to verify the corrosion resistance of the materials.

The purpose of this work is to investigate the corrosion phenomena of the high temperature alloys used for HTR-PM and compare them with the corrosion behavior of the other two common alloys in the steam generator. Corrosion experiments of the four alloys were carried out for 48 hours at 950°C in an impure helium atmosphere. The quality change, surface morphology and element distribution of the samples were analyzed.

## 2. Experimental Procedures

The alloys used in this work are: Inconel 617, Hastelloy X, Incoloy 800H and T-22. The chemical composition of these alloys is shown in Table 1.

**Table 1.** Chemical composition of four alloys.

| Alloys | C | Cr | Fe | Mn | Ti | Al |
|---|---|---|---|---|---|---|
| Inconel 617 | 0.01 | 24.3 | 0.29 | 0.04 | 0.72 | 1.23 |
| Hastelloy X | 0.01 | 22.7 | 24.0 | 0.68 | 0.33 | 0.18 |
| Incoloy 800H | 0.39 | 21.8 | Base | 0.53 | 1.03 | 0.79 |
| T-22 | 0.01 | 2.11 | Base | 0.54 | - | 0.01 |

The samples were processed into 20*40*2mm pieces. The final heat treatment temperature of the material was 1180°C, and water cooling was used for 10 mins. Both sides of the samples were mechanically polished by abrasive paper from 600# to 2000#. Then, the samples were ultrasonically degreased in an acetone mixture, dried in air, and weighed with an electronic balance with an accuracy of 0.1mg.

For the corrosion test, eight samples (two samples for each alloy) can be exposed at the same time, being placed in a separate quartz tubes, which are housed in a high-temperature furnace. The corrosion test is carried out in a flowing impure helium gas at atmospheric pressure and at a flowing rate of 0.1 ml $s^{-1}$ $cm^{-2}$ sample surface. The tubes are made of quartz to avoid the influence of the test device in this test atmosphere. The impurities of the gas were configured before the test, and are shown in Table 2. The flow rate of the gas is controlled by the mass flow meter with 200 mL/min. The samples were heated at a rate of 5 °C/min and cooled at a rate of 10 °C/min in the test atmosphere.

**Table 2.** Impurity content in helium for $P_{tot}$ = 0.1MPa

| Impurities | $O_2$ | $H_2$ | $CH_4$ | CO | $H_2O$ |
|---|---|---|---|---|---|
| Content(ppm) | 1.0 | <0.1 | <0.05 | <0.05 | 6.0 |

After the corrosion test, the sample was weighed with EX224ZH balance, which is produced by OHAUS of USA, with an accuracy of 0.1mg. XQ-1 Metallographic Specimen Inlay Machine was utilized to press thermosetting plastics for the sample, which would be helpful for the observation. Just like before, samples were mechanically polished by abrasive paper from 600# to 2000# until there was no scratches and stains on the alloy surface. Finally, the samples characterized by the scanning electron microscopy (SEM) with the energy dispersive spectrometer (EDS) system and the electron probe microanalyzer (EPMA). The morphology, element distribution and content with the depth of the corroded samples were obtained in the following sections.

## 3. Results and Discussion

### *3.1. Mass Gain*

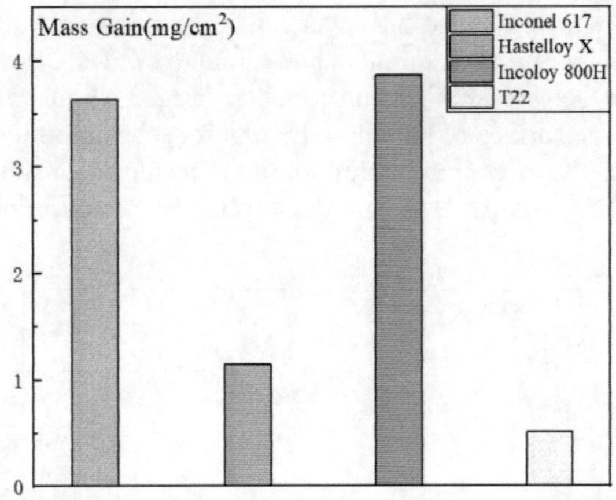


**Figure 1.** Mass gains of the four alloys after the test.

As shown in Fig. 1, the four alloys showed a mass increases after the corrosion test. They all showed a significant mass transfer from the atmosphere, where impurities were transferred to the alloys through surface reactions. Hastelloy X and T-22 have a low mass gain, indicating a potentially good corrosion resistance. This is consistent with the previous test results of Tsinghua University and the findings of C.J.Tsai [9]. This result needs to be further verified by SEM with EDS system and EPMA in the next section.

### *3.2. Inconel 617*

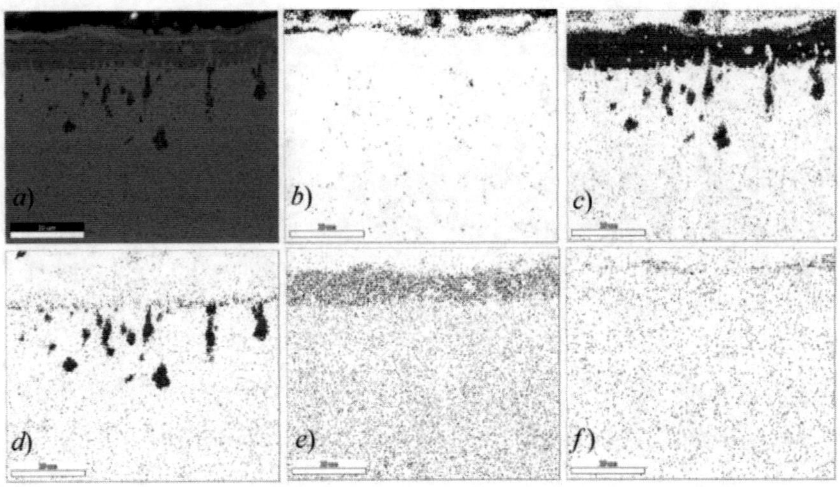


**Figure 2.** The cross-sectional SEM micrographs with EDS for Inconel 617 alloy and the distribution of various elements

Figure 2 presents the cross-sectional SEM micrographs with EDS for Inconel 617 alloy after 48 hours corrosion at 950°C. From figure b) to f), the EDS system shows the distribution of carbon, oxygen, aluminum, chromium and titanium. The chromium content in the alloy is high, so it combines with free oxygen to form a $Cr_2O_3$ scale. According to figures c) and e), it can be obviously seen that there are $Cr_2O_3$ scales on the Inconel 617 surface. In addition, large amounts of spinel can be observed below the surface oxide layers. The internal and inter-granular $Al_2O_3$ is well developed due to the preferential oxidation of Al in Alloy 617. The extensive development of internal oxides may prove the protection from the surface oxide scale of Inconel 617. This is consistent with the results of C. Jang et al [10].

Figure 3 shows the distribution of various elements in Inconel 617 alloy with the depth measured by EPMA. In this figure, the thickness of the oxide layer can be quantitatively determined to be about 4μm, and the scale is composed of chromium, aluminum and titanium oxides, of which chromium is the dominant element. According to the change of carbon content in Fig. 3, slight carburization occurred in the range of 15μm-30μm from the surface of the alloy. In addition, the chromium content below the oxide layer is very low. It is due to the migration of chromium to the surface, resulting in the emergence of a chromium depleted zone. This is consistent with the chromium depletion phenomenon researched by Quadakkers et al [5].

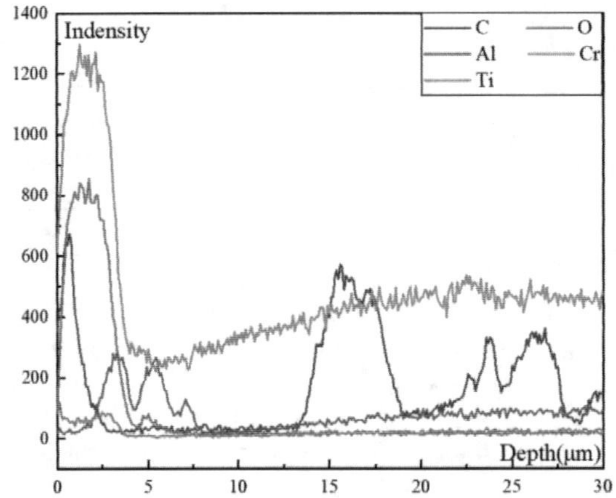


**Figure 3.** The change curve of alloying element content with depth obtained by EPMA.

### *3.3. Hastelloy X*

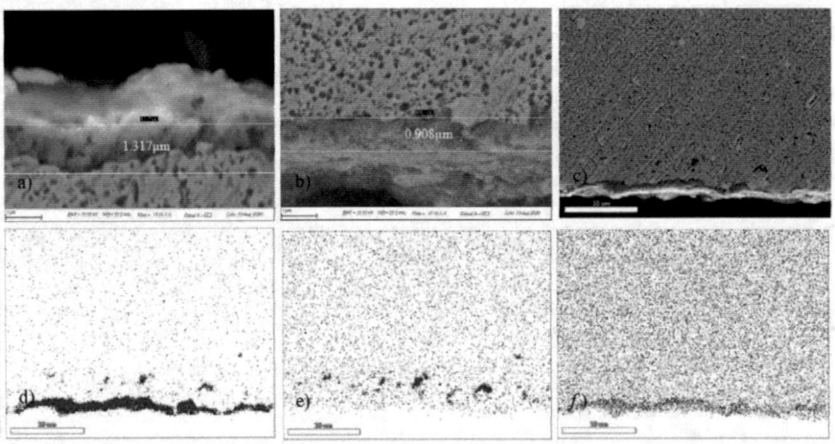


**Figure 4.** The cross-sectional SEM micrographs with EDS for Hastelloy X and the distribution of oxygen, aluminum, chromium elements

As shown in Fig. 4, Hastelloy X has also formed an oxide layer in this atmosphere. The thickness of the upper sample layer is about 1.3 μm and the thickness of the bottom layer is about 0.9 μm as measured by SEM in figures a) and b). This scale is dense, and it consists mainly of chromium and manganese oxides. According to the micrographs, there is less internal oxide in this alloy, which means the corrosion depth is shallow. This phenomenon also reflects the strong protective effect of the oxide layer on the Hastelloy X surface.

Figure 5 shows the depth dependent Hastelloy X element content. According to elemental analysis, there might be a very thin chromium carbide layer on the surface of the alloy, indicating that the slight carburization may have occurred on a surface. Relative to the other alloys, the manganese content in the surface layer of Hastelloy X is high. So, it formed the dense $MnCr_2O_4$ layer which is on the top of the $Cr_2O_3$ layer. It is the main contributor to the strong oxidation resistance of Hastelloy X. This is very similar to the Haynes 230 [10].

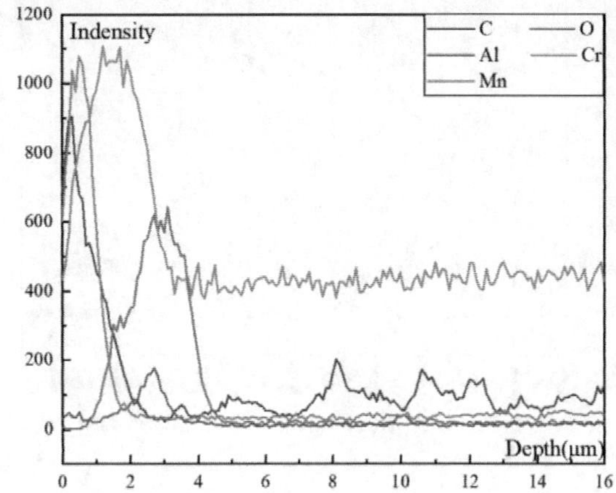


**Figure 5.** The change curve of alloying element content with depth obtained by EPMA.

### *3.4. Incoloy 800H*

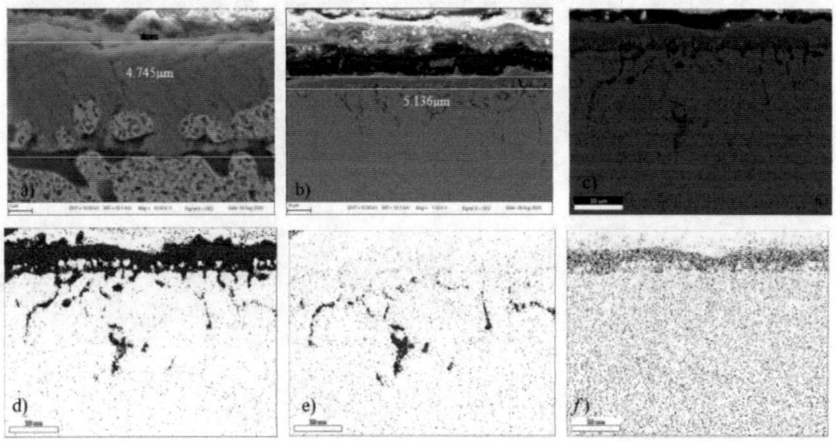


**Figure 6.** The cross-sectional SEM micrographs with EDS for Incoloy 800H and the distribution of oxygen, aluminum, chromium elements

As shown in Fig. 6, an oxide scale of about 5 μm thickness has formed on the surface of Incoloy 800H the alloy, which is thicker than that of Inconel 617 and Hastelloy X. However, a thicker oxide layer does not mean better corrosion resistance. On the contrary, 800H alloy shows the worst oxidation resistance. Severe internal oxidation occurred in this alloy and a large amount of $Al_2O_3$ spinel oxide was formed. According to the SEM data, the corrosion depth was more than 30 μm, which indicates that the surface oxide layer provides poor protection.

According to the curve in Fig. 7, it can be clearly seen that there is obvious internal oxidation along the lines on the sample swept by EPMA, and the identified oxide is $Al_2O_3$. In the surface layer of the alloy, the change of oxygen content is completely consistent with that of chromium, indicating that the surface oxide is mainly $Cr_2O_3$. In addition, the carbon content inside the alloy is relatively high and fluctuates constantly, which may be due to the deep carburizing behavior. Therefore, in this test atmosphere, the main corrosion phenomena of Incoloy 800H alloy are internal oxidation and deep carburization.

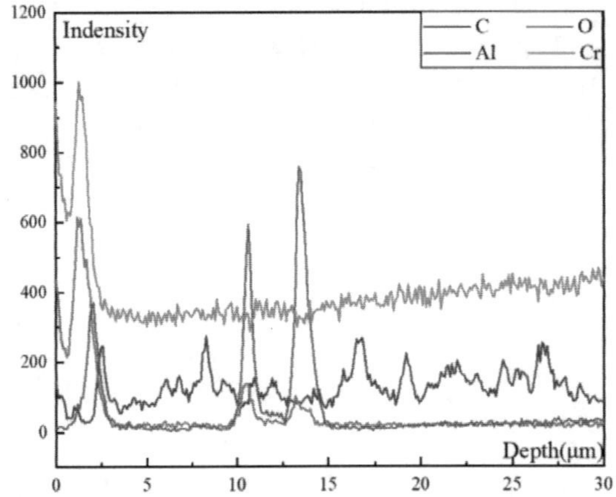


**Figure 7.** The change curve of alloying element content with depth obtained by EPMA.

### *3.5. T-22*

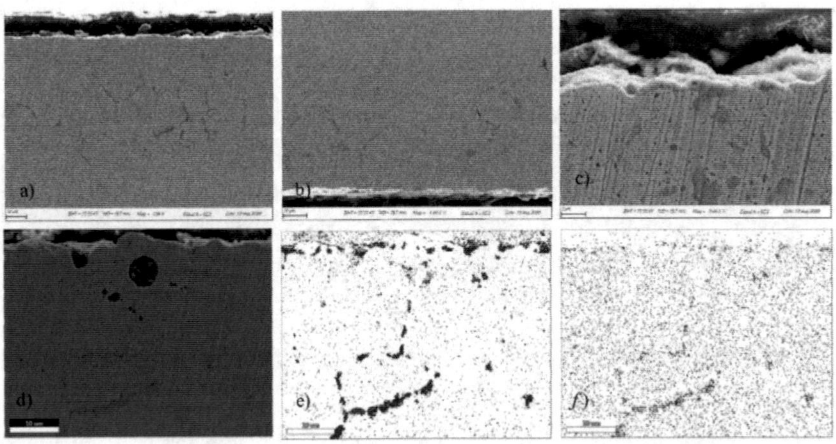


**Figure 8.** The cross-sectional SEM micrographs with EDS for T-22 and the distribution of oxygen, chromium elements.

T-22 alloy is a low alloy steel, its composition and structure are different from the other three alloys. Figure 8 shows the cross-sectional micrographs of T-22 alloy under scanning electron microscope with the EDS system. It can be seen that the overall corrosion resistance is good, without decarburization and severe carburization occurring. Fig. 8 e) and f) show that there are large volumes of chromium oxide in the deep regime of T-22, which may be due to the changes of the material structure during processing of the alloy, and not being necessarily due to this corrosion

. Figure 9 shows the relationship between the content and depth of the main elements in the T-22 alloy. Due to the low content of chromium, aluminum and other elements in T-22, only a very thin oxide layer was formed on the surface. Except for some potentially attached carbon on the surface, the carbon content inside the alloy is the lowest among the four alloys, indicating that there is no carbon transfer between the alloy and the atmosphere. According to the test results, T-22 alloy has good corrosion resistance despite its low content of alloying elements, which may be related to the metallogenic structure (Ferrite + Bainite) [11] and material structure. At present, there are few tests for of the T-22 alloy in the HTGR field. Thus, more experiments are needed to study the corrosion resistance of T-22.

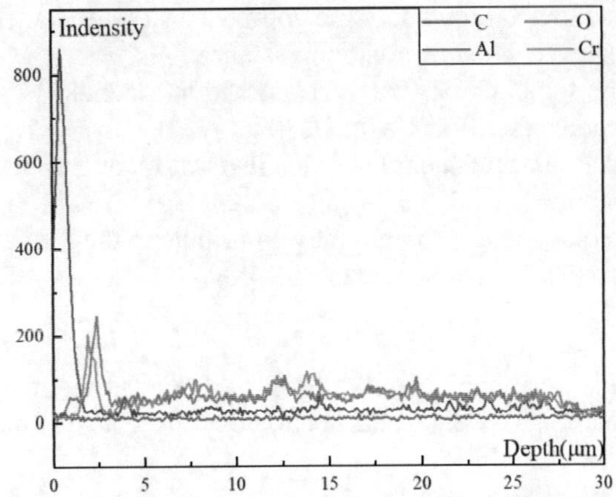


**Figure 9.** The change curve of alloying element content with depth obtained by EPMA.

### *3.6. Discussion*

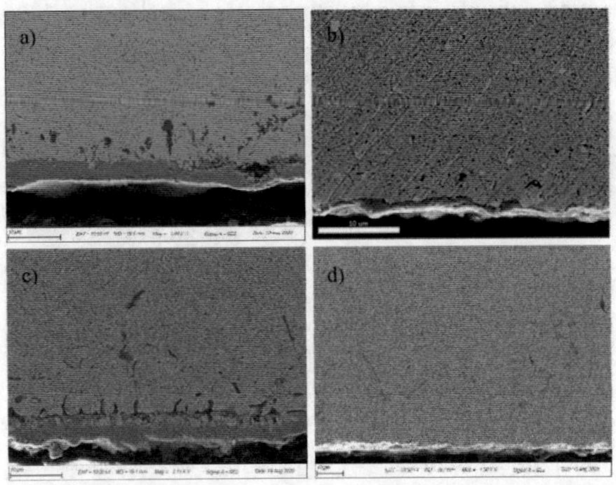


**Figure 10.** SEM cross-sectional micrographs for the four alloys, followed by that a). Inconel 617; b). Hastelloy X; c). Incoloy 800H; d).T-22

All the four alloys developed oxide scales in the test atmosphere, and the comparison of corrosion was shown in Figure 10. A dense oxide scale was formed on the surface of Hastelloy X, which can effectively avoid further corrosion. The internal oxidation is not obvious, which suggested that the oxide layer has better protection. Meanwhile, the mass gain of Hastelloy X alloy is very low, which indicates that this alloy has good corrosion resistance. The mass gain and corrosion behavior of Inconel 617 are similar to the Incoloy 800H. Both of them developed 4-5μm thick oxide layer, but spinel oxides could still be identified inside the sample, indicating that their protective effect were poor. Incoloy 800H has the highest mass gain and the deepest corrosion, so it can be determined to have the worst corrosion resistance. T-22 alloy has a thin oxide layer due to its low chromium content, but its corrosion resistance is also good according to the SEM figure. In particular, T-22 has a strong inhibition on carbon transfer between the alloy interior and the atmosphere.

## 4. Conclusion

The four Ni(Fe) base alloys foreseen to be used for the heat exchanger tubes of the steam generator in HTGR were corroded for up to 48 hours in an impure helium atmosphere at 950°C. The corrosion results were analyzed and discussed based on SEM and EMPA, and the four alloys showed different corrosion phenomena.

1. T-22 alloy and Hastelloy X alloy show the good corrosion resistance under the test conditions, and Incoloy 800H has the worst corrosion resistance;
2. The formation of the spinel oxides can be observed in Inconel 617 and 800H, which is similar to the previous research results on Hayens 230 alloy;
3. The chromium depletion occurs near the oxide layer of Inconel 617 and it may be caused by the migration of chromium;
4. A proper increase of manganese content may contribute to the formation of a dense oxide layer, thus improving the oxidation resistance of the alloy;

**Acknowledgement**
This work was supported by National Natural Science Foundation of China (NSFC) (Grant No. 11875176), and the Major National Science and Technology Projects of China (Grant No. ZX069).

**References**

[1] Shindo M , Quadakkers W J , Schuster H . Corrosion behaviour of high temperature alloys in impure helium environments[J]. Journal of Nuclear Materials, 140(2):94-105, 1986.
[2] Kurata Y, Ogawa Y, Nakajima H. Effect of Carburizing Helium Environmant on Creep-Behavior of Ni-Base Heat-Resistant Alloys for High-Temperature Gas-Cooled Reactors[J]. Tetsu to Hagane-Journal of The Iron and Steel Institute of Japan, 74(11): 2185-2192, 1988.
[3] Kurata Y, Ogawa Y, Nakajima H. Effect of Decarburizing Helium Environmant on Creep-Behavior of Ni-Base Heat-Resistant Alloys for High-Temperature Gas-Cooled Reactors[J]. Tetsu to Hagane-Journal of The Iron and Steel Institute of Japan, 74(2): 380-387, 1988.
[4] Quadakkers W J, H. Schuster. Corrosion of High Temperature Alloys in the Primary Circuit Helium of High Temperature Gas Cooled Reactors. Part I: Theoretical Background[J]. Materials and Corrosion, 36(8):141-150, 1985.
[5] Quadakkers W J. Corrosion of High Temperature Alloys in the Primary Circuit Helium of High Temperature Gas Cooled Reactors. Part II: Experimental Results[J]. Materials & Corrosion, 36(8):335-347, 1985.
[6] Shimpei HAMAMOTO, Nariaki SAKABA, Yoichi TAKEDA. Control Method of Puriˆcation System of Helium Coolant for Suppressing Decarburization of Heat-Resistant Alloy Used in Very High Temperature Gas Cooling Reactors[J]. Japanese Journal of Atomic Energy Society of Japan, 9(2), 174-182, 2010.
[7] LI Jufeng, WU Xiaobo, DUAN Hongwei, etc. Study on Localization of SA213 T-22 Transfer Heat Tube for Nuclear Safety Class One[J]. Hot Working Technology, 45(08), 82-84, 2016.
[8] LI Jufeng, YANG Sengai, YU Liyuan, ect. First Time Localization Practice of Steam Generator Tubes of Incoloy 800H for Nuclear Power Plant, 44(18), 92-94, 2015.
[9] Tsai C J. High Temperature Oxidation Behavior of Nickel and Iron Based Superalloys in Helium Containing Trace Impurities[J]. Corrosion Science and Technology. 2019, 1(18): 8-15.
[10] Jang C, Kim D, Kim D, et al. Oxidation behaviors of wrought nickel-based superalloys in various high temperature environments[J]. Transactions of Nonferrous Metals Society of China, 21(7):0-1531, 2011.
[11] LI Jufeng, WU Xiaobo, DUAN Hongwei, etc. Study on Localization of SA213 T-22 Transfer Heat Tube for Nuclear Safety Class One[J]. Hot Working Technology, 45(08):82-84, 2016.

# Drop analysis of Active Magnetic Bearing with rolling-sliding integrated auxiliary bearing

**Mingqi Wang[1,2,3], Xingnan Liu[1,2,3], Yulan Zhao[4], Guojun Yang[1,2,3], Jianqiang Chen[1,2,3], Zhengang Shi[1,2,3]**

[1]*Institute of Nuclear and New Energy Technology, Tsinghua University, Beijing, China*

[2]*Collaborative Innovation Center of Advanced Nuclear Energy Technology, Beijing, China*

[3]*The Key Laboratory of Advanced Reactor Engineering and Safety, Ministry of Education, Beijing, China 4Central Academy, Harbin Electric Corporation, Harbin, China*

Corresponding author's e-mail: shizg@tsinghua.edu.cn

**Abstract**. The Active Magnetic Bearing (AMB) technology is introduced in the High Temperature Reactor-Pebble-bed Modules (HTR-PM) demonstration nuclear power plant, which is being constructed in Shandong province, China. The auxiliary bearing is one of the most important components guaranteeing the reliability of the AMB. It also has an important impact on the reliability of the whole reactor system. Compared with the traditional auxiliary bearing, a novel one proposed by the authors has a smaller impact force and the rotor center orbit is much more concentrated during the rotor drop. This paper establishes an analytical model of drop of rolling-sliding integrated auxiliary bearing to analyze the above phenomena. Based on the Hertz contact theory, the complex structure inside the rolling bearing is simplified through a spring damping model. The overall impact model of the rolling-sliding integrated auxiliary bearing is established. Then, according to the structural characteristics of the rolling-sliding integrated auxiliary bearing, the tangential force inside the rolling- sliding integrated auxiliary bearing can be obtained by applying the angular momentum theorem. Finally, a four-degree-of-freedom horizontal rotor drop model is established to analyze and calculate the center orbit and motion state of the rotor. The analytical model is helpful in the selection and design of auxiliary bearing for AMB. In further research this contact model can be used to calculate the center orbit and contact forces in the application of the rolling-sliding integrated auxiliary bearing.

## 1. Introduction

The Active Magnetic Bearing (AMB) is a typical type of mechanical and electronic product. It has a lot of advantages, such as active suppression of vibration, ultra-high speed, lubrication-free, no mechanical friction, high energy density, low operation and maintenance costs and so on. AMB can solve the problem of traditional mechanical dynamics, and it gradually becomes a focus of research on the application of the high-speed rotating machinery [1]. In the High Temperature Reactor-Pebble-bed Modules (HTR-PM) demonstration nuclear power plant, which is being constructed in Shandong province, China, the AMB is used to suspend the rotor of the main helium blower [2, 3]. The rotor will lose support and fall on the auxiliary bearings in case of emergency such as power failure, overload, or outage for maintenance. The auxiliary bearings are also called backup bearings or protection bearings. When the rotor falls off, the auxiliary bearing accelerates rapidly and bears the collision and friction, which can avoid the damage caused by the rotor falling off. Therefore, auxiliary bearing is one of the most important components guaranteeing the reliability of the AMB. It also directly affects the reliability of the whole reactor system.

Generally speaking, there are two basic types of auxiliary bearings, rolling bearings and sliding bearings. Compared with sliding bearings, the rolling auxiliary bearings can effectively reduce the friction inside the bearing when the rotor falls down. However, the contact between the rolling element and the inner and outer rings is point contact, which has large local stress. And the rolling auxiliary bearing is more susceptible to damage. Prashad et al. [4] proposed the Double Decker Rolling Bearing (DDRB) formed by connecting two high-precision rolling bearings to each other via an adapter ring. As an auxiliary bearing, it will effectively reduce the dynamic impact of the rotor drop. But due to its complicated structure and difficult design, its application is limited. The sliding auxiliary bearing has a simple structure and large starting friction resistance. It is mostly used in low- speed and heavy-load rotor system. OKBM institute of Russia [5~7] applied sliding auxiliary bearing with damping systems in the helium turbine modular high temperature gas cooled reactor to provide temporary support for the rotor. Moreover, they applied the electromagnetic bearing to the 600MW GT-MHR system. In addition, some scholars improved the structure of auxiliary bearings according to different engineering application requirements, and proposed Planetary Gear Auxiliary Bearings, Zero Clearance Auxiliary Bearings (ZCAB) [8], External Clearance Auxiliary Bearings [9] and hybrid auxiliary bearings which combined different types of auxiliary bearings or mechanical parts. The auxiliary bearing can effectively avoid the catastrophic accident of the electromagnetic bearing suspension rotor system. [10]

G. J. Yang et al. [11] presented a new-type auxiliary bearing called rolling-sliding integrated auxiliary bearing. It is a design of novel arrangement with outer clearance structure. For this novel arrangement, the rolling bearing is fixed on the rotor, and there is interference fit or small clearance fit between the inner ring of the rolling bearing and the rotor. The speed of the outer ring will be equal to or smaller than the speed of the rotor. When the magnetic bearing system fails, the rolling bearing will fall on the bearing housing with the rotor. J. Q. Chen et al. [12, 13] studied the performance of this new auxiliary bearing by simulation with software LS- Dyna. X. N. Liu et al. [14] conducted a rotor drop experiment on a horizontal high-speed motor with an AMB system, and compared the rotor center orbit and the maximum impact force of the rolling-sliding integrated auxiliary bearing and the traditional auxiliary bearing.

The structure of the rolling-sliding integrated auxiliary bearing is shown in Fig. 1. In this paper, a drop dynamics model for the rolling-sliding integrated auxiliary bearing is proposed. The dynamic characteristics and internal friction between the rolling-sliding integrated auxiliary bearing and the rotor are studied in the falling process of the horizontal rotor, so as to analyze the dynamics of the dropping rotor.

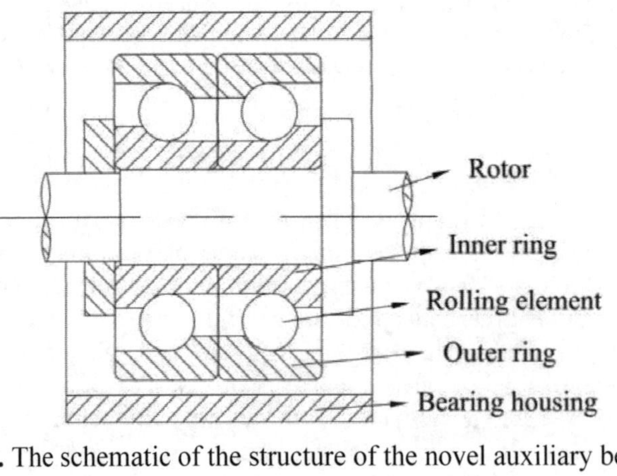


**Figure 1.** The schematic of the structure of the novel auxiliary bearing.

## 2. Hertz Contact

According to the Hertz contact theory, the Hertz contact force F is expressed as:

$$F = \begin{cases} K\delta^e + C\dot{\delta}, \delta > 0 \\ 0, \delta \leq 0 \end{cases} \tag{1}$$

where $\delta$ represents the relative normal deformation of the contacting bodies, $K$ and $C$ are respectively the generalized stiffness parameter and generalized damping parameter, $e$ is the contact coefficient and its value is determined by the contact type: for point contact, $e$=3/2, for line contact, $e$=10/9 and for surface contact, $e$=1 [15]. The generalized parameter $K$ is dependent on contact type and material properties.

There are two main types of contact between horizontal rotor and the rolling-sliding integrated auxiliary bearing. The radial contact between the rolling bearing and the bearing housing is line contact, while between the internal rolling element of the rolling bearing and the inner and outer rings is point contact. The bearing characteristics of the rolling- sliding integrated auxiliary bearing is determined by the above two contact types.

According to the relative normal deformation of the contacting bodies $\delta$, the line contact stiffness parameter can be calculated by the empirical formula proposed by Palmgren [16]:

$$K_1 = 0.7l^{8/9}\left[\frac{(1-\upsilon_1{}^2)}{E_1} + \frac{(1-\upsilon_2{}^2)}{E_2}\right]^{-1} \tag{2}$$

where $l$ is the line contact length, $E_1$ $E_2$ are respectively the elastic modulus of two contact surfaces, $\upsilon_1$ 、$\upsilon_2$ are the Poisson's ratios of two contact surfaces.

If no load is applied, the contact between the rolling element and the inner and outer rings is a point contact. When the load is applied, the contact is a surface contact, and the contact surface is elliptical. It is considered that point contact occurs between the rolling element and the inner and outer rings. Point contact stiffness parameter $K_p$ can be expressed as [17]:

$$K_p = \frac{1}{2}\sqrt{\frac{2\pi^3\mu^3}{3\left[\frac{(1-\upsilon_1{}^2)}{E_1} + \frac{(1-\upsilon_2{}^2)}{E_2}\right]^2 \Gamma^3 \sum\rho}} \tag{3}$$

where $\mu$ is the Hertz contact coefficient, $\Gamma$ is the complete elliptic integral of the first kind and $\sum\rho$ is the sum of radius of curvature of two contact bodies on two orthogonal planes.

## 3. Internal Contact Stiffness Parameter of Rolling Bearings

The rolling bearing is an important component of the rolling-sliding integrated auxiliary bearing. When the horizontal rotor falls down, the internal forces of the rolling bearing directly affect the rotor drop. This section will analyze the contact force inside the rolling bearing. According to the structural characteristics of the rolling-sliding integrated auxiliary bearing, the rotor and inner ring are considered as a whole. The load is applied to the bearing and transmitted to the bearing housing through the rolling element and outer ring. It is considered that the rotor is rigid and elastic deformation occurs in the contact process between the rotor and the auxiliary bearing. Considering material damping, the internal contact of rolling bearing can be simplified through a spring damping model with mass block.

Hertz contact will occur inside the rolling-sliding integrated auxiliary bearing when the rotor falls. Although radial load can reduce the contact angle of angular contact ball bearing, it has little effect on its size. Considering the material elasticity and ignoring the influence of the radial load and position of the rolling element on the size of the contact angle, the contact angle of auxiliary bearing is constant during the loading process. The internal contact stiffness parameter of angular contact ball bearing is shown in Fig. 2.

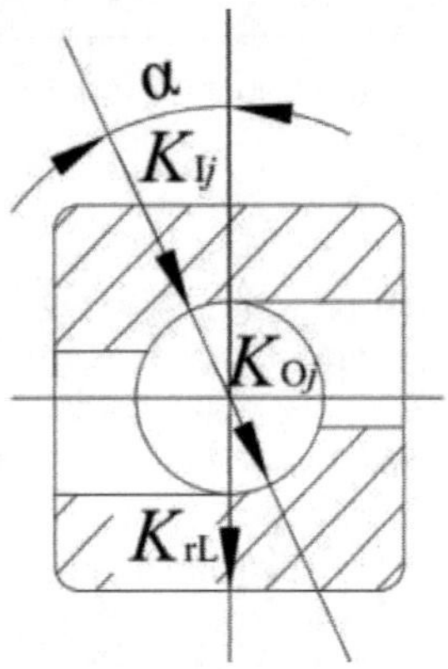


**Figure 2.** Internal contact stiffness parameter of angular contact ball bearing.

In Fig. 2, $K_{Ij}$, $K_{Oj}$ are respectively the contact stiffness parameter between the j th rolling element and the inner and outer rings. According to equation (3), the contact stiffness parameter between all rolling elements and the inner and outer rings has nothing to do with the position of the rolling element. $K_{rL}$ is the contact stiffness parameter between the outer ring and the bearing housing, and α is the bearing contact angle. When the horizontal rotor falls down, the axial force of the rolling-sliding integrated auxiliary bearing is small, which has little effect on the motion state of the rotor [14]. Therefore, the axial contact stiffness parameter is not analyzed here. The spring structure in contact with the inner and outer rings of the rolling element is regarded as a series spring, and all rolling elements are regarded as parallel springs. According to the structure of the bearing, the total stiffness of the *j*-th rolling element (series connection of the inner and outer rings) can be expressed as:

$$K_{Bj} = \frac{1}{\left(K_{Ij}{}^{-2/3} + K_{Oj}{}^{-2/3}\right)^{3/2}} \tag{4}$$

The radial displacement of the *j* th rolling element is $\delta_{rBj}$, the radial force of the *j*-th rolling element can be expressed as:

$$K_{rBj} = K_{Bj}\left(\frac{\delta_{rBj}}{\cos\alpha}\right)^{3/2}\cos\alpha = K_{Bj}\cdot\delta_{rBj}{}^{3/2}\cdot(\cos\alpha)^{-1/2} \tag{5}$$

Based on equations (4~6), the radial component of the total stiffness parameter of the *j*-th rolling element can be expressed as:

$$K_{rBj} = \frac{1}{\left(K_{Ij}{}^{-2/3} + K_{Oj}{}^{-2/3}\right)^{3/2}}(\cos\alpha)^{-1/2} \tag{6}$$

If the external radial load is Fr, the radial deformation of the rolling element in the direction of the maximum radial load is $\delta_{rB}$, and the included angle between the adjacent rolling element and the center of the rolling bearing is β. According to the formula of spring series and parallel connection, and considering the force balance:

$$F_r = K_{rBj}\delta_{rB}{}^{3/2} + 2K_{rBj}(\delta_{rB}\cdot\cos\beta)^{3/2}\cos\beta + 2K_{rBj}(\delta_{rB}\cdot\cos2\beta)^{3/2}\cos2\beta + \cdots \tag{7}$$

If is the number of rolling elements is NB, the equation (7) can be simplified as [16]:

$$F_r = K_{rBj}\frac{N_B}{4.36}\delta_{rB}{}^{3/2} \tag{8}$$

According to the combination of contact stiffness parameter of all stressed rolling elements, the radial contact stiffness parameter of the rolling element in the direction of the maximum radial load is obtained by

$$K_{rB} = \frac{K_{rBj} N_B}{4.36} \tag{9}$$

The rolling element is simplified as the spring damping model, and the normal contact force is replaced by the linear spring damping force. When the rotor collides with the rolling-sliding integrated auxiliary bearing, the rolling element's comprehensive radial embedding depth $\delta_{rB}$ is positive, i.e., $\delta_{rB} > 0$. According to the Hertz contact theory, the comprehensive radial contact force between the rolling element and the inner and outer rings can be obtained as follows:

$$F_{rB} = K_{rB} {\delta_{rB}}^{3/2} + C_{rB} \dot{\delta}_{rB} \tag{10}$$

Thus, we can obtain the relationship between the overall deformation amount of the bearing (or elastic approaching amount) and the load. The contact stiffness parameter of the bearing can be obtained after some manipulation. The comprehensive radial contact force between the rolling element and the inner and outer rings can also be calculated.

## 4. The Contact Model of Rolling- Sliding Integrated Auxiliary Bearing

When the electromagnetic bearing system fails, the rotor immediately loses the electromagnetic control and falls on the auxiliary bearing. In the falling process, the various degrees of freedom of the rotor have extremely strong coupling relationships. The rotor drop process is highly nonlinear. The study of the contact force exerted by the dropping rotor on the auxiliary bearing is based on the accurate contact model. In this section, with the help of the Hertz contact theory and considering the damping characteristics in the contact process, a nonlinear contact force model of dropping rotor on the auxiliary bearing is established.

According to the Hertz contact theory, the internal contact force of the rolling-sliding integrated auxiliary bearing is analyzed. When the rotor falls, line contact occurs between the outer ring and bearing housing. The radial depth $\delta_{rL}$ of insertion between outer ring and bearing housing satisfies $\delta_{rL} > 0$. The radial contact force between the outer ring and the bearing housing can be obtained as follows:

$$F_{rL} = K_{rL} {\delta_{rL}}^{10/9} + C_{rL} \dot{\delta}_{rL} \tag{11}$$

where $K_{rL}$, $C_{rL}$ are respectively the line contact stiffness parameter and damping parameter between the outer ring and bearing housing. Therefore, the overall impact model of the rolling-sliding integrated auxiliary bearing is shown in Fig. 3.

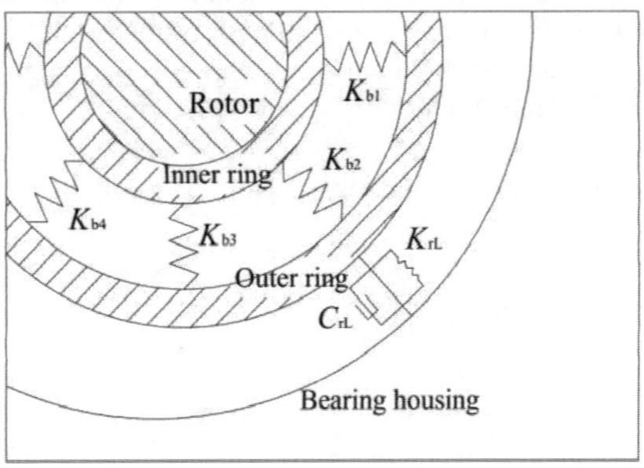


**Figure 3.** The contact model of rolling-sliding integrated auxiliary bearing.

According to the model structure:

$$F_r = F_{rB} = F_{rL} \tag{12}$$

$$\delta_{rB} + \delta_{rL} = \delta_r \tag{13}$$

here Fr is the comprehensive contact force between the rotor and the bearing housing and $\delta_r$ is the comprehensive radial embedding depth of the auxiliary bearing. With $\delta_r$, the coupling formula (10~13) can be used to calculate the magnitude of $F_r$, $\delta_{rB}$ and $\delta_{rL}$. The expressions of contact stiffness parameters are given above. Due to the complexity of bearing damping calculation, damping is generally not involved in the analysis of bearing in the existing literature. When damping is required, it is usually measured experimentally. The internal elasticity and damping of the rolling-sliding integrated auxiliary bearing greatly buffer the force on the bearing housing when the rotor falls down.

## 5. Tangential Contact Force Between the Horizontal Rotor and the Rolling-Sliding Integrated Auxiliary Bearing

When the electromagnetic bearing system fails, the rotor falls on the rolling-sliding integrated auxiliary bearing. The interaction inside the bearing is shown in Fig. 4

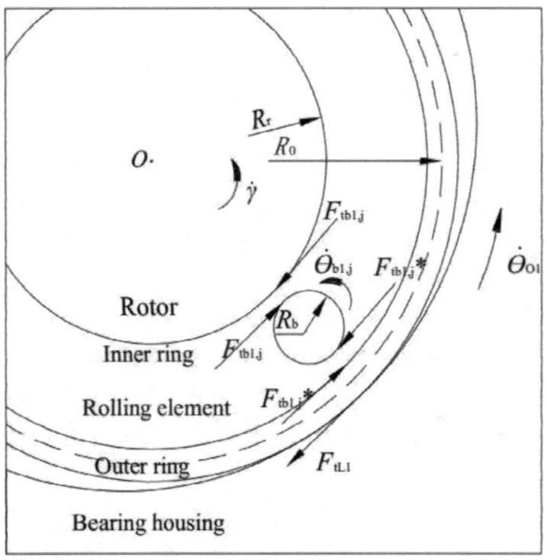


**Figure 4.** The drop model of the rotor

In the falling process of the horizontal rotor, the rotation process of the left and right rolling-sliding integrated auxiliary bearings is driven by the radial friction of the bearing housing and the rotor. When the rolling element rotates, there is not only a rotation around its own central axis, but also a revolution around the center of the bearing. In the case of the rotation of the rolling element, the rolling element rotates around a central axis. The angular velocity is the absolute angular velocity relative to the ground, such as relative to a fixed horizontal line. It is stipulated that the vertical paper facing outwards is the positive direction. Based on the angular momentum theorem, the rotational motion of the rotor and the left and right rolling-sliding integrated auxiliary bearings can be obtained.

$$\ddot{\gamma} J = -(F_{tb1} + F_{tb2})R_r \tag{14}$$

$$\ddot{\theta}_{b1} I_b = -(F_{tb1} + F_{tb1}^{*})R_b \tag{15}$$

$$\ddot{\theta}_{b2} I_b = -(F_{tb2} + F_{tb2}^{*})R_b \tag{16}$$

$$\ddot{\theta}_{O1} I_O = (F_{tb1}^{*} - F_{tL1})R_O \tag{17}$$

$$\ddot{\theta}_{O2} I_O = (F_{tb2}^{*} - F_{tL2})R_O \tag{18}$$

where $J$, $I_b$, $I_O$ are respectively the moment of inertia of rotor (including inner ring), rolling element and outer ring, $R_r$, $R_b$, $R_O$ are the radius of the rotor (including inner ring), rolling element and the outer ring, $\dot{\gamma}$ is the speed of rotor, $\dot{\theta}_{b1}$, $\dot{\theta}_{b2}$ are the rolling element speed of the left and right auxiliary bearing, $\dot{\theta}_O$ is the speed of outer ring, $F_{tb1}$, $F_{tb2}$ are respectively tangential forces between the left and right auxiliary bearing rolling element and the rotor, $F_{tb1}{}^*$, $F_{tb2}{}^*$ the tangential forces between the left and right auxiliary bearing rolling element and the outer ring and $F_{tL1}$, $F_{tL2}$ the tangential forces between the left and right auxiliary bearing outer ring and the bearing housing.

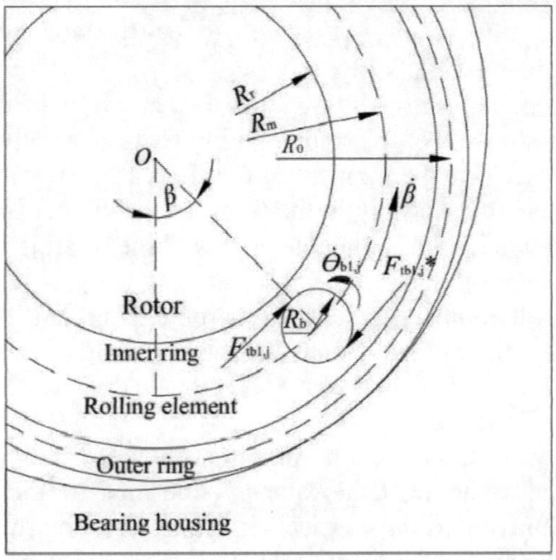


**Figure 5.** The drop model of the rotor (Consider the revolution of the rolling element).

It is also considered that the angular velocity of the rolling element is absolute ?? the angular velocity to the ground, such as relative to a fixed horizontal line. Ignoring the gravity of the rolling element, it is also stipulated that the vertical paper facing outwards is the positive direction. The angular momentum theorem about the rolling element is established relative to the bearing center [18, 19]:

$$-I_b\ddot{\theta}_{b1}\cos\alpha + m_b R_m{}^2\ddot{\beta}_1 = F_{tb1}R_r - F_{tb1}{}^*R_O \tag{19}$$

$$-I_b\ddot{\theta}_{b2}\cos\alpha + m_b R_m{}^2\ddot{\beta}_2 = F_{tb2}R_r - F_{tb2}{}^*R_O \tag{20}$$

where Rm is the revolution radius of the rolling element and $\dot{\beta}_1$, $\dot{\beta}_2$ are respectively the revolution speed of the rolling element of the left and right rolling-sliding integrated auxiliary bearings. Moreover, the contact angle of the rolling element is ignored here. The spin axis of the rolling element is considered to be perpendicular to the surface of the paper.

According to the characteristics of the structure of the rolling-sliding integrated auxiliary bearing, the moment of inertia of the rolling element and the outer ring is considered to be very small compared to the rotor. In order to simplify the calculation model, it is assumed that sliding friction always occurs between the outer ring and the bearing housing and rolling friction always occurs between the rolling element and the inner and outer rings during the falling of the horizontal rotor. As for the structure, the rolling bearing can be regarded as a planet wheel. When standing on the rolling element (planet wheel) for observation, the rotor, the rolling element and the outer ring all rotate around a central axis. The angular velocities of the three should be subtracted from the velocity of the rotating coordinate system, that is, the velocity of the rolling element.

$$R_r(\dot{\gamma} - \dot{\beta}_1) = R_b(\dot{\theta}_{b1} - \dot{\beta}_1) = R_O(\dot{\theta}_{O1} - \dot{\beta}_1) \tag{21}$$

$$R_r(\dot{\gamma} - \dot{\beta}_2) = R_b(\dot{\theta}_{b2} - \dot{\beta}_2) = R_O(\dot{\theta}_{O2} - \dot{\beta}_2) \tag{22}$$

The following formula can be obtained by using the pure rolling hypothesis:

$$F_{tL1} = \mu_d F_{rL1} \tag{23}$$

$$F_{tL2} = \mu_d F_{rL2} \tag{24}$$

where μd is the coefficient of dynamic friction between the outer ring and the bearing housing. FrL1, FrL2 are respectively the radial forces between the left and right auxiliary bearing outer ring and bearing housing, and the calculation formula has been given above. Considering the revolution and rotation of the rolling element, $F_{tb1}$, $F_{tb2}$, $F_{tb1}{}^{*}$, $F_{tb2}{}^{*}$ can be obtained according to the formula (14~24). The results can be obtained explicitly.

In fact, the friction between the rolling-sliding integrated auxiliary bearing and the bearing housing is more complex in the falling process of the rotor. Rolling friction and sliding friction occur staggered in the whole falling process. Because the moment of inertia of the outer ring is small, the outer ring is rapidly slowed down by the bearing housing in the rotor fall behind. After bouncing, the outer ring is subjected to the force transmitted by the rolling element, and the rotating speed has a certain degree of improvement. Ignoring acceleration and deceleration time, rotor spinning and other state, it can be considered that only sliding friction occurs between the outer ring and the bearing housing, and only rolling friction occurs between the rolling element and the inner and outer rings.

## 6. 4 DOF Horizontal Rotor Drop Model

In order to ensure the stability of the suspension rotor in normal operation, the rotor is controlled in six degrees of freedom. The axial rotation of the rotor is controlled by the motor. The four degrees of freedom of the rotor – in horizontal and vertical direction, are controlled by two radial magnetic bearings respectively. The axial degree of freedom of the rotor is controlled by an axial electromagnetic bearing. It is assumed that the rotor is rigid and affected by the gravity of the rotor itself and the auxiliary bearings during the falling process of the rotor. A four-degree- of-freedom horizontal rotor falling model is established as follows.

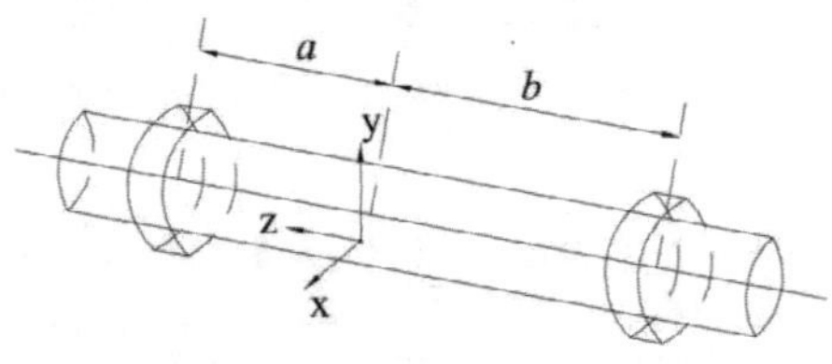


**Figure 6.** Horizontal rotor diagram.

In Fig. 6, a and b are respectively represent the positions of the left and right auxiliary bearing sections. The Cartesian coordinate system is established at the center of the rotor with the bearing housing centroid as the origin.

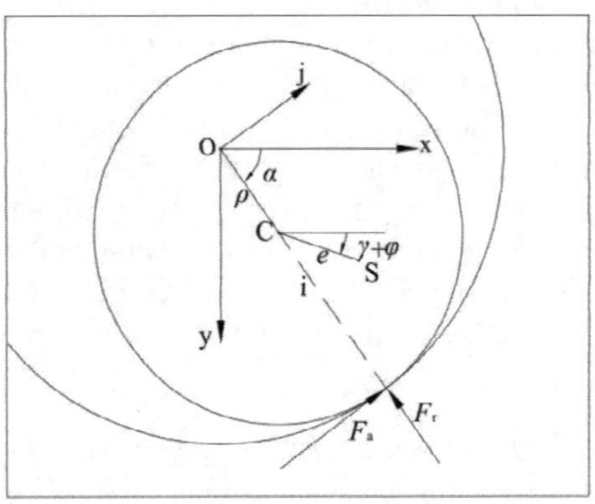


**Figure 7.** Radial friction between rotor and auxiliary bearing.

When the electromagnetic bearing fails, the rotor immediately loses its control in the x, y directions and the support of four degrees of freedom. Radial contact occurs between dropping rotor and auxiliary bearing.

According to the contact model of the rolling- sliding integrated auxiliary bearing established above, the motion state of the rotor is analyzed. In Fig.7, O is the bearing housing centroid, C is the rotor centroid, S is the rotor barycenter, ρ is the distance between O and C, e is the eccentricity, $\dot{\alpha}$ is the rotor vortex speed, $\dot{\gamma}$ is the rotor rotation speed and φ is the initial phase. According to the geometric relationship, the displacements of the rotor barycenter S are as follows:

$$\begin{cases} x_s = \rho\cos\alpha + e\cos(\gamma+\varphi) \\ y_s = \rho\sin\alpha + e\sin(\gamma+\varphi) \end{cases} \tag{25}$$

$$\begin{cases} \dot{x}_s = \dot{\rho}\cos\alpha - \dot{\alpha}\rho\sin\alpha - e\dot{\gamma}\sin(\gamma+\varphi) \\ \dot{y}_s = \dot{\rho}\sin\alpha + \dot{\alpha}\rho\cos\alpha + e\dot{\gamma}\cos(\gamma+\varphi) \end{cases} \tag{26}$$

Denote the displacements of the left and right auxiliary bearing centroid in the $x$ direction and the $y$ direction as respectively, $x_1$, $x_2$, $y_1$, $y_2$, then the displacements of the rotor centroid C are as follows:

$$\begin{cases} x = \dfrac{bx_1 + ax_2}{a+b} \\ y = \dfrac{by_1 + ay_2}{a+b} \end{cases} \tag{27}$$

The rotation angles of the rotor around the X-axis and Y-axis are Θx、Θy respectively:

$$\begin{cases} \theta_x = -\dfrac{y_1 - y_2}{a+b} \\ \theta_y = -\dfrac{x_1 - x_2}{a+b} \end{cases} \tag{28}$$

The displacement of the left and right auxiliary bearing centroid in the $x$ and $y$ directions can be expressed:

$$\begin{cases} x_1 = \rho\cos\alpha - a\theta_y \\ y_1 = \rho\sin\alpha - a\theta_x \\ x_2 = \rho\cos\alpha + b\theta_y \\ y_2 = \rho\sin\alpha + b\theta_x \end{cases} \tag{29}$$

Under the global coordinate system, the acting forces of the left and right auxiliary bearings on the rotor $F_{x1}$, $F_{y1}$, $F_{x2}$, $F_{y2}$ are:

$$F_{x1} = -F_{r1}\frac{x_1}{\sqrt{{x_1}^2+{y_1}^2}} + F_{tb1}\frac{y_1}{\sqrt{{x_1}^2+{y_1}^2}} \tag{30}$$

$$F_{y1} = -F_{r1}\frac{y_1}{\sqrt{{x_1}^2+{y_1}^2}} - F_{tb1}\frac{x_1}{\sqrt{{x_1}^2+{y_1}^2}} \tag{31}$$

$$F_{x2} = -F_{r2}\frac{x_2}{\sqrt{{x_2}^2+{y_2}^2}} + F_{tb2}\frac{y_2}{\sqrt{{x_2}^2+{y_2}^2}} \tag{32}$$

$$F_{y2} = -F_{r2}\frac{y_2}{\sqrt{{x_2}^2+{y_2}^2}} - F_{tb2}\frac{x_2}{\sqrt{{x_2}^2+{y_2}^2}} \tag{33}$$

where $F_{r1}$, $F_{r2}$ are the radial contact force between the left and right auxiliary bearing and the rotor, $F_{tb1}$, $F_{tb2}$ are the tangential force between the rolling element of the left and right auxiliary bearing and the rotor. The calculation formulas have been given above. After the horizontal rotor falls, components of the force exerted by the rolling-sliding integrated auxiliary bearing on the rotor are:

$$F_x = F_{x1} + F_{x2} \tag{34}$$

$$F_y = F_{y1} + F_{y2} \tag{35}$$

In order to analyze the mechanical properties of the falling rotor, the dynamic model of the horizontal rotor is established according to the Lagrange equations as follows:

$$\frac{d}{dt}\left(\frac{\partial T}{\partial \dot{q}_1}\right) - \frac{\partial T}{\partial q_1} + \frac{\partial V}{\partial q_1} = Q_1 \tag{36}$$

$$T = \frac{1}{2}m(\dot{x}_s{}^2 + \dot{y}_s{}^2) + \frac{1}{2}I_p\dot{\theta}_x{}^2 + \frac{1}{2}I_p\dot{\theta}_y{}^2 + \frac{1}{2}J\dot{\gamma}^2 \tag{37}$$

$$V = mg\rho\sin\alpha + mge\sin(\gamma + \varphi) \tag{38}$$

where qi is the generalized coordinate, Qi is the generalized force, T is the kinetic energy of the rotor, V is the gravitational potential energy of the rotor, m is the quality of rotor, Ip is the equatorial moment of inertia of the rotor, and J is the polar moment of inertia of the rotor.

According to the above analysis, the rotor state during the rotor falling process can be obtained as follows:

$$\ddot{\alpha} = \frac{1}{\rho}\left[\frac{-F_t}{m\rho} - e\ddot{\gamma}\cos(\alpha - \gamma - \varphi) - g\cos\alpha - e\dot{\gamma}^2\sin(\alpha - \gamma - \varphi) - 2\dot{\rho}\dot{\alpha}\right] \tag{39}$$

$$\ddot{\rho} = -\frac{F_n}{m} - e\ddot{\gamma}\sin(\alpha - \gamma - \varphi) + e\dot{\gamma}^2\cos(\alpha - \gamma - \varphi) + \dot{\alpha}^2\rho - g\sin\alpha \tag{40}$$

$$I_p\ddot{\theta}_x = aF_{y1} - bF_{y2} - J\dot{\gamma}\dot{\theta}_y \tag{41}$$

$$I_p\ddot{\theta}_y = aF_{x1} - bF_{x2} - J\dot{\gamma}\dot{\theta}_x \tag{42}$$

where $F_n$ and $F_t$ respectively represents the normal contact force and tangential friction between the rotor and the auxiliary bearing:

$$F_n = -(F_x\cos\alpha + F_y\sin\alpha) \tag{43}$$

$$F_t = F_x\sin\alpha - F_y\cos\alpha \tag{44}$$

According to the relative displacement of the rotor and the auxiliary bearing center, the collision state can be evaluated. The forward insertion depth indicates radial contact between the rotor and the auxiliary bearing. Otherwise, no contact occurs. The contact force can be obtained according to the relation between the Hertz contact force and the deformation, which has been described in detail above.

## 7. Results and Outlook

Based on the Hertz contact theory, the complex structure inside the rolling bearing is simplified to the spring damping model, and obtain the comprehensive radial contact force inside the rolling bearing. The overall impact model of the rolling-sliding integrated auxiliary bearing is established. Then, according to the structural characteristics of the rolling-sliding integrated auxiliary bearing, the tangential force inside the rolling-sliding integrated auxiliary bearing can be obtained by applying the angular momentum theorem. Finally, a 4-degree-of-freedom horizontal rotor drop model is established to analyze and calculate the center orbit and motion state of the rotor. Thus, the drop analysis of the horizontal dropping rotor of the rolling-sliding integrated auxiliary bearing is carried out.

At present, the experimental verification of the impact model has been completed. The research in near future will focus on the solution of the model and the comparison of calculation and experimental results. Furthermore, a quantitative comparison will be made between the rolling-sliding integrated auxiliary bearing and the traditional rolling bearing to verify the model predictability.

**References**

[1] Schweizer, G., Bleuler, H., and Traxler, A., Active Magnetic Bearings—Basics, Properties and Application of Active Magnetic Bearings (Translated by Yu, L., and Yuan, C. J.), Beijing: New Time Press, 1997.

[2] Z. Y., Zhang, Y. D., Dong, F., Li, et al, The Shandong Shidao Bay 200 MWe High-Temperature Gas-Cooled Reactor Pebble-Bed Module (HTR-PM) Demonstration Power Plant: An Engineering and Technological Innovation, Engineering, 2(1), pp. 112-118, 1916.

[3] G. J. Yang, Z. G. Shi, and N. Mo, Technical Design and Engineering Prototype Experiment of Active Magnetic Bearing for Helium Blower of HTR-PM, Annals of Nuclear Energy, 71, pp. 103-110, 2014.

[4] Prashad Har, A New Generation Double Decker High Precision Rolling Element Bearing — Concept, Development and Investigations, Tribology Transactions, 44(2): 203-208, 2001.

[5] Kodochigov N G, Belov A, Borovkov S E, et al, Development of the GT-MHR vertical turbomachine design, The 4th International Topical Meeting on High Temperature Reactor Technology, Washington DC, USA, 2008.

[6] Baxi C, Telengator A, Razvi J, Rotor Scale Model Tests for Power Conversion Unit of GT-MHR, Nuclear Engineering and Design, 251: 344-348, 2012.

[7] Belov S E, Borovkov M N, Golovko V F, et al, Approaches to experimental validation of high-temperature gas-cooled reactor components, Nuclear Engineering and Design, 251: 2-17, 2012.

[8] Heshmat H., and H. M. Chen, Zero Clearance Auxiliary Bearing for Providing Rotor Shock Tolerance, US Patent No. 5,752,774, 1998.

[9] T. W. Liu, L. Chen, and D. L. Shi, An Auxiliary Bearing with Outer Clearance Structure, Bearing, (9), pp. 36-40, 2011. (in Chinese)

[10] Penfield Scott, Rodwell Ed, Auxiliary Bearing Design Considerations for Gas Cooled Reactors, Technology Insights, 7: 5-7, 1997.

[11] G. J. Yang, Z. G. Shi, Y. Xu, and X. N. Liu, A Type of Rolling-Sliding Integrated Auxiliary Bearing, CN 201210258948.8, 2012.

[12] J. Q. Chen, Z. Sun, G. J. Yang, X. N. Liu, and Z. G. Shi, Research on Rolling-Sliding Integrated Auxiliary Bearing and its Application in High Temperature Reactor, International Conference on Nuclear Engineering, Proceedings, ICONE 25th, Shanghai, China, July 2-6, 2017.

[13] J. Q. Chen, X. N. Liu, G. J. Yang, and Z. G. Shi, Preliminary simulation study on rolling-sliding integrated auxiliary bearings, Lubrication Engineering, 42(10), pp. 98-103, 2017. (in Chinese)

[14] X. N. Liu, Y. Zhou, X. S. Yan,J. J. Zhao, Z. G. Shi, J. Q. Chen, Y. L. Zhao, G. J. Yang*, Experimental study on the novel rolling-sliding integrated auxiliary bearing in active magnetic bearing during rotor drop, Annals of Nuclear Energy , 2019 (136), 107044.

[15] Harris T A, Rolling Bearing Analysis, New York: J. Wiley, 1991.

[16] Okamoto Junichiro, Design calculation of ball bearing (Translated by Huang, Z. Q.), Beijing: China Machine Press, 2003.

[17] Hamrock B J, Dowson D, Ball Bearing Lubrication, John Wiley& Sons, 1981.

[18] Y. C. Wu, Conservation of angular momentum in the rotation of a rigid body on a variable axis, Physics Bulletin, 2001(01):7-8. (in Chinese)

[19] Daniel Kepler, Robert Kolenkow, An introduction to mechanics (Translated by Liu, S. X.), Beijing: China Machine Press, 2018.

# ASME Code Rules and ASTM Standards Integration for Ceramic Composite Core Materials and Components[1]

**J W Geringer[1], Y Katoh[1], S Gonczy[2], T Burchell[1], M Mitchell[3], M Jenkins[4], and W Windes[5]**

[1] Materials Science & Technology Division, Oak Ridge National Laboratory
One Bethel Valley Rd, Oak Ridge, TN 37830, USA
phone: +1-865-241-8510, geringerj@ornl.gov
[2]Gateway Materials, 221 S. Emerson, Mt. Prospect, IL 60056, USA
[3]USNC, 2288 W Commodore Way Ste 300, Seattle, WA 98199-1465, USA
[4]Bothell Engineering & Science Technologies, 17815-93rd Pl NE, Bothell, WA 98011, USA
[5] Idaho National Laboratory, 775 MK Simpson Blvd, Idaho Falls, ID 83401, USA

**Abstract.** Fiber-reinforced ceramic matrix composites have many desirable properties for high-temperature nuclear applications, including excellent thermal and mechanical properties and reasonable to outstanding radiation resistance. Over the last 20 years, the use of ceramic composite materials has already expanded in many commercial nonnuclear industries as fabrication and application technologies mature. The new ASME design and construction rules under Section III, Subsection HH, Subpart B lay out the requirements and criteria for materials, design, machining and installation, inspection, examination, testing, and the marking procedure for ceramic composite core components, which is similar to the established graphite code under Section III, Subsection HH, Subpart A. Moreover, the general requirements listed in Section III, Subsection HA, Subpart B are also expanded to include ceramic composite materials. The code rules rely heavily on the development and publication of standards for composite specification, classification, and testing of mechanical, thermal, and other properties. These test methods are developed in the American Society for Testing and Materials Committee C28 on Advanced Ceramics with a current focus on ceramic composite tubes. Details of the composites code, design methodology, and similarities to the graphite code, as well as guidance for the development of specifications for ceramic composites for nuclear application and recent standard developments, are discussed. The next step is to "close the gap" to support licensing aspects by validating the code with benchmarking data.

[1] This manuscript has been authored by UT-Battelle, LLC, under contract DE-AC05-00OR22725 with the US Department of Energy (DOE). The US government retains and the publisher, by accepting the article for publication, acknowledges that the US government retains a nonexclusive, paid-up, irrevocable, worldwide license to publish or reproduce the published form of this manuscript, or allow others to do so, for US government purposes. DOE will provide public access to these results of federally sponsored research in accordance with the DOE Public Access Plan

## 1. Introduction

Continuous fiber-reinforced ceramic matrix composites (CMCs) are enabling materials for various advanced energy systems, including high-temperature reactors (HTRs). Promising material properties—such as low neutron absorption, excellent high-temperature strength, maintained mechanical properties, and, in some cases, chemical inertness—make it ideal candidate materials for core applications. The American Society for Mechanical Engineers (ASME) under Boiler and Pressure Vessel Code (BPVC) Section III, Division 5 published its first design rules for CMCs in the 2019 edition. The code addresses the construction requirements for nuclear reactor applications of silicon carbide matrix with silicon carbide fibers (SiC/SiC) and carbon-based matrix with a carbon fiber (C/C) composite material.

## 2. The Purpose of Codes and Standards

The US Nuclear Regulatory Commission's (NRC) objective is to ensure public health and safety in the operation of commercial nuclear power plants as it relates to reactors, materials, and waste [1]. Besides licensing and inspection of nuclear facilities and the possession, use, and disposal of nuclear materials, it is also part of the regulator's mission to establish regulations and requirements. From this stance, it supports the development of industry consensus codes and standards, which is valuable to both industry and the regulator [2]. Codes and standards provide guidance as to what constitutes good practice, and it enables technology for life cycle applications [3].

When applying for a license, the process requires applicants to specify the design methodology, material specifications, quality assurance, and inspection and installation requirements for NRC approval, as stipulated under 10 CFR 50 regulations. Applicants or designers can use in-house developed standards or industry consensus standards. ASME is a professional standards organization that has developed codes, specifications, and standards for metal, concrete, and graphite components.

In particular, ASME Section III, "Rules for Construction of Nuclear Facility Components," under Division 5, "HTRs," has incorporated the general and technical requirements for CMCs under Subsection HA, Subpart B, "General Requirements for Graphite and Composite Materials" [4], and Subsection HH, Subpart B, "Composite Materials" [5]. Moreover, the code rules rely on the guidelines and test standards, which were concurrently developed by the American Society for Testing and Materials (ASTM).

## 3. Ceramic Matrix Composites and Potential Applications

The ASME BPVC defines CMCs as a material consisting of two or more materials, in which the first matrix component is a ceramic, while the secondary or reinforcing component, may also be a ceramic, or something else like a glass-ceramic, metal, or organic in nature. "These components are combined on a macroscale to form a useful engineering material possessing certain properties or behaviors not possessed by the individual constituents" [4].

Two types of materials systems were previously identified [6] and are currently allowed for the application of HTR core components: SiC/SiC and C/C. Guidance for the classification of SiC/SiC and C/C for structural applications is provided in ASTM C1835 [7] and ASTM C1836 [8], respectively.

Potential nuclear applications for HTRs include control rod guide tubes, tie rods, and restraint straps for core supports. Identified composite core components for HTR application are not intended to be used as pressure-retaining parts and therefore do not need to be leak-tight to maintain their function. This is different for accident-tolerant fuel cladding applications in light water reactors, which require composite tubes to be hermetically sealed. Other nuclear applications include blanket structures and flow channel inserts for fusion technologies [9].

## 4. ASME Section III, Division 5 Nonmetallic Rules for Ceramic Composite Components

The composite rules integrate with the graphite rules under Class SN, nonmetallic core components.

### *4.1. General Requirements for CMC Component and Assemblies*

The general requirements for nonmetallic core components (Section III, Division 5, Subsection HH subpart A) are applicable to graphite and ceramic composites, core components, and assemblies. They provide the rules for component classification, as well as the roles and responsibilities for the owner, designer, and the material organization. They further provide the requirements for a quality assurance program and the appointment of an authorized inspector. They elaborate on how to obtain certificates and data reports from ASME and reference the applicable standards that must be applied.

The owner or owner designee is responsible for preparing the design specification, but compliance of the code remains the responsibility of the owner. The material organization is the party responsible for supplying the materials, machining the components, and installing the core components in the core assembly.

### *4.2. Technical Requirements for CMC Component and Assemblies*

The design rules for CMCs (Section III, Division 5, Subsection HH subpart B) specifically focus on composites materials and lay out the requirements and criteria for materials, design, machining and installation, inspection, examination, testing, and the marking procedure for ceramic composite core components. They are similar to the graphite rules in that they use a probability of failure (POF) approach over the component's lifetime. However, they are distinctly different in that they do not use the maximum deformation energy, or equivalent stress, theory that allows stresses to be combined as it is applied for graphite. Instead, they use the maximum failure mode for stress analysis, which differentiates between primary and secondary stresses.

## 5. Ceramic Matrix Composite Material Requirements, Specifications, and Test Standards

Composites are a "new" material system tailored for a specific component. Composites have different design rules and failure mechanisms than metals and monolithic ceramics. The rules for materials are addressed in Article-2000 [10].

CMCs have some key issues. Both SiC/SiC and C/C composites are complex in fibers, matrix, and porosity with a wide range of constituents, different properties, and many distinctly different densification techniques. The reinforcement architectures can vary widely with marked anisotropy, giving anisotropic physical and mechanical properties. The component properties can vary widely based on the constituents, architecture, and processing. Moreover, the component requirements can vary widely, depending on the design requirements and composite material architectures.

For this reason, the material must be specified in the early stages of component development. The component geometry and component primary and secondary loads must be well understood. The two ASTM standards, C1783 and C1793 [11–12], were adopted and applied in Subsection HH, subpart B. The standards provide guidance on how to specify the constituents, structure, desired engineering properties, methods of testing, manufacturing process requirements, quality assurance requirements, and traceability for composites needed for nuclear reactor applications.

The rules also require designers to obtain the necessary composite design data and provide material data sheets that must be populated, which include as-manufactured, irradiation and oxidation, or chemical attack properties, as well as material behavior being subjected to stress-time-temperature effects.

Since the initiation of code rule development for composite component nuclear application, it was realized that another important undertaking was required to develop standards to collect material properties. This effort was led by Committee C28, the Committee on Advanced Ceramic Standards—specifically subcommittee C28.07, which focuses on CMCs. A recent development includes the new standard, ASTM C1899, to perform flexure strength tests on tubes [13]. A list of standards for this application is published elsewhere [14].

## 6. Design Approach for Ceramic Composite Components

The design rules are structured to allow for multiple applications and the continual development of CMCs. The general design requirements are addressed in Article-3000 [15].

The design rules allow for future applications because they are not limited to the current material systems. They are also process based because they provide guidance for the permissibility of the materials and specify how to qualify the material systems.

As mentioned, the rules are probabilistic because failure is derived from the variability in the material strength and accommodates the material changes due to environment exposure, such as irradiation, chemical attack, and/or stress-time-temperature effects.

The rules provide two design approach options. Designers can either follow a design-by-analysis method or a design-by-test method. For the design-by-analysis method, two key concepts are noteworthy. First, the failure mode related to the allowable stress should be applied to determine the POF. Second, the design margin is implied from the statistical analysis of the material test data, and no specific safety factor is used in the stress assessment.

The design-allowable stress is based on the statistically determined margin from the proportional limit and ultimate limit strengths. The minimum value for both limits will be considered. The design-by-analysis method defines several steps:

- Identify the potential failure modes and loading criteria (either static or time-dependent).
- Define the component classification and acceptable POF.
- Develop models to determine the component stress and derive the maximum mode stress from the application specific failure modes.
- Statistically characterize the material reliability.
- Determine the design allowable stresses based on component POF.
- Perform the structural reliability assessment.

If the design loading or geometry is too complex to rely on analysis, it is possible to follow the design-by-test method. The design-by-test method requires multiple components and a demonstration of the requirements stipulated in the design specification.

## 7. Next Steps

The NRC recently completed its endorsement review of ASME Section III, Division 5 from the 2017 edition. With a few explicit exceptions and limitations, Section III, Division 5 largely passed the assessment [16].

However, the 2017 edition does not have a section on composites, which was first published in the 2019 edition. There will likely be a continuous review to include the newer sections of the code.

No HTR with composite core components has ever been constructed to serve as a basis for the safety, sustainability, or licensing case for the NRC. Because of the lack of a demonstration in previous HTRs and a need to validate the existing rules, it is necessary to develop a technical basis that supports the rules with the conditions described in the code. Working together with current HTR vendors, this can be done by producing benchmarking data.

Several activities have been undertaken. Some of these activities are also supported by efforts from the light water reactor and advanced fuels technology communities that are driving forces for the development of the SiC fuel claddings and core component applications for accident-tolerant fuel designs. Specific concerns for cladding and channel box applications include component bowing due to fluence-temperature effects.

The supply of material and qualification thereof will not be a small undertaking because of the material's complex nature. The challenge will be to reduce the time to adopt new material for nuclear reactor use.

## 8. Summary and Conclusion

The ASME CMC design and construction rules were first published in the ASME BPVC Section III, Division 5 in the 2019 edition under Subsection HA, Subpart A, and Subsection HH, Subpart B. It is an attractive material because of its low thermal expansion, superior high-temperature performance, light weight, and moderate to outstanding radiation resistance.

CMCs are complex material structures with variability in material properties, which requires probabilistic assessment methods for composite component design.

Subsection HH, Subpart B is structured to allow for multiple applications and continual development because it is process based. Most developed ASTM standards align with material testing and support the requirements of the material data sheet.

**Acknowledgment**

This work is supported by the U.S. Department of Energy's Office of Nuclear Energy under Contract No. DE-AC05-00OR22725 with UT-Battelle LLC.

**References**

[1] US NRC, About NRC, https://www.nrc.gov/about-nrc.html, last accessed August 2021.
[2] R. Sowinski, Update on DOE consensus-based standards efforts, Nuclear Regulatory Commission Standards Forum, Rockville, MD, September 11, 2018.
[3] Thomas A. Hunter, Designing to Codes and Standards, Materials Selection and Design, Vol 20, ASM Handbook, Edited By George E. Dieter, ASM International, 1997, p 66-71, https://doi.org/10.31399/asm.hb.v20.a0002430
[4] ASME Boiler and Pressure Vessel Code, Section III, Div. 5, HAB, The American Society of Mechanical Engineers, Two Park Avenue, NY (2019)
[5] ASME Boiler and Pressure Vessel Code, Section III, Div. 5, HHB, The American Society of Mechanical Engineers, Two Park Avenue, NY (2019)
[6] W.R. Corwin et al., Generation IV Reactors Integrated Materials Technology Program Plan: Focus on Very High Temperature Reactor Materials, ORNL/TM-2008/129, 2008.
[7] ASTM Standard C1835-16, "Standard Classification for Fiber Reinforced Silicon Carbide-Silicon Carbide (SiC-SiC) Composite Structures," ASTM International, West Conshohocken, PA (2016).
[8] ASTM Standard C1836-16, "Standard Classification for Fiber Reinforced Carbon-Carbon Composite Structures," ASTM International, West Conshohocken, PA (2016).
[9] Yutai Katoh, "Recent Development in SiC Composite Technologies for Nuclear Energy Applications", in Transactions of the American Nuclear Society, Vol. 118, Philadelphia, Pennsylvania, June 17-21, 2018.
[10] ASME Boiler and Pressure Vessel Code, Section III, Div. 5, HHB-2000, American Society of Mechanical Engineers, Two Park Avenue, NY, 2019.
[11] ASTM Standard C1783-15, "Standard Guide for Development of Specifications for Fiber Reinforced Carbon-Carbon Composite Structures for Nuclear Applications1," ASTM International, West Conshohocken, PA (2015).
[12] ASTM Standard C1793-15, "Standard Guide for Development of Specifications for Fiber Reinforced Silicon Carbide-Silicon Carbide Composite Structures for Nuclear Applications1," ASTM International, West Conshohocken, PA (2015).
[13] ASTM Standard C1899-21, "Standard Guide for Development of Specifications for Fiber Reinforced Silicon Carbide-Silicon Carbide Composite Structures for Nuclear Applications1," ASTM International, West Conshohocken, PA (2021).
[14] ASTM International. 2021. ASTM Volume 15.01 Refractories, Activated Carbon; Advanced Ceramics West Conshohocken, PA (2021).
[15] ASME Boiler and Pressure Vessel Code, Section III, Div. 5, HHB-2000, American Society of Mechanical Engineers, Two Park Avenue, NY, 2019.
[16] J. Poehler. "Acceptability of ASME Code, Section III, Division 5, High Temperature Reactors", US NRC, DG-1380, August 2021.

Journal of Physics: Conference Series **2048** (2021) 012021 doi:10.1088/1742-6596/2048/1/012021

# Current Status of Purification of Indonesian Natural Graphite as a Candidate for Nuclear Fuel Matrix by Hydrometallurgy and Pyrometallurgy Methods

**D Mustika, Torowati, Sudirman [1], A Dimyati [1], A Fisli [1], I M Joni [2], and R Langenati**

Center for Nuclear Fuel Technology – BATAN, PUSPIPTEK AREA, Setu, South Tangerang, Banten, Indonesia, 15346
phone :+62-85217039494, dmustika@batan.go.id
[1]Center for Science and Technology of Advanced Materials – BATAN, PUSPIPTEK AREA, Setu, South Tangerang, Banten, 15346
[2]Functional Nano Powder University Center of Excellence (FiNder U-CoE), Directorate of Research and Community Development - Padjadjaran University, Jl. Raya Bandung – Sumedang Km 21, Jatinangor, Sumedang Regency, West Java, Indonesia, 45363

**Abstract.** Indonesia has natural graphite reserved in Sulawesi, Sumatera and Kalimantan islands. The highest graphite content was observed in Sanggau Region, West Kalimantan. Indonesian natural graphite has the potential to be used as fuel matrix in Pebble Bed Reactor (PBR) type - High Temperature Gas Cooled Reactor (HTGR). To increase self-reliance of graphite supply and decrease graphite import for fuel matrix purposes, it is necessary to master the purification technology of graphite. Graphite matrix in Pebble Bed Reactor (PBR) fuel has an important role. It is not only used as neutron moderator and structural material to protect nuclear fuel but also as heat transfer media. Therefore, the graphite matrix must meet the physical and chemical criteria specified for PBR fuel. This paper focuses on current status of purification of Indonesian natural graphite as a candidate for nuclear fuel matrix using hydrometallurgy and pyrometallurgy. Acid and acid mixtures such as HF, $HNO_3$+$H_2SO_4$ and HF+HCl+$H_2SO_4$ were used for the hydrometallurgy purification process, while Arc Plasma System were used for pyrometallurgy methods. Characterization for the purified graphite includes physical and chemical properties. The result showed that Indonesian natural graphite obtained from hydrometallurgy was classified into low nuclear grade graphite but it still could be used as nuclear fuel matrix PBR - HTGR. The graphitization degree needs to be increased and the impurity content needs to be decreased for the purified Indonesian graphite using hydrometallurgy method. The Indonesian natural graphite obtained from preliminary pyrometallurgy methods has 96.78 % graphite content according to SEM (surface) observation and the graphite content needs to be increased into nuclear grade graphite.

## 1. Introduction

Graphite, natural mineral consisting of carbon, has hexagonal crystal system and low level of hardness (1 to 2 Mohs scale) [1, 2]. Graphite has number of uses, it is used as heat resistant material, dry battery, lubricant additive material, paint, crucible material, electrode, brake friction material, steel smelting industry, pencil industry, and nuclear fuel matrix [3, 2, 3, 4, 5, 6, 7, 8].

China is currently by far the largest producer of natural graphite (66 %), followed by India (14 %, Brazil (7 %), Turkey (3%), Canada (3%) and North Korea (3%) [9]. In Indonesia, natural graphite deposits are distributed in several regions. Latambago Subdistrict, part of Kolaka District of Southeast Sulawesi Province, has natural graphite with carbon content 2.36 to 4.51 % [2,10]. In Balau sebut, located in Sanggau District of West Kalimantan, there is also fine-flake graphite with carbon content 1.25 to 65.56 % in $SiO_2$ material [2]. The other regions are Muara Saiti, Pangkalan and Tanjung Balit, Lima Puluh District; Ombilin area, around Singkarak Lake and Siberlabu, Payakumbuh in West Sumatra Province [1].

Graphite in nature still contains some mineral impurities and thus several purification methods are required to eliminate the impurities and increase the carbon content. Indonesian graphite purification was performed by Florena et.al. via flotation method. Florena et. al added $Na_2CO_3$ (pH controller), sodium silicate (lowering the amount of confounding mineral), diesel oil, $C_{12}H_{23}$ (collector) and pine oil (frother). The purity of the graphite could be increased from 3% to 61% [10]. The flotation method by using Denver-like flotation cell, addition of diesel fuel (DEX) as graphite coat, pine oil as stabilized froth, and caustic soda as pH controlled could produce graphite with carbon content up to 91 % [11]. Naturally, graphite could float in water because of its hydrophobic properties and several reagents are usually added to produce the best recovery [10]. Thus, flotation method is usually chosen to separate and increase graphite concentration based on physicochemical interface [10].

High Temperature Gas Cooled Reactor (HTGR) is a type of nuclear reactor with safety and flexible application feature. There are two main types of HTGR: pebble bed type (e.g., 10 MW HTR 10 from China) and prismatic type (e.g., 30 MW HTTR from Japan). Pebble bed type utilized spherical fuel elements which consist of spherical fuel area measuring about 50 mm in diameter and fissile material in the form of coated particle dispersed in graphite material. Outer fuel free shell with 5 mm thick graphite matrix content surrounded spherical fuel area. Every spherical fuel element contains 8300 coated particles. Graphite matrix works as neutron moderator, heat transfer media, and structural materials to protect against outside forces [3, 4, 6, 12, 13].

Pebble bed and prismatic type fuel use graphite matrix with the same composition which is A3-3 contains 64% natural graphite, 16% synthetic graphite, and 20% phenolic resin. Prismatic type is compacted by uniaxial method while pebble bed type used isostatic method [3, 4, 6, 7, 8]. Based on HTR-10 physical reactor design, a total of 27,000 spherical fuel elements should be filled up in the reactor core to reach a state of equilibrium [3, 14]. In China, 60 tons graphite had been used for HTR-10 and 1000 tons graphite will be used for HTR-PM as structural material and graphite matrix [15]. If HTR 10 power reactor type were going to be built in Indonesia, 105 pebble fuels per day is required for steady state operation [13].

Natural graphite for nuclear application has requirements such as the graphite content > 99 %, surface area from 4.8 to 5.5 $m^2/g$, 100 % of particle size below 80 μm [4, 8] and 50 % below 32 μm [7], ash content around 100 μg/g, lithium content <0,005 μg/g, Equivalent Boron Content (EBC) < 1 μg/g, high thermal conductivity, high density, high mechanical, low thermal expansion, good corrosion resistance, and stable under neutron irradiation [4, 6]. Xiang-wen Zhou used natural graphite as the base material of A3-3 with EBC 0.223 μg/g and ash content 10 μg/g [17]. Impurities may reduce corrosion resistance and other fuel performances because of the species which may attack outer pyrolytic layer or diffuse into silicon carbide (SiC) layer. Density may influence mechanical strength of nuclear fuel [4,6].

Indonesian natural graphite has the potential to be used as fuel matrix in Pebble Bed Reactor (PBR) type - High Temperature Gas Cooled Reactor (HTGR). Until now, Indonesia still does not have nuclear graphite that fulfills the required qualifications [16]. To increase self-reliance of graphite supply and decrease graphite import for fuel matrix purposes, it is necessary to master the purification technology of graphite. This paper focuses on the current status of purification of Indonesian natural graphite as a candidate for nuclear fuel matrix using hydrometallurgy and pyrometallurgy. Thus, it is expected to provide a picture of Indonesian natural graphite purification process which has been performed as well as the resulting purified graphite.

## 2. Hydrometallurgy

Hydrometallurgy purification consists of flotation method, acid-base method, and fluoride method. Flotation purification is the lowest in cost which make advantage of graphite floating properties to increase purity. Acid base method is an alkaline fusion and sodium hydroxide (NaOH) method where impurity reacted with NaOH. In fluoride method, impurities reacted with hydrofluoric acid (HF) forming soluble fluoride in water. Hydrometallurgy purification method is most often used because of the low infrastructure cost, easy implementation despite time-consuming, and causing serious pollution [9].

In China, hydrometallurgy purification method of natural graphite used hydrochloric acid (HCl) and sodium fluoride (NaF) resulted graphite with carbon content 98.37 %. The carbon content is increasing compared to initial carbon content which was 83.08 % [18]. The mixture of NaOH and HCl-HF was also used to purify flake graphite and to obtain high purity graphite [19]. The natural graphite in Henan province, China, was purified by adding HCl (36 %) and sulfuric acid ($H_2SO_4$ 98 %) with 1:10 ratio in high temperature hydrothermal to produce purified graphite for anode material of Li-Ion battery [5]. In Brazil, graphite was purified by using $H_2SO_4$ (30 %) and NHxFy (30 %) [20]. Microwave radiation purification with HCl/$HNO_3$ obtained graphite with carbon content of 98.57 %. On the other hand, the purification using HF successfully produced graphite with carbon content 99.957 % [21]. In Indonesia, natural graphite was purified by HF with 5:1 ratio. The materials were mixed for 2 hours using magnetic stirrer and then cleaned until the pH reach 7. As the result, the carbon content was increased from 76.502 into 92.36 to 98 % [22,23]. In China, the natural graphite used as fuel matrix was purified by a mixture of HF, HCl and $H_2SO_4$. The resulting graphite contained ash, lithium, and equivalent boron content as much as 100, <0.005 and < 1 ppm respectively [3, 4, 7].

Indonesian natural graphite purification for nuclear fuel matrix used acid leaching with acid variation of HF, $H_2SO_4$+$HNO_3$ (1:1 ratio) and HF+HCl+$H_2SO_4$ (1:1:1 ratio). Graphite and acid or mixture acid were mixed for leaching at a 1:5 weight ratio. The mixtures were stirred for 3 hours and washed by distilled water for several times until free-acid graphite was obtained. The yielded free-acid graphite was dried at 115°C in an oven and subsequently crushed. The observed graphite has the characteristics of 2H poly type, hexagonal crystal structure and P 63 m c space group. The lattice parameters of graphite changed during acid purification as shown in Table 1 [16,24].

**Table 1.** Crystal lattice parameter of Indonesian natural graphite before and after purification [16,24].

| Graphite | Crystal lattice parameter | |
|---|---|---|
| | a (Å) | c (Å) |
| Before acid treatment | 2.4673 | 6.7344 |
| HF | 2.4594 | 6.7435 |
| $HNO_3$ + $H_2SO_4$ | 2.4616 | 6.7356 |
| HF+HCl+$H_2SO_4$ | 2.4622 | 6.7419 |

The graphite purified with $HNO_3$ + $H_2SO_4$ has the nearest value to single crystal graphite with 0.94 in deviation when compared to perfect graphite crystal (2.461 Å). The density of graphite after $HNO_3$+$H_2SO_4$ and HF+HCl+$H_2SO_4$ purification differs but insignificantly from the theoretical density. The density of graphite before purification was 2.3273 g/cm$^3$. After purification with HF, $HNO_3$+$H_2SO_4$ and HF+HCl+$H_2SO_4$, the density of graphite changed into 2.1808, 2.2203 and 2.2752 g/cm$^3$ respectively [16,24].

The surface area of the Indonesian natural graphite decreases after purification and still higher than nuclear grade graphite. The surface area of graphite before purification was 10.346 m$^2$/g and after purification with HF, $HNO_3$+$H_2SO_4$, and HF+HCl+$H_2SO_4$ changed into 6.177, 5.831 and 7.63 m$^2$/g respectively. It was observed that the average of particle size decreases from 29.65 μm (before purification) to 23.12 μm (after purification). According to IAEA Technical Document number 1674, the recommended graphite particle diameter is 50% smaller than 32 μm. The IAEA recommendation could be met by graphite before and after acid purification with diameter at 50% of 19.87 and 17.47 μm [24].

The results of SEM – EDS, analysis using ZAF method of qualitative analysis without standard, show that the carbon content of natural graphite of pre-purification process, post purification with HF, $H_2SO_4$ + $HNO_3$ and HF+HCl +$H_2SO_4$ were 89.68 %, 99.52 %, 93.98 % and 96.21 % with fitting coefficient of 0.1994; 0.4178; 0.3976 and 0.4400 respectively. The highest increase of graphite mass percentage was obtained by HF purification and fulfilled the characteristic for nuclear grade natural graphite [25].

The carbon content was analyzed using carbon sulfur analyzer. The results show that the carbon content of graphite before and after purification with HF, $H_2SO_4$+$HNO_3$ and HF+HCl+$H_2SO_4$ are 89.60±1.50 %, 99.20±0.35 %, 94.26±0.39 % and 97.5±1.36%, respectively. The highest carbon rate was obtained from HF purification with 99.20 %, which fulfilled the characteristics of nuclear grade natural graphite. This result is in accordance with the result obtained from EDS analysis [25].

Ash content for graphite before and after purification with HF, $H_2SO_4$+$HNO_3$ and HF+HCl+$H_2SO_4$ were 9.587 %, 0.796 %, 1.781 % and 1.054 %, respectively. The lowest ash content was obtained in purification with HF followed by HF+HCl+$H_2SO_4$ and $H_2SO_4$+$HNO_3$. This result is also in accordance with EDS and CS analyzer result. However, compared with nuclear grade natural graphite characteristics, the ash content of acid purified graphite is still higher [25].

**Table 2.** The concentration of impurities in graphite before and after purification (μg/g) [25,26]

| Element | Content Impurities (μg/g) | | | | Method |
|---|---|---|---|---|---|
| | Pre | HF | $H_2SO_4$ + $HNO_3$ | HF+ HCl+$H_2SO_4$ | |
| Al | 741 ± 45 | 725 ± 40 | 696 ± 17 | 593 ± 15 | NAA |
| B | <0.44 | < 0.44 | 156.63 ± 0.04 | < 0.44 | ICP |
| Cd | <0.05 | <0.05 | <0.05 | <0.05 | ICP |
| Co | 5.59 ± 0.47 | 1.49 ± 0.06 | 4.13 ± 0.2 | 4.09 ± 0.32 | NAA |
| Cr | 74.80 ± 0,14 | 46.41± 0.01 | 54.62 ± 0.01 | 51.05 ± 0.01 | AAS |
| Cu | 60,675 ± 2.14 | 1,088 ± 59 | 925 ± 58 | 835 ± 57 | NAA |
| Dy | 24,540 | < 0.09 | < 0.09 | < 0.09 | ICP |
| Eu | < 0.03 | < 0.03 | < 0.03 | < 0.03 | ICP |
| Fe | 1379.20 ± 80,00 | 216.47±0.01 | 153.21±0.01 | 580.13±0.01 | AAS |
| Gd | <0.03 | <0.03 | <0.03 | <0.03 | ICP |
| K | 163.70±0.01 | 21.65± 0.01 | 71.48±0.01 | 21.58 ± 0.01 | AAS |
| La | 3.56 ± 0,33 | 3.09 ± 0.16 | 2.15 ± 0.14 | 2.27 ± 0.16 | NAA |
| Li | < LD 0.01 | < LD 0.01 | < LD 0.01 | < LD 0.01 | AAS |
| Mg | 253.40 ± 4,60 | 27.20±1.99 | 175.70±8.99 | 15.76±0.33 | AAS |
| Mn | 9.04 ± 0.38 | 2.05 ± 0.07 | 2.7 ± 0.07 | 1.87 ± 0.08 | NAA |
| Na | 171 ± 10.6 | 170 ± 8.8 | 39.2 ± 1.3 | 29.4 ±1.19 | NAA |
| Ni | 70.60 ± 0,24 | 21.73±0.002 | 31.79±0.02 | <0.02 | AAS |
| Pb | 190 ± 0,18 | 221.398±0.075 | 200.03±0.01 | 143.16±0.05 | AAS |
| Sb | 5,514±14 | 93±2,4 | 4,348±49 | 3,421±37 | NAA |
| Sc | 0.28 ± 0.03 | 0.14 ± 0.01 | nd | nd | NAA |
| Sm | <0.03 | <0.03 | <0.03 | <0.03 | ICP |
| V | 27.5 ± 1.26 | 15.09 ± 0.54 | 9.1 ± 0.31 | 14.6 ± 0.51 | NAA |
| W | 19.4 ± 1.67 | 16.59 ± 0.63 | 18.8 ± 0.74 | 19.14 ± 0.78 | NAA |
| Zn | 408 ± 34.7 | 14.74 ± 1.02 | nd | nd | AAN |
| Sum | 94,246.66 | 2,684.73 | 6,888.78 | 5,139.75 | |

Determination of graphite impurity was performed with two methods, non-destructive test by neutron activation analysis (NAA) and destructive test by Atomic Absorption Spectroscopy (AAS) and ICP – OES. Table 2 display the result of impurity assessment graphite before and after acid leaching purification. From Table 2 it can be observed that the total impurities before and after purification graphite obtained by NAA, AAS and ICP-OES, are 94246.66 µg/g, 2684.73 µg/g, 6888.78 µg/g and 5139.75 µg/g, respectively. The lowest impurity was obtained in graphite with HF purification. This is in accordance with EDS, CS analyzer and ash content analysis [25].

In determining the EBC total (Table 2), elements such as B, Dy, Eu, Gd, Sm, Li and Cd content showed different result after the purification process. Before purification process, the graphite had Dy with 24,540 µg/g concentration. Graphite which was purified using $H_2SO_4$+$HNO_3$ contained B around 156.63 µg/g. The concentrations for impurity elements of purified graphite are below LoD for B, Dy, Eu, Gd, Sm, Li and Cd with each being 0.44 µg/g, 0.09 µg/g, 0.03 µg/g, 0.03 µg/g, 0.03 µg/g, 0.01 µg/g and 0.05 µg/g, respectively. EBC before and after purification graphite with $H_2SO_4$ + $HNO_3$ was higher than nuclear graphite (EBC < 1 µg/g), while graphite obtained purification with HF and HF+HCl+$H_2SO_4$ fulfilled the EBC requirements for nuclear graphite [25].

From the physical density and particle size distribution point of view, the Indonesian natural graphite obtained from acid purification can be used as nuclear fuel matrix for PBR - HTGR, but the graphitization degree needs to be increased and the surface area needs to be decreased [24]. From the chemical view, the HF was the best reagent to eliminate the graphite impurities which results the graphite of low purity grades approach for nuclear application [25, 26].

## 3. Pyrometallurgy

Pyrometallurgy purification method is divided into chlorination roasting and high temperature method. Chlorination roasting method is roasting the graphite in certain temperature and adding chlorine gas to chlorinate the impurities in graphite, producing gas phase or condensed complex compound with low melting and boiling point. Purification efficiency with this method is high (up to 98%) but in the other hand, it requires high cost and difficult gas handling. The second method is high temperature method. Graphite is heated up to 4892 °C, causing impurities with low boiling point to evaporate, leaving 99.995 % graphite. This method requires large scale infrastructure investment and high electricity consumption [9].

Several companies in China purified natural graphite with high temperature method by using furnace. Graphite is inserted from above and pass high temperature area (up to 3000 °C) with induction method and in inert condition. The graphite degree could be obtained more than 90 % [19].

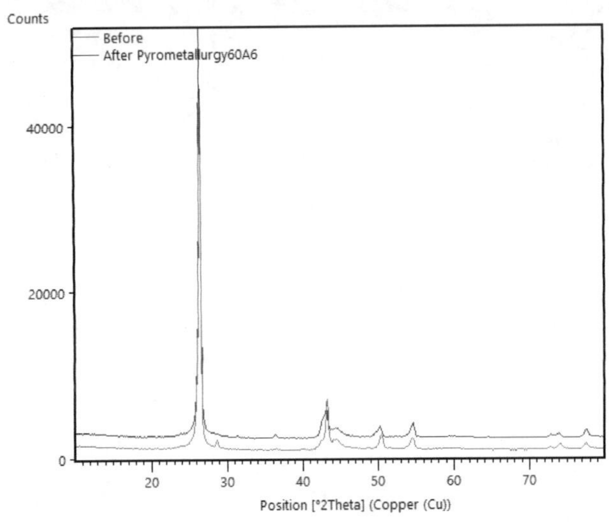


**Figure 1.** Graphite diffraction pattern before and after pyrometallurgy purification.

Journal of Physics: Conference Series **2048** (2021) 012021 doi:10.1088/1742-6596/2048/1/012021

Indonesian natural graphite purification by preliminary stage of pyrometallurgy method was performed by using Arc Plasma System (APS). Material purification by plasma in APS occurs through utilizing the different melting points of each element or phases with only one step. Natural graphite purification process by plasma could occur through melting or evaporating other compound by the intense heat caused by plasma exposure. Graphite powder was formed into pellet and further purification process was performed by using APS in 60 Amperes under time variation 2, 4 and 6 minutes. Graphite characterization was performed before and after purification.

Crystallography diffraction pattern analysis was done with 2 Theta from 20 to 80. The result of local graphite before and after purification process by APS was graphite 2H with hexagonal crystal system with P 63 m c space group. The decrease and absent of peak in graphite purified by APS indicates the decrease of impurity content occurred in graphite sample.

Fig. 2 shows graphite SEM-EDS result before and after purification process by Arc Plasma Sintering. Analyzed by ZAF quantitative analysis method, it appeared that C content before and after purification was increasing up to 96,78 %. The increasing of C content occurred in 60 A 6 minutes parameter.

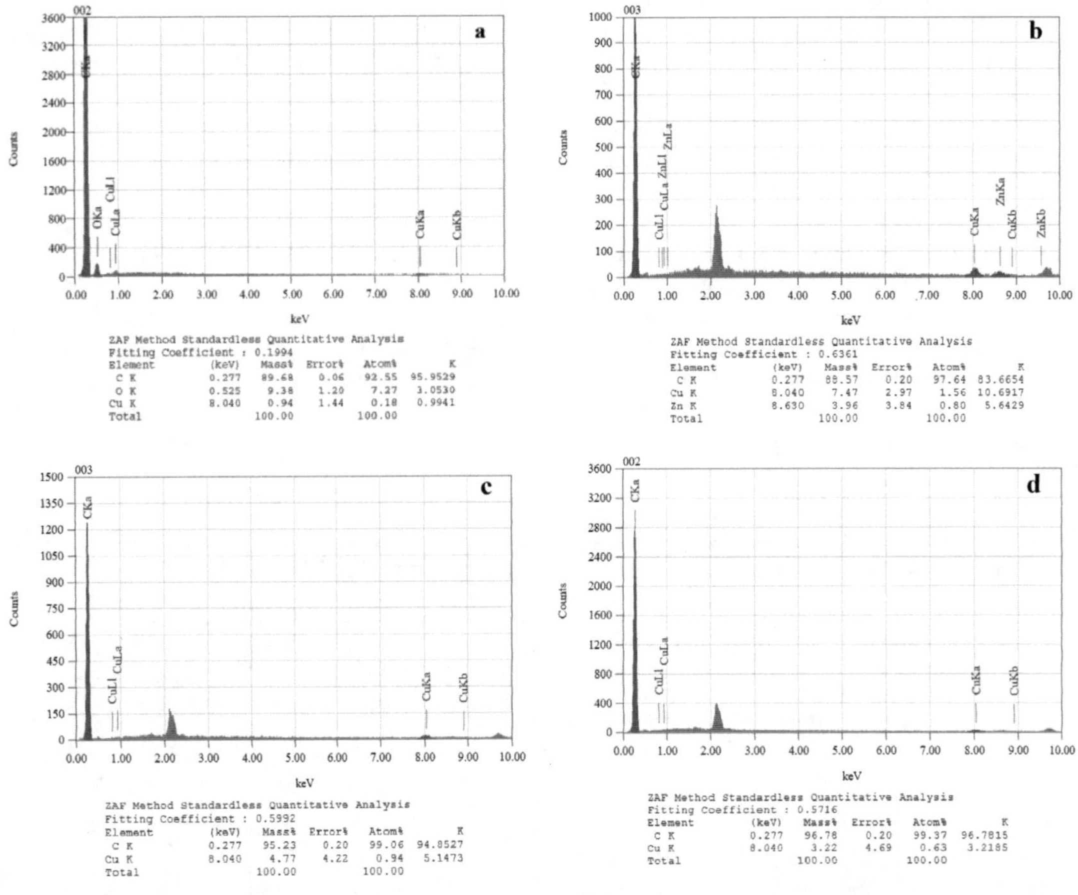


**Figure 2.** SEM – EDS graphite result before and after purification process by Arc Plasma Sintering, a. Pre b. 60 A 2 minutes c. 60 A 4 minutes d. 60 A 6 minutes

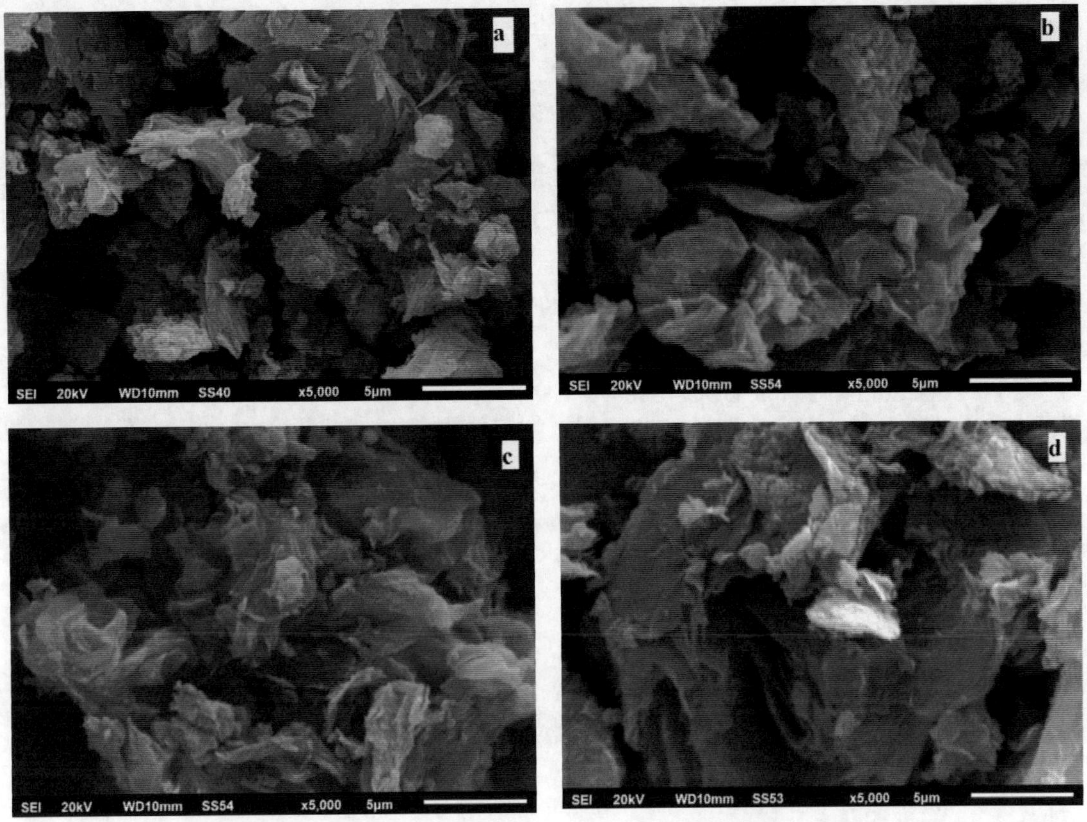


**Figure 3.** SEM picture (a) Graphite before and after pyrometallurgy purification, (b) 60 A 2 minutes, (c) 60 A 4 minutes dan (d) 60 A 6 minutes

From the SEM picture in Figure 3, it is apparent that after purification process, graphite has smoother surface compared to before purification graphite. The smooth surface was obtained from the reduction of impurities on the graphite surface.

## 4. Conclusion

The Current status of purification of Indonesian natural graphite as a candidate for nuclear fuel matrix use hydrometallurgy and pyrometallurgy method. Acid and acid mixtures such as HF, $HNO_3$+$H_2SO_4$ and HF+HCl+$H_2SO_4$ were used for the hydrometallurgy purification process, while Arc Plasma System were used for pyrometallurgy methods. Characterization for the purified graphite includes physical and chemical properties. The result showed that Indonesian natural graphite obtained from hydrometallurgy was classified into low nuclear grade graphite. However, it still could be used as nuclear fuel matrix PBR - HTGR. The graphitization degree needs to be increased and the impurity content needs to be decreased for the purified Indonesian graphite using hydrometallurgy method. The Indonesian natural graphite obtained from preliminary pyrometallurgy methods has 96.78 % graphite content according to SEM (surface) observation and the graphite content needs to be increased into nuclear grade graphite. The increasing graphite content and graphitization degree could be expected by optimization of parameters and modification or development of methods.

## References

[1] Sukandarrumidi. "Minerals Industry Relating to Malihan Stone" in *Industrial Minerals*, Gadjah Mada University Press, Yogyakarta, 2017, pp. 223–24.

[2] Marza, Reza, et al. "The Mineral Graphite Prospects on the Borneo and Sulawesi Islands"

*Proceeding of Annual Activities of Center for Mineral Resources, Coal and Geothermal Fiscal Year 2017.* vol. Book 2 : B, 2018, pp. 219–29

[3] Tang, Chunhe, et al. "Design and Manufacture of the Fuel Element for the 10 MW High Temperature Gas-Cooled Reactor." *Nuclear Engineering and Design*, vol. 218, no. 1–3, 2002, pp. 91–102, doi:10.1016/S0029-5493(02)00201-7.

[4] Zhao, Hongsheng, et al. "Manufacture and Characteristics of Spherical Fuel Elements for the HTR-10." *Nuclear Engineering and Design*, vol. 236, no. 5–6, 2006, pp. 643–47, doi:10.1016/j.nucengdes.2005.10.023.

[5] Zhao, Haipeng, et al. "Purification and Carbon-Film-Coating of Natural Graphite as Anode Materials for Li-Ion Batteries." *Electrochimica Acta*, vol. 52, no. 19, 2007, pp. 6006–11, doi:10.1016/j.electacta.2007.03.050.

[6] IAEA. "High Temperature Gas Cooled Reactor Fuels and Materials." *IAEA Tecdoc 1645*, 2010, pp. 1–182, doi:IAEA-TECDOC-1645.

[7] IAEA. "Advances in High Temperature Gas Cooled Reactor Fuel Technology." *IAEA TECDOC CD 1674*, 2012, pp. 1–690.

[8] Yeo, Sunghwan, et al. "Fabrication Methods and Anisotropic Properties of Graphite Matrix Compacts for Use in HTGR." *Journal of Nuclear Materials*, vol. 499, Elsevier B.V., 2018, pp. 383–93, doi:10.1016/j.jnucmat.2017.11.055.

[9] Jara, Allah D. et. al. "Purification, Application, and Current Market trend of Natural Graphite : A Review". *International Journal of Mining Sciennce and Technology*. Volume 29, Issue 5, September 2019.

[10] Florena, Fenfen Fenda, et al. "Floatability Study of Graphite Ore from Southeast Sulawesi (Indonesia)." *AIP Conference Proceedings*, vol. 1712, 2016, doi:10.1063/1.4941888

[11] Joni, I. Made, et al. "Synthesis and Dispersion of Nanoparticles, and Indonesian Graphite Processing." *AIP Conference Proceedings*, vol. 1554, 2013, pp. 20–26, doi:10.1063/1.4820275.

[12] Li, Junfeng, et al. Recent Advances in Treatments of Irradiated Graphite : A Review. *Annals of Nuclear Energy* 110. 2017. Pp 140 – 147.

[13] Setiadipura, Topan., et.al. Coolong Passive Safety Features of Reaktor Daya Eksperimental. *AIP Conference Proceeding 1984.020034*. American Institute of Physics. 2018

[14] Kuntjoro, Sri, et.al. The Analysis for Inventory analysis of Experimental Reactor High Temperature Gas Reactor Type. *Urania Jurnal Ilmiah Daur Bahan Bakar Nuklir*. Vol.22 No.1. February 2016.

[15] Zhou, Xiang-wen, et al. "Nuclear Graphite for High Temperature Gas Cooled Reactors. *New Carbon Materials*, Volume 32, Issue 3, June 2017. Pp193-204

[16] Mustika, Deni., "The Potential of Indonesian Graphite as RDE Fuel Matrix". *Indonesian Journal Material Science*. Vol. 20, No. 2, January 2019

[17] Zhou, Xiang-wen, et al. "Study on the Comprehensive Properties and Microstructures of A3-3 Matrix Graphite Related to the High Temperature Purification Treatment." *Hindawi Science and Technology of Nuclear Installation*, 2018.

[18] Xie, Wei, et al. "Fixed Carbon Content and Reaction Mechanism of Natural Microcrystalline Graphite Purified by Hydrochloric Acid and Sodium Fluoride." *International Journal of Mineral Processing*, vol. 155, Elsevier B.V., 2016, pp. 45–54, doi:10.1016/j.minpro.2016.08.002.

[19] Shen, ke, et.al. "*Advantages of Natural Microcrystalline Graphite Filler Over Petroleum Coke in Isotropic Graphite Preparation*". Carbon 90. 2015, pp 197-206

[20] Zaghib, K., et al. "Purification Process of Natural Graphite as Anode for Li-Ion Batteries: Chemical versus Thermal." *Journal of Power Sources*, vol. 119–121, 2003, pp. 8–15, doi:10.1016/S0378-7753(03)00116-2.

[21] Li, Yu Feng, et al. "Selectivity Heating Effect of Microwave on Purifying of Natural Graphite." *Applied Mechanics and Materials*, vol. 174–177, 2012, pp. 810–15, doi:10.4028/www.scientific.net/AMM.174-177.810.

[22] Panatarani, Camellia, et al. "Preparation of Graphite Oxide by Sodium Cholate Intercalation and

Sonication from Indonesian Natural Graphite." *AIP Conference Proceedings*, vol. 1712, no. March 2016, 2016, doi:10.1063/1.4941908.

[23] Joni, I. Made, et al. "Augmenation of Graphite Purity from Mineral Resources and Enhancing % Graphitization Using Microwave Irradiation : XRD and Raman Studies" Diamond & Related Materials Volume 88. 2018. September 2018. Pp 129 - 136.

[24] Mustika, Deni., et.al. "Purification of Indonesian Natural Graphite by Acid Leaching Method as Nuclear Fuel Matrix : Physical Characterization". *International Journal of Chemistry*, Vol. 11, No. 1. 2019

[25] Mustika, Deni., et. al "Purification of Indonesian Natural Graphite as Candidate for Nuclear Fuel Matrix by Acid Leaching Method : Chemical Characterization. *Urania Journal Ilmiah Daur Bahan Bakar Nuklir*. Vol. 26 No 3. 2020

[26] Fisli, Adel., et.al. "Determination of Elements in Acid Leaching of Graphite Using Instrumental Neutron Activation Analysis". *International Journal of Chemistry*, Vol. 12, No. 1. 2020

# Study on the Implementation of Quality Assurance Aspect on High-Temperature Gas Cooled Reactor (HTGR)

**Sunarto, Sigit Santosa[1], Khusnul Khotimah[2], Sriyana[3]**

Center for Nuclear Standardization and Quality Unit Tangerang Selatan, Indonesia
phone: +62895 3403 83049,

coresponding author's e-mail : narto@batan.go.id

**Abstract** – High-Temperature Gas Cooled Reactor (HTGR) Power Reactors have a layered safety system with the concept of a double barrier system. However, quality assurance is required to ensure the fulfillment of technological analysis weightings on power chamber materials, power ratings, fabrication components of High- Temperature Gas Cooled Reactor (HTGR) fuel elements, primary and secondary coolant pressures to meet customer requirements and be carried out continuously systematic and objective. This study analyzes the application of quality assurance, safety, security, the correctness of test/calibration results, increasing competitiveness, consumer protection and building trust (brand image) in the use of HTGR reactors to provide a reliable level of safety and security. The study method used is based on the literature review. The output of this study is the document of the HTGR reactor quality assurance systems to fulfill the IAEA-TECDOC-1645 requirements according to safety and standardization in frameworks design, material, fuel, and physical properties of the quality management systems. HTGR reactor has technical qualification, good performance of HTGR fuel, safety and accident analysis source term analysis, control of multi-modular HTGR and related human factor analysis, also optimizing radiation protection of HTGR

## 1. Introduction

Nuclear reactor technology is always evolving to improve the factors in question, namely Quality Assurance (QA) and safety, which will minimize the risks associated with accidents and avoid improvement in the event of an accident. The experience of turning commercial power reactors or nuclear power plants for six decades in 33 countries around the world has occurred 3 (three) major accidents namely the Three Mile Island reactor, United States (radioactive substances are still confined), the Chernobyl reactor, Ukraine and the Fukushima Dai-ichi reactor, Japan. In the last two- reactor accidents the release of radioactive substances into the environment. The accident caused human death due to the Chernobyl reactor accident with a total casualty of 56 people [1]. This reflects that the nuclear power plant is a power generation system that has a higher level of security in nuclear reactors.

Based on the Power Reactor Information System (PRIS) provided by the International Atomic Energy Agency (IAEA), at the end of 2018 there were 454 PLTN commercial operations [2]. Of all the NPPs, around 97% are cooling water-based NPPs. The rests are 3 Fast Breeder Reactors (FBR) and 14 Gas Cooled Graphite Moderated Reactors (GCR). The NPP supplies around 298.65 GW of world energy demand [3]. Nuclear reactors are generally designed to have an operating life of around 30 years. Unfortunately, around 63% of them are more than 30 years old whose operations must be immediately extended following the aging management requirements or deactivated and replaced with new ones. But in the end, there are also nuclear reactors in the world that are operated beyond the design life. This depends on the physical condition and function of each component, system, and reactor structure [4].

As a part of the old NPP replacement and the need of massive energy in some developing country especially in China and India, there are about 56 under construction commercial NPPs around the world that is dominated by water coolant-based reactors [1]. The interesting thing is one of the under-construction reactors are Generation IV nuclear reactor based on High Temperature Gas Cooled Reactor (HTGR) technology that is located in China [5]. HTGR is an advanced development of the Gas Cooled Reactor (GCR) technology. GCR uses carbon dioxide gas as its primary coolant. One disadvantage of carbon dioxide as a coolant is at a relatively high operating temperature. Oxidation of carbon dioxide against moderator graphite can be ruled out only at temperatures below 675°C [6]. At higher temperatures, carbon dioxide undergoes radiolitic oxidation which produces carbon monoxide and attacks graphite so that it has the potential to accelerate the degradation process. Therefore, to produce higher operating temperature around 900°C, HTGR adopts Helium as its coolant. As an inert gas, helium does not react to graphite and other reactor components which make it one of the determinants in their inherent safety concept.

Base on the Generation IV International Forum (GIF) system arrangements and memoranda of understanding as of January 2014, China, Europe Union, France, Japan, South Korea, Switzerland, and the USA are the active countries researching HTGR as the part of Generation IV reactor development [7]. GIF has also agreed on two types of HTGR designs, prismatic and pebble beds as the standard basis of Generation IV HTGR technology. Both HTGR types use Tri-structural-isotropic (TRISO) spherical fuel particle as the smallest part of its fuel component. Graphite is used as the neutron moderator of reflector also has the function as the core structure. Helium gas is chosen as the cooling system because of its inert characteristic that will able to minimize the degradation because of the chemical reaction between core components with the coolant. The aim, however, is to build future nuclear fuel cycles in concert with the aim of the Generation IV International Forum and includes nuclear reactor applications for process heat, hydrogen production, and electricity generation. Moreover, developmental work is ongoing and focuses on the burning of weapon-grade plutonium including civil plutonium and other transuranic elements using the deep-burn concept or inert matrix fuels, especially in HTGR systems in the form of coated particle fuels, which broadly covers several aspects of coated particle fuel technology, namely: manufacture of coated particles, compacts, and elements of quality assurance requirements [7].

Therefore, the study in this paper has been conducted to harmonize the interest of quality assurance in carrying out of the characterization of TRISO coated particles in HTGR systems and comparative study of modular HTGR procedures being implemented in INET Tsinghua University, China and Japan Atomic Energy Agency (JAEA). For that purpose, on the rest of this paper. Section 2 describing the methodology used in this study. Section 3 discussing the study result. And finally, in Section 4 this paper will be closed by the conclusion.

## 2. Methodology

The methodology used in this paper based on literature review, includes collecting data and information from various libraries, journals and other publications related to the implementation of quality assurance aspects and analyzed using descriptive qualitative analysis methods.

The stages of the literature review are as follows [6]: (1) Organize; i.e., organizing the kinds of literature that will be reviewed. The literatures will be selected based on its relevance with the theme of the literature review. The stages in organizing kinds of literature are identifying the ideas, general purpose, and conclusion of the literature by reading the abstract, some of the introductory paragraph, and its conclusion, as well as grouping the kinds of literature based on certain categories; (2) Synthesize; i.e. combining the result of literature organization into an integrated summary by looking at the intertextuality between the literatures; (3) Identify; i.e. identifying the controversial issues of the literature. Controversial issues are issues that are deemed important to be analyzed to produce an interesting article to read; (4) Formulate; i.e., formulating the findings that require further research

For that purpose, we are doing some stage of study starting from literature study, applying current standards and guidance that usually used for quality assurance requirements, developing new methodology if needed, and finally establishing and proposing the appropriate graded approach for the real graded approach implementation. This paper is part of preliminary study and because of that, the methods used are adopted directly from current IAEA publications, JAEA, INET Tsinghua University as HTGR developers. IAEA has published some standards, guidance and technical report for graded approach purposes. One of that publication is IAEA TECDOC 1645 regarding graded approach for quality assurance requirements for High Temperature Gas Cooled Reactor Fuels and Materials. It would be useful to have a comparative study of QA procedures being implemented in HTGR developers.

## 3. Result and Discussion

HTGR safety is based on an inherent safety feature that does not have the potential to lead serious radiological hazard if the quality and integrity of inherent safety feature related components are well preserved [4]. The main features of HTGR are enhanced safety, high thermal efficiency, economic competitiveness, and proliferation resistance, and these make this technology a potential candidate for the nuclear power plant deployment. One of the driving forces behind the HTGR philosophy is its utilization in the production of process heat. Net thermal efficiencies greater than 45% are within the reach in some of the designs of HTGR. The foremost motivation for the development of HTGR technology is its enhanced safety features along with its high- temperature capabilities. The enhanced safety of the HTGR fuel is based on its coated fuel particle design consisting of uranium oxide/carbide particles coated with layers of pyrolytic carbon and silicon carbide. Coated particles are so designed that they can withstand high internal gas pressure without releasing any fission products to the environment. The understanding gained through the quality assurance characterization of TRISO coated particles [8]. The analysis of the quality assurance process schematic for TRISO coating deposition is given in Fig. 1. The four coating layers are deposited on kernels in a heated furnace (see Fig. 2) by a process called chemical vapor deposition (CVD) [8].

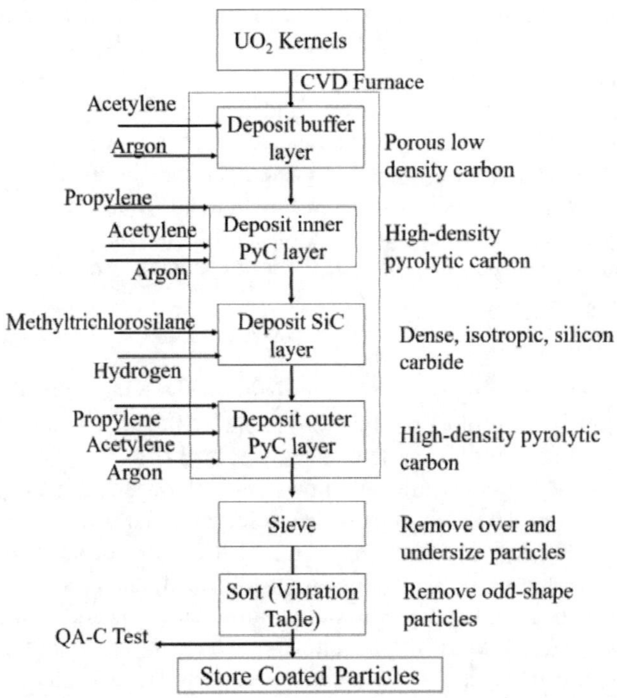


**Figure 1.** Analysis of quality assurance in coating process [8]

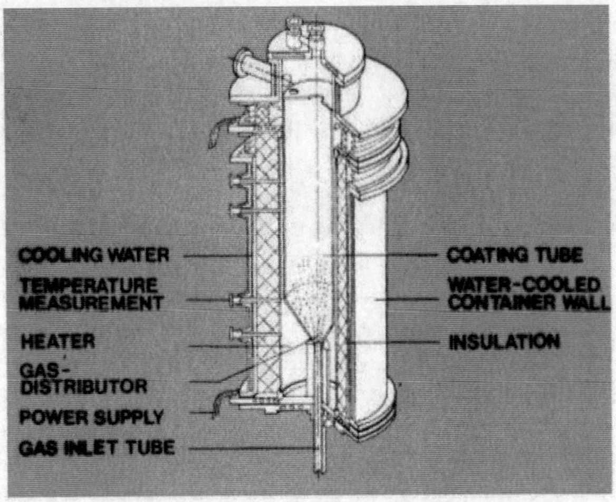


**Figure 2.** Schematic of a High temperature fluidized bed coating reactor used in HTGR fuel fabrication [8]

As the part of inherent safety feature, TRISO fuel of HTGR consist of low enrichment uranium or plutonium. The fission material is coated by three- layer, high-density Pyrolytic Carbon (PyC), low-density PyC, and Silicon Carbide (SiC) with the size only about 0.9 mm. Low density with high porosity PyC layer able to capture almost all the fission products. The next layers consist of high-density PyC and SiC becomes the next deterrent against the release of fission products [9]. The use of large amounts of graphite material both in the TRISO fuel layer and as a moderator neutron, the reflector, and also the structure gives a negative reactivity coefficient, low power density, and high thermal conductivity characteristics. All of these characteristics cause the reactor temperature to never exceed the predetermined threshold even without inserting the control rod. Although has different core design, both of prismatic and pebble-bed HTGR using similar fuel, moderator, and cooling concepts [10].

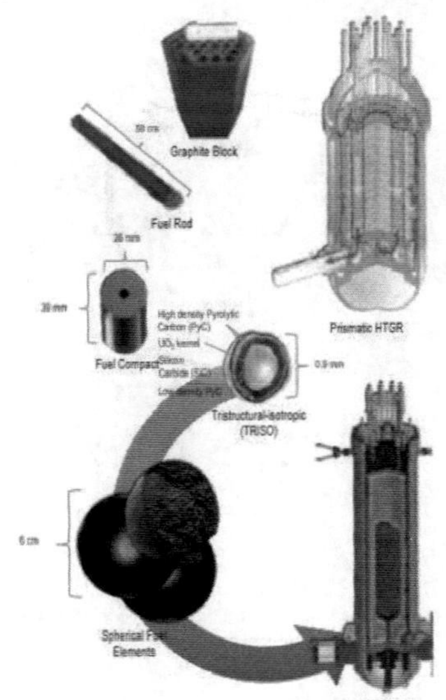


**Figure 3.** Pebble bed reactor design and prismatic reactor design [4]

The combination of TRISO fuel, graphite moderator, and helium. create an inherent safety design that is the main requirement of the Generation IV nuclear reactor. The similarity and differences between those design furthermore can be seen in Fig.3 [4]. Both prismatic and pebble-bed HTGR use B4C material as their control rod that can be inserted on the hole beside the reflector. In the case of loss of cooling accident, the core reactor power and temperature will become transient below the safety limit [12]. As the backup, the control rod is possibly needed to return the reactor to normal conditions faster and avoid component degradation due to excessive temperatures exposure. The backup reactivity control of prismatic HTGR is designed base on B4C pellets that can be inserted into the channels bored in the control rod blocks. The pebble bed HTGR be equipped with B4C pebbles that can be inserted as the reactivity control backup system [11].

Quality Assurance, Quality Control, and Testing go hand in hand to ensure the quality of the product and client satisfaction. Quality Assurance is the process by which development and/or production is 'guided' to ensure the system will attain the objectives set for it and ensure the quality of the product and client satisfaction. Quality Control is in essence a set of procedures laid down to evaluate a work product. Products are evaluated by testing against stringent specifications whether they are raw materials, intermediate products, or final products. However, The Nuclear industry is far more rigid and stringent in defining its requirements, standards, and specifications as the client always involves the safety of the greater public [8].

Coated fuel particles for development and testing purposes must be manufactured and controlled following a documented QA program that has been established following an appropriate standard, for example, IAEA TECDOC1645, ASME NQA-1 (American Society of Mechanical Engineers - Quality Assurance Requirements for Nuclear Facility Applications) provide for : (a) Product and material specifications to prescribe the technical and quality requirements that must be met; (b) Appropriate sampling procedures and acceptance criteria for determining that the specified values have been met; (c) Performance of work following written manufacturing and test instructions; (d) Calibration and control of measuring and test equipment; (e) Identification and control of materials and product, and (f) Generation of reports following established formats and maintenance of appropriate QA records [8]. Figure 4 contains a list of typical QA-QC tests and the preferred techniques used to diagnose TRISO coated particles. Some of them are (1) TRISO particle size and shape analysis (PSA); (2) Optical anisotropy; (3) Kernel, buffer and layer density determination; (4) Layer thickness determination: Micro-radiography; (5) SiC layer integrity: Burn-leach testing; (6) Thermal conductivity; (7) Elasticity modulus.

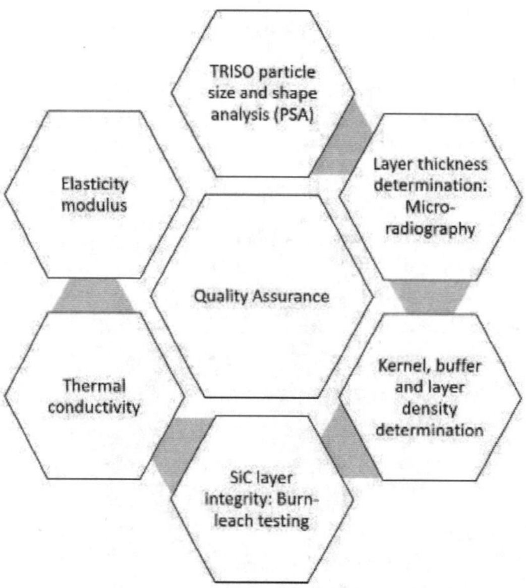


**Figure 4.** List of typical QA-QC tests and the preferred techniques used to diagnose TRISO coated particles

The first type, TRISO particle size and shape analysis (PSA) have the benchmark apparatus for measuring particle diameters (and their associated volumes) for spherical particles in the size range applicable to kernels and coated particles is an automated optical particle analyzer with pneumatic particle transport, custom developed by Seibersdorf for NUKEM. It is a reliable, accurate, and precise method that relies on the intensity dip observed by a detector when a particle passes through a light beam. For spherical particles, it is possible to achieve a linear response between an appropriately defined function of the intensity dip and the particle diameter. Accurate calibration of the system is achieved through standard steel balls. Particles are pneumatically transported, separated, and passed through the light beam where they are counted and measured. Although a maximum rate of about 50 particles per second is achievable, the feed rate is chosen to match the desired accuracy and precision of the application [12], [15].

**Table 1.** Properties and preferred test of TRISO particle size and shape analysis (PSA) [13], [14], [15]

| Properties | Test |
|---|---|
| Uranium enrichment | Mass spectrometric analysis using thermal ion<br>Mass spectrometry or gamma-ray spectrometry |
| Equivalent boron content (impurities) | Spectroscopic analysis using plasma source mass spectrometry or emission<br>spectrometry |
| Stoichiometry (O:U ratio) | Thermo-gravimetric analysis |
| Diameter and sphericity | Particle Size Analyzer (PSA) Shadow-scope techniques using an optical microscope and image analysis system |
| Density | Geometrical determination by means of PSA Mass by helium pycnometry or mercury porosimetry |
| Density of buffer layer<br>95 μm; | Geometrical determination by means of PSA |
| Density of other layers | Gradient column (sink- float method) |
| Microstructure | Microscopy on ceramographic sections |
| Layer thickness and symmetry | Micro-radiography Ceramography using image analysis techniques |
| PyC layers<br>PyC layer: 40 μm; must be impermeable; have an isotropic texture | Advanced Two-Modulator Generalized Ellipsometry Microscope (2-MGEM) |
| SiC layer integrity β-SiC with a cubic structure; equiaxed microstructure with fine grains and as few flaws as possible | Burn-leach testing Micro- radiography |

The second type, Optical anisotropy. Recently, advanced ellipsometry techniques have been applied to the measurement of pyrocarbon anisotropy in TRISO fuels. A system developed by Oak Ridge National Laboratory (ORNL) called the Two- Modulator Generalized Ellipsometry Microscope (2MGEM) was designed to completely determine the polarization effect on light reflected off of a polished pyrocarbon cross-section [16], [17]. This ellipsometer provides a very accurate determination of the pyrocarbon anisotropy with a selectable spatial resolution down to a few micrometers. It is a reliable, accurate, and precise method that relies on the intensity dip observed by a detector when a particle passes through a light beam. For spherical particles, it is possible to achieve a linear response between an appropriately defined function of the intensity dip and the particle diameter.

The third type, Kernel, buffer, and layer density determination Silicon carbide and pyrocarbon (PyC) densities are measured through suitable density gradient columns [18]. A density gradient column is created by filling a glass column with two liquids of different density, where the ratio of the two liquids is varied during filling to create a linear density gradient as a function of the column height. This linear density gradient is determined by measuring the zero-buoyancy position of calibrated floats. Samples of the Inner-PyC (IPyC), SiC, and outer-PyC (OPyC) layers are obtained by fracturing the coatings of individual TRISO particles.

The fourth type, Layer thickness determination: Micro-radiography Although PSA analysis can be used to derive layer thickness, the method becomes increasingly imprecise for outer layers due to error propagation. To achieve good statistics of intrinsic layer variation over a large number of particles (100 – 200), X-ray microradiography can be utilized [19], [20]. A single layer of particles is positioned directly on the emulsion of a high-resolution photographic film (about 1 μm resolution) and illuminated with an X-ray source approximately 300 mm away.

The fifth type, SiC layer integrity: Burn-leach testing A very important test for SiC layer integrity is the burn-leach test. A representative sample of coated particles of statistically significant size is selected. Under clean laboratory conditions, these are burned down to the SiC layers and the remaining particles and ash are leached under reflux for an extended period in a nitric acid solution. A sample of the liquid is then preconcentrated in a rotary evaporator and analyzed for uranium with an extremely sensitive analytical technique such as fluorimetry, mass spectrometry methods, or delayed neutron counting (after activation in a reactor). When there is no defective SiC coatings, the analytical result reflects the unconfined uranium content. The number of broken particles or defective SiC layers can be calculated after the division of the total concentration by the expected contribution per particle [8].

The sixth type, Thermal conductivity, the most important property for predicting the in-reactor fuel temperature is the thermal conductivity. For the graphite element (compact or sphere) this property can easily be obtained by the conventional laser flash method. The thermal properties of coated particles must also be evaluated to improve the prediction of in-reactor behavior [8]. Thermal characterization applied to dense PyC layers Thermoreflectance microscopy has been applied to characterize dense pyrolytic carbon layers of TRISO particles. Measurements have been performed at room temperature [21], and tests at temperatures of up to 1500°C are currently in progress. Thermal characterization applied to the buffer layer thermal property measurements can be performed at room temperature. The diffusivity obtained for the dense parts of the buffer layer is $5.2 \pm 0.5$ $mm^2.s^{-1}$ [21].

The seventh type, Elasticity modulus Elastic modulus measurements were performed with a Nano indenter NT 600 (Micro Materials Limited) that allows indentation displacement of 50 μm. The penetration of the nondeformable diamond indenter is measured by a capacitive sensor with about 0.01 nm accuracy.

Quality assurance analysis for program Fuel Fabrication Process Improvements: (a) Reduced human interactions in the process: Eliminated tabling with 3D sieving of coated particles, Improved matrix production (dry mixing and jet milling), Improved overcoating with automated fluidized bed over-coater, Multi cavity compacting press with automatic fill; (b) Kernel fabrication: Internal gelation to improve sphericity, Method of carbon addition modified to improve distribution of oxide and carbide phases; (c) Improved chemical vapor deposition process control: Argon dilution during Si-coating, Coater chalice and multiport nozzle to improve process yields (>95%), Mass flow controllers to control gas flows during deposition of each coating layer, improved MTS vaporizer (Si-C layer deposition); (d) Specifications on source materials, production processes and process limits; (e) Specifications on kernel, coating, and compact properties; (f) Specifications on defect populations that may impact performance [22]. Therefore, current Industrial Interest in TRISO-fueled power. HTGR reactor has a technical qualification, good performance of HTGR fuel, safety and accident analysis source term analysis, control of multi- modular HTGR, and related human factor analysis, also optimizing radiation protection of HTGR. The quality control and assurance system have been successfully practiced in fuel fabrication for the HTGR.

In addition, China's long-term development plan of nuclear power, the Institute of Nuclear and New Energy Technology (INET) of Tsinghua University developed and designed a Modular HTGR demonstration plant, named high-temperature gas- cooled reactor pebble bed module (HTR-PM). The

HTR-PM came into the construction phase at the end of 2012. The HTR-PM aims to demonstrate safety, economic potential and modularization technologies towards future commercial applications. Based on experiences obtained from the HTR-PM project with respect to design, manufacture, construction, licensing and project management, a further step aiming to promote commercialization and market applications of the MHTGR is expected. To this purpose, INET is developing a commercialized MHTGR named HTR-PM600 and a conceptual design is under way accordingly. HTR-PM600 is a pebble-bed MHTGR power generation unit with a sixpack of 250MWth reactor modules. The objective is to cogenerate electricity and process heat flexibly and economically in order to meet a variety of market needs. The design of HTR-PM600 closely follows HTR-PM with respect to safety features, system configuration and plant layout. HTR-PM600 will have the six modules feeding one steam turbine to generate electricity with capacity to extract high temperature steam from various interfaces of the turbine for further process heat applications. A standard plant will consist of two HTR-PM600 units. Base on the economic information of HTRPM, a preliminary study is carried out on the economic prospect of HTR-PM600 [23].

The modular high temperature gas-cooled reactor (MHTGR) is an inherently safe nuclear energy technology for efficient electricity generation and process heat applications. The MHTGR is promising in China as it may replace fossil fuels in broader energy markets.

Meanwhile, Progresses in Hydrogen Production and Application for Establishment of Low-carbon Society in Japan. Hydrogen (H2) is expected to be a new energy carrier for independent from dependency on fossil fuels. Hydrogen system driven by high temperature gas cooled reactor (HTGR) of inherent safety reactor is one of practical technologies for establishment of low-carbon society post Fukushima. The high temperature engineering test reactor (HTTR) in Japan Atomic Energy Agency (JAEA) has demonstrated heat output at 950oC which is relatively higher-quality energy than one from other type reactors. For efficient utilization of the high thermal energy, it is useful thermodynamically to be used as a heat source of endothermic chemical reaction. Then, thermochemical hydrogen (H2) production from water by using heat from HTGR is rational way. A thermo-chemical Iodine-Sulfur (IS) process is a process which can produce H2 at less than 900°C in liquid-gas flowing type reactor. The IS process in HTTR demonstrated continuous $H_2$ production of 30 NL/h for a week the world's first in 2004. Establishment of $H_2$ consumption and supply systems is needed for practical $H_2$ energy system. A new energy system of Active Carbon Recycle Energy System (ACRES) driven by HTGR has been proposed as low-carbon energy system. A smart iron making system based on ACRES (iACRES) is been discussed in Iron and Steel Institute of Japan. $H_2$ is important energy material for reduction of carbon dioxide into useful carbon materials in iACRES. Progresses in hydrogen production and application are been expecting for establishment of low-carbon society [23].

## 4. Conclusions

Quality Assurance, Quality Control, and Testing go hand in hand to ensure the quality of the product and client satisfaction. Specified criteria on both process conditions and fuel properties The main features of HTGR are enhanced safety, high thermal efficiency, economic competitiveness, and proliferation resistance, and these make this technology a potential candidate for the nuclear power plant deployment. Thus, HTGR for quality assurance program cover: (1) Acceptance stages for kernel batches, kernel composites, particle batches, particle composites, and compacts; (2) Specified mean values and/or critical limits on the dispersion for variable properties, such as diameter, stoichiometry, layer thickness, layer density, micro- structure; (3) Specified maximum defect fractions for attribute properties, such as SiC defects, PyC defects, exposed kernel defects.

## References

[1]. International Energy Agency, World Energy Outlook 2017, Int. Energy Agency Together Secure. Sustain, 2017.
[2]. International Atomic Energy Agency, Nuclear Power Reactors in the World, Vienna, 2018.
[3]. International Energy Agency, World Energy Outlook 2017, Int. Energy Agency Together Secure.

Sustain., 2017.
[4]. I. W. Ngarayana, K. Murakami, High Temperature Gas Cooled Reactor Regulation Development- Operation & Maintenance Perspective, Conference Paper Transactions on GIGAKU 6(1)(2019)06004/1-11, https://www.researchgate.net/publication/33312 8351, May 2019.
[5]. G. Zhao et al., Endurance test of full-scale mock- up helium circulator for HTR-PM, Nucl. Eng. Des., vol. 329, no. April 2017, pp. 20–24, 2018.
[6]. B. J. Marsden and G. N. Hall, Graphite in gas- cooled reactors, vol. 4, no. April 2015, 2015.
[7]. Pioro, Ed., Handbook of Generation IV Nuclear Reactors, Woodhead P. Duxford, UK: Elsevier, 2016.
[8]. International Atomic Energy Agency (IAEA) TECDOC-1645 - High Temperature Gas Cooled Reactor Fuels and Materials, IAEA, Vienna, March 2010.
[9]. S. Nakagawa, K. Takamatsu, Y. Tachibana, N. Sakaba, and T. Iyoku, Safety demonstration tests using high temperature engineering test reactor, Nucl. Eng. Des., vol. 233, no. 1–3, pp. 301–308, 2004.
[10]. T. Nishihara, X. Yan, Y. Tachibana, and T. Shibata, Excellent Feature of Japanese HTGR Technologies, Tokai-mura, 2018.
[11]. International Atomic Energy Agency, Fundamental Safety Principles, Safety Fundamentals, vol. 2, no. No.SF-1. p. 37, 2006.
[12]. International Atomic Energy Agency (IAEA) - NS-R-1 and International Atomic Energy Agency, Safety of Nuclear Power Plants: Design (NS-R-1), vol. 1, 2016.
[13]. Hunn, J.D., Quality Assurance and Quality Control for Coated Particles and Fuel Compacts, Eurocourse on coated particle fuel, Petten, NL, December 2007.
[14]. Sowder, W.K., Quality Assurance Program Plan for AGR Fuel Development and Qualification Program, INEEL/EXT-04-01825, Idaho National Engineering and Environmental Laboratory, Idaho Falls, Idaho, October 2003.
[15]. HUNN, J.D., Quality Assurance and Quality Control for Coated Particles and Fuel Compacts, presented in Eurocourse on coated particle fuel, Raphael Project, Petten, NL, December 2007.
[16]. Jellison, jr., g.e., hunn, j.d., lowden, R.A., Optical Characterization of Tristructural Isotropic Fuel Particle Cross-sections Using Generalized Ellipsometry (Proc. E-MRS 2005 Spring mtg,Symp), J. Nucl. Mater. 352, p. 6-12, 2006
[17]. Jellison, jr., g.e., hunn, j.d., Optical Anisotropy Measurements of TRISO Nuclear Fuel Particle Cross-sections: The Method, J. Nucl. Mater. 372, p. 3644, 2008.
[18]. ASTM International, Standard Test Method for Density of Plastics by the Density Gradient Technique, ASTM D1505-98, ASTM International, West Conshohocken, PA, 1999).
[19]. Kim, w.k., et al., Non-destructive Measurement of the Coating Thickness in the Simulated TRISO-Coated Fuel Particle for the HTGR, 3nd International Topical Meeting on High Temperature Reactor Technology, Johannesburg– South Africa, 2006.
[20]. Price, J.R., et al., New Developments in Image- based Characterization of Coated Particle Nuclear Fuel (Proc. Machine Vision Applications in Industrial Inspection XIV), SPIE Vol. 6070, p.153-162, 2006.
[21]. Rochais, D., Le Meur, g., Basini, v., Domingues, G., Microscopic Thermal Characterization of HTR Particle Layers, Proc. 3nd International Topical Meeting on High Temperature Reactor Technology, Johannesburg – South Africa, 2006.
[22]. Z Xiorning FU* Masashi TAKAHASHI, Shouhei UETA and Kazuhiro SAWA, Current Status and Technical Description of the Chinese 2 ×250MWth HTR-PM Demonstration Plant, Nuclear Engineering and Design, v239, p.1212, 2009.
[23]. HTR, 7$^{th}$ International Topical meeting on High Temperature reactor technology, Weihai, 2014.

# Accurate Nodal Diffusion Modelling on the High Temperature Test Reactor (HTTR)

**M. Rizki Oktavian, Volkan Seker[1], Brendan Kochunas[1], Yunlin Xu[2]**

School of Nuclear Engineering, Purdue University, 516 Northwestern Ave., West Lafayette, IN 47906, United States
phone: +1-734-882-9329, rizkiokt@purdue.edu
[1]Department of Nuclear Engineering And Radiological Sciences., University of Michigan, 2355 Bonisteel Blvd, Ann Arbor, MI 48109 United States
[2]School of Nuclear Engineering, Purdue University, 516 Northwestern Ave., West Lafayette, IN 47906, United States

**Abstract.** The High Temperature Test Reactor is a 30-MWth helium-cooled, graphite-moderated, prismatic-type gas reactor developed by the Japan Atomic Energy Agency (JAEA). The hexagonal shape of fuel blocks in the HTTR core combined with complex inner structures containing TRISO particles results in the double-heterogeneity effect that increases the simulation challenge of the reactor. This research has a goal to accurately model the HTTR fuel blocks employing the standard two-step procedure of a reactor analysis: employ a lattice physics calculation to generate homogeneous cross sections and use them in a nodal diffusion calculation. The implementation of the diffusion approximation results in a faster calculation with acceptable accuracy compared to the high-resolution lattice calculation. An advanced method called Triangular Polynomial Expansion Nodal (TriPEN) method was used in this work for the nodal diffusion calculation to accurately model the flux discontinuity effect between blocks by generating discontinuity factors in each surface and corner point. To do this, the heterogeneous solutions obtained from the lattice physics calculation, which is done by Serpent Monte Carlo in this case, are utilized by TriPEN to generate the discontinuity factors. Due to its capability to simulate any reactor geometry with a high-resolution, the results generated from Serpent calculation were also used as the reference cases for this work. In this work, the TriPEN method is implemented in the PARCS core neutronic module inside AGREE, a U.S. N.R.C. Multiphysics code system for the High Temperature Reactor (HTR). Test cases conducted for this method involved the original design of the HTTR. The 4-hex model built consisted of the central control-rod block of HTTR together with 6 of the half-fuel-blocks surround it. The differences in material composition in each assembly block in HTTR resulted in flux discontinuity effects on the assembly block interfaces. To correct this discrepancy, discontinuity factors were applied in order to make the homogenous solutions from the nodal calculation agree with the heterogeneous solutions from the lattice physics calculation. Applying this procedure to the HTTR nodal models, TriPEN is able to produce exact results in the eigenvalue compared to Serpent calculation, the rod worth calculated perfectly matched the reference, and the flux and power distribution only has negligible discrepancies.

Journal of Physics: Conference Series **2048** (2021) 012023 doi:10.1088/1742-6596/2048/1/012023

## 1. Introduction

One of the six advanced reactors proposed by the Generation IV Forum (GIF) in 2002 is the High Temperature Reactor (HTR) or High Temperature Gas Reactor (HTGR) or also called Very High Temperature Reactor (VHTR)[1], which is a reactor characterized with its higher output temperature than a conventional nuclear reactor and the gas coolant employed instead of water. The high temperature heat produced by this reactor results in a more efficient power cycle, capable to generate more electricity with the same number of nuclear fuels as the conventional Light Water Reactor (LWR). Other than the efficiency, the heat generated by HTR can possibly be used as a cogeneration facility: not only utilized to generate electricity, but also for heat application[2]. Some of the most popular heat application from HTR are seawater desalination, hydrogen production and district heating[3].

Table 1. Specification of HTTR

| | |
|---|---|
| Reactor Thermal Power | 30 MW |
| Reactor Coolant | Helium Gas |
| Reactor Outlet Coolant Temperature | 850 °C/950 °C |
| Reactor Inlet Coolant Temperature | 395 °C |
| Primary Coolant Pressure | 4 MPa |
| Core Material | Graphite |
| Core Diameter | 290 cm |
| Average Power Density | 2.5 W/cm$^3$ |
| Fuel | Low Enriched Uranium Oxide |
| Fuel Element Type | Prismatic Block |
| Uranium Enrichment | 3 |
| Reactor Pressure Vessel | Steel (21 /4 Cr-Mo) |

Given the various interesting features offered in the HTR, it is indeed important to create an optimized design to maximize the potential of the HTR. To do that, an accurate model of the reactor should be able to be generated in the current computer technology. As a result, a Verification and Validation (V&V) of nuclear codes and analysis method need to be conducted to this reactor. Unfortunately, unlike light water reactors, not many experimental data and specific nuclear analysis codes available for gas reactors. One of the experimental data available to use is from the Japan Atomic Energy Agency (JAEA) in the High Temperature Test Reactor (HTTR)[4].

The HTTR is a 30-MWth helium-cooled, graphite-moderated, prismatic-type gas reactor developed by JAEA[5]. The establishment of the reactor has a purpose to improve the technological basis for advanced gas reactors while also to conduct various tests for high temperature research. This reactor is fueled with enriched uranium in the form of TRISO particles dispersed in the fuel compact, then the fuel compacts are stacked together and inserted in the prismatic hexagonal block of graphite. Five fuel blocks are stacked with the addition of two reflectors in the upper and lower side of the stacks. There are 30-33 stacks in the reactor core with some replaceable control rod blocks distributed in the core and reflector blocks surround them. Some major specifications of HTTR are presented in the Table 1.

The hexagonal shape of fuel blocks in the HTTR core combined with complex inner structures containing TRISO particles result in the double-heterogeneity feature. As a result, this will create more simulation challenge because the heterogeneity properties will produce a more prominent self-shielding effect in the fuel[6]. The effect may cause the homogeneous nodal calculation will overestimate the capture effect in the fuel. Other than the double-heterogeneity effect, more challenge will arise due to the significant different fuel enrichment for each fuel blocks and the existence of control rod blocks in the reactor core. These will create a non-negligible flux discontinuity effect between blocks in the nodal diffusion calculation.

This research has a goal to accurately model the HTTR fuel blocks employing the standard two-step procedure of reactor analysis: employ a lattice physics calculation to generate homogeneous cross sections and use the cross sections in a nodal diffusion calculation. An advanced method called Triangular Polynomial Expansion Nodal (TRIPEN) method[7] will be used in the nodal diffusion calculation to accurately model the flux discontinuity effect between blocks by generating discontinuity factors in each surface and corner point. To do this, the heterogeneous solutions obtained from lattice physics calculation, which is done by Serpent in this case, will be utilized by TRIPEN to generate the discontinuity factors.

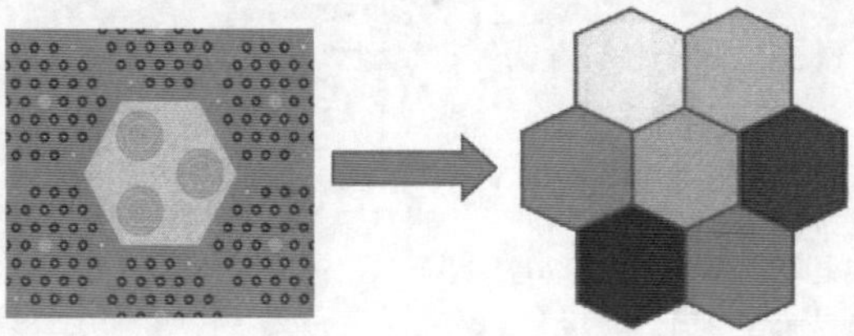

**Figure 1.** Example of a homogenization result in the lattice physics calculation

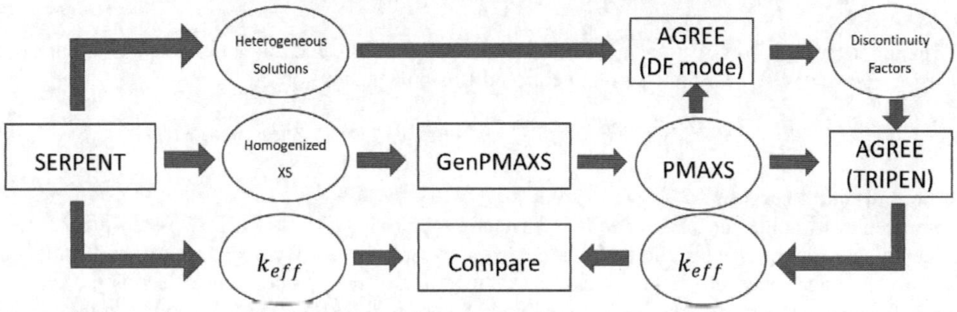


**Figure 2.** Procedure applied to model HTTR blocks

## 2. Theory

The homogenization process in the lattice physics calculation to generate multigroup homogenized cross-sections to use in nodal diffusion code is illustrated in Figure 1. This process could eliminate the self-shielding effect occurred in the heterogeneous model, especially in the resonance energy region. This is mainly caused due to fewer neutrons exist in the centers of fuel regions than in the edges, resulting in overestimating overall capture rate in the homogenized model. To handle the self-shielding effect, lattice physics codes generate the homogenized cross-sections using the flux-weighted averaging method[8]:

$$\Sigma_g^{hom} = \langle \Sigma_g \rangle_{node} = \frac{\int_R \int_{E_g}^{E_{g-1}} \Sigma(x,E)\phi(x,E)\, dE\, dV}{\int_R \int_{E_g}^{E_{g-1}} \phi(x,E)\, dE\, dV} \tag{1}$$

where: $g$ is the energy group index and $R$ is the region of lattice calculated.

The homogenized parameters defined should obey the relationship between the heterogeneous and homogeneous group-wise reaction rate and surface current[9]:

$$\int_R \Sigma_g^{hom}(\boldsymbol{x})\phi_g^{hom}(\boldsymbol{x})\, dV = \int_R \Sigma_g^{het}(\boldsymbol{x})\phi_g^{het}(\boldsymbol{x})\, dV \tag{2}$$

and

$$\int_{\partial R} \boldsymbol{\nabla} \cdot \mathrm{J}^{hom}(\boldsymbol{x})\, dS = \int_{\partial R} \boldsymbol{\nabla} \cdot \mathrm{J}^{het}(\boldsymbol{x})\, dS \tag{3}$$

However, some experiments[9–11] suggest that the conventional homogenization methods persistently produced large error in the solution even though the exact flux-weighted cross sections are already employed in the calculation. This problem arises as an inaccurate approximation of the leakage terms (defined in Equation (3)) are a significant source of error[9]. As a matter of fact, in the node boundary, neutron flux should be continuous, and this is true for the heterogeneous solution. On the other hand, the homogeneous solution does not conserve this condition, and it will get worse when there is a significant difference in material composition between nodes. Additional term called Discontinuity Factor (DF) should be included in the calculation, such that the flux continuity condition in the interface between nodes can be preserved.

$$\phi_i^{hom,+} f_i^{+} = \phi_{i+1}^{hom,-} f_{i+1}^{-} \tag{4}$$

where: $i$ is the index number of the calculated node, and the discontinuity factors defined as:

$$f_i^{+} = \frac{\phi_i^{het,+}}{\phi_i^{hom,+}} \tag{5a}$$

$$f_{i+1}^{-} = \frac{\phi_{i+1}^{het,-}}{\phi_{i+1}^{hom,-}} \tag{5b}$$

The heterogeneous solution can be easily obtained in the lattice physics calculation. Also, the heterogeneous flux can also be written in terms of partial neutron current using a simple relation from the diffusion theory.

$$\phi_i^{het,+} = 2\left(J_i^{het,-} + J_i^{het,+}\right) \tag{6}$$

The homogenized cross-sections obtained from lattice physics calculation are then used in the nodal diffusion code in the standard multigroup neutron diffusion equation:

$$-D_{i,g}\nabla^2\phi_{i,g} + \Sigma_{r,i,g}\phi_{i,g} = \frac{\chi_{i,g}}{k_{eff}}\sum_{g'} \nu\Sigma_{f,i,g'}\phi_{i,g'} + \sum_{g'} \Sigma_{s,i,g'\to g}\phi_{i,g'} \tag{7}$$

## 3. Methods and Procedures

The procedures implied in this research is basically employing the standard two-step procedure of nuclear reactor analysis with additional input called discontinuity factors used to handle the flux discontinuity effect between HTTR blocks. The illustration of the procedure practiced is presented in Figure 2. The nodal diffusion method utilized in this work is TRIPEN which is applied in the PARCS nodal diffusion code under the AGREE executable. The AGREE code system have the capability to do multiphysics analysis on the HTR-type reactor. PARCS uses cross-section files called PMAX, which is generated by GenPMAXS code using the homogenized cross-section data from the lattice physics code, which is Serpent in this case.

Serpent uses Monte Carlo methods to do the lattice physics calculation in the reactor and further to obtain homogenized cross sections to use in nodal diffusion calculation. Unlike deterministic methods, Monte Carlo methods do not solve the neutron transport equation, rather they simulate individual particles (neutrons) and record some aspects of their average behavior to obtain results intended by the users. The accuracy of Monte Carlo calculation depends highly on the number of particle histories included in the calculation, causing this method is very cost-extensive in terms of computation resource if one wants to obtain an accurate result. Nevertheless, Monte Carlo is reliable to solve any arbitrary and complicated three-dimensional problems because there are no averaging approximations required in space, energy and time.

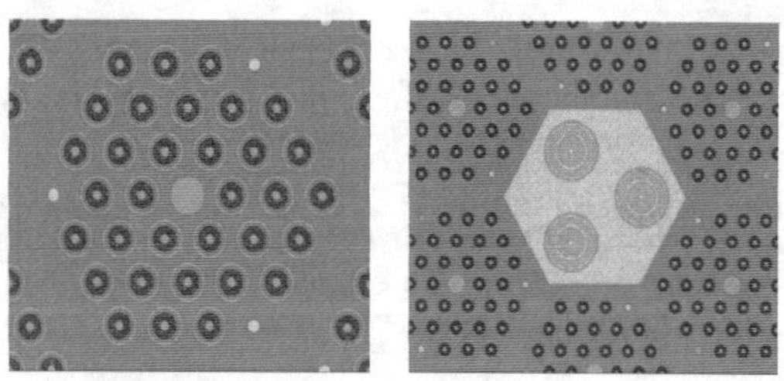

**Figure 3.** Two-dimensional (2D) Serpent model used: 1-hex fuel block (left) and 4-hex fuel blocks with central control rod block (right).

Figure 3 presents the two-dimensional (2D) HTTR blocks model used in this research generated by Serpent geometry plotter. The 1-hex model uses the zone 1-1 fuel block defined by JAEA memo[12] and the 4-hex model is based on the zone 1-1 to zone 1-6 fuel blocks with the central control rod block included. The 4-hex model basically consists of one central control rod block with 6-half fuel blocks surround it, and reflective boundaries are placed in all directions of the system. The use of 4-hex model instead of 7-hex model is because of Serpent geometry feature that require all cells and universes defined should be enclosed in a surface. As the 4-hex model can easily fit a hexagonal surface, it is the most possible option to model the simplest color-set of parts of HTTR core.

The next step after the homogenized cross sections generated by Serpent and converted to PMAX files by GenPMAXS is to use TRIPEN method to do the nodal diffusion calculation. TRIPEN is an improved method from Triangle-based Polynomial Expansion Nodal (TPEN) method to solve the diffusion equation in hexagonal lattice by uncoupling the three-dimensional hexagonal lattice into two-dimensional triangle-based polynomial expansion and one-dimensional polynomial expansion in the axial direction[13]. Unlike TPEN that still solve the hexagonal problem, TRIPEN treat explicitly the triangle nodes as individual homogeneous region[7]. As a result, it is possible to model one half of a hexagon or even one sixth of the hexagon if needed. While TPEN cannot reproduce the 4-hex model we used as reference, TRIPEN can easily model it.

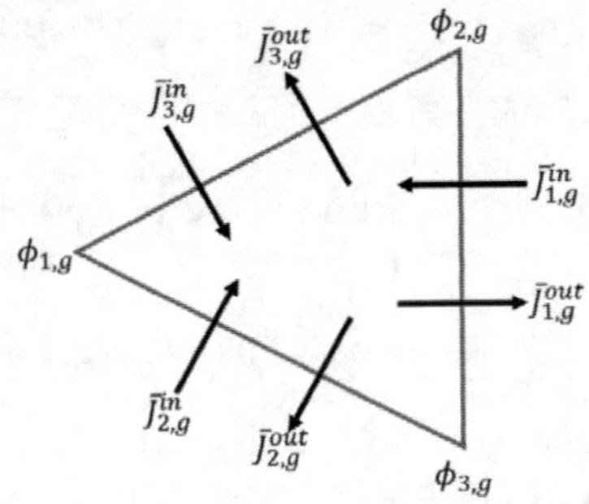


**Figure 4.** TRIPEN knowns and unknowns in a single node

Figure 4 represents a single triangle node in TRIPEN. Even though TRIPEN uses triangle-nodes, Serpent cannot generate triangle-wise homogenized cross-sections. As consequence, the same cross-sections were applied in the triangle nodes of the same hexagon, and this will assume the net current in the surfaces inside the hexagon are zero.

As mentioned before, the discontinuity factors are included in the nodal diffusion calculation to handle the flux discontinuity between hexagonal blocks surfaces. Heterogeneous solutions from Serpent are needed to be produced with the order: node flux, surface flux, surface net current, corner point flux and the reference eigenvalue. All the mentioned heterogeneous solutions need to be obtained for each node properties. Since Serpent and TRIPEN use different indexing, a careful converting of Serpent output needs to be conducted to obtain the right solution for each triangle-nodes. For the 1-hex problem, Figure 5 and Table 2 illustrate the indexing comparison between Serpent and TRIPEN. It is also important to be noted that the $x - y$ direction of the Serpent model and TRIPEN model is different, so a justified rotation need to be done before apple-to-apple compare the index numbers.

**Table 2.** TRIPEN result with and without ADF for 1-Hex model and comparison with TPEN

| Neutron Histories | SERPENT K-eff | SERPENT Stdev | TPEN K-eff | TPEN Error (pcm) | ADF in TRIPEN | TRIPEN K-eff | TRIPEN Error (pcm) |
|---|---|---|---|---|---|---|---|
| $1 \times 10^8$ neutrons | 0.99179 | 10 | 0.99174 | -5 | Off | 0.99174 | -5 |
| | | | | | On | 0.99179 | 0 |
| $4 \times 10^8$ neutrons | 0.99167 | 5 | 0.99165 | -2 | Off | 0.99165 | -2 |
| | | | | | On | 0.99167 | 0 |

## 4. Results and Discussion

### *4.1. Two-dimensional 1-Hex Model*

Table 3 presents the result calculated from TRIPEN without and with assembly discontinuity factor (ADFs). This problem is quite simple, since it only consists of one fuel assembly in the two-dimensional model, therefore without ADF included in the calculation, the result was already almost exact compared to the reference result (Serpent).

Without ADFs included in the calculation, TRIPEN produced different error compared to the reference. It also matched perfectly with results from TPEN as shown in the Table 3 as well. When the ADFs involved in the TRIPEN calculation, it results in no error relative to the reference solution. It can be observed that in this case, the ADFs can slightly improve the nodal diffusion solution given by the TRIPEN. It is also possible to provide exact results compared to the reference solution with smaller neutron histories by applying ADFs in TRIPEN.

*4.2. Two-dimensional 4-Hex Model*

The two-dimensional 4-hex model is indeed more complicated with 1-hex model solved in previous discussion. In this case, 4-hex model is created due to the constraint in Serpent to have all universes and cells in one surface. On the other hand, TPEN, which is usually used as one of the methods to do nodal diffusion calculation on hexagonal lattice, cannot reproduce the 4-hex model. It might be possible that TPEN can model the 4-hex system using the 7-hex model possibly modeled in TPEN, but of course only for certain cases.

Depicted in Figure 7 are the two-dimensional 4-hex models used in this research based on the HTTR central control rod block and zone-1 fuel blocks. Calculation results in this model can be observed in Table 4. In the table, TRIPEN prove to have better approaches to the original 4-hex models than TPEN. While TPEN produced thousands pcm errors in this case, TRIPEN only results in around a hundred pcm errors and even less. Also, for the rod worth comparison, TPEN generated more than 5000 pcm different with the reference's rod worth, while TRIPEN only differs 47 pcm $\Delta\rho$ of rod worth from the reference. TRIPEN results can still be improved to expectedly zero pcm error by applying the assembly discontinuity factors into calculation, which are also presented in this report.

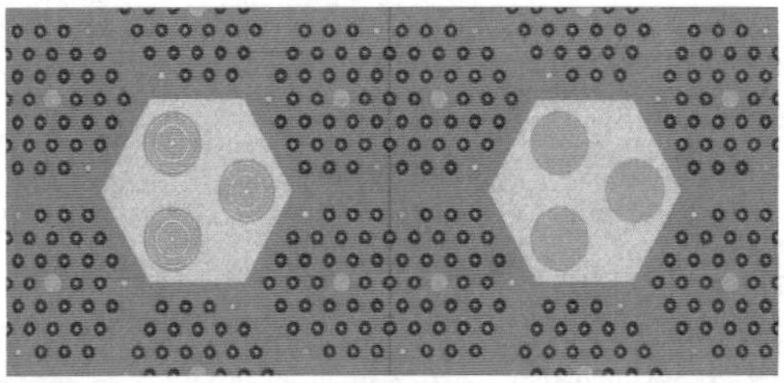

**Figure 5.** Two-dimensional 4-hex model: rodded (left) and unrodded (right).

**Table 3.** Comparison of TRIPEN results without and with ADF

| Control Rods | SERPENT | | TRIPEN | | TRIPEN (+ADF) | |
|---|---|---|---|---|---|---|
| | K-eff | Stdev | K-eff | Error (pcm) | K-eff | Error (pcm) |
| Un-rodded | 1.13051 | 4 | 1.13170 | 119 | 1.13051 | 0 |
| Rodded | 1.00628 | 3 | 1.00675 | 47 | 1.00628 | 0 |
| **Rod Worth (Δρ)** | **10920** | **5** | **10967** | **46** | **10920** | **0** |

As discussed before, the results of TRIPEN in Table 4 can be further improved by applying Assembly Discontinuity Factors (ADFs) on the inter-block surfaces. Table 3 presents the comparison of TRIPEN calculation for 4-Hex model without and with ADFs included in the calculation. Applying ADFs in this calculation caused TRIPEN to produce exact results with reference, i.e., 0 pcm difference in the $k_{eff}$. As consequence, the calculated rod worth also matched perfectly with the one from reference (Serpent). This implies the possibility to accurately model the HTTR core which has a significant heterogeneity effect using this method. However, it is obvious that to do full core modeling of the reactor, an excessive and meticulous works should be made to correctly transfer the heterogeneous solutions obtained from Serpent into TRIPEN. If not, the ADFs generated by TRIPEN will not represent the true heterogeneous calculation from Serpent.

To further verify the results for TRIPEN with ADFs included in the calculation, radial power comparisons are depicted in Figure 10-11 and group-wise radial flux are compared in Table 8-9. The comparisons were conducted between TRIPEN calculation without and with ADF with all other inputs remain the same, therefore effects of ADFs can be implied from these results.

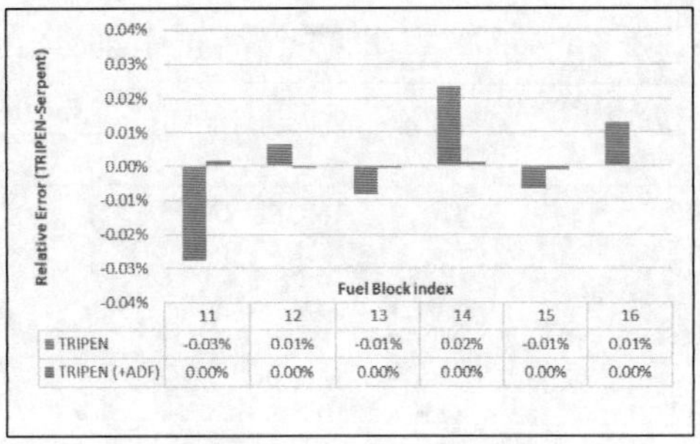


**Figure 6.** Relative error in radial power for the un-rodded case of 4-Hex model

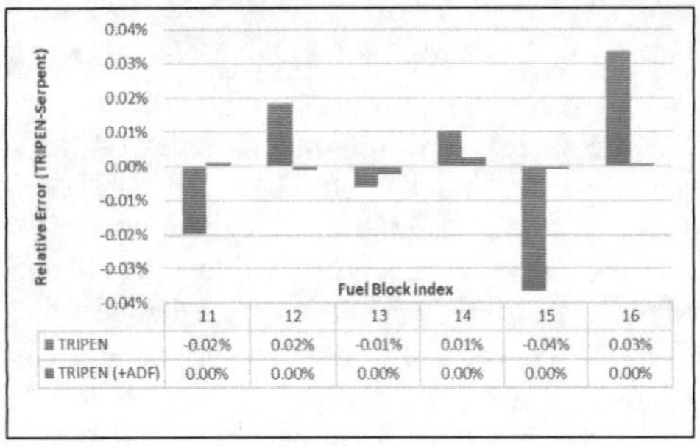


**Figure 7.** Relative error in radial power for the rodded case of 4-Hex model

The relative radial power error presented in Figure 10-11 gives a clear insight that with ADFs included in TRIPEN, a better approach can be reached in the power calculation. However, the improvement is not so significant in this case. It can be observed in Figure 10 and 11 that the maximum error from both cases, un-rodded and rodded, in TRIPEN without ADFs are just 0.03% and 0.04% respectively. These errors are pretty small as such when both results are plotted together, there will be hardly any difference. A larger improvement is expected for a case when the heterogeneity effect is higher than this case.

A more prominent improvement of applying ADFs in TRIPEN can be observed from the energy group-wise radial flux comparison presented in Table 8 and 9. With ADFs, TRIPEN results in almost exact approach compared to the reference with average error just less than 0.01% for both cases. These excellent results prove that this method can be used to model HTTR in the nodal diffusion code and can be used for multiphysics transient analysis.

Higher error in TRIPEN calculation without ADFs are found in the fast neutron, especially in the group 1 of flux. The reason is quite clear: higher energy neutrons will have longer distance to travel before absorbed in the system. This will cause more neutrons to leak out of or into the block, and the discontinuity effect will again worsen the nodal diffusion calculation.

**Table 4.** Relative error in group-wise radial flux for the un-rodded case of 4-Hex model

| Energy Group | Relative Error TRIPEN | | | | | | | Relative Error TRIPEN (+ADF) | | | | | | |
|---|---|---|---|---|---|---|---|---|---|---|---|---|---|---|
| | Block Index | | | | | | | Block Index | | | | | | |
| | 50 | 11 | 12 | 13 | 14 | 15 | 16 | 50 | 11 | 12 | 13 | 14 | 15 | 16 |
| 1 | 20.38% | 3.40% | 3.35% | 3.37% | 3.32% | 3.37% | 3.33% | 0.00% | 0.00% | 0.01% | 0.01% | 0.01% | 0.00% | 0.01% |
| 2 | 8.91% | 2.14% | 2.10% | 2.11% | 2.06% | 2.11% | 2.08% | 0.01% | 0.00% | 0.01% | 0.00% | 0.00% | 0.00% | 0.00% |
| 3 | 1.90% | 0.56% | 0.54% | 0.54% | 0.53% | 0.55% | 0.54% | 0.00% | 0.00% | 0.00% | 0.00% | 0.00% | 0.00% | 0.00% |
| 4 | 0.41% | 0.16% | 0.16% | 0.20% | 0.17% | 0.15% | 0.16% | 0.00% | 0.00% | 0.00% | 0.03% | 0.01% | 0.02% | 0.01% |
| 5 | 0.50% | 0.15% | 0.19% | 0.19% | 0.19% | 0.16% | 0.16% | 0.01% | 0.01% | 0.00% | 0.01% | 0.01% | 0.02% | 0.00% |
| 6 | 0.37% | 0.20% | 0.13% | 0.18% | 0.15% | 0.16% | 0.17% | 0.00% | 0.01% | 0.02% | 0.01% | 0.00% | 0.01% | 0.02% |
| 7 | 2.13% | 0.07% | 0.11% | 0.10% | 0.12% | 0.08% | 0.11% | 0.00% | 0.00% | 0.01% | 0.01% | 0.00% | 0.01% | 0.01% |

Journal of Physics: Conference Series **2048** (2021) 012023 doi:10.1088/1742-6596/2048/1/012023

**Table 5.** Relative error in group-wise radial flux for the rodded case of 4-Hex model

| Energy Group | Relative Error TRIPEN | | | | | | | Relative Error TRIPEN (+ADF) | | | | | | |
|---|---|---|---|---|---|---|---|---|---|---|---|---|---|---|
| | Block Index | | | | | | | Block Index | | | | | | |
| | 50 | 11 | 12 | 13 | 14 | 15 | 16 | 50 | 11 | 12 | 13 | 14 | 15 | 16 |
| 1 | 20.67% | 3.53% | 3.46% | 3.53% | 3.49% | 3.53% | 3.48% | 0.01% | 0.01% | 0.02% | 0.00% | 0.00% | 0.01% | 0.01% |
| 2 | 9.65% | 2.39% | 2.32% | 2.37% | 2.34% | 2.38% | 2.35% | 0.00% | 0.00% | 0.02% | 0.01% | 0.00% | 0.01% | 0.02% |
| 3 | 2.50% | 0.71% | 0.68% | 0.69% | 0.68% | 0.68% | 0.69% | 0.00% | 0.00% | 0.01% | 0.00% | 0.00% | 0.00% | 0.01% |
| 4 | 0.16% | 0.11% | 0.14% | 0.13% | 0.13% | 0.11% | 0.10% | 0.00% | 0.00% | 0.02% | 0.00% | 0.01% | 0.01% | 0.01% |
| 5 | 0.09% | 0.12% | 0.15% | 0.15% | 0.16% | 0.15% | 0.12% | 0.01% | 0.00% | 0.00% | 0.02% | 0.00% | 0.01% | 0.01% |
| 6 | 1.15% | 0.20% | 0.17% | 0.20% | 0.18% | 0.19% | 0.17% | 0.00% | 0.00% | 0.01% | 0.01% | 0.00% | 0.01% | 0.00% |
| 7 | 0.42% | 0.11% | 0.15% | 0.14% | 0.14% | 0.06% | 0.16% | 0.00% | 0.00% | 0.01% | 0.06% | 0.00% | 0.06% | 0.01% |

Another large error in TRIPEN is observed in the block index 50, which is the central control rod block. This can be explained as the central block is a full hexagon, compared with other six blocks which are a half of hexagon. While one half of hexagon has only three inter-block surfaces, the full hexagon has six, therefore the central block has more discontinuity effect than the other six fuel blocks. Also, all six surfaces in the control rod block are directly connected with the fuel blocks, creating a non-negligible discontinuity effect in each surface. On contrary, only one surface of each fuel block that is connected with the control rod block.

To have a better insight about the calculation improvement in TRIPEN after having ADFs included, a plot of group-wise flux in the central block is depicted in Figure 12. In the figure, it is observed that TRIPEN has some obvious discrepancies in the first three energy-groups of neutron flux, and also some small error in other groups as well based on Table 9, which is hard to see in the plot. The ADFs applied in TRIPEN has corrected the discrepancies, and the plot can match perfectly with the reference plot from Serpent.

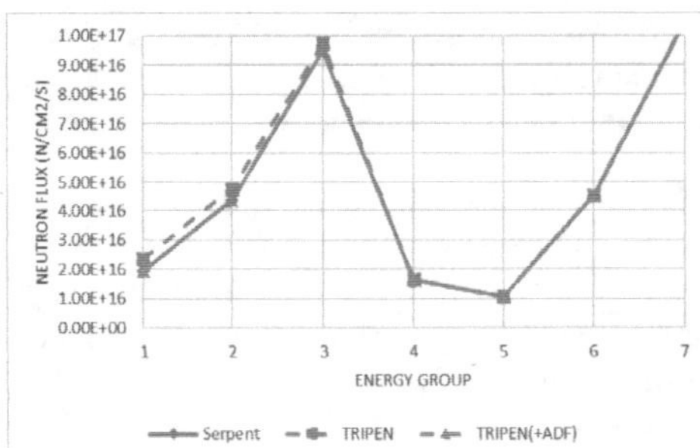


**Figure 8.** Comparison of group-wise neutron flux spectrum in central control rod block in the rodded case

## 5. Conclusion

The HTTR fuel blocks can be accurately modeled using the methods proposed in this research: employ a lattice physics calculation to generate homogeneous cross sections and use the cross sections in a nodal diffusion calculation with the addition discontinuity factors involved in the calculation. The utilization of TRIPEN method in the nodal diffusion calculation provide a flexibility in the design of hexagonal lattice due to its capability to handle a hexagon into six triangular nodes. The calculation results by TRIPEN indeed can be further improved when Serpent has the capability to generate triangle-wise cross-sections to use in nodal diffusion calculation.

## References

[1] Generation IV International Forum, A Technology Roadmap for Generation IV Nuclear Energy Systems, 2002.
[2] IAEA, High Temperature Gas Cooled Reactor Fuels and Materials, Vienna, 2010.

[3] K. Kugeler, Z. Zhang, Modular High-Temperature Gas-Cooled Reactor Power Plant, Springer Berlin Heidelberg, 2018.
[4] J. Ortensi, J.J. Cogliati, M.A. Pope, J.D. Bess, R.M. Ferrer, A. Bingham, A.M. Ougouag, Deterministic Modeling of the High Temperature Test Reactor With, 2010.
[5] Japan Atomic Energy Agency, "High Temperature Test Reactor;" https://httr.jaea.go.jp/eng/index.html; (current as of Apr. 18, 2019).
[6] U. Rohde, S. Baier, S. Duerigen, E. Fridman, S. Kliem, B. Merk, Nucl. Eng. Des. 251 (2012) 412–422.
[7] B. Kochunas, Y. Xu, T. Downar, Development Of The Triangular Nodal Method Tripen For Prismatic HTR Analysis, American Nuclear Society.
[8] J.J. Duderstadt, L.J. Hamilton, Nuclear Reactor Analysis, John Wiley & Sons, Inc., 1976.
[9] K.S. Smith, Assembly Homogenization Techniques For Light Water Reactor Analysis, 1986.
[10] K.S. Smith, 17 (1980) 148.
[11] G. Gomes, Importance of Assembly Discontinuity Factors In Simulating Reactor Cores Containing Highly Heterogeneous Fuel Assemblies, n.d.
[12] N. Nojiri, M. Nakano, N. Fujimoto, K. Yamashita, M. Tateuchi, S. Fujisaki, Benchmark Problem's Data for The HTTR's Start-up Core Physics Experiment, 1998.
[13] J.Y. Cho, H.G. Joo, B.-O. Cho, S.Q. Zee, Hexagonal Cmfd Formulation Employing Triangle-Based Polynomial Expansion Nodal Kernel, 2001.

International Conference on High Temperature Reactor Technology (HTR) 2021 IOP Publishing
Journal of Physics: Conference Series **2048** (2021) 012024 doi:10.1088/1742-6596/2048/1/012024

# Evaluation of PBMR-400 Core Design Steady State Condition with Serpent and AGREE

**H Ardiansyah[1], V Seker[1], T Downar[1], S Skutnik[2], and W Wieselquist[2]**

[1]Department of Nuclear Engineering and Radiological Sciences, University of Michigan, 1906 Cooley Building, 2355 Bonisteel Boulevard, Ann Arbor, Michigan, USA 48109-2104
phone: +1 (734) 239-3250, harun@umich.edu
[2]Oak Ridge National Laboratory, 1 Bethel Valley Rd, Oak Ridge, TN 37830

**Abstract.** The significant recent advances in computer speed and memory have made possible an increasing fidelity and accuracy in reactor core simulation with minimal increase in the computational burden. This has been important for modeling some of the smaller advanced reactor designs for which simplified approximations such as few groups homogenized diffusion theory are not as accurate as they were for large light water reactor cores. For narrow cylindrical cores with large surface to volume ratios such the Ped Bed Modular Reactor (PBMR), neutron leakage from the core can be significant, particularly with the harder neutron spectrum and longer mean free path than a light water reactor. In this paper the core from the OECD PBMR-400 benchmark was analyzed using multigroup Monte Carlo cross sections in the HTR reactor core simulation code AGREE. Homogenized cross sections were generated for each of the discrete regions of the AGREE model using a full core SERPENT Monte Carlo model. The cross sections were generated for a variety of group structures in AGREE to assess the importance of finer group discretization on the accuracy of the core eigenvalue and flux predictions compared to the SERPENT full core Monte Carlo solution. A significant increase in the accuracy was observed by increasing the number of energy groups, with as much as a 530 pcm improvement in the eigenvalue calculation when increasing the number of energy groups from 2 to 14. Significant improvements were also observed in the AGREE neutron flux distributions compared to the SERPENT full core calculation.

## 1. Introduction

The "two-step" few group, homogenized method for solving the neutron transport equation has been used successfully for the analysis of most all large Light Water Reactors [1]–[4]. However, the methods have not been as accurate for reactor cores that are not as optically thick and are not scattering-dominant system which is the case for some of the smaller advanced reactor concepts. The research here focused on the High Temperature Reactor (HTR) which is one of the six type reactor designs that were proposed in the Generation IV Forum (GIF) in 2002 [5]. The neutronic modeling of the HTR using the few group homogenized diffusion approximations has several limitations, particularly for the PBMR-400 core analyzed here which introduces the additional complexity of the double heterogeneity in modeling Pebbles with TRISO fuel [5].

The analysis here was performed using the OECD PBMR-400 Benchmark. The Monte Carlo Code SERPENT and the deterministic core simulator AGREE were used to analyze the PBMR-400. PBMR-400 is the reactor of choice in this analysis due to the data availability of PBMR-400 benchmark results. Some works related to PBMR-400 steady-state and transient analysis has been done in the past [6][7]. This work is meant to be a part to verify the use of two-step method using Monte Carlo generated cross sections and diffusion theory to obtain k-eigenvalue, power, and flux distribution. Using this analysis, similar analysis can be done in the future for any advanced reactor, especially HTR, which has similar system to PBMR-400.

This work was performed as part of a collaboration between ORNL and Department of Nuclear Engineering and Radiological Sciences, University of Michigan to assess and verify the SCALE/PARCS/AGREE code system for advanced reactor analysis. One particular task in this project is to perform full core analyses of PBMR-400 benchmark by generating nodal data from Monte Carlo method to model the full core with the cylindrical diffusion kernel in the AGREE code.

## 2. OECD PBMR-400 Benchmark

The Pebble-Bed Modular Reactor (PBMR) is a pebble-type High Temperature Gas Cooled Reactor (HTGR) that incorporates a closed cycle primary coolant system utilizing helium as coolant to transfer heat energy from modular core to a recuperative Brayton Cycle power conversion unit with a single-shaft turbine/compressor/generator. This type of reactor provides simplification and a substantial increase in overall system and efficiency and inherent safety with lower capital and operational cost.

The core contains approximately 451,527 fuel pebbles with a packing fraction of 0.61. The packing fraction of 0.61 was achieved by randomizing the pebble positions using Serpent's capability to model pebble position explicitly. The uranium loading is 9 g per fuel-sphere with the $^{235}U$ enrichment at 9.6%. The inner 5 cm of the fuel sphere contains about 15,000 $UO_2$ TRISO-coated micro-spheres within a graphite matrix and surrounded by an outer graphite fuel free zone. Each coated particle acts as a fission product barrier [6].

**Table 1.** PBMR-400 design characteristics

| | |
|---|---|
| Installed thermal capacity (MW) | 400 |
| Core height (m) | 11 |
| Core configuration | Vertical with fixed center graphite reflector |
| Inner core diameter (m) | 2 |
| Outer core diameter (m) | 3.7 |
| Primary coolant | Helium |
| Primary coolant pressure (MPa) | 9 |
| Moderator | Graphite |
| Core outlet temperature (°C) | 900 |
| Core inlet temperature (°C) | 500 |

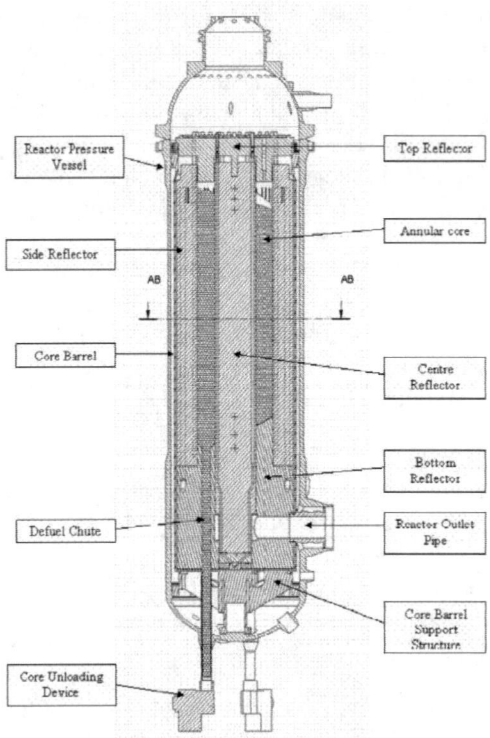


Figure 1. PBMR schematics

Table 2. PBMR-400 core characteristics

| | |
|---|---|
| Fuel pebble diameter | 6 cm |
| Outer graphite shell thickness | 0.5 cm |
| Heavy metal content per pebble | 9 g |
| Fuel enrichment | 9.6% |
| Number of fuel kernels | 15000 |
| $UO_2$ kernel radius | 0.0025 cm |
| $UO_2$ density | 10.4 g/cm$^3$ |
| Coating layer material | PyC/PyC/SiC/PyC |
| Coating layer thickness | 0.0095/0.004/0.0035/0.004 cm |
| Coating layer densities | 1.05/1.9/3.18/1.9 g/cm$^3$ |
| Density of graphite matrix | 1.77 g/cm$^3$ |
| Reflector material | Graphite |
| Reflector density | 1.78 g/cm$^3$ |
| Control rod material | $B_4C$ |
| B-10 content of $B_4C$ | 6 ppm |
| Total number of pebbles | 451,527 |

In the benchmark design, core analysis was performed using the Very Superior Old Program (VSOP) which utilized a set of two-group macroscopic cross-section data for each distinct core region which included fuel regions with different mixtures of burned pebbles, as well as reflector and control rod regions [8]. The cross sections were prepared stored in multi-dimensional tables as a function of five state-parameters, to include fuel temperature, moderator temperature, xenon concentration, as well as fast and thermal buckling to represent the leakage spectral effects. All cross terms dependencies were included which were determined by linear interpolation on a 5-dimensional space [6].

## 3. Core Simulation

*3.1. Monte Carlo Neutronics*
The Serpent Monte Carlo code, developed at VTT Technical Research Centre of Finland, is a continuous-energy Monte Carlo particle code. It has been enabled to perform lattice physics calculations to obtain homogenized cross sections for use in nodal diffusion calculations. Although a large number of particle histories can be required to minimize the statistical uncertainty and provide accurate multi-group data, Monte Carlo methods are attractive for lattice physics calculations since they are able to solve any arbitrary and complicated three-dimensional problems with minimal physics approximations [9], [10]. This is particularly attractive for modeling the HTR with complex physics such as the double heterogeneity introduced by the TRISO fuel form.

Serpent has unique capabilities with regards to the modeling of pebble bed reactors. Serpent can not only model the random pebble distribution, but it can also model the random TRISO distribution inside the pebbles. This modeling is done explicitly in which the location of each pebble is generated using an automated disperser routine. Serpent only requires a file with the position of each pebble's center point. Serpent uses this information to explicitly represent the location of pebbles in the core without applying any homogenization.

For the analysis of the PBMR-400 in this work, Serpent was used for preparation of the multi-group homogenized cross sections as well as to provide a detailed reference calculation without energy, angular, or spatial discretization error. The version of Serpent used in this work is 2.1.31.

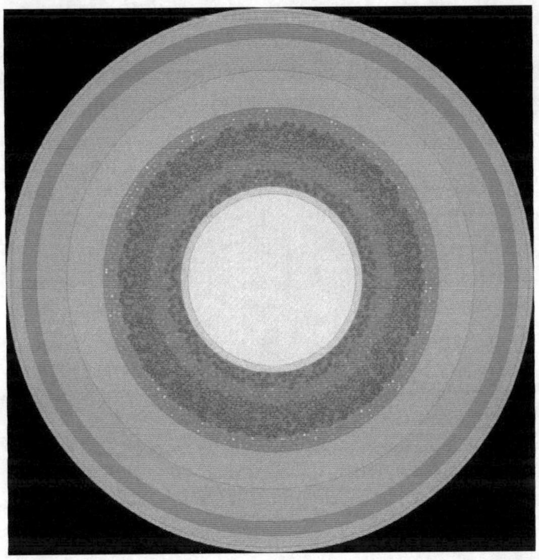

**Figure 2.** Radial configuration of Serpent PBMR-400

*3.2. AGREE HTR Simulator*
Cross sections that were calculated in Serpent were processed by the cross-section data converter GenPMAXS to generate a PMAXS cross section file that would be read by AGREE. Cross section was prepared for each of the distinct core regions of the PBMR-400. These cross sections contain 110 cross section data for 110 fuel regions and 470 reflector region that has been defined in the benchmark document. region division is shown in Figures 2 and 3.

**Figure 3.** Axial configuration of Serpent PBMR-400

The AGREE (Advance Gas Reactor Evaluator) was developed for the U.S. NRC as a thermo-fluids code to solve the steady state and time dependent mass, momentum, and energy equations in three-dimensions for High Temperature Gas Cooled reactor analyses. AGREE has two separate versions, one for Pebble Bed type reactor applications and another for Prismatic type reactors. The pebble bed version of AGREE was recently updated to provide functionality for the Fluoride salt-cooled High temperature Reactor (FHR) designed by Kairos Power [11].

### *3.3. Core Calculation*

The procedure used here to perform core simulation is depicted in Fig. 5. Serpent was used to generate nodal cross sections for the AGREE code, as well as full core reference calculations. The Serpent k-eff eigenvalue and power distribution results will be used as reference for AGREE results.

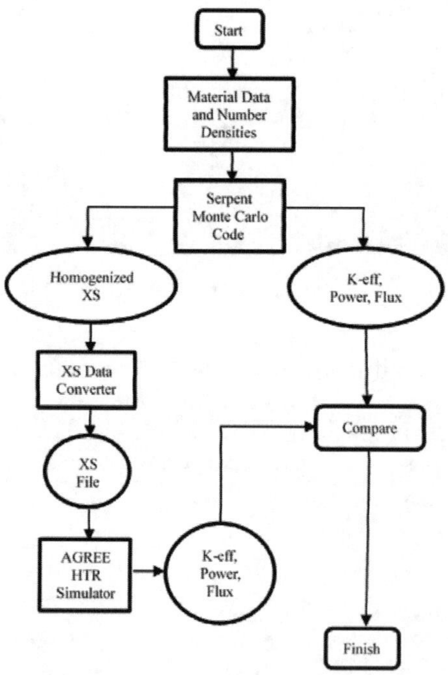


**Figure 4.** Research method employed in this work

The type of two-step code system method has been used in previous modeling of High-Temperature Gas Reactor, as for example by Argonne National Laboratory (ANL) using DRAGON as lattice transport code and DIF3D as nodal diffusion code. In this study, significant errors were reported using the two-step method compared to the result of Monte-Carlo code [12].

PBMR-400 cross sections were calculated using Serpent with various few-group configurations using ENDF 7.1 Library. Energy cut-offs for each group is tabulated in Table 3. In each calculation, 500,000 neutron histories were used in order to minimize statistical standard deviation to approximately 10pcm. For full core calculations, a vacuum boundary condition was used.

**Table 3.** Energy cut-off boundaries (Unit: eV) [13]

| 23 | 14 | 7 | 4 | 2 |
|---|---|---|---|---|
| 3.679E+06 | | | | |
| 1.353E+06 | | | | |
| 5.000E+05 | 5.000E+05 | 5.000E+05 | | |
| 1.110E+05 | 1.110E+05 | | | |
| 6.738E+04 | 6.738E+04 | | | |
| 9.118E+03 | 9.118E+03 | 9.118E+03 | 9.118E+03 | |
| 3.673E+02 | 3.673E+02 | | | |
| 4.000E+00 | 4.000E+00 | 4.000E+00 | | |
| | | | | 3.059E+00 |
| 1.500E+00 | | | | |
| 1.097E+00 | 1.097E+00 | 1.097E+00 | | |
| 1.045E+00 | | | | |
| 9.720E-01 | 9.720E-01 | | | |
| 8.500E-01 | 8.500E-01 | | 8.500E-01 | |
| 5.000E-01 | 5.000E-01 | 5.000E-01 | | |
| 4.000E-01 | | | | |
| 3.500E-01 | 3.500E-01 | | | |
| 3.000E-01 | | | | |
| 2.500E-01 | | | | |
| 1.800E-01 | | | | |
| 1.400E-01 | 1.400E-01 | | | |
| 1.000E-01 | | 1.000E-01 | 1.000E-01 | |
| 5.000E-02 | 5.000E-02 | | | |

## 4. Results and discussions

### *4.1. k-eff Eigenvalue Comparison*

Homogenized multi-group cross section data was generated for 580 regions of the full core model of the PBMR-400, including 110 regions of fuel assemblies and 470 region of non-fuel assemblies. In this section, comparison of k-eff eigenvalue results between Serpent and AGREE is provided with the standard deviation for Monte Carlo calculation and also the overall absolute difference between Serpent and AGREE. These results are tabulated in Table 4.

As indicated in Table 4 the k-eff eigenvalue difference between Serpent and AGREE decreases as the number of energy groups used in the calculation increases. However, from 14-groups to 23-groups, the difference is not as significant as the previous few-groups. In Serpent, the number of neutrons used per cycle is 500,000. To assess the statistical uncertainty of the results, 1,000,000 neutrons per cycle is also calculated and the results are tabulated in Table 5 and as indicated 500,000 histories appear to be sufficient.

**Table 4.** k-eff eigenvalue results of AGREE and Serpent with 500,000 neutrons per cycle, 600 cycles

| Groups | Serpent | | AGREE | Δk-eff |
|---|---|---|---|---|
| | k-eff | σ (pcm) | k-eff | (pcm) |
| 2 | 0.995002 | 4.6 | 1.002107 | 710.5 |
| 4 | 0.995039 | 4.6 | 0.999852 | 481.3 |
| 7 | 0.994955 | 4.6 | 0.997337 | 238.2 |
| 14 | 0.994805 | 4.7 | 0.996580 | 177.5 |
| 23 | 0.994795 | 4.6 | 0.995914 | 111.9 |

**Table 5.** k-eff eigenvalue results of AGREE and Serpent with 1,000,000 neutrons per cycle, 1200 cycles

| Groups | Serpent | | AGREE | Δk-eff |
|---|---|---|---|---|
| | k-eff | σ (pcm) | k-eff | (pcm) |
| 2 | 0.995028 | 2.3 | 1.002132 | 710.4 |
| 4 | 0.995034 | 2.4 | 0.999804 | 477.0 |
| 7 | 0.995005 | 2.1 | 0.997323 | 231.8 |
| 14 | 0.994788 | 2.2 | 0.996559 | 177.1 |
| 23 | 0.994763 | 2.3 | 0.995913 | 115.0 |

The general conclusion from the eigenvalue results is that more than 2 or 4 energy groups are necessary to accurately describe the core leakage and achieve a reasonable prediction of the core eigenvalue for modeling the PBMR-400.

*4.2. Flux Distribution Comparison*

The group-wise neutron fluxes from the full core Serpent calculation are compared to the AGREE calculation in this section. Because of space limitations, the results shown focus on the radially and integrated distributions of the thermal fluxes for each of the multi-group calculations shown in Table 5. The radial flux distributions are obtained by volume averaging the axial fluxes in each ring. The results are displayed in Fig. 5 to Fig. 9.

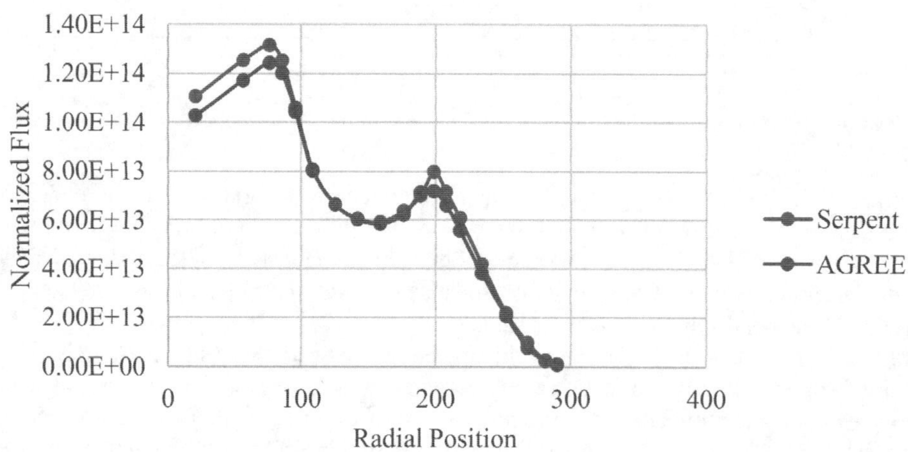


**Figure 5.** Radial thermal flux of 2-groups core

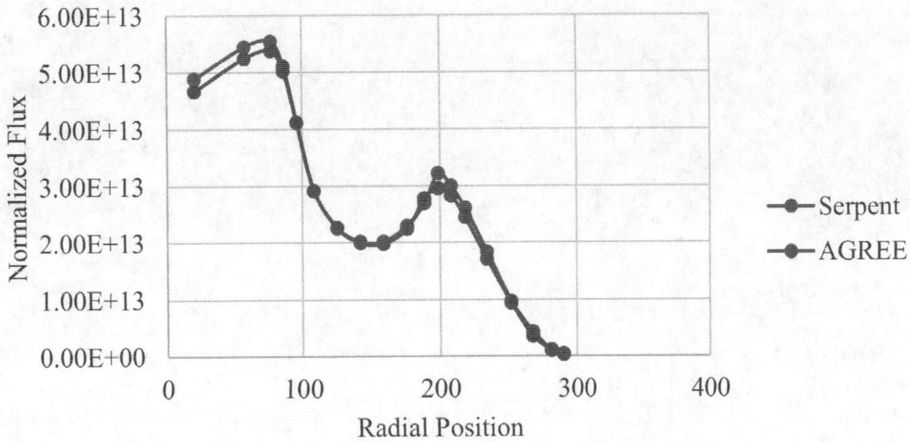


**Figure 6.** Radial thermal flux of 4-groups core

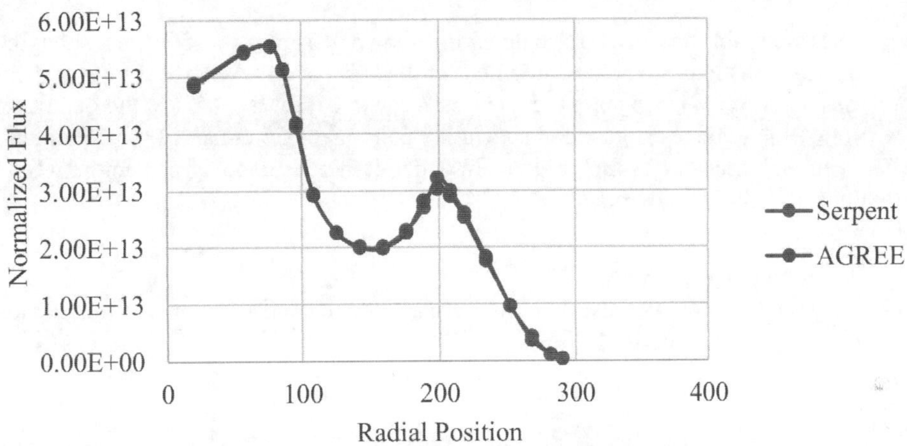


**Figure 7.** Radial thermal flux of 7-groups core

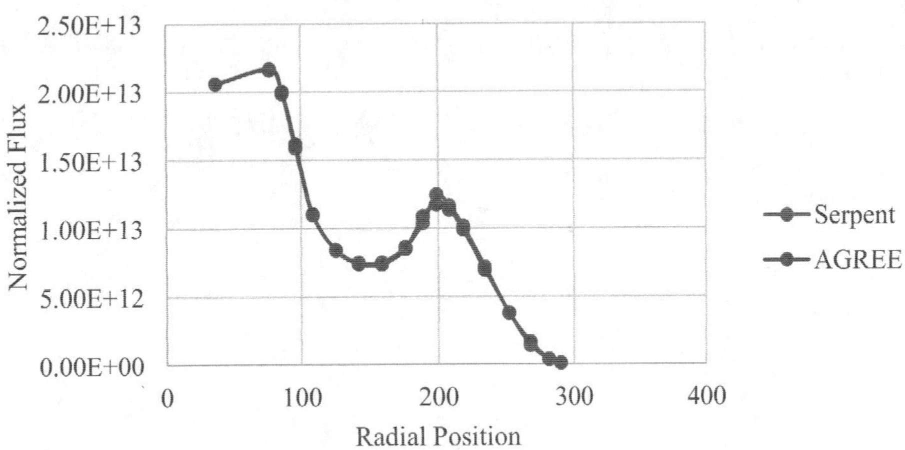


**Figure 8.** Radial thermal flux of 14-groups core

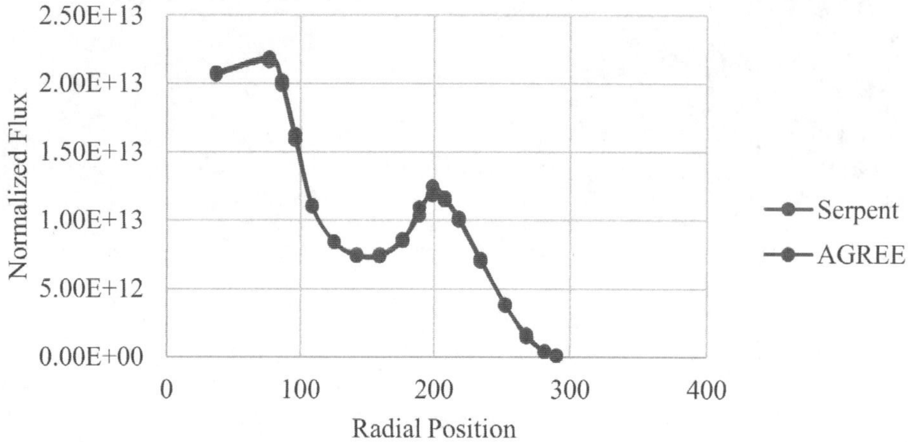


**Figure 9.** Radial thermal flux of 23-groups core

Similar to the results for the eigenvalue calculation shown in Tables 4 and 5, the results for the radial thermal flux distributions indicate better agreement of the Serpent and AGREE results as the number of groups increases. For the 23-group core, the maximum relative error is 14.5% at the outermost position of the core. Noticeable relative errors are observed at position 96.025 cm and 188.975 cm, which is the interface between the reflector and fuel regions. In general, there is good agreement between the radial flux distributions of AGREE and Serpent.

### *4.3. Power Distribution Comparison*

The radially integrated axial power distributions were also edited and are shown in this section for each of the few group calculations in Fig. 10 to Fig. 14.

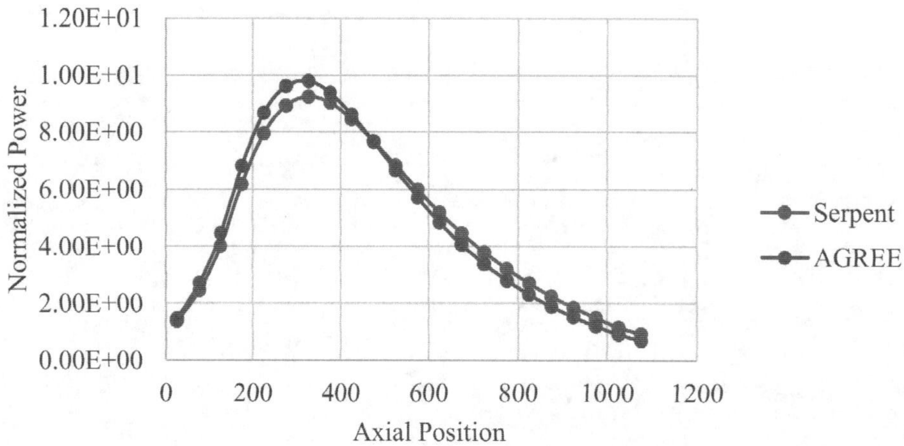


**Figure 10.** Axial power distribution of 2-groups core

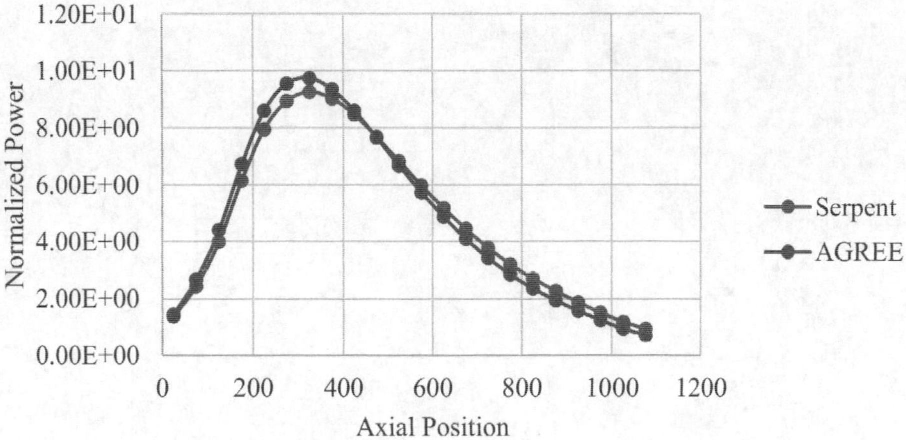


**Figure 11.** Axial power distribution of 4-groups core

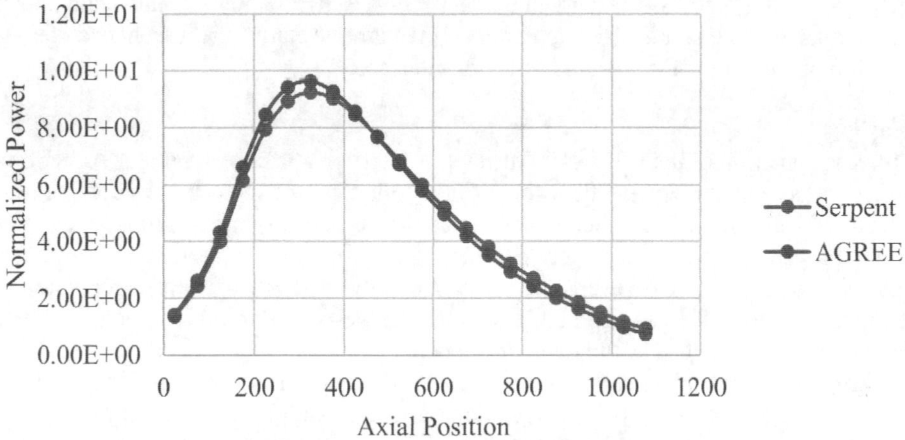


**Figure 12** .Axial power distribution of 7-groups core

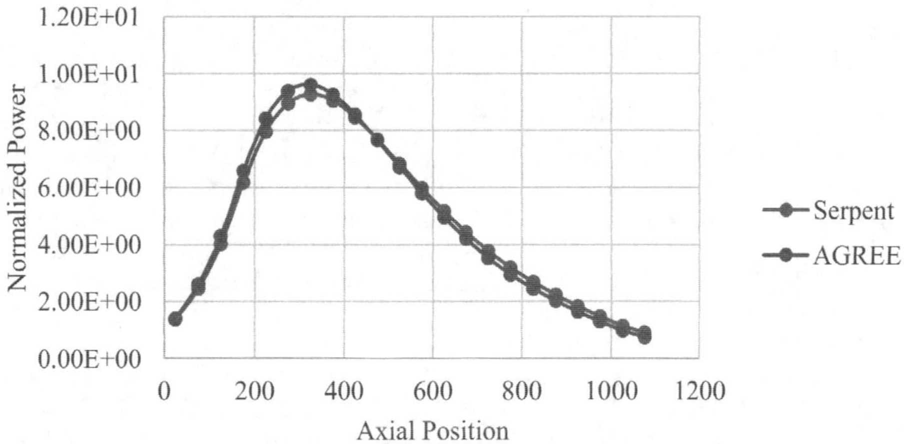


**Figure 13.** Axial power distribution of 14-groups core

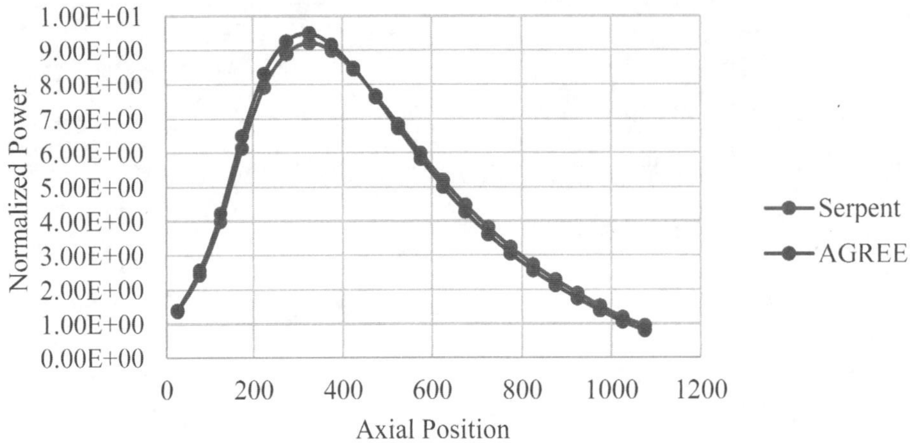


**Figure 14.** Axial power distribution of 23-groups core

As indicated in the figures, the agreement between AGREE and Serpent again improves with increasing number of groups. It is also apparent that the highest relative error from each few-group core is at the bottom of the core at the fuel and reflector interface.

## 5. Conclusions

The neutronics simulation of the PBMR-400 using the deterministic core simulator AGREE with multi-group cross sections generated using the Monte Carlo code Serpent showed considerable improvement in the agreement with the full core Serpent result as the number of energy groups was increased. An eigenvalue improvement of approximately 530 pcm was observed when the number of energy groups was increased from 2 to 23. However, even with 7 energy groups sufficiently accurate results were obtained with could be considered acceptable for core analysis. Similar improvements were observed in the flux and power distributions as the number of energy groups were increased.

Work is continuing on the incorporation of assembly discontinuity factors into the deterministic core calculation, as well as the analysis of calculations at the full range of core power and temperature conditions. This work will involve the assessment of using color set or supercell models at the various temperature conditions instead of relying on full core Monte Carlo for every branch calculation necessary for practical reactor simulation.

## References

[1] A. Dambrosio, M. Ruščák, G. Mazzini, and A. Musa, "Neutronic analysis of the LVR-15 research reactor using the PARCS code," *Ann. Nucl. Energy*, vol. 117, pp. 145–154, 2018, doi: 10.1016/j.anucene.2018.03.009.

[2] S. Silva Pinto Wahnon, L. Ammirabile, J. L. Kloosterman, and D. Lathouwers, "Multi-physics models for design basis accident analysis of sodium fast reactors. Part I: Validation of three-dimensional TRACE thermal-hydraulics model using Phenix end-of-life experiments," *Nucl. Eng. Des.*, vol. 331, no. February, pp. 331–341, 2018, doi: 10.1016/j.nucengdes.2018.02.038.

[3] S. Choi, K. S. Smith, H. Kim, T. Tak, and D. Lee, "On the diffusion coefficient calculation in two-step light water reactor core analysis," *J. Nucl. Sci. Technol.*, vol. 54, no. 6, pp. 705–715, 2017, doi: 10.1080/00223131.2017.1299648.

[4] Z. Wu, Q. Zhang, and A. K. Hany, "Hybrid Monte Carlo-deterministic methods for reactor analysis," *Nucl. Technol.*, vol. 180, no. 3, pp. 372–382, 2012, doi: 10.13182/NT12-A15350.

[5] G. Baiocco, A. Petruzzi, S. Bznuni, and T. Kozlowski, "Analysis of a small PWR core with the PARCS/Helios and PARCS/Serpent code systems," *Ann. Nucl. Energy*, vol. 107, pp. 42–48, 2017, doi: 10.1016/j.anucene.2017.04.008.

[6] F. Reitsma, K. Ivanov, T. Downar, H. De Haas, and H. D. Gougar, "The OECD/NEA/NSC PBMR coupled neutronics/thermal hydraulics transient benchmark: The PBMR-400 core design," *PHYSOR-2006 - Am. Nucl. Soc. Top. Meet. React. Phys.*, vol. 2006, no. May 2016, 2006.

[7] IAEA, "Evaluation of High Temperature Gas Cooled Reactor Performance: Benchmark Analysis Related to the PBMR-400, PBMM,GT-MHR, HTR-10 and the ASTRA Critical Facility," Vienna, 2013. [Online]. Available: http://dx.doi.org/10.1016/j.cirp.2016.06.001%0Ahttp://dx.doi.org/10.1016/j.powtec.2016.12.055%0Ahttps://doi.org/10.1016/j.ijfatigue.2019.02.006%0Ahttps://doi.org/10.1016/j.matlet.2019.04.024%0Ahttps://doi.org/10.1016/j.matlet.2019.127252%0Ahttp://dx.doi.o.

[8] K. Kugeler and Z. Zhang, *Modular High Temperature Gas Cooled Reactor.* 2019.

[9] J. Leppänen, M. Pusa, T. Viitanen, V. Valtavirta, and T. Kaltiaisenaho, "The Serpent Monte Carlo code: Status, development and applications in 2013," *Ann. Nucl. Energy*, vol. 82, pp. 142–150, 2015, doi: 10.1016/j.anucene.2014.08.024.

[10] J. Leppänen, M. Pusa, and E. Fridman, "Overview of methodology for spatial homogenization in the Serpent 2 Monte Carlo code," *Ann. Nucl. Energy*, vol. 96, pp. 126–136, 2016, doi: 10.1016/j.anucene.2016.06.007.

[11] V. Şeker and T. Downar, "KP-AGREE - Advance Gas Reactor Evaluator User's Manual," 2018.

[12] T. A. Taiwo and T. K. KIm, "Evaluation of the DRAGON Code for VHTR Design Analysis," 2006. doi: 10.2172/929210.

[13] W. S. Yang and C. H. Lee, "Status report on multigroup cross section generation code development for high-fidelity deterministic neutronics simulation system.," 2008. [Online]. Available: http://www.osti.gov/servlets/purl/1028602/.

# Study on the Curved Channel Model in the Initial Core Loading of Pebble Bed High Temperature Reactors

**B Xia, J Zhang, J Guo, C Wei, and Fu Li**

Institute of Nuclear and New Energy Technology, Collaborative Innovation Center of Advanced Nuclear Energy Technology, Key Laboratory of Advanced Reactor Engineering and Safety of Ministry of Education, Tsinghua University
Energy Science Building, Tsinghua University, Beijing 100084, China phone: +86-10-62784822, xiabing@tsinghua.edu.cn

**Abstract.** Continuous on-line fuel cycling is the essential feature of the pebble bed high temperature reactor (PB-HTR). The flow speed of the fuel pebbles in a PB-HTR presents a radial distribution in the reactor core, mainly due to the friction between the pebbles and the wall and the conical structure at the core bottom. In the VSOP fuel shuffling model, the simulation of unequal pebble flow speed is achieved by dividing the reactor core into some vertical flow channels with different numbers of the equal-volume regions in each channel. However, the fuel shuffling with equal-volume batches bring complexity when dealing with the change of fuel composition, such as the fuel fraction of fuel-graphite pebble mixture, during the initial core loading and early running-in phase. In this work, a curved channel model with unequal flow speed and the bottom cone is established based on the DEM simulation of pebble flow in the HTR-PM. The batch-wise fuel shuffling strategy is adapted to fit the complex situation during mixing and re-assigning the discharged fuels by employing a rounding strategy for the actual volume of fuels with similar irradiation history. The key of the adapted strategy is to divide the total number of the mixed batches with similar irradiation history by the number of flow channels, and round the quotient as the number of reloaded batches in each top region. The fuel loading process to build up the initial core, accompanied by the low-power reactor running to compensate the reactivity provided by the fresh fuels, is simulated by using the fuel shuffling model mentioned above. On the other hand, the simulation on the same process with an effective cylindrical core mesh and straight flow channels is carried out, in which dividing and rounding the batch numbers are unneeded. The results of both models are compared, indicating that the curved channel model presents less core reactivity and shorter fuel loading period than those of the cylindrical model. From the point of view of fidelity, the former is more suitable for the simulation of initial core loading process. The results in this work are important for enhancing the economy of fuel cycling of PB-HTRs.

## 1. Introduction

High temperature gas-cooled reactors (HTGRs) present the unique feature of the spherical fuel elements with diameter of 6 cm flowing downward within the pebble bed reactor core. The simulation of the fuel pebble flow is important to the neutronics calculations since the on-line fuel recycling is carried out all the time. In the model of the well-verified PB- HTR code V.S.O.P. [1], the simulation of pebble flow is carried out by dividing the pebble bed into several vertical channels. Each channel is then divided into some regions with equal volumes in the axial direction, as shown in Fig. 1.

During the pebble flow simulation, all the fuels in the regions can be simultaneously shuffled to the next regions in the corresponding channels or to the so- called "storage boxes" representing the fuels in the discharge tube under the pebble bed core for a certain time interval, i.e., the shuffling cycle. The fuels in one single region are subdivided into some equal-volume logical parts named "batches", which are the basic units of fuel content in PB-HTR neutronics calculations and represent the fuels with different irradiation histories. The pebble flow speed varies in the radial direction, mainly due to the friction between the pebbles and the wall and the conical structure at the core bottom. Consequently, the pebbles near the core axis move faster than those near the side reflector. The radial difference of pebble speed can be simulated by assigning the region number proportional to the fuel residence time for each channel in the V.S.O.P. model.

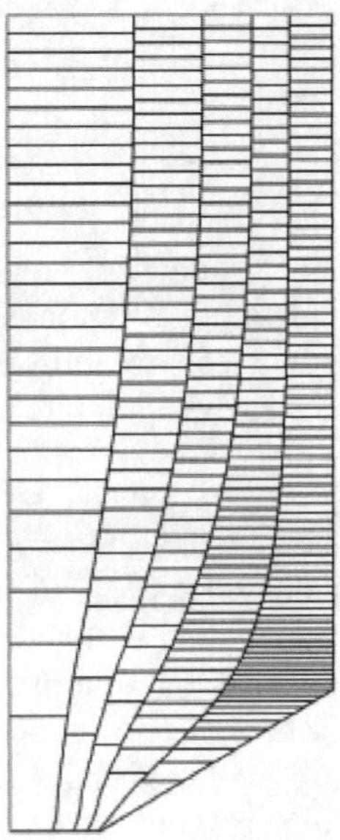

**Figure 1.** Schematic figure of pebble flow channels and regions in a PB-HTR. Note that all the volumes of the regions are equal and the region number in each channel is proportional to the fuel residence time in this channel.

During the pebble flow simulation, all the fuels in the regions can be simultaneously shuffled to the next regions in the corresponding channels or to the so- called "storage boxes" representing the fuels in the discharge tube under the pebble bed core for a certain time interval, i.e., the shuffling cycle. The fuels in one single region are subdivided into some equal-volume logical parts named "batches", which are the basic units of fuel content in PB-HTR neutronics calculations and represent the fuels with different irradiation histories. The pebble flow speed varies in the radial direction, mainly due to the friction between the pebbles and the wall and the conical structure at the core bottom. Consequently, the pebbles near the core axis move faster than those near the side reflector. The radial difference of pebble speed can be simulated by assigning the region number proportional to the fuel residence time for each channel in the V.S.O.P. model.

For the core physics design of the HTR-PM, sufficient precision can be achieved by using the simple cylindrical channel model, i. e. the region numbers of all the channels are equal and the bottom cone structure is replaced by an effective cylinder with the same volume, since the pebble flow speed values at different radial position are similar. In this work, the model with curved channels and bottom cone structure is called "the curved channel model", while the model with cylindrical channels is called "the cylindrical channel model". Both models are equally suitable for the fuel shuffling of the equilibrium core because the batches in a region are all filled with fuels and present the regular pattern from the shortest irradiation period to the longest one. On the other hand, circumstance becomes complicated when the curved channel model is utilized for the initial core and running-in phase. As shown in Fig. 2, the front of regions filled with fuel- graphite pebble mixture in the central channel reaches the core bottom earlier than those in outer channels. Therefore, the fuel-graphite pebble mixture in the central-bottom region will be mixed with the graphite pebbles in the bottom regions of other channels, and be equally divided into all the channels when reloaded to the core top. Unfortunately, the volume of reloaded batches is usually unequal to that of the original batches. Hence, one has to deal with the "fractional batches" for most of the cases of the curved channel model, which is the most challenging feature in the curved channel model.

| | | | | |
|---|---|---|---|---|
| $7_1:8_G$ | $7_1:8_G$ | $7_1:8_G$ | $7_1:8_G$ | $7_1:8_G$ |
| $7_1:8_G$ | $7_1:8_G$ | $7_1:8_G$ | $7_1:8_G$ | $0:15_G$ |
| $7_1:8_G$ | $7_1:8_G$ | $7_1:8_G$ | $0:15_G$ | $0:15_G$ |
| $7_1:8_G$ | $7_1:8_G$ | $7_1:8_G$ | $0:15_G$ | $0:15_G$ |
| $7_1:8_G$ | $7_1:8_G$ | $0:15_G$ | $0:15_G$ | $0:15_G$ |
| $7_1:8_G$ | $7_1:8_G$ | $0:15_G$ | $0:15_G$ | $0:15_G$ |
| $7_1:8_G$ | $0:15_G$ | $0:15_G$ | $0:15_G$ | $0:15_G$ |

**Figure 2.** An example of the logical layout ofregions near the core bottom. The columns represent the channels, while a single row corresponds to the pebbles unloaded within a certain period. The figure in each region represents the ratio of fuel pebbles to graphite pebbles. The subscripts of number mean the pass number of fuels and the subscripts of G mean the graphite pebbles

## 2. Analysis Models

In this work, the curved channel model and cylindrical model based on the HTR-PM are established as reference models based on the HTR- PM. The active core of the HTR-PM can be equivalent to a cylinder with the diameter of 150 cm and the height of 1100 cm according to the volume equivalence, which bases the cylindrical channel model in this work. On the other hand, a more realistic model, namely the curved channel model with an upper cylinder and a bottom cone structure is established based on the actual layout of the reactor core. In the hypothetical models of this work, the active core is divided into 5 channels. In the curved channel model, the region numbers of the channels from core axis to reflector are set as 20, 21, 23, 25 and 26, respectively, while the cylindrical channel model also contains 5 channels with 23 regions for each channel. The ratio of fuel pebble number to the graphite pebble number is set as 7:8, and the fuel-graphite pebble mixture are filled in the top 9 regions in each channel of both models while the lower parts are both filled with graphite pebbles. In order to load more fuel-graphite mixture, depletion must be introduced to compensate the further reactivity introduced by the loading of more fuels. In this work, the reactor power is set as 10% reactor full power (RFP), i.e., 25MW. Another boundary condition for the calculations is the reactor can be operated at full power when the whole cores are totally filled with the pebble mixture.

| | | | | | |
|---|---|---|---|---|---|
| $7_1:8_G$ | $7_1:8_G$ | $7_1:8_G$ | $7_1:8_G$ | $7_1:8_G$ | $7_1:8_G$ |
| $7_1:8_G$ | $7_1:8_G$ | $7_1:8_G$ | $7_1:8_G$ | $0:15_G$ | $5.6_1:9.4_G$ |
| $7_1:8_G$ | $7_1:8_G$ | $7_1:8_G$ | $0:15_G$ | $0:15_G$ | $4.2_1:10.8_G$ |
| $7_1:8_G$ | $7_1:8_G$ | $7_1:8_G$ | $0:15_G$ | $0:15_G$ | $4.2_1:10.8_G$ |
| $7_1:8_G$ | $7_1:8_G$ | $0:15_G$ | $0:15_G$ | $0:15_G$ | $2.8_1:12.2_G$ |
| $7_1:8_G$ | $7_1:8_G$ | $0:15_G$ | $0:15_G$ | $0:15_G$ | $2.8_1:12.2_G$ |
| $7_1:8_G$ | $0:15_G$ | $0:15_G$ | $0:15_G$ | $0:15_G$ | $1.4_1:13.6_G$ |

**Figure 3.** The logical layout of regions near the core bottom of the curved channel model in this work. The boundary of fuel shuffling strategy change is between the uncolored regions and green-colored ones. The right column presents the fractional fuel batches to be reloaded to core top.

Since the ratio of fuel pebble number to the graphite pebble number is set as 7:8, it is natural to divide one region into 15 batches for both models. For the initial core loading process, the general fuel shuffling strategy is unloading the graphite pebbles from the core bottom, recycling 8/15 of them to the core top and loading fresh fuel pebbles with number of 7/15 of the unloaded pebbles to ensure the reloaded fuel to graphite ratio equal to 7:8. For the fuel shuffling simulation of the cylindrical channel model, the recycled batches with the same batch serial number from 5 bottom regions are mixed into one composition called "storage box" before they are divided evenly back to 5 top regions. This strategy ensures no mixing between fuel pebbles and graphite pebbles, as well as no mixing between fuels with different refueling history.

The logical layout of regions near the core bottom of the curved channel model is shown in Fig. 3, containing the batch numbers of fuels and graphite pebbles which should be assigned to the top regions under the restriction of equal batch volumes. Unfortunately, the fractional batch numbers are unacceptable in V.S.O.P. However, the sums of the fractional batch numbers are integers equal to the actual batch number sum of fuels and graphite pebbles divided by the channel number. On the other hand, the same integer sums as those mentioned above can be achieved by rounding the fractional batch numbers. Hence, the rounded batch numbers can be treated as the recycled batch numbers in the fuel shuffling simulations, for example, $6_l$:$9_G$, $4_l$:$11_G$, $3_l$:$12_G$ and $1_l$:$14_G$, corresponding the fractional batch numbers in Fig. 3.

The refueling strategy should be decided after rounding the batch numbers for each layer. For the cylindrical model, 3 batches of graphite pebbles will be replaced by 3 batches of fuels after all the graphite pebbles unloaded from the core, i.e., the initial core, resulting the reloaded fuel to graphite ratio of 10:5. There should be a mandatory boundary between the fuel shuffling strategies before and after the initial core, which is presented by color difference in Fig. 3 for the curved channel model. Consequently, the actual graphite batch number to be replaced for each region is determined by both the shuffling strategy and the rounded batch numbers. For example, 6 batches of graphite pebbles should be replaced by 6 batches of fresh fuels for the bottom layer in Fig. 2, while 4 batches of graphite pebbles should be replaced by 4 batches of fresh fuels for the sixth- lowest layer in Fig. 3. Thus, the challenge of curved channel model is overcome by rounding the fractional batch numbers after mixing the unloaded fuel and graphite batches.

## 3. Results and Discussions

In order to investigate the difference between the cylindrical channel model and the curved channel model, simulations for both models are carried out. As mentioned above, the final core state after 10% RFP operation along with fuel loading must be able to reach 100% RFP with proper control rod position. Hence, the irradiation period and the control rod position have to be adjusted carefully.

The evolution of average control rod position (CRP) during the initial core loading process is illustrated in Figure 4. The initial CRP values and the final CRP values are similar for both models, indicating that the initial and final excess reactivity values are also similar for both models. That is the natural results of the requirement of full power operation for the final state. However, the irradiation period of cylindrical channel model is significantly longer than that of curved channel model (about 8% longer), which means the reactor can be depleted less for the latter than the former. It should be considered that there are three kinds of reactivity increment/decrement which satisfy the equation below

$$\rho_{load}^{+} = \rho_{burn}^{-} + \rho_{rod}^{-} \quad (1)$$

in which $\rho_{load}^{+}$ is the reactivity increment originated from fuel loading, $\rho_{burn}^{-}$ is the reactivity decrement from fuel depletion and $\rho_{rod}^{-}$ is the reactivity decrement from control rod insertion. Since the depth values of control rod insertion in both models are quite similar, it is reasonable to consider the $\rho_{burn}^{-}$ values in both models are also similar. Consequently, the reactivity increment $\rho_{load}^{+}$ in the curved channel model, corresponding to the less depletion, is less than that in the cylindrical channel model.

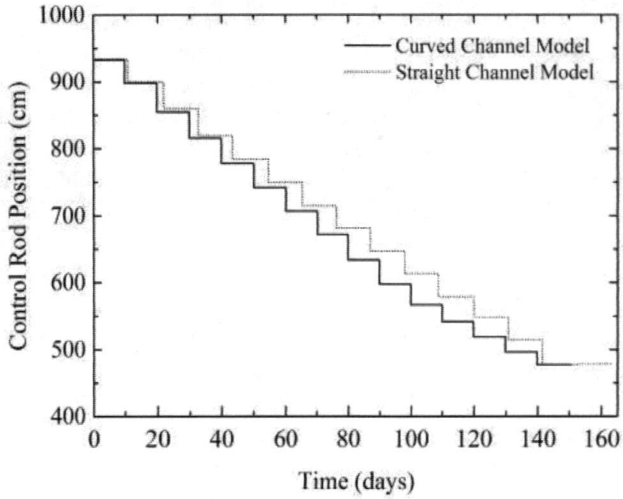


**Figure 4.** The time evolution of the average CRP values of curved channel model and cylindrical channel model. The stepped evolutions are shown since the depletion process has to be simulated by using a discrete time step model.

The results of irradiation period can be explained as below. For the final state of the cylindrical model, the whole reactor core is totally filled with fuel- graphite pebble mixture with fuel to graphite ratio of 7:8. On the other hand, there exist some pure graphite zones around the outer bottom of the core in the final state of the curved channel model. Moreover, the fuel pebbles reloaded near the end of final state of the curved channel model contain some irradiated fuel pebbles, corresponding to the fuels in the green zones in Fig. 3. Those facts indicate that the final state of the curved channel model presents not only less fuel pebbles, but less fresh fuel pebbles than that of the cylindrical channel model. Consequently, the former can be depleted for a shorter period than the latter to obtain the same excess reactivity.

Moreover, it can be observed through the evolution of the CRP values that there exists depletion with remarkable variable speed during the loading process in the curved channel model. For the earlier refueling cycles, the increase values of insertion depth of control rods are much larger than those for the latter cycles. These results reveal that the accumulation of reactivity in the earlier cycles is larger than in the latter cycles, which can also explain by the lack of fuel pebbles, especially fresh fuel pebbles, during the latter process of the curved channel model.

On the other hand, a calculation test is performed to evaluate the calculation error of the rounding process. The keff values, corresponding to 1 batch and 2 batches of fuels reloaded to the core when reloading the bottom layer of mixtures in Fig. 3, are calculated, as listed in Table 1. Both values are quite close to each other and the reactivity difference is only 2.8 pcm, which may only be treated as calculation error and is definitely negligible. Similarly, the discrepancy of reactivity introduced by rounding 1.4 batches of fuels to 1 batch of fuels must be also negligible. Hence, the batch number rounding in the curved channel model is sufficiently accurate since the total batch number of the whole reactor core maintains unvaried.

**Table 1.** Comparison between keff corresponding to 1 batch and 2 batches of fuels reloaded to the core when reloading the bottom layer of mixtures in Fig. 3.

| Reloaded batch number | keff value | Difference of reactivity (pcm) |
|---|---|---|
| 1 | 1.001599 | 2.8 |
| 2 | 1.001571 | -- |

Compared with the cylindrical channel model, the curved channel model provides higher fidelity. It means that the errors on estimating the period length of initial core loading with the simpler model of cylindrical channels can be corrected by the curved channel model. Since the length of commissioning process, including the initial core loading process, is highly related to the cost of the plant operation, the accurate determination of the initial core loading period length is important to the cost control of fuel cycling of PB-HTRs.

## 4. Conclusions

In this work, a curved channel model for the HTR- PM core design is established, with 5 vertical pebble flow channels in radial direction and the equal-volume region numbers for channels from inside to outside of 20, 21, 23, 25 and 26. These region numbers are proportional to the averaged passing-through time in the channels derived from the DEM simulations of the pebble flow. Compared with the traditional cylindrical channel models, the curved channel models encounter complicated situation when dealing with the refueling process before reaching equilibrium core, such as the running-in phase and the initial core loading. The main challenge is the possible fractional batch numbers after the refueling process, which can be solved by rounding the fractional batch numbers.

The simulation of initial core loading process with the curved channel model mentioned above is implemented in this work, based on the solution of rounding fractional batch numbers. It is revealed that the irradiation period of cylindrical channel model is about 8% longer than that of curved channel model, which can be explained by the difference of distribution of fuels and graphite pebbles between the both models. Furthermore, the error of batch number rounding process is analyzed and proved negligible for the keff results. The fidelity of the curved channel models is important for the design and analysis on the complicated refueling process of PB-HTRs. The analysis upon the running-in phase will be focused in the future works.

**Acknowledgments**

This work is jointly supported by the National S&T Major Project (Grant No. 2017ZX06901027), the National S&T Major Project (Grant No. 2013ZX06906007) and the National Nuclear Develop Program of China.

**References**

[1] H. J. Rütten, K. A. Haas, H. Brockmann and W. Scherer, "VSOP (99/05) computer code system for reactor physics and fuel cycle simulation", Jül-4189, Forschungszentrum Jülich (2005).

# Performance Improvement for Multi-recycling HTGR Incorporated with MA burning

**Y Fukaya, M Goto, and X L Yan**

Japan Atomic Energy Agency,4002, Oarai-machi, Higashi Ibaraki-gun, Ibaraki-ken 311-1394, Japan

E-mail: fukaya.yuji@jaea.go.jp

**Abstract.** Multi-recycling HTGR has been investigated by JAEA in order to reduce the environmental burden and non-proliferation of Pu. In the previous study, it is found that all actinoids except neptunium, which is not problematic from the viewpoint of toxicity and proliferation, can be recycled. However, the cycle length is slightly decreased compared with uranium fueled core due to the cumulated fertile TRU in the fuel composition. In the present study, Pu recycling HTGR is designed to incorporate with MA burning. As a result, the cycle length is increased by approximately 15% compared with TRU multi-recycling core, and if the MA burner can be achieved by IFR, the cost is decreased by 0.14 yen/kWh.

## 1. Introduction

TRansUranium (TRU) multi-recycling concept with thermal neutron High Temperature Gas-cooled Reactor (HTGR) has been investigated [1]. In the concept, the multi-recycling is formed by providing uranium-235 from outside of the cycle to reduce environmental burden and proliferation risk of fissile plutonium. This cycle can consume the TRU provided from outside of the cycle. The function is almost the same as Fast Breeder Reactors (FBRs).

On the other hand, FBR cycle incorporated with Minor Actinoid (MA) burning by Accelerator-Driven System (ADS) has been researched [2]. With the incorporation, the advantage may be obtained. Unfortunately, no advantage is found in this case with the multi-faced evaluation. The reason can easily be guessed that the role and characteristics of FBR and ADS are similar because of the Fast Reactor (FS) system for both reactors.

However, it is expected that the incorporation with the MA burner reactor such as ADS would bring certain advantages to the HTGR multi-recycling fuel cycle because of the thermal reactor.

Then, the specifications of the fuel cycle of multi-recycling HTGR incorporated with MA burning is evaluated in the present study. The outline of the fuel cycle and reactor concept is described in Section 2. The design method is described in Section 3. The specifications of the fuel cycle with MA burner are summarized and discussed in Section 4. The requirement for MA burner is described in Section 5.

## 2. Concept of multi-recycling HTGR

We proposed multi-recycling HTGR in the previous study [1]. The objectives are to reduce potential toxicity and fissile plutonium from the viewpoint of environmental burden and proliferation risk, respectively. The detailed concept is described as follows.

### *2.1. Concept of fuel cycle*

Figure 1 shows the fuel cycle concept proposed in the previous study. The major characteristics is providing the fissile uranium-235 from outside of the fuel cycle. Actually, natural uranium is provided and it is enriched in the enrichment facility in the fuel cycle. Then, depleted uranium is defecated. In the enriched facility, the recovered uranium is also enriched and reused. The depleted uranium is particular because it includes a relatively larger amount of uranium-234 and uranium-236 due to the multi-recycling. However, it was confirmed that the toxicity is not problematic from the viewpoint of potential toxicity in the previous study. The nuclides disposed of as waste is Fission Products (FPs) and neptunium. Neptunium is not problematic from the viewpoint of potential toxicity and public dose by the groundwater model [3]. Moreover, the cycle length of the HTGR is significantly reduced with neptunium recycling. Therefore, the neptunium is aggressively disposed of in the representative scenario. The burden of MA recycling is found at this stage. In addition, this concept employs 4-group partitioning [4] to recover MA. Therefore, significant waste volume reduction can be achievable because of the high-loading glass canister and Sr-Cs calcined waste package.

In the present study, the fuel cycle with MA burner reactor is proposed as shown in Fig.2 to reduce the burn to the HTGR specification. The burning of neptunium is not essential even with the MA burner in the present study. The MA burner implicitly includes its fuel cycle because that may be different from that of power generation strata as same as the pyro-reprocessing of ADS [5].

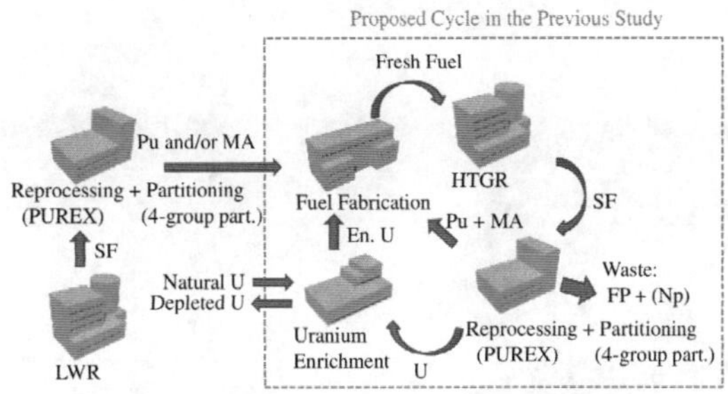


**Figure 1.** Fuel cycle proposed in the previous study.

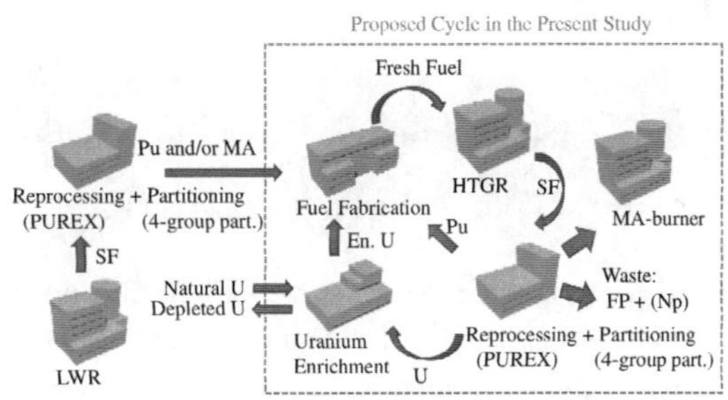


**Figure 2.** Fuel cycle proposed in the present study.

### *2.2. HTGR reactor concept*

The multi-recycled HTGR was designed based on GTHTR300 [6], which is a commercial-scale HTGR design with a 600 MW thermal power output. The detailed specifications and core configuration are described in Table 1 and Fig.3. Its annular core, which comprises two batches of fuel blocks, is loaded with 14 wt.% enriched uranium fuels. The cycle length is 730 days. The fuel columns are composed of eight fuel block layers aligned in the axial direction. Each fuel block is approximately 1 m high, yielding an approximate core height of 8 m. Because of the axial arrangement of the GTHTR300 core parts, an axial fuel reloading is assumed. As the loading pattern for GTHTR300 design, JAEA devised and implemented a method called sandwich refueling [6]. The fuel blocks are divided into irradiated and fresh fuel batches. The irradiated fuel blocks are sandwiched between the fresh fuel blocks.

Also, the uranium inventory is slightly reduced from its original 7.09 t [7], as the fuel structure was revised from the viewpoint of fuel fabrication [8]. The target cycle length and average discharged burn-up are 730 days and 120 GWd/t, respectively.

**Table 1.** Major specification of GTHTR300.

| Item | Value |
|---|---|
| Thermal power (MWt) | 600 |
| Electric generation (MWe) | |
| Gross: | 280 |
| Net: | 274 |
| Uranium inventory (ton) | 7.01 |
| $^{235}$U enrichment (wt%) | 14.0 |
| Cycle length (days) | 730 |
| Number of batch (-) | 2 |
| Discharge burn-up (GWd/t) | 120 |

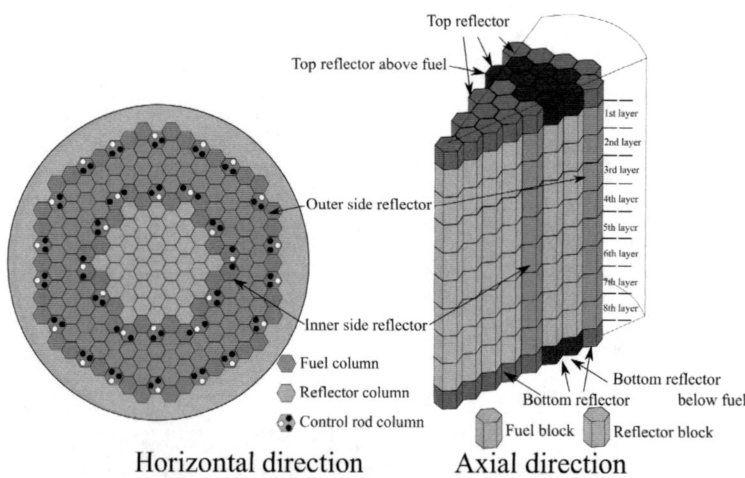


**Figure 3.** Core configuration of GTHTR300.

Table 2 shows the comparison of the specifications between the standard design of GTHTR300 and TRU multi-recycling HTGRs. The cycle length of the standard design is reduced by 100 days because of the revision of the design and improvement of the calculation code and nuclear data. The uranium enrichment is limited to be lower than 20 wt% in any part of the fuel cycle. In the enrichment facility, the uranium is enriched to 19.9 wt%. Later, it is mixed with the mixture of recovered plutonium and uranium. In Japan, the treatment of pure plutonium is prohibited and the recovered plutonium should be mixed with the same amount of the recovered uranium from the viewpoint of proliferation according to the Japan-U.S. reprocessing negotiation [9]. As a result, the uranium enrichment of fabricated fuel is reduced to approximately 18 wt%. It is increased by 4 wt% compared with the standard design. Even with the compensation of 4 wt% enrichment increase, the cycle length becomes lower than half due to the cumulated TRU for the whole TRU recycled case (TRU multi-recycling with Np). In the case of disposing of neptunium (TRU multi-recycling), the cycle length is slightly reduced compared with the standard design. Therefore, the case was selected as representative of the multi-recycling HTGR.

The other specifications of the multi-recycling HTGR are the almost same or improved. The excess reactivity becomes lower than half. The delayed neutron fraction is almost the same even with TRU recycling because the fission of uranium-235 is dominant due to the high enrichment fuel. The temperature coefficient becomes a more negative value. As described above, TRU multi-recycling is not problematic from the viewpoint of reactor safety.

**Table 2.** Comparison of major specifications between HTGR designs.

| | GTHTR300 | TRU multi-recycling | TRU multi-recycling with Np |
|---|---|---|---|
| Uranium Enrichment (wt%) | 14.0 | 18.4 | 17.9 |
| Cycle length (day) | 630 | 610 | 240 |
| Discharged burn-up (GWd/t) | 107.8 | 104.4 | 41.1 |
| Excess reactivity (BOC) (%Δk/kk') | 18.2 (0.06%) | 8.0 (0.13%) | 2.2 (0.57%) |
| Delayed neutron fraction (BOC) (%) | 0.606 (3.3%) | 0.540 (3.3%) | 0.529 (3.5%) |
| Delayed neutron fraction (MOC) (%) | 0.547 (2.9%) | 0.521 (3.9%) | 0.533 (3.1%) |
| Delayed neutron fraction (EOC) (%) | 0.517 (3.2%) | 0.514 (3.3%) | 0.512 (3.3%) |
| Temp. coeff. (BOC) (pcm/K) | -2.29 (6.5%) | -5.82 (2.6%) | -7.49 (2.5%) |
| Temp. coeff. (MOC) (pcm/K) | -3.84 (3.9%) | -5.71 (3.2%) | -6.54 (2.7%) |
| Temp. coeff. (EOC) (pcm/K) | -5.31 (3.2%) | -6.68 (2.8%) | -6.56 (2.8%) |

*The values in parentheses stand for statistics error corresponding to 1σ.

## 3. Design method of multi-recycled HTGR

To design the multi-recycled HTGR, several processes are necessary to evaluate the whole fuel cycle not only for the core design.

### *3.1. Design method of whole fuel cycle*

Figure 4 shows the mass flow of the proposed fuel cycle with the lead, lag time, and loss ratio. As described in Section II.B, the enrichment facility treats both of the natural uranium and recovered uranium. The enrichment is limited lower than 20 wt% at this stage. That is mixed with recovered plutonium with the same amount of uranium according to the Japan-U.S. reprocessing negotiation. Recovered MA is burned in the MA-Burner.

To reduce the potential toxicity, the loss ratio of TRU is limited to lower than 0.1 % in the whole fuel cycle [10]. Here, the loss of the reprocessing is set at 0.1 % instead of 0 % in fuel fabrication.

To accelerate the iteration of the calculation and to obtain an accurate result, the decay calculation of the fuel cycle and the burn-up calculation of the reactor is performed by using a point burn-up calculation code ORIGEN [11]. The calculation time is so short less than 1 second that the number of iterations can be spent enough to obtain saturated solutions.

With the fuel composition evaluated in the fuel cycle calculation, Core burn-up calculation is performed as described in Section III.B. The calculation is also iterated until to obtain the saturated discharge fuel composition. At the same time, the cross-sections used by ORIGEN code in the fuel cycle calculation are revised at this stage because that should be prepared for the target reactor.

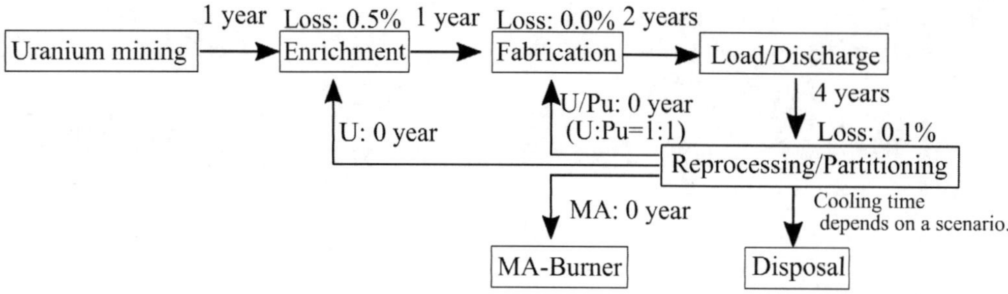


**Figure 4.** Fuel cycle mass flow of multi-recycle HTGR.

*3.2. Design method of multi-recycled HTGR*

The burn-up characteristics are evaluated by core burn-up calculation implemented in MVP [12] code, a Monte Carlo neutron transport code with evaluated nuclear data of JENDL-4.0 [13]. Moreover, the double heterogeneity of Coated Fuel Particles (CFPs) is directly analyzed using a statistical geometric model [14]. The MVP calculations were implemented in three-dimensional whole-core models. The core is composed of two batches as described in Section II.B. To evaluate equilibrium cycle core, the fuels were reloaded several times to obtain a saturated state according to the sandwich reloading scheme as described in Section II.B. To evaluate temperature coefficient, the reactivities are compared with a reference state and temperature increased state (100K increased for each region). Moreover, this study evaluates effective delayed neutron yields by using the prompt method [15].

*3.3. Evaluation of enriched uranium composition*

In the proposed cycle, recovery uranium is also enriched and recycled. Uranium isotopes except for uranium-235 and uranium-238 are important as well. Uranium-236 would be accumulated and affect criticality, and other components are released as depleted uranium to the environment and might have significant toxicity. To assess the feasibility of this cycle, the evaluation method for multi-component enrichment of uranium is necessary.

In general, to evaluate multi-component separation, matched abundance ratio cascade theory, which is extended the ideal cascade theory of two-component to match the abundance ratio in each fed point of cascade [16]. The abundance ratio is determined as a ratio of the mole number of targets to that of a key component. In general, uranium-238 is selected as the key component. In two components system, the target component is uranium-235 and the key component is uranium-238. By reducing the problem with each target component and common key component, the two components theory is extended to the multi-component theory. The target would be uranium-232, uranium-233, uranium-234, uranium-235, uranium-236 and, etc.

To evaluate the enriched composition by using the multi-component theory, the separation factor is necessary, and that is evaluated by assuming gas centrifuge [17] with the data of the peripheral velocity from 400-600 m/s and the temperature of 300K.

## 4. Specifications with MA burner

The specifications of plutonium multi-recycling HTGR with MA Burner is evaluated in the present study described as follows.

*4.1. Specifications of Pu multi-recycling HTGR*

Table 3 lists the calculation result of HTGR specification with a comparison with standard design and TRU multi-recycling HTGR. The cycle length and discharged burn-up shows a significant increase of approximately 10 %. The excess reactivity increases 5% Δk/kk' along with the improvement of criticality. However, that is lower than that of standard design by 5% Δk/kk'. The delayed neutron fraction and reactivity coefficient of temperature is almost the same as that of the standard design.

Table 4 lists the fresh fuel composition of each design. In the plutonium multi-recycling HTGR fuel, the americium and curium are excluded, and the neptunium is originally excluded in the stage of TRU multi-recycling design due to the no effect to the environmental burden. With the reduction of 1.8 wt% of MA and 0.6 wt% of fertile plutonium, the significant specification improvement can be obtained.

**Table 3.** Comparison of major specifications between HTGR designs.

| | GTHTR300 | TRU multi-recycling | Pu multi-recycling |
|---|---|---|---|
| Uranium enrichment (wt%) | 14.0 | 18.4 | 18.8 |
| Cycle length (day) | 630 | 610 | 700 |
| Discharged burn-up (GWd/t) | 107.8 | 104.4 | 119.8 |
| Excess reactivity (BOC) (%Δk/kk') | 18.2 (0.06%) | 8.0 (0.13%) | 13.0 (0.13%) |
| Delayed neutron fraction (BOC) (%) | 0.606 (3.3%) | 0.540 (3.3%) | 0.560 (3.5%) |
| Delayed neutron fraction (MOC) (%) | 0.547 (2.9%) | 0.521 (3.9%) | 0.541 (3.5%) |
| Delayed neutron fraction (EOC) (%) | 0.517 (3.2%) | 0.514 (3.3%) | 0.527 (3.2%) |
| Temp. coeff. (BOC) (pcm/K) | -2.29 (6.5%) | -5.82 (2.6%) | -2.12 (8.0%) |
| Temp. coeff. (MOC) (pcm/K) | -3.84 (3.9%) | -5.71 (3.2%) | -2.66 (6.5%) |
| Temp. coeff. (EOC) (pcm/K) | -5.31 (3.2%) | -6.68 (2.8%) | -2.61 (6.4%) |

*The values in parentheses stand for statistics error corresponding to 1σ.

**Table 4.** Fuel composition of fresh fuel (wt%).

| | GTHTR300 | TRU multi-recycling | Pu multi-recycling |
|---|---|---|---|
| $^{234}$U | - | 0.3 | 0.3 |
| $^{235}$U | 14.0 | 18.4 | 18.8 |
| $^{236}$U | - | 9.9 | 9.8 |
| $^{237}$Np | - | - | - |
| $^{238}$Pu | - | 1.3 | 1.1 |
| $^{239}$Pu | - | 1.0 | 0.9 |
| $^{240}$Pu | - | 0.7 | 0.5 |
| $^{241}$Pu | - | 0.4 | 0.4 |
| $^{242}$Pu | - | 1.1 | 0.9 |
| Am | - | 0.7 | - |
| Cm | - | 1.1 | - |

### *4.2. Specifications for waste package generation and disposal*

Table 5 lists the number of waste packages generated by electricity generation. The number is mainly determined by the reprocessing method and waste package specification [5]. The amount of MA is negligible compared with FPs, and the decay heat also negligible at this stage. With partitioning case, that is "GTHTR300 with partitioning"," TRU multi-recycling", and "Pu multi-recycling", the number of waste packages is reduced by 60 % compared with an ordinary reprocessing case of "GTHTR300".

On the other hand, the repository footprint is listed in Table 6. That depends on partitioning, cooling time, and disposal method. In the case of "GTHTR300 with partitioning", the longer cooling time of 150 years realize the horizontal emplacement. With the reduction of the number of waste packages, the repository footprint is reduced by 88.3 % compared with the ordinary reprocessing case in the soft rock repository. With transmutation of americium-241 and long cooling time of 330 years, the decay heat can be minimized. With the small decay heat, the compact emplacement, in which bundled waste packages are piled up as shown in Fig. 5, can be realized. With the compact disposal, the footprint can be reduced by 99.7 % for TRU multi-recycling HTGR and plutonium multi-recycling HTGR.

**Table 5.** Number of waste package generation (canister/TWeh).

| | GTHTR300 | GTHTR300 with partitioning | TRU multi-recycling | Pu multi-recycling |
|---|---|---|---|---|
| Vitrified waste | 2.31 | 0.502 | 0.515 | 0.521 |
| Sr calcined waste | - | 0.153 | 0.152 | 0.153 |
| Cs calcined waste | - | 0.178 | 0.193 | 0.192 |
| Total | 2.31 | 0.833 | 0.860 | 0.866 |

**Table 6.** Specifications for waste disposal.

| | GTHTR300 | GTHTR300 with partitioning | TRU multi-recycling | Pu multi-recycling |
|---|---|---|---|---|
| Disposal method | Vertical | Horizontal | Compact | Compact |
| Cooling time from repro | 50 years | 150 years | Vitrified: 60 years<br>Calcined: 330 years | Vitrified: 60 years<br>Calcined: 330 years |
| Repository footprint in soft rock ($m^2$/TWeh) | 209 | 24.3 | 0.658 | 0.663 |
| Repository footprint in hard rock ($m^2$/TWeh) | - | - | 0.823 | 0.829 |

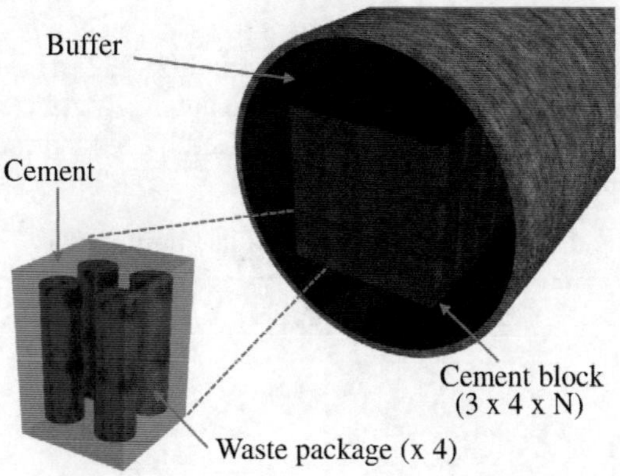


**Figure 5.** Compact emplacement disposal.

*4.3. MA generation from Pu multi-recycling HTGR*

Tables 7 and 8 list the MA amount and its composition from PWR, GTHTR300, TRU and plutonium multi-recycling HTGR, with and without neptunium, respectively. The MA generation per electricity generation of GTHTR300 is smaller than that of PWR because of the higher thermal efficiency. The thermal efficiencies are 34.5 % and 45.6 %, respectively for PWR and HTGR. The MA generation from plutonium multi-recycling HTGR is five times larger than that from GTHTR300 because of the generation of neptunium from cumulated uranium-236, and that of americium and curium from cumulated plutonium. However, the MA generation can significantly be reduced by excluding neptunium the toxicity is not problematic due to its long lifetime.

For the MA composition of americium and curium, the amount of high order nuclides is a lager with the plutonium multi-recycling HTGR because of the cumulated plutonium-242, which exists almost the same amount of plutonium-239.

To confirm the reactivity worth of the MAs, that is evaluated by the equivalent fissile method [18], which is also employed to manage fuel composition in the prototype FBR Monju. The equivalent fissile method is as follows,

$$y^i = \nu\sigma_f^i - \sigma_a^i , \tag{1}$$

$$\eta^i = y^i / y^{key} , \tag{2}$$

$$W = \textstyle\sum_i \alpha^i \eta^i , \tag{3}$$

where,

$y^i$ : equivalent fissile value for i-th nuclide (cm$^{-2}$),
$y^{key}$ : equivalent fissile value for key nuclide (cm$^{-2}$),
$\nu\sigma_f^i$ : microscopic production cross-section for i-th nuclide (cm$^{-2}$),
$\sigma_a^i$ : microscopic absorption cross-section for i-th nuclide (cm$^{-2}$),
$\eta^i$ : equivalent fissile coefficient for i-th nuclide (-),
$\alpha^i$ : atomic number fraction for i-th nuclide (-),
W : reactivity worth of fuel material (-).

In general, plutonium-239 is selected as the key nuclide to manage plutonium composition, and this method is used to determine plutonium enrichment to keep certain reactivity worth of fuel material. In the present study, neptunium-237 is selected as the key nuclide to elucidate the reactivity worth of MAs. MA burner should be fast neutron systems such as FBR and ADS. Therefore, the condensed cross-section by FBR neutron spectrum prepared as ORIGEN code library named 1500MXIC in ORLIB-J40 [19]. That is represented for the MOX part of the inner core of large commercial FBR.

The reactivity worth is listed in Table 9. The worth shows the negative value for positive reactivity because of the negative equivalent fissile value of neptunium-237. The MA from plutonium multi-recycling HTGR contributes criticality, and it is significant for MAs excluding neptunium. For the ADS fuel design, the MA content should slightly be diluted by the matrix material to compensate for the increased criticality worth.

**Table 7.** MA amount and its composition.

| | PWR | GTHTR300 | Pu multi-recycling |
|---|---|---|---|
| MA amount (kg/TWeh) | 3.2 | 2.0 | 10.1 |
| Composition (wt%) | | | |
| Np-237 | 53.00 | 52.29 | 62.32 |
| Am-241 | 30.34 | 26.05 | 8.31 |
| Am-242m | 0.09 | 0.11 | 0.07 |
| Am-243 | 11.98 | 16.26 | 19.39 |
| Cm-243 | 0.05 | 0.06 | 0.04 |
| Cm-244 | 4.17 | 4.89 | 8.95 |
| Cm-245 | 0.34 | 0.31 | 0.87 |
| Cm-246 | 0.03 | 0.02 | 0.06 |

**Table 8.** MA amount and its composition without Np.

| | PWR | GTHTR300 | Pu multi-recycling |
|---|---|---|---|
| MA amount (kg/TWeh) | 1.5 | 0.9 | 3.8 |
| Composition (wt%) | | | |
| Am-241 | 64.55 | 54.60 | 22.07 |
| Am-242m | 0.19 | 0.24 | 0.17 |
| Am-243 | 25.49 | 34.09 | 51.46 |
| Cm-243 | 0.10 | 0.12 | 0.09 |
| Cm-244 | 8.88 | 10.26 | 23.74 |
| Cm-245 | 0.73 | 0.66 | 2.30 |
| Cm-246 | 0.06 | 0.04 | 0.16 |

**Table 9.** Reactivity worth of MAs in FR by equivalent fissile method (-)

| | PWR | GTHTR300 | Pu multi-recycling |
|---|---|---|---|
| MA | 0.59 | 0.49 | 0.27 |
| MA without Np | 0.12 | -0.07 | -0.96 |

## 5. Requirement for MA burner

To consume MA generated from plutonium multi-recycling HTGR, the introduction of MA burner is considered in the present study. Major topics are as follows.

### *5.1. Installation capacity of MA burner*

To consider the installation capacity of MA burner, ADS is assumed because of the small fuel cycle due to the heavy loading of MAs. ADS is designed as small-sized Pb-Bi cooled FR, and the coolant also plays a role of spallation reaction target of proton beam as a neutron source to drive the subcritical reactor. The reactor power is 800MWt, and the transmutation rate of MA is 250 kg/y [20]. According to these specifications and MA generation amount, the installation unit number of ADS is evaluated, and the result is listed in Table 10. The number stands for the installation unit number of ADS per electricity generation of each reactor in an equilibrium state. Comparing between PWR and GTHTR300, the installation number of ADS for GTHTR300 is very small because of the less MA generation. On the contrary, that of plutonium multi-recycling HTGR is very large due to the more MA generation. However, by excluding neptunium the insulation unit becomes close that of PWR for the whole MA, which is the representative scenario of ADS.

**Table 10.** Number of ADS per electricity capacity (unit/GWe)

| | PWR | GTHTR300 | Pu multi-recycling |
|---|---|---|---|
| MA | 0.090 | 0.062 | 0.318 |
| MA without Np | 0.042 | 0.030 | 0.120 |

*5.2. Cost impact to introduce MA burner*

To consider the cost impact to introduce MA burner HTGR the difference in electricity cost between TRU multi-recycling HTGR and plutonium multi-recycling HTGR with MA burner. Neptunium is excluded as a transmutation target because of the unnecessity. In the future, a detailed analysis should be performed. However, some cost-related terms are considered and the cost feasibility is confirmed. The conditions and cost-related terms are as follows.

- Based on GTHTR300 cost evaluation [21] revised to the latest condition [22].
- The cycle length change is considered via a change of capacity factor and fuel fabrication.
- The plutonium multi-recycling HTGR is regarded as a representative case in the comparison because the cycle length is almost the same as the design target of GTHTR300.
- MA burner cost is simply converted by the introduced capacity from the cost increase of 0.12 yen/kWh in LWR scenario [23].

Based on the latest electricity generation cost evaluation of LWR in Japan [24], where the cost is evaluated as 10.3 yen/kWh, the revised cost GTHTR300 is to be 9.0 yen/kWh. It is composed of a capital cost of 2.4 yen/kWh, the operation cost of 2.3 yen/kWh, the fuel cost of 1.8 yen/kWh, and social cost of 1.5 yen/kWh. The cost change is evaluated and the result is listed in Table 11. The capacity factor is slightly reduced by 1% in TRU multi-recycling HTGR. It increases the cost relating to capital cost and operational cost. Totally, the cost is increased by 0.07 yen/kWh. The fuel fabrication cost is 0.53 yen/kWh. Because of the reduced cycle length, the cost increased by 0.08 yen/kWh. Finally, the cost of TRU multi-recycling HTGR is increased by 0.15 yen/kWh. On the other hand, the cost of the plutonium multi-recycling core is increased by 0.16 yen/kWh. From the viewpoint of the cost, the cost is slightly increased by introducing MA burner. According to the cost evaluation of ADS [23], the cost may reduce to 0.01 yen/kWh by employing FR corresponding to ADS due to the cost reduction by removing accelerator and increasing of electricity generation. In that case, the installation of MA burner can improve the economy of multi-recycling HTGR by 0.14 yen/kWh.

**Table 11.** Cost change by MA recycling (yen/kWh).

| | TRU multi-recycling | Pu multi-recycling |
|---|---|---|
| Capacity factor | +0.07 | - |
| Fuel fabrication | +0.08 | - |
| MA burner | - | +0.16 |
| Total | +0.15 | +0.16 |

*5.3. Safety requirement of MA burner*

In the ADS core, the neutron source did not affect to the transmutation characteristics. The neutron population in the subcritical reactor is expressed as follows,

$$M = \frac{sl}{1-k_{eff}}, \tag{4}$$

where,

$M$ : neutron population in the reactor (-),
$s$ : neutron source strength ($s^{-1}$),
$l$ : a lifetime of a neutron (s),
$k_{eff}$ : effective multiplication factor (-).

The effective multiplication factor of ADS is designed around 0.95. Due to the eq.4, one neutron generated from the neutron source is multiplied by 20 times. In other words, 95% of a neutron is generated from the chain reaction. The transmutation characteristics are not different from that of critical FR.

The reason that ADS designed as a subcritical reactor is to ensure safety. However, the safety can be ensured not only by the neutronic characteristics but also by the thermal characteristics. In general, inherent safety feather of self-regulation of the reactor power in LWR is very famous. This safety feature can be realized by the characteristics of the thermal reactor and reduced moderation design [25]. On the contrary, in FR, positive reactivity is inserted when the coolant voided due to the threshold fission reaction. It is called positive sodium void reactivity. In general, commercial FBR occurs power burst and core melt, when a scrum is failed during the loss of forced coolant [10]. However, inherent safety can be realized even by FR with a large safety margin in thermal design. In the accident, the power is settled down safely by the Doppler effect if the coolant is not voided. This reactor concept is called the Integral Fast Reactor (IFR) [26]. IFR is designed as small-sized FR as same as ADS. MA burner based on IFR should be investigated to improve the economy of multi-recycling HTGR.

**Summary**

To find the advantage of incorporation of multi-recycling HTGR cycle with MA burner, the specification of plutonium multi-recycle HTGR and the requirement for MA burner have been investigated. Major conclusions are as follows.

- According to the previous study, there is no advantage to the incorporation of FBR multi-recycling with ADS.
- Plutonium multi-recycling HTGR can realize significant toxicity reduction and waste volume reduction as same as FBR and ADS, and the cycle length and discharged burn-up are increased by 15% comparing with TRU multi-recycling HTGR. On the other hand, the cycle needs to incorporate with MA burner.
- The installation capacity of MA burner is almost the same as the representative ADS scenario by excluding neptunium from the transmutation target even with the more MA generation characteristics.
- The cost increase by introducing MA burner is slightly larger than the cost reduction by the improvement of the specification of HTGR when ADS is assumed as the MA burner. If FR without accelerator can be introduced, the cost improvement of 0.14 yen/kWh can be expected.
- The neutron source of ADS does not affect its transmutation characteristics, and the subcritical design is to ensure safety. IFR may achieve enough safety as MA burner reactor, and the feasibility should be investigated in the future.

As summarized above, it is found that there is an advantage for the incorporation of multi-recycling HTGR with MA burner based on IFR.

**References**

[1] Fukaya Y, Goto M, Ohashi H, et al. 2018. Uranium-based TRU Multi-recycling with Thermal Neutron HTGR to Reduce Environmental Burden and Threat of Nuclear Proliferation Journal of Nuclear Science and Technology v55 i11 p.1275

[2] Nishihara K. 2004. Multi-faceted Evaluation for Nuclear Fuel Cycles with Transmutation Japan Atomic Energy Agency JAEA-Research 2014-032

[3] Japan Nuclear Cycle Development Institute. 2000. Second Progress Report on Research and Development for the Geological Disposal of HLW in Japan; H12: Project to Establish the Scientific and Technological Basis for HLW Disposal in Japan, Project Overview Report Japan Nuclear Cycle Development Institute, JNC TN1410 2000-001

[4] Kubota M, Morita Y. 1997. Preliminary Assessment on Four Group Partitioning Process Developed in JAERI Proc. GLOBAL'97 Tokyo Japan Oct. 5-10 1997

[5] Nishihara K Nakayama S Morita Y et al. 2008. Impact of Partitioning and Transmutation on LWR High-Level Waste Disposal Journal of Nuclear Science and Technology v.45 i.1 p.84

[6] Yan X L, Kunitomi K, Nakata K, et al. 2003. GTHTR300 Design and Development Nuclear Engineering and Design v.222 p.248

[7] Nakata T, Katanishi S, Takada S, et al. 2003. Nuclear, Thermal and Hydraulic Design for Gas Turbine High Temperature Reactor (GTHTR300) Transaction of Atomic Energy Society of Japan v.14 i.3 p. 478 [in Japanese]

[8] Fukaya Y Goto M Nishihara T. 2015. Development on Nuclear Design Model for Detailed Design of Clean Burn HTGR Japan Atomic Energy Agency JAEA-Technology 2015-017 [in Japanese]

[9] U.S. Government. 1988. United States-Japan Nuclear Cooperation Agreement: Hearings before the Committee on Foreign Affairs House of Representatives One Hundredth Congress First and Second Sessions U.S. Government Printing Office

[10] Advanced Nuclear System Research and Development Directorate Research and Development Department and The Japan Atomic Power Company 2011 Fast Reactor Cycle Technology Development Project (FaCT Project) -Phase I Report- Japan Atomic Energy Agency JAEA-Evaluation 2011-003 [in Japanese]

[11] Croff A G. 1983. ORIGEN2: A Versatile Computer Code for Calculating the Nuclide Compositions and Characteristics of Nuclear Material Nuclear Technology v62 p.335

[12] Nagaya Y, Okumura K, Mori T. 2006. A Monte Carlo neutron/photon transport code MVP 2 Transactions of the American Nuclear Society v.95 p.662

[13] Shibata K, Iwamoto O, Nakagawa T, et al. 2011. JENDL-4.0: A New Library for Nuclear Science and Technology Journal of Nuclear Science and Technology v.48 i.1 p.1

[14] Murata I, Takahashi A, Mori T, et al. 1997. New Sampling Method on Continuous Energy Monte Carlo Calculation for Pebble Bed Reactors. Journal of Nuclear Science and Technology v.34 i8 p.734.

[15] Meulekamp R, Marck S. 2006, Calculating the Effective Delayed Neutron Fraction with Monte Calro Nuclear Science and Engineering v.152 p.142

[16] Garza A Garrett G A Murphy J E. 1961. Multicomponent Isotope Separation in Cascades Chemical Engineering Science v.15 i.3-4 p.188

[17] Benedict M Thomas H P and Hans L W. 1981. Nuclear Chemical Engineering Mcgraw-Hill Book Company

[18] Nakae N, Ito M, Mishima T, et al.1986. Control of Plutonium Content Using a Concept of Physical Accounting Method for Adjusted Fissile Enrichment Dounen Gihou 1986- Jun-70, p.77 [in Japanese]

[19] Okumura K Sugino K Kojima K et al. 2013. A Set of ORIGEN2 cross section libraries based on JENDL-4.0; ORLIBJ40 Japan Atomic Energy Agency JAEA-Data/Code 2012-032.

[20] OECD/NEA, Actinide and Fission Product Partitioning and Transmutation, p.417. OECD/NEA, 2015.

[21] Kunitomi K Shiozawa S and Yan X L. 2007. Basic Design and Economical Evaluation of Gas Turbine High Temperature Reactor 300 (GTHTR300) #7375 Proc. of ICAPP 2007 Nice France 13-18 May207.
[22] JAEA, Brochure of JAEA, URL:https://www.jaea.go.jp/04/o-arai/nhc/en/assets/images/brochure/brochure.pdf
[23] Tujimoto K. 2011. Transmutation Technology with ADS Forum of "Nuclear, Biology and Physics", Kyoto Japan 8-10 Oct 2011. URL:http://www2.yukawa.kyoto-u.ac.jp/~soken.editorial/sokendenshi/vol13/nbp
[24] Matuo Y. 2015. Overview of Assessment by Power Generation Cost Verification Working Group IEEJ. URL: https://eneken.ieej.or.jp/data/6362.pdf
[25] E Lewis. 1977, Nuclear Power Reactor Safety. p. 648 John Wiley & Sons inc
[26] Wade D and Chang Y. 1988. The Integral Fast Reactor Concept, Physics of Operation and Safety Nuclear Science and Engineering v.100 p.507

Journal of Physics: Conference Series **2048** (2021) 012027 doi:10.1088/1742-6596/2048/1/012027

# Optimization of PeLUIt-150 Conceptual Design

**T Setiadipura[1], W Luthfi[1], S Bakhri[1], Suwoto[1], Zuhair[1], Z Li[2], and Y Sun[2]**

[1]Center for Nuclear Reactor Technology and Safety, Puspiptek Area Building 80$^{th}$, South Tangerang, BANTEN, Indonesia
phone: +62-21-7560912, tsdipura@batan.go.id
[2]Institute of Nuclear and New Energy Technology, Tsinghua University, Beijing 100084, China

**Abstract.** A 150MWt pebble bed high temperature reactor, called PeLUIt-150, is proposed as a solution for distributed energy demand including the electricity and various co-generation potentials. In current study an optimization of the design is performed. The optimization includes its optimum power density to have a compact core design including the height-to-diameter (H/d) ratio. As several computer codes is used in this study, PEBBED-THERMIX codes, comparison of results from different code is also discussed. Constrain of the design at current stage are the maximum fuel temperature under depressurized loss of forced cooling (DLOFC) accident which represent the passive performance of the core, and discharge burnup which represent the fuel utilization performance of the core. Current study achieves an optimized design with core diameter and height of 260 cm and 601.11cm, a total active core volume of 31.9 m$^3$. The average power density is 4.7W/c m$^3$ with discharge burnup of 80.82MWd/Kg and the maximum fuel temperature after DLOFC is 1619.9°C.

## 1. Introduction

A specific geographical condition of Indonesia required a particular energy or electricity supply. A nuclear reactor type of high temperature pebble bed reactor (PBR) is one of appropriate technology for this energy and electricity challenge. Not only to supply distributed small yet continuous electricity demand, the cogeneration feature of PBR is also an interesting technology to supply high temperature steam for natural resource processes [1]. As a follow up of national program to develop a small experimental 10MWt PBR called *Reaktor Daya Eksperimental*, a 150MWt PBR development, called PeLUIt-150, was already started [2]. The design was based on the Chinese HTR-PM design [3]. The specification of pebble fuel was also maintained to take advantage of all the fuel test experiment which already done for the HTR-PM fuel. One of the challenges of the 150MWt PBR is the economics of the design. As one of the efforts to decrease the cost of the reactor is to have a design with smaller main component specially the Reactor Pressure Vessel (RPV). To have a smaller RPV, the active core is further optimized to get a more compact core while maintaining the efficient fuel utilization and passive safety feature of the design. Previous optimization [2] results in a core with diameter 300cm, height 6.63m with power density of 3.2W/m3. Burnup value which represents the efficient fuel utilization of previous optimization was 87.69 MWd/Kg. The Helium outlet from the core is 750°C and steam output from the steam generator is 540°C. This high temperature output of the PeLUIt-150 design is very potential for cogeneration application including the medium high temperature hydrogen production from Cu-Cl or Mg-Cl cycles [4.5]. Purpose of this study is to further optimized the core size of PeLUIt-150 by increasing the power density of the core. The selective criteria of the optimized design is to have an efficient fuel utilization represent by minimum discharge burnup of 80MWd/Kg, and a strong passive safety feature which represent by having a maximum fuel temperature under depressurized loss of forced cooling (DLOFC) accident scenario below 1620°C. Calculation method including the optimized parameters of the design is given in the later chapter, followed by the calculation results and its discussion, and finally closed by a conclusion of this study.

## 2. Calculation method

The configuration of Pebble Bed type HTGR from the general in-vessel component including the active core down to its TRISO coated fuel particle can be seen in Figure 2. A ceramic based material including its fuel guarantee the capability to withstand a high temperature condition. In addition, the high heat conductivity and high heat capacity of the graphite ceramic make a good thermal hydraulic performance of the core. The diameter of the pebble bed type HTGR generally limited to 300cm also to assure the capability of the core in releasing the heat outside passively. The PeLUIt design development is based on the HTR-PM design including its pebble fuel design of 7g/pebble and 8.5% enrichment. The HTR-PM design then downscale to have an optimum design of PeLUIt 150MWt.

**Table 1.** The main parameter of PeLUIt-150 reactor

| Reactor Parameter | Nominal |
|---|---|
| Thermal Power (MWt) | 150 |
| Helium inlet/outlet temp (°C/°C) | 250 / 750 |
| Minimum Average Discharge Burnup (MWd/t-HM) | 80 |
| Max. Fuel Temperature under any accident (°C) | 1620 |
| Core diameter/height | Optimized |
| Average/Maximum Core power density (MW/m$^3$) | Optimized |
| Number of pebble loading/day | Optimized |

The power conversion system of PeLUIt-150 is kept as in the previous optimization [2] where the superheated steam temperature is 540°C with pressure of 14 MPa and flowrate of 59.5 Kg/s.

The optimization study was started by increasing power density from the previous 3.2MW/m3 design by keeping its diameter up to highest possible power density which fulfill the optimization criteria. To optimized the design further, a lower of core diameter was chosen.

Neutronic analysis of this study was performed using PEBBED [6,7] code and other codes which already include in it. This includes the COMBINE code for spectrum analysis for fast and thermal spectrum each having a 4-group neutron energy. For the thermal hydraulic analysis there are two option available in PEBBED, first is to use the 1-d analysis and second is to couple this calculation to THERMIX thermal hydraulic module. Thermal hydraulic analysis in this study was performed using the THERMIX code which already coupled with PEBBED by INL. It adopts a two-dimensional R-Z cylindrical geometry, where the geometrical definition applied in PEBBED is directly transferred to THERMIX. It has been approved to be applied in the design development of several PBR design such as AVE, THTR, HTR-500 and HTR-Module [8] and recently also applied in HTR-PM design development. It includes modules of heat conductivity in the matrix graphite of fuel element based on empirical relationship of German fuel. Zehner-Schlunder [9] formula is applied to accommodate the effects of different heat transfer mechanism of radiation, gas and solid conduction and represent with an effective heat conductivity for uniform pebble-bed. Formula of the German safety guide KTA3102.2 for heat transfer coefficient of the surface of pebble fuel elements. While German KTA Safety Guide KTA3102.1 for helium thermal physical property parameters is applied. Specific reflector graphite thermal physical property in which the heat conductivity of reflector is already accommodate the effect of fast neutron radiation.[3]

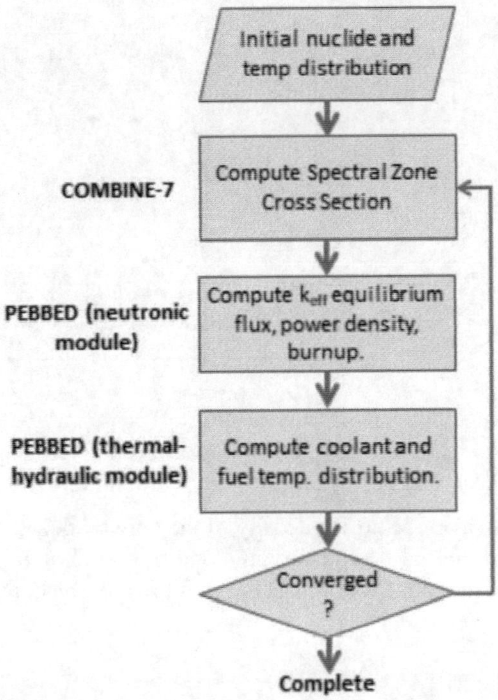


**Figure 1.** Calculation scheme for equilibrium core and DLOFC accident analysis.

## 3. Results and Discussions

Start from the previous optimized core design with power density of 3.2 W/cm3 [2], the initial effort is to increase the power density as high as possible by maintaining the active core diameter of 300cm. Figure 2 shows the maximum axial profile of the power density in the core. In general, the axial profile is not changed by increasing the power density for same geometry. However, as the core height is decreasing a small increase of power density in the upper part near the void cavity and in the bottom part near the bottom reflector was shown. This phenomenon is also strengthened by the increase of power peaking value as the average power density increasing or the height of the core is decreasing as shown in Figure 3.

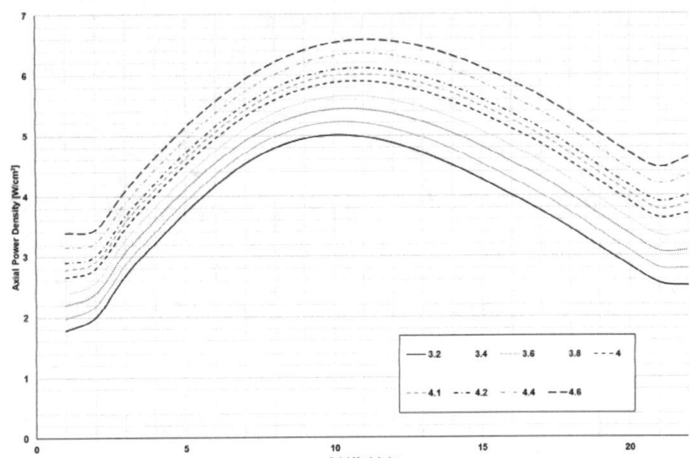


**Figure 2.** Axial power densities profile of cores with diameter 300cm.

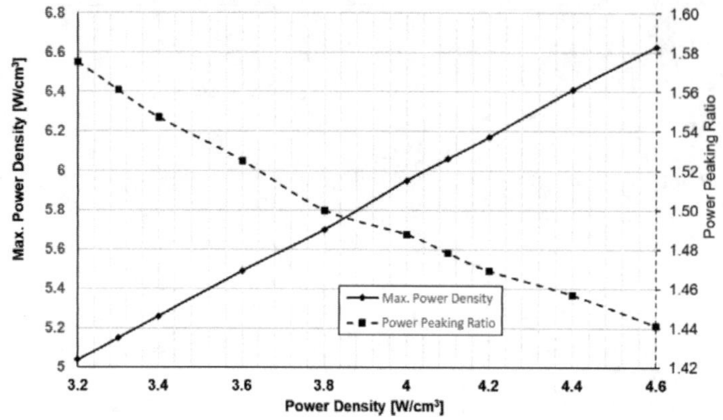


**Figure 3.** Maximum Axial power densities for different average power density and its power peaking values of cores with diameter 300cm.

As expected, increasing the average power density of the core by decreasing its height gives a higher average and peak fuel temperature in the equilibrium condition as shown in Figure 4. For the integrity of the fuel, it will give a more heat loading on the fuel as it crosses the core for 15 times.

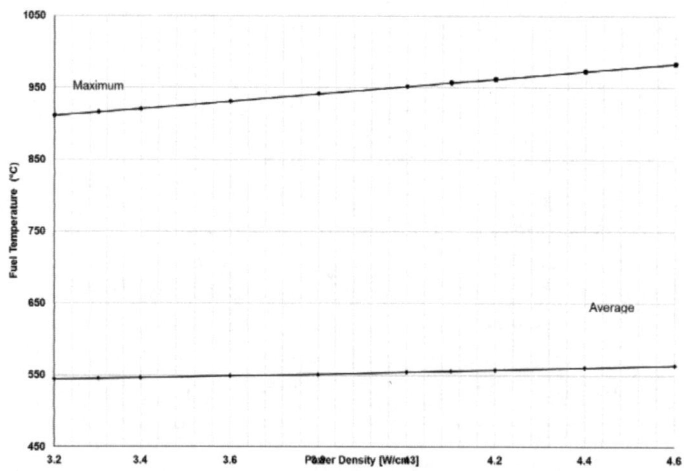


**Figure 4.** Maximum and average fuel temperature in the cores with increasing average power density for diameter 300cm.

Fuel utilization efficiency in the core was shown to be decreasing for higher average power density. This efficiency decrease is shown by lower discharge burnup and, as a result, more fuel pebbles are needed in the equilibrium operation as shown in Figure 5. Increasing average power density from 3.2 W/cm$^3$ to 4.6 W/cm$^3$ which decrease the active core height of ~200cm from 663.15cm result in the decrease of discharge burnup ~4MWd/Kg. The size benefit seems worth for that small decrease of discharge burnup, which means that increasing average fuel density is one of good approach for current optimization.

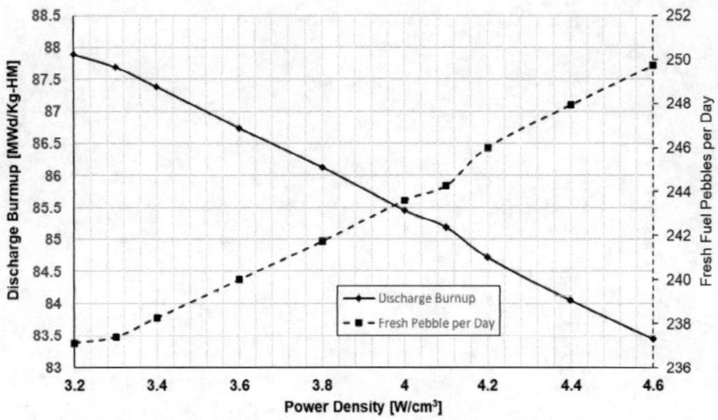


**Figure 5.** Discharge Burnup and fresh fuel pebbles per day in the cores with increasing average power density for diameter 300cm.

However, passive safety feature of the core was not fulfilled for all the increased power density fuel. Results of the transient maximum fuel temperature after DLOFC accident scenario as shown in Figure 6 show that for core diameter of 300cm, the accepted power density was only up to 4 W/cm$^3$ where the maximum fuel temperature is 1610.0c. An increase of power density to 4.1 W/ cm$^3$ gives an unacceptable maximum fuel temperature of 1624 W/cm$^3$ which slightly higher than the limit.

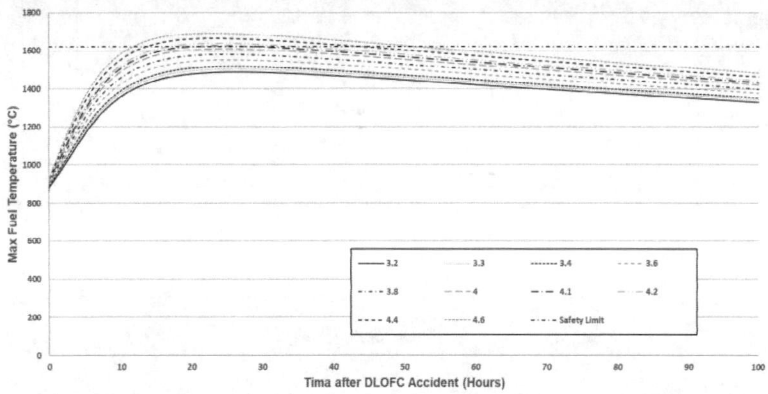


**Figure 6.** Transient of fuel temperatures after DLOFC of cores with higher power density with diameter 300cm.

Results for optimization which involved a decrease of core diameter to suppressed the maximum fuel temperature are given in following figures.

Maximum fuel temperature after DLOFC accident scenario for different average power density and different core diameter is given in Figure 7. It shows that decreasing the core diameter is an effective way to decrease the maximum fuel temperature after DLOFC. For certain core diameter we have an optimum power density which still gives a core with strong passive feature. A step-by-step increment of core diameter in Figure 7 shows that we can achieve high power density or more compact core which still survive the DLOFC accident passively.

However, this method of decreasing the diameter of the core in the same time also decrease the fuel utilization efficiency shown by lower discharge burnup as given in Figure 8. Applying the minimum burnup target of 80MWd/Kg, the optimum design in current study is the 4.7W/cm$^3$ design with core diameter and height of 260 cm and 601.11cm, a total volume of 31.9 m$^3$. The burnup of this optimized design is 80.82MWd/Kg and the maximum fuel temperature after DLOFC is 1619.9°C, slightly below the limit.

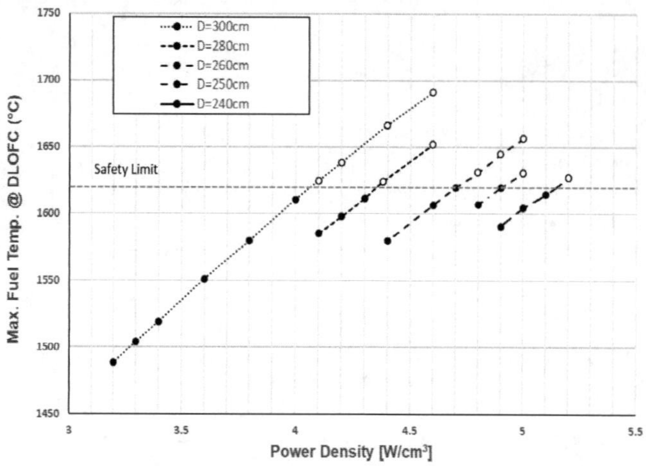


**Figure 7.** Results of optimized cores with higher power density for different active core diameter constrained with maximum fuel temperature under DLOFC accident scenario.

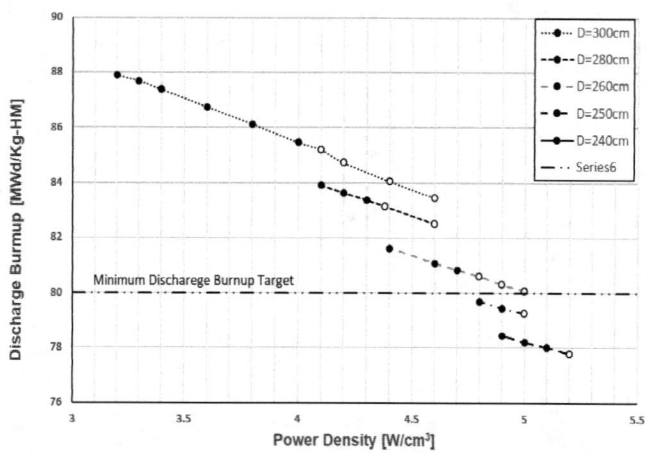


**Figure 8.** Results of optimized cores with higher power density for different active core diameter constrain with maximum fuel temperature under DLOFC accident scenario.

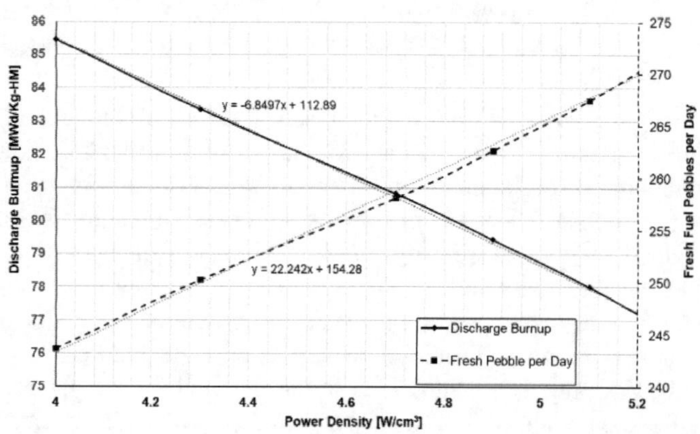


**Figure 9.** Discharge burnup and fresh pebble fuel per day for optimized core for each average power density.

Figure 9 compiles all the optimum acceptable design for each core diameter which also give certain power density and shows their fuel utilization performance. Higher power density, achieved from lower core diameter, will have a lower discharge burnup. A simple linear approach shows that for an increment of 1 W/cm$^3$ will caused a decrease of discharge burnup of ~7MWd/Kg, and it will increase the required daily fresh pebble fuels of ~22 pebbles.

## 4. Conclusion

Optimization of PeLUIt-150 PBR design is already performed. Keeping the fuel specification and fuel recirculation with 15 passes as in HTR-PM, current study achieves an optimized design with core diameter and height of 260 cm and 601.11cm, a total active core volume of 31.9 m$^3$. The average power density is 4.7W/c m$^3$ with discharge burnup of 80.82MWd/Kg and the maximum fuel temperature after DLOFC is 1619.9°C. The design fulfills the target of more compact core design and maintain the fuel utilization efficiency and its strong passive safety feature in which it can survive DLOFC accident scenario passively.

**Acknowledgement**

This research is supported by the National Key Research and Development Program of China (No. 2017YFE0102100). Additional supporting fund also given from the Indonesia Ministry of Research, Technology, and Higher Education through INSINAS-Flagship 2019 grant program.

## References

[1] T. Setiadipura, S. Bakhri, G.R. Sunaryo, D.S. Wisnubroto, "Cooling passive safety features of Reakto Daya Eksperimental", AIP Conference Proceedings, 1984, 020034, 2018

[2] T. Setiadipura, D. Irwanto, Suwoto, Zuhair, "Pebble Bed High Temperature Reactor for Electric and Cogeneration Application", Proceedings of International Conference on Energy Sciences (ICES2018), Bandung, Indonesia, 2018

[3] Z.Y. Zhang, Z.X. Wu, D.Z. Wang, Y.H. Xu, Y.L. Sun, F. Li, Y.J. Dong, Current Status and Technical Description of the Chinese 2×250MWth HTR-PM Demonstration Plant, Nuclear Engineering and Design, v239, p.1212, 2009.

[4] H. Ozcan, I. Dincer, "Comparative performance assessment of three configurations of magnesium-chlorin cycle", International Journal of Hydrogen Energy, 41, p845-856, 2016

[5] W. Wu, H.Y. Chen, J.J. Hwang, "Energy Analysis of a class of copper-chlorin (Cu-Cl) thermochemical cycles, International Journal of Hydrogen Energy, 42(25), p15990-16002,2017

[6] Terry W.K., Gougar H.D., Ougouag A.M," Direect deterministic method for neutronics analysis and computation of asymptotic burnup distribution in a recirculating pebble-bed reactor", Annals of Nuclear Energy, 29, p1345-1364, 2002

[7] H.D. Gougar, A.M. Ougouag, W.K. Terry, Automated design and optimization of pebble bed reactor cores, Nuclear Science and Engineering, 165, p245-269, 2010

[8] Y. Zheng, J. Lapins, E. Laurien, L. Shin, Z. Zhang, "Thermal hydraulic analysis of a pebble-bed modular high temperature gas-cooled reactor with ATTICA3D and THERMIX codes", Nuclear Engieering and Design, 246, p.286-297, 2012

[9] H. Gerwin, W. Scherer, E. Teuchert, TINTE modular system for computational simulation of transient processes in the primary circuit of a pebble-bed high-temperature gas-cooled reactor, Nuclear Science and Engineering, 102, p302-312, 1989.

# Multi-group cross section library generation for HTGR lattice physics code XPZ

**Lerui Zhang[1], Ding She[1], Lei Shi[1], Richard Chambon[2] and Alain Hébert[2]**

[1] Institute of Nuclear and New Energy Technology,
Collaborative Innovation Center of Advanced Nuclear Energy Technology,
Key Laboratory of Advanced Reactor Engineering and Safety of Ministry of Education, Tsinghua University, Beijing 100084, China

[2] Polytechnique Montréal, Institut de Génie Nucléaire, P.O. Box 6079, Station "Centre-Ville," Montréal, Quebec H3C 3A7, Canada

Email: sheding@mail.tsinghua.edu.cn

**Abstract.** The XPZ code was previously developed for the lattice physics computation in High Temperature Gas-cooled Reactors (HTGRs), which adopted the multi-group cross section library converted from the existing open-source DRAGON library. In this paper, a new format of multi-group cross section library named XPZLIB has been implemented in XPZ code. XPZLIB is designed in binary and HDF5 formats, including detailed data contents for resonance, transport and depletion calculations. A new data-processing module named XPZR is developed based on NJOY-2016 to generate nuclide dependent XPZLIB from the most recent evaluated nuclear data, and besides, the PyNjoy-2016 system is developed for automatic generation of integrated XPZLIB including a complete set of nuclides. The new generated XPZLIB is presented with the XPZ code. Numerical results demonstrate the accuracy of the new library XPZLIB and the reliability of the data processing scheme. Moreover, the influence of different versions of ENDF/B data is investigated.

## 1. Introduction

The multi-group cross section library is the basis and prerequisite for the lattice physics calculation of neutron transport in reactor analyses. The library can provide all kinds of different nuclear data, including nuclides properties, temperature-dependent cross sections, burnup information and some other related quantities required by lattice physics computations. Therefore, the accuracy of a lattice physics code can be significantly influenced by the multi-group cross section library [1]. The multi-group cross section library utilized directly by the lattice code is processed from the evaluated nuclear data library by using the specific data processing code. The ENDF/B [2] library established by the American Cross Section Evaluation Working Group (CSEWG) is the most comprehensive and widely used evaluated nuclear data library around the world. The NJOY nuclear data processing system developed by Los Alamos National Laboratory (LANL) is a computer code package that uses a modular program structure to produce pointwise and multi-group nuclear cross sections and other quantities from evaluated nuclear data [3].

Most lattice physics codes have their own multi-group cross section libraries. For instance, WIMS developed through various versions at the UK laboratory AEE/Winfrith uses the library WIMSLIB [3]. WIMSLIB is developed continuously by a Co-ordinated Research Project (CRP) WIMS Library Update Project (WLUP) supported by IAEA [4]. DRAGLIB is a cross section library for lattice code DRAGON which is developed by Polytechnique Montréal [5]. The PyNjoy-2012 system that can simplify the management of all the NJOY runs is a set of Python scripts dedicated to the production of DRAGLIB [6]. In addition to WIMS and DRAGON, many other codes use the MATXS format libraries and corresponding post-processing program to generate dedicated cross section libraries [1][7][8].

In our previous work, the XPZ code was developed for lattice physics calculation, as well as for the generation of broad-group constants [9] in High Temperature Gas-cooled Reactors (HTGRs). XPZ utilized a cross section library converted from the open-source library DRAGLIB. The latter was processed from the ENDF/B-VII.0 nuclear data by NJOY-2012.

This paper introduces a new format of multi-group cross section library named XPZLIB that has been recently implemented in XPZ code. The new library is processed from the ENDF/B data by developing a new data-processing module named XPZR in the open-source NJOY-2016 code. Besides, a processing system PyNjoy-2016, based on PyNjoy-2012, is developed to realize the automatic generation of multiple sets of XPZLIB.

The remainder of the paper is organized as follows. Section 2 introduces the format and characteristics of XPZLIB as well as generation flow and scheme of XPZR. Numerical results of critical and burnup calculations based on produced libraries are presented for validation in Section 3. Finally, concluding remarks are given in Section 4.

## 2. Generation of the Multi-group Cross Section Library

### *2.1. XPZLIB Format and Characteristics*

XPZLIB has two types of formats: binary format and HDF5 format [10].

Binary format XPZLIB consists of four basic data files, i.e., NUCLIDES, XSDIR, DEPL_CHAIN and ENERGY.

The NUCLIDES file contains one- and two- dimensional cross sections of all nuclides. As a binary file, it can save storage space and realize fast reading. Since the microscopic cross sections stored in a cross-section library are usually dependent on the background cross section and temperature [11], the format of the file is organized in multi-loop structure. As is shown in Table 1, the structure includes the nuclide loop, the temperature loop and the dilution loop from the outside in. And the NUCLIDES file structure is shown in Fig. 1.

The XSDIR file stores the list of nuclides and the address of data blocks in the NUCLIDES file for each nuclide, which is used for fast data access. The DEPL_CHAIN file contains the depletion chains used for burnup calculations. The ENERGY file is used to describe the energy group structure.

Although the binary format can realize fast reading and storage space saving, the users cannot read and look up the specific nuclear data directly. In order to maintain the advantages of binary format and make it convenient to look up nuclear data, XPZR is developed to generate the library in a HDF5 format. The HDF5 format library has only one file: NUCLIDES.h5. The file contains cross sections of all nuclides in multi-loop structures as the same as the binary format, energy group structure and depletion related data.

Table 1: Multi-loop structure

| LOOP | Parameter |
|---|---|
| 1 | Nuclide-e.g. U235 |
| 2 | Temperature-e.g. TMP00XX |
| 3 | Background XS-e.g. BGXS00XX |

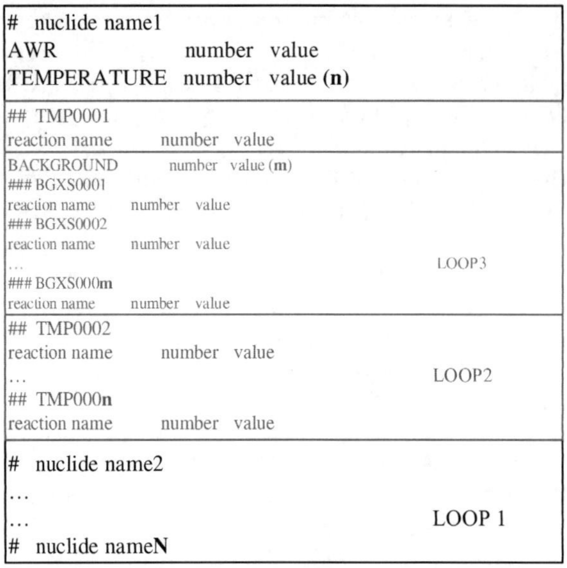


**Figure 1.** The NUCLIDES file structure.

The data contents comprised in XPZLIB are as detailed as DRAGLIB, which is well suited for general fission reactors. For example, the XPZLIB processed from ENDF/B-VII.0 using SHEM-361 [12] energy structure is summarized as follows:

- Evaluated nuclear data libraries: ENDF/B-VII.0;
- Number of nuclides: 314;
- Number of fissile nuclides: 31;
- Number of heavy nuclides: 42;
- Number of fission fragments: 272;
- Number of resonance nuclides: 68;
- Energy group structure: SHEM-361;
- Energy range: $1.964\times10^{7}$-$1.100\times10^{-5}$ eV;
- Range of resonance energy groups and energy: 31-173 group, $3.2065\times10^{5}$-22.536 eV; 52-173 group, $1.8585\times10^{4}$-22.536 eV;
- S(α, β) data: including all important available S(α, β) materials in ENDF/B data, such as H in $H_2O$, C in graphite, etc. ;
- Maximum Legendre order: P1;
- Temperatures: typically including five temperature grid points, i.e., 293.0K, 550.0K, 900.0K, 1200.0K, and 2000.0K;
- Background cross sections: The number of background cross sections for most resonance nuclides is limited to less than or equal to 10, but for the following nuclides that have a considerable resonance effect, it is 20, including $^{232}$Th, $^{235}$U, $^{238}$U, $^{238}$Pu, $^{239}$Pu, $^{240}$Pu, $^{241}$Pu, $^{242}$Pu and $^{241}$Am;
- Reactions or quantities dependent on temperature: (n, tot), (n, n) (n, n'), (n, 2n), (n, 3n), (n, 4n), (n, f), (n, np), (n, γ), (n, p), (n, d), (n, t), (n, α), (n, 2α), $\nu\sigma_f$ (neutron number per fission multiply fission cross section), fission spectrum and scattering matrix;
- Reactions or quantities dependent on background cross section: (n, tot), (n, n), (n, f), (n, γ), $\nu\sigma_f$ and scattering matrix;
- Depleting channels: (n, 2n), (n, 3n), (n, 4n), (n, f), (n, np), (n, γ), (n, p), (n, d), (n, t), (n, α), (n, 2α) and radioactive decay.

Journal of Physics: Conference Series **2048** (2021) 012028 doi:10.1088/1742-6596/2048/1/012028

### 2.2. XPZLIB Generation Flow and Scheme

The generation flow of XPZLIB is presented in Fig.2. The ENDF/B data are processed by NJOY-2016. Several modules are available to process the cross-section data from neutron sub-library of ENDF/B. The specific modules are as follows: MODER, RECONR, BROADR, UNRESR, THERMR and GROUPR. After processing from module GROUPR, the output file is in GENDF format [3], which is further processed by the post-processing module XPZR. The XPZR module performs the final conversion from GENDF format towards XPZLIB format.

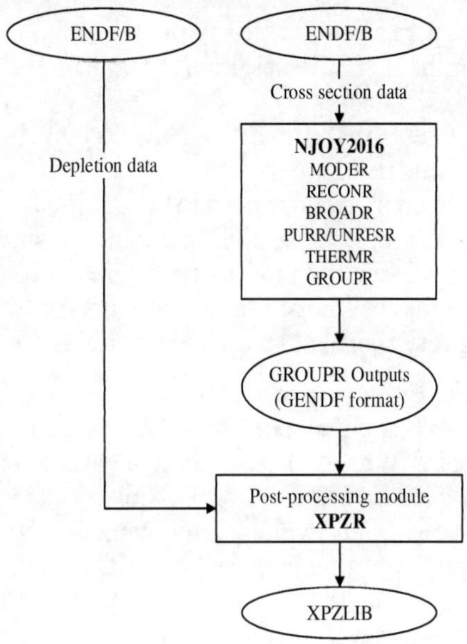


**Figure 2.** Flow chart of XPZLB generation.

The development of XPZR is based on DRAGR module in NJOY-2012 [13]. XPZR has two functions: one is to provide available data required by XPZ from GENDF files and the other is to generate the depletion file from decay and neutron fission yield sub-libraries of ENDF/B.

An important issue is the generation of fission- related data, i.e., fission spectrum and$\nu\sigma_f$ values. The following equations are used [13] [11] in XPZR.

$$\chi_g = \frac{\sum_{g'} \sigma_{f,g'\to g}\phi_{g'} + \chi_{d,g}\sum_{g'} \nu_{d,g'}\sigma_{f,g'}\phi_{g'}}{\sum_g \sum_{g'} \sigma_{f,g'\to g}\phi_{g'} + \sum_{g'} \nu_{d,g'}\sigma_{f,g'}\phi_{g'}} \quad (1)$$

$$\nu_g\sigma_{f,g} = \sum_{g'} \sigma_{f,g'\to g} + \nu_{d,g}\sigma_{f,g} \quad (2)$$

$$\chi_{d,g} = \frac{\nu_{d,g}}{\sum_{g'} \nu_{d,g'}} \quad (3)$$

where,

$\chi_g$ : fission spectrum,
$\chi_{d,g}$ : fission spectrum of delayed neutron,
$\sigma_{f,g'\to g}$ : fission matrix,
$\sigma_{f,g}$ : fission cross section,
$\nu_g$ : number of neutrons generated by a fission,
$\nu_{d,g}$ : number of delayed neutrons generated by a fission,
$\phi_g$ : weighting flux.

The scattering matrix can be obtained by the following equation [13] in XPZR.

$$\sigma_{scat,g'\to g} = \sigma_{diffusion} + \sigma_{n2n,g'\to g} + \sigma_{n3n,g'\to g} \quad (4)$$

where,

$\sigma_{scat,g'\to g}$ : scattering matrix,
$\sigma_{diffusion}$ : diffusion matrix,
$\sigma_{n2n,g'\to g}$ : (n, 2n) reaction matrix,
$\sigma_{n3n,g'\to g}$ : (n, 3n) reaction matrix.

Above the thermal cut-off energy, the static scattering matrix including elastic and inelastic scattering is used as the diffusion matrix. In the thermal energy range, coherent and incoherent scattering matrix is requested as the diffusion matrix.

To reduce the storage requirement of the scattering matrix, XPZR uses the same sparse-matrix storage approach as in MATXSR module [3].

In thermal energy range, the total cross sections need to be modified. Specifically, the static scattering cross section is deducted from the total cross section and the corresponding thermal scattering cross sections including coherent and incoherent thermal scattering are added to the total cross sections.

As for burnup data, XPZR inherits the lumped fission product treatment [14] from DRAGR, which removes those nuclides that have very short half-lives and small fission yields.

### *2.3. Automated Generation System PyNjoy-2016*

The processing system PyNjoy-2016 is developed for automatic generation of XPZLIB containing a complete set of nuclides. The system is made of three components: the NJOY-2016 program including post-processing module XPZR, a generic Python script PyNjoy.py and a collection of Python datasets.

As is shown in Fig.3, in the system, the Python script, named PyNjoy.py, has been used to define corresponding functions to prepare input files required by NJOY modules automatically, and then to execute the modules in correct order. As for Python datasets, firstly, they can define parameters of all nuclides, which are used during processing, such as temperature, background cross section, Legendre order, energy group structure and so on. Secondly, the datasets can import functions in PyNjoy.py to execute NJOY-2016 to process a large number of nuclides in the defined directory.

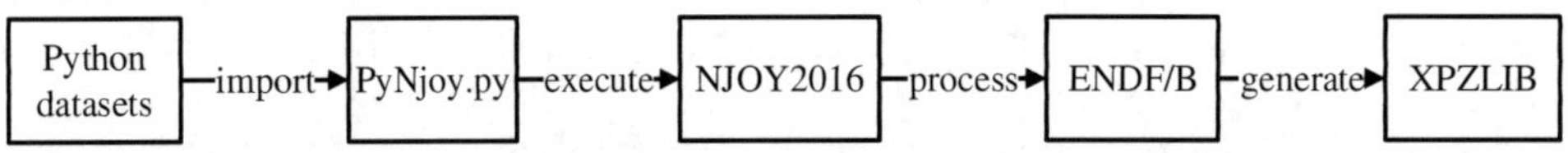


**Figure 3.** The generation flow of PyNjoy-2016 system.

The specific generation flow is shown in Fig. 4: the function self.pendf() is used to process the ENDF-6 format file to PENDF format file; the function self.gendf() is used to process PENDF format file to GENDF format file; the function self.xpzlib() can process the GENDF format file to XPZLIB; and besides, the function self.burnup() can process the burnup data.

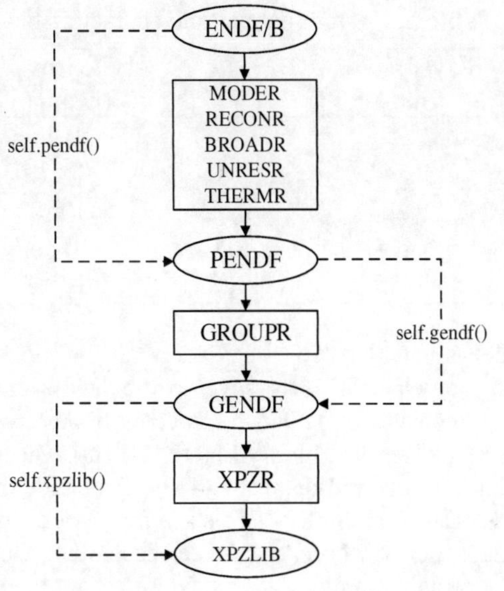


**Figure 4.** Functions from PyNjoy.py used in XPZLIB generation flow.

## 3. Numerical Validation and Analyses

### *3.1. Numerical Validation*

In order to validate the processed XPZ libraries, the realistic fuel pebble in HTR-10 reactor [15] is calculated. The HTR-10 fuel pebble model is shown in Fig. 5. The pebble consists of the fuel zone and the graphite shell, having the radius of 2.5 cm and 3.0 cm, respectively. And the fuel zone is filled with dispersed fuel particles. The dispersed particle with four coated layers is shown in Fig. 6.

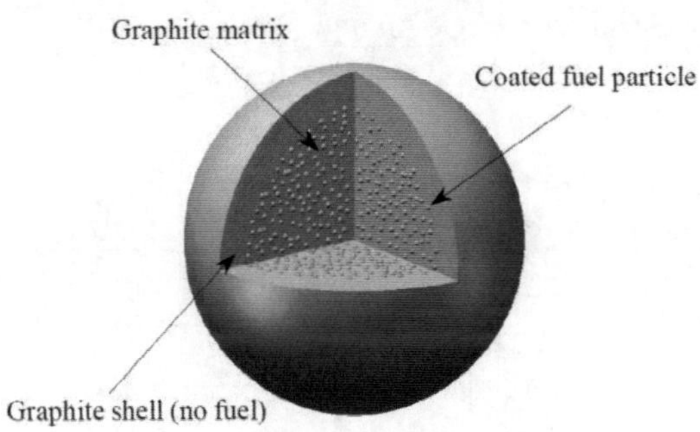


**Figure 5.** HTR-10 Pebble fuel element.

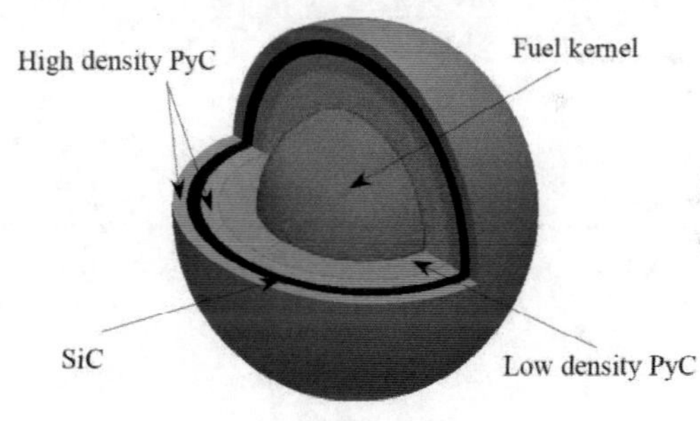


**Figure 6.** Coated fuel particle.

Table 2 and 3 give the parameters of the realistic HTR-10 fuel ball and coated fuel particle [15].

**Table 2.** HTR-10 Pebble fuel element characteristics.

| | |
|---|---|
| Diameter of ball(mm) | 60 |
| Diameter of fuel zone(mm) | 50 |
| Density of graphite in matrix and outer shell (g/cm$^3$) | 1.73 |
| Heavy metal (U) loading per ball (g) | 5.0 |
| Enrichment of $^{235}$U | 17% |
| Equivalent natural boron contents of impurities in uranium | 4 ppm |
| Equivalent natural boron contents of impurities in graphite | 1.3 ppm |
| Volumetric filling fraction of coated fuel particle in the fuel zone | 0.05 |

**Table 3.** Coated fuel particle characteristics.

| Layer radius (mm) | Material | Density (g/cm$^3$) |
|---|---|---|
| 0.25 | $UO_2$ | 10.4 |
| 0.34 | PyC | 1.1 |
| 0.38 | PyC | 1.9 |
| 0.415 | SiC | 3.18 |
| 0.455 | PyC | 1.9 |

The HTR-10 pebble model is calculated by XPZ adopting the old library and the new XPZLIB, respectively. The Mont Carlo code OpenMC [16] developed by Massachusetts Institute of Technology is taken as the reference code, which uses an HDF5-format continuous cross section library. All libraries are based on the same evaluated nuclear data library ENDF/B-VII.0. The calculation results of OpenMC have standard deviations being $10^{-4}$ magnitude. Table 4 and 5 provide the $k_{eff}$ calculation results. It is seen that the $k_{eff}$ results of XPZ based on new XPZLIB show very good agreement with the results based on the old library, with only a few pcm differences between each other. Besides, the differences between XPZ and OpenMC are in an acceptable range.

**Table 4.** $k_{eff}$ calculation results of XPZ based on old library and new XPZLIB.

| Filling ratio | XPZ | | Difference (PCM) |
|---|---|---|---|
| | Old Lib | New Lib | |
| 5.025% | 1.691781 | 1.691780 | -0.1 |
| 10.049% | 1.543318 | 1.543312 | -0.6 |
| 20.099% | 1.355486 | 1.355481 | -0.5 |

**Table 5.** $k_{eff}$ calculation results of OpenMC and XPZ based on new XPZLIB.

| Filling ratio | OpenMC | XPZ | Difference (PCM) |
|---|---|---|---|
| 5.025% | 1.69124 | 1.691780 | 54.0 |
| 10.049% | 1.54485 | 1.543312 | -153.8 |
| 20.099% | 1.35547 | 1.355481 | 1.1 |

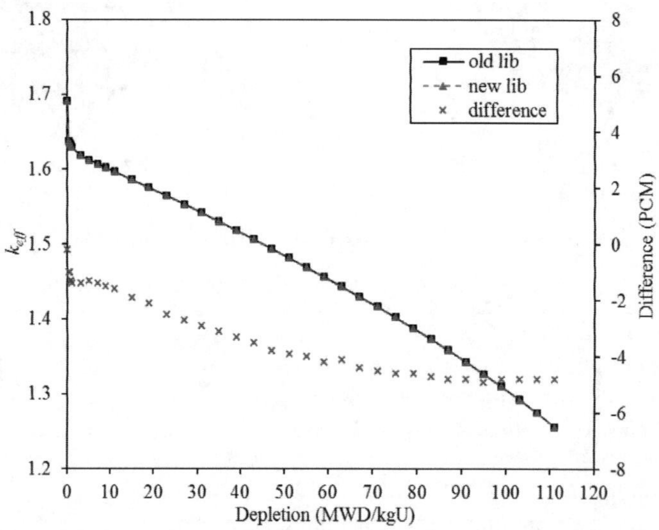


**Figure 7.** HTR-10 fuel ball burnup calculation results based on old library and new XPZLIB.

Burnup calculations are performed for a more comprehensive validation of the XPZLIB, especially for the burnup data. In the test, the filling ratio is 5.025% and the power density is 90W/gU. Fig. 7 shows dependence of $k_{eff}$ on burnup in HTR-10 pebble. The result based on old library is regarded as the reference data. The difference at every burnup step is within 5 pcm, which demonstrates the accuracy of the new library XPZLIB and the reliability of the data processing scheme.

### 3.2. Comparisons on different versions of ENDF/B data

Table 6 gives the $k_{eff}$ results calculated by XPZ based on ENDF/B-VII.0, ENDF/B-VII.1 and ENDF/B-VIII.0. It is found that version of evaluated nuclear data file can make a big influence on the results. The old library is processed from ENDF/B-VII.0. After updating the evaluated nuclear data library to ENDF/B-VIII.0, the result values will decrease by about 0.3%-0.6%.

**Table 6.** $k_{eff}$ calculation results differences between different ENDF/B versions.

| Filling ratio | XPZ VII.0 | XPZ VII.1 | XPZ VIII.0 |
|---|---|---|---|
| 5.025% | 1.691780 | 1.686013 | 1.681245 |
| 10.049% | 1.543312 | 1.540592 | 1.536338 |
| 20.099% | 1.355481 | 1.354254 | 1.351402 |

In addition to $k_{eff}$ calculation, Fig. 8 gives the burnup calculation results based on different evaluated nuclear data libraries. The result based on ENDF/B-VII.0 is considered as the reference. Then, it can be seen that there exist about 0.3%-0.5% differences between ENDF/B-VII.0 and ENDF/B-VII.1, while 0.5%-0.7% differences between ENDF/B-VII.0 and ENDF/B-VIII.0. It is noted that all the above XPZ calculation results based on binary format is almost the same as HDF5 format, which the difference is within 0.2 pcm.

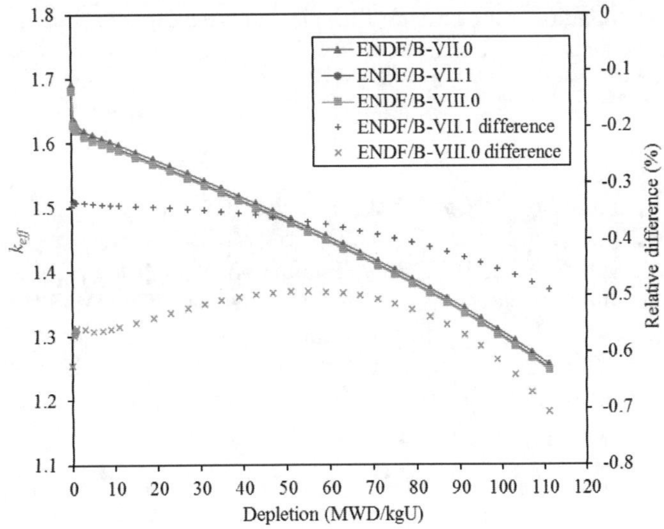


**Figure 8.** HTR-10 fuel ball burnup calculation results based on different evaluated nuclear data libraries.

## 4. Conclusions

This paper introduces the development of the XPZR module in NJOY-2016 to generate the multi-group cross section library XPZLIB for lattice physics code XPZ. Numerical results demonstrate the accuracy of the new library XPZLIB and the reliability of the data processing scheme. Comparison studies on different versions of ENDF/B data are also presented, which will be further investigated in our future work.

Journal of Physics: Conference Series **2048** (2021) 012028 doi:10.1088/1742-6596/2048/1/012028

**References**

[1] A. Yamamoto, K. Tada, N. Sugimura, T. Ushio, M. Mori, Generation of Cross Section Library for Lattice Physics Code, AEGIS, PHYSOR-2006, Vancouver, BC, Canada, 10-14 Sept. 2006.
[2] A. Trkov, M. Herman, D.A. Brown, ENDF-6 Formats Manual, BNL-203218-2018-INRE, p. 1, Brookhaven National Laboratory, New York, 2018.
[3] D.W. Muir, R.M. Boicourt, A.C. Kahler, J.L. Conlin, W. Haeck, The NJOY Nuclear Data Processing System, Version 2016, LA-UR-17-20093, p. 1, p. 187-271, p. 451-489, p. 555-575, Los Alamos National Laboratory, New Mexico, 2019.
[4] D. Lopez Aldama, F. Leszczynski, A. Trkov, WIMS-D Library Update, p. 1, International Atomic Energy Agency, Vienna, 2007.
[5] A. Hébert, G. Marleau, R. Roy, A Description of the DRAGON and TRIVAC Version5 Data Structures, IGE-351, p. 142-145, École Polytechnique de Montréal, 2019.
[6] A. Hébert, PyNjoy-2012: A system for producing cross-section libraries for the DRAGON lattice code, ND2016: International Conference on Nuclear Data for Science and Technology, Bruges, Belgium, 11-16 Sep. 2016.
[7] H. Bei, J.K. Zhao, Q.C. Chen, S.Y. Si, Design and Processing of Multi-Group Cross Section Library for SONG, Nuclear Power Engineering, v35, p. 173, 2014.
[8] R.E. MacFarlane, TRANSX 2: A Code for Interfacing MATXS Cross-Section Libraries to Nuclear Transport Codes, LA-12312-MS, Los Alamos National Laboratory, New Mexico, 1992.
[9] D. She, Z.H. Liu, L. Shi, XPZ: Development of a lattice code for HTR, Annals of Nuclear Energy, v97, p. 183, 2016.
[10] S. Koranne, Hierarchical data format: 5 HDF5, In: Handbook of Open Source Tools, p. 191–200, Springer, New York, 2011.
[11] D. Knott, A. Yamamoto, Lattice Physics Computations, In: Handbook of Nuclear Engineering, p. 959-965, Springer, New York, 2010.
[12] A. Hébert, A. Santamarina. Refinement of the Santamarina-Hfaiedh Energy Mesh Between 22.5 eV and 11.4 keV, International Conference on Reactor Physics, Interlaken, Switzerland, 14-19 Sep. 2008.
[13] D.W. Muir, R.M. Boicourt, A.C. Kahler, J.L. Conlin, W. Haeck, The NJOY Nuclear Data Processing System, Version 2012, LA-UR-12-27079, p. 575-581, Los Alamos National Laboratory, New Mexico, 2017.
[14] A. Hébert, R. Chambon, A PYNJOY-2012 Tutorial, IGE-361, p. 1-13, École Polytechnique de Montréal, 2019.
[15] K. Kunitomi, Y. Sun, S. Ball, H.L. Brey, Evaluation of high temperature gas cooled reactor performance: Benchmark analysis related to initial testing of the HTTR and HTR-10, IAEA-TECDOC-1382, p. 234-235, International Atomic Energy Agency, Vienna, 2003.
[16] P.K. Romano, N.E. Horelik, B.R. Herman, A. G. Nelson, B. Forget, K. Smith, OpenMC: A state-of-the-art Monte Carlo code for research and development, Annals of Nuclear Energy, v82, p. 90, 2015.

# Impact of Different Nuclear Data Library on Control Rod Reactivity Worth Calculation of Small Pebble Bed Reactor

**Suwoto*, H Adrial, T Setiadipura, Zuhair, and S Bakhri**

Center for Nuclear Reactor Technology and Safety National Nuclear Energy Agency of Indonesia Kawasan Puspiptek Gd.80, Serpong, Tangerang Selatan, Banten, Indonesia
Phone:+62(21)7560912,

*Corresponding author: suwoto@batan.go.id

**Abstract.** One of the main critical issues on a nuclear reactor is safety and control system. The control rod worth plays an important role in the safety and control of nuclear reactors. The control rods worth calculation is used to specify the safety margin of the reactor. The main objective of this work is to investigate impact of different nuclear data libraries on calculating the control rod reactivity worth on small pebble bed reactor. Calculation of the control rod reactivity worth in small high temperature gas cooled reactor has been conducted using the Monte Carlo N-Particle 6 (MCNP6) code coupled with a different nuclear data library. Famous evaluated nuclear data libraries such as JENDL-40u, ENDF/B-VII.1 and JEFF-3.2 continuous cross section-energy data libraries were used. The overall calculation results of integral control rod worth show that the ENDF/B-VII.1, JENDL-40u and JEFF-3.2 files give values of -17.814%□k/k, -18.0204 %□k/k and -18.0267%□k/k, respectively. Calculations using ENDF/B-VII.1 give a slightly lower value than the others, while the JENDL-4.0u file gives results that are close to JEFF-3.2 file. The different nuclear data libraries have a relatively small impact on the control rod worth of small pebble bed reactor. Accurate prediction by simulation of control rod worth is very important for the safety operation of all reactor types, especially for new reactor designs.

**Keywords:** Control rod worth, pebble bed reactor, MCNP6, ENDF/B-VII.1, JENDL- 40u, JEFF-3.2

## 1. Introduction

One of the main critical issues on a nuclear reactor is safety and control system. In high temperature gas cooled reactor (HTGR) type small pebble bed reactor designs, only the reflector control rods are used for reactivity control [1]. The main purpose of a reactivity control system is to get the desired level of output power from the system, to maintain at the desired power level, and turn it off during routine reactor operation [2]. Neutron absorber rods are installed in most reactors to provide adjustable reactivity control. This absorber rod can be inserted or withdrawn from the reactor core [3].

The control rod has the maximum effect if it is placed in the reactor where the flux is maximum [2]. The exact amount of reactivity that is inserted per control rod depends on the design of the reactor. Changes in reactivity caused by control rod movements are referred to as control rod worth. Integral control rod worth is the total reactivity worth of the rod at a certain withdrawal level [3]. The differential control rod worth is the change in reactivity per unit of rod and is usually expressed as $\rho$/cm, and is measured by $\Delta k/k$ per cm, or pcm/cm.

However, sufficient calculation efforts using sophisticated methods such as the Monte Carlo method have not been conducted in this small pebble bed reactor, especially in calculating the control rod worth. In this report, the Monte Carlo calculation for control rod worth of a small pebble bed reactor core will be presented, because one of the main issues of a nuclear reactor is safety and control system.

The main objective of this work is to investigate impact of different nuclear data libraries on calculating the control rod reactivity worth on small pebble bed reactor. In this paper, the control rod reactivity worth (CRW) of small pebble bed reactor is presented. All calculations were performed using the Monte Carlo N-Particle MCNP6[4] code combined with a variety of different continuous energy cross- sections taken from the ENDF/B-VII.1[5], JENDL- 40u [6]and JEFF-3.2 [7] files.

## 2. Description of Small Pebble Bed Reactor

Indonesia through BATAN and its stakeholders have been carried out the design a small pebble bed reactor called *Reaktor Daya Eksperimental* (Experimental Power Reactor), one of the GEN-IV type reactors. This type of small modular variety will be very suitable for remote islands in Indonesia. The RDE reactor is designed to generate 10 MW thermal power and produce a core output temperature of around 700 °C and around 3 MWe of electricity. The Indonesian Experimental Power Reactor (RDE) [8,9] is a type of the fourth-generation reactor, a type of high temperature reactor cooled by helium. RDE refers to the design and technology of the German High Temperature Gas-cooled Reactor (HTR-Module) which is applied to HTR-10 in China and has inherent safety features [10]. RDE is designed using TRISO coated fuel particles [11] which are dispersed in a spherical fuel with a radius of 3 cm known as pebble. Theoretically, RDE reactor can use TRISO- coated fuel particles with kernels containing uranium dioxide as well as thorium [12] dioxide without changing the shape and size of the reactor geometry [9]. The fuel and core design parameters of small pebble bed reactor are displayed in Table 1.

**Table 1.** Core and fuel data parameter of small pebble bed reactor (RDE) [9,13]

| Reactor Core Parameter | Value |
|---|---|
| Thermal Reactor Power, MW | 10 |
| Equivalent Core Radius, cm | 90 |
| Equivalent Core Height, cm | 197 |
| Reactor Core Volume, cm3 | 5 |
| Volumetric filling fraction of balls in the core, % | 61 |
| Height of the empty cavity above the pebble bed, cm | 41.7 |
| Radius of fuel discharging tube, cm | 25 |
| TRISO Coated Fuel Particle (CFP) | |
| Fuel kernel material | $UO_2$ |
| Kernel diameter, cm | 0.05 |
| Enrichment of U-235, % | 17 |
| Kernel density, $g/cm^3$ | 10.4 |
| Coating layer material from inside | C/IPyC/SiC/OPyC |
| Coating layer thickness, cm | 0.095/0.040/0.035/0.04 |
| Coating layer density ($g/cm^3$) | 1.1/1.90/1.38/1.90 |
| Spherical Fuel Pebble | |
| Diameter of fuel pebble, cm | 6 |
| Diameter of fuel zone, cm | 5 |
| Thickness of graphite outer shell | 0.5 |
| Heavy metal (uranium) loading (weight) per ball, g | 5 |
| Density of graphite in matrix and outer shell, $g/cm^3$ | 1.73 |

*2.1 Design and Modeling of Control Rod*

One of the main safety components of RDE is the control rod. Ten control rods function to control the fission reaction in the reactor, where each control rod consists of five boron carbide ring segments [14]. Each control rod is located 102.5 cm from the center and placed on the side of the reflector. The inner and outer diameter of the ring is 6 cm and 12 cm. The reactor is designed with a high level of safety.

The RDE reactor has ten control rods located in ten channels on the side of the reflector in a vertical position and uniformly distributed encircling the reactor core. This control rod system is designed to work at high temperatures, high radiation and in the helium environment. Control rod material made from Boron Carbide ($B_4C$) with a density of 1.7 g/cc composed of Carbon 20 %w, B-10 15.84 %w and B- 11 64.16 %w is used as neutron absorber [15].

**Table 2.** Main data of detail geometry and material specification of control rod [14-16]

| | |
|---|---|
| Number of Control Rod (identically) | 10 |
| Length of control rod, cm | 275 |
| Radial position of channel center, cm | 102.1 |
| Control Rod channel diameter, cm | 13 |
| Neutron absorber material | $B_4C$ |
| Density of Boron Carbide ($B_4C$), g/cm3 | 1.7 |
| Helium Channel radius, mm | 27.5 |
| ID ring Boron Carbide ($B_4C$), cm | 6.0 |
| OD ring Boron Carbide ($B_4C$), cm | 10.5 |
| Number of segments $B_4C$ | 5 |
| Length of each segment $B_4C$, cm | 48.7 |
| length of each joint, cm | 3.6 |
| length of lower and upper metallic end, cm | 4.5/2.3 |
| Density of steel sleeve (SS), g/cm3 | 7.9 |
| ID/OD inner part of steel sleeves, cm | 5.5/5.9 |
| ID/OD outer part of steel sleeves, cm | 10.6/11 |
| Thickness of steel sleeve, cm | 0.02 |
| Gap between steel sleeve and $B_4C$, cm | 0.05% |
| Radial zone/thickness, (from center), mm | He/27.5; SS/2; Gap/0.5; $B_4C$/22.5; Gap/0.5; SS/2 |
| Axial coordinate of CR lower end → CR fully inserted, cm | 394.2 |
| Axial coordinate of CR lower end → CR fully withdrawn | 119.2 |
| Chemical composition of steel sleeve SS (%wo) | see below |

Chemical composition of steel sleeve SS (%wo):

| element composition | weight composition of Steel Sleeve (%w) |
|---|---|
| Cr | 18 |
| Fe | 68.1 |
| Ni | 10 |
| Si | 1 |
| Mn | 2 |
| C | 0.1 |
| Ti | 0.8 |

Each control rod has five B4C ring segments which are housed in the area between an inner and outer sleeve of stainless steel. The steel sleeves housing the neutron absorber material ($B_4C$) are assumed to have a density of 7.9 g/cc. The isotopes composition of steel sleeves are Cr-18%w, Fe-68.1%w, Ni-10%w, Si-1%w, Mn-2%w, C-0.1%w, and Ti-0.8%w. These are then connected together by a metallic joint [15].

The inner and outer diameters of the $B_4C$ ring are 6.0 cm and 10.5 cm, respectively, while the length of each ring segment is 48.7 cm. The inner/outer diameters of the inner part steel sleeves are 5.5 cm/5.9 cm and of the outer part of steel sleeve are 10.6 cm/11.0 cm. The length of each joint is 3.6 cm. The length of lower and upper metallic end are 4.5 cm and 2.3 cm, respectively [16].

Detailed geometry and specification data of control rod are presented in Figure 1 and Table 2. Figure 1 illustrates the schematic geometry of the RDE control rod. The geometry of the complexity control rod is modeled in detail and explicitly by special treatment in Figure 2.

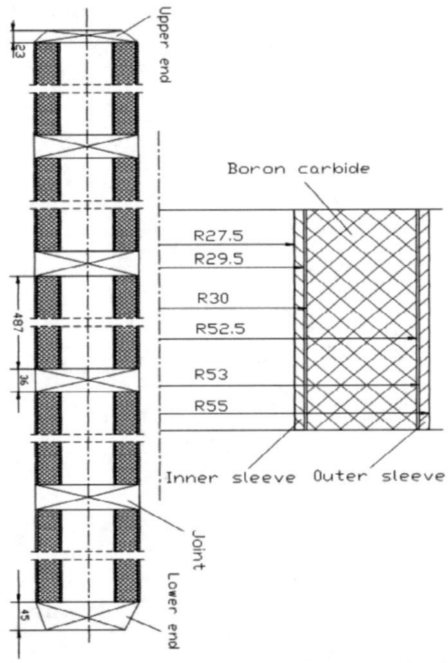


**Figure 1.** Schematic geometry of RDE control rod [15],

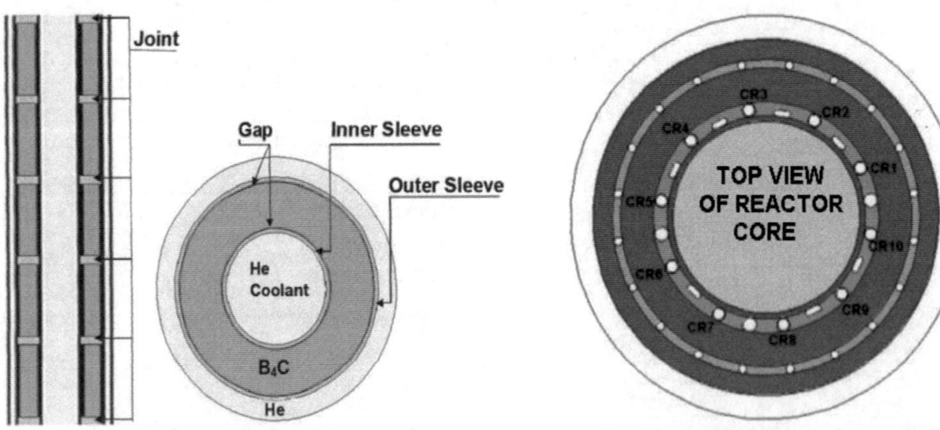


a. Control rod modeling b. Placement of 10 control rods

**Figure 2.** Modeling and placement location of control rod using MCNP6 code

## 3. Calculation Methodology

The calculation of control rod reactivity worth of a small pebble bed reactor performed using the Monte Carlo transport code MCNP6 coupled with several continuous energy nuclear data libraries such as ENDF/B-VII.1, JENDL-4.0u and JEFF-3.2 files. The MCNP6 code provides detailed description capabilities of geometrical elements and a very precise representation of the continuous energy nuclear data cross-sections. Whereas other code (diffusion code) that uses a geometry approach and uses a multi-group cross section library.

MCNP6 is capable of solving the double heterogeneity problem [17,18]. The double heterogeneity model in MCNP6 is built into regular TRISO particles in the pebble fuel and pebble arrangement in the core. The first step is to calculate the total reactivity of the control rod (control rod worth) using all the control rods inserted into the core and the second step is all the control rods withdrawn by the core to calculate the excess reactivity. All calculations use some original nuclear data taken from ENDF/B-VII.1, JENDL-4.0u and JEFF-3.2 files, and the next calculation is using substitution some nuclides such as Boron, Carbon, Oxygen and Uranium in the ENDF/VII.1 file as reference nuclear data library.

### *3.1. Reactivity coefficients*

Core reactivity is the most global parameter that helps to understand the behavior of all types of nuclear reactor. The precise calculation of core reactivity is a major concern of neutron physicists and engineers and the branch of physics that deals with it must be well understood. Defining it is not as easy as it seems at first.

The amount of reactivity (q) in the reactor core determines the manner of neutron population. This term is defined as [19-20]

$$a = \frac{k_{eff} - 1}{k_{eff}} \tag{1}$$

where $k_{eff}$ is effective reactor multiplication factor. The reactivity is affected by many factors such as fuel depletion, temperature, or neutron poisons.

### *3.2. Control Rod Worth*

The control rod worth is calculated using the excess reactivity (□ex) of the core configuration. The core excess reactivity is calculated according to the global multiplication factor with all control rods withdrawn completely from the core, this is expressed in equation (1)[19].

$$q_{es} = \frac{k_{eff-CRout} - 1}{k_{eff-CRout}} \tag{2}$$

Whereas CRW (Control Rod Worth) is calculated using the following formula [3,20-21]:

$$CRW = q_{es} - \frac{k_{eff-CRin} - 1}{k_{eff-CRin}} (in \frac{0_k}{k}) \tag{3}$$

Or simply equation (3) becomes:

$$CRW = q_{es} - \frac{k_{eff-CRout} - k_{eff-CRin}}{k_{eff-CRout} \times k_{eff-CRin}} (in \frac{0_k}{k}) \tag{4}$$

where:
$k_{eff-CRout}$ = reactivity of the core with all control rods fully withdrawn from the core
$k_{eff-CRin}$ = reactivity of the core with all control rods fully inserted in the core

When a control rod is inserted into a reactor core, it absorbs the surrounding neutrons and results in distortion of the neutron flux distribution. The effect of absorber control rod can be explained by considering a reactor in which the maximum neutron flux is maintained constant, with or without insertion of control rod, as illustrated in Figure 3.

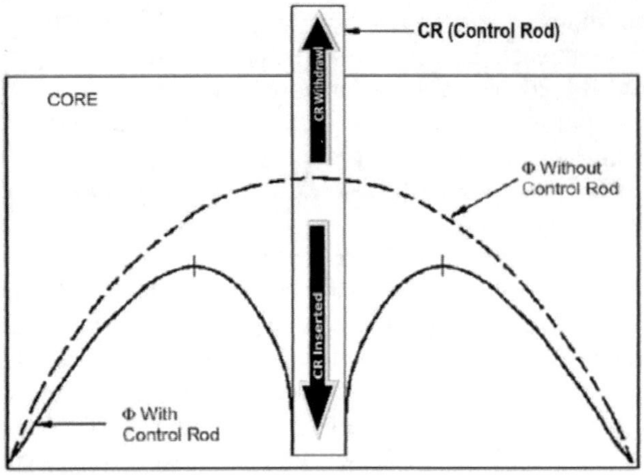


**Figure 3.** Illustration of control rod insertion effect on radial neutron flux distribution [3].

## 4. Result and Discussions

In order to ensure reactivity control in reactor core operations, a full understanding of neutron physics needed. Achieving a full understanding of the complex physical mechanisms that occur in nuclear power reactor ensures good design and safe operation.

The control rod worth results calculated by MCNP6 combined with several different continuous energy nuclear data file such as ENDF/B-VII.1, JENDL-4.0u and JEFF-3.2 files for fresh core are presented in Table 3. All calculations run on MCNP6 code using 210 cycles including 10 cycles skipped of 5000 particles per cycle to obtain convergent results. The curve calculated from the integral control rod worth (CRW) of small pebble bed reactor (RDE) is particularly important in reactor operation as shown in Figure 4. In Figure 4, this phenomenon shows the reactivity change caused by moving the control rod with the unit distance at a certain height. when the control rod is inserted from the initial reference position to a certain height, the reactivity introduced in the process same as the control rod integral worth at the insertion height.

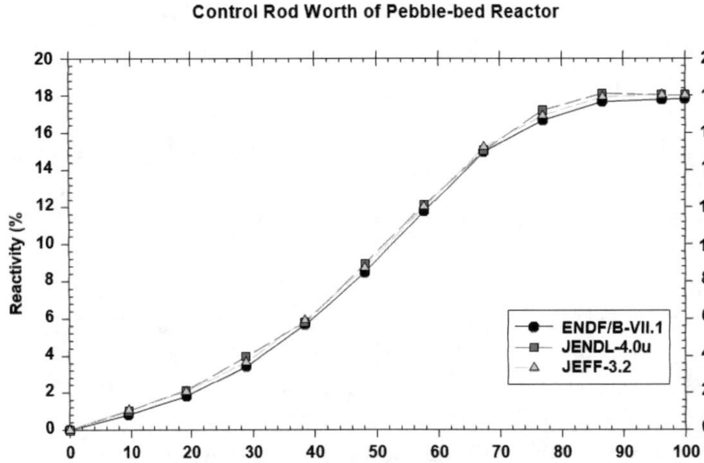


**Figure 4.** Calculated curve of Control Rod Worth of small pebble bed reactor (RDE)

The calculation results shown in Table 3 use original data according to each of the mentioned nuclear data files. the results of all CRW calculations give relatively the same results, the ENDF / B-VII.1 file although the CRW value is slightly lower compared to JENDL-4.0u file which is close to JEFF- 3.2 file.

**Table 3.** The global calculated value of effective multiplication factor and CRW from original nuclear data file

| Nuclear Data File Library | $K_{eff\text{-}CRout}$ | $K_{eff\text{-}CRout}$ | ρ (%Δk/k) | CRW (%Δk/k) |
|---|---|---|---|---|
| ENDF/BVII.1 | 1.11678 ± 0.00084 | 0.93147 ± 0.00098 | 10.4568 | 17.8140373 |
| JENDL-4.0u | 1.11679 ± 0.00079 | 0.92969 ± 0.00092 | 10.4577 | 18.0203869 |
| JEFF-3.2 | 1.11993 ± 0.00080 | 0.93181 ± 0.00088 | 10.7087 | 18.0267205 |

Meanwhile in Table 4 and Table 5, the results are calculated using the nuclide substitution for U-235, U-238 and O-16 taken from JENDL-4.0u and JEFF-3.2 files, while the rest of the nuclides are taken from ENDF/ B-VII.1 file.

Table 4 shows the calculation results of the criticality and CRW values with the nuclide substitution in which the ENDF/B-VII.1 file is retained, while the JENDL-4.0u and JEFF-3.2 files are replaced for kernel fuel nuclides ($UO_2$) such as Uranium (U-235, U-238) and Oxygen (O-16) and other nuclides are taken from the ENDF/B-VII.1 file.

The differences in *K*eff value to the ENDF/B-VII.1 standard reference file is 0.073-0.102% and 0.0306- 0.260% for the JENDL-4.0u and JEFF-3.2 files, respectively.

**Table 4.** The effect of nuclide substitution of $UO_2$ (kernel) on *K*eff and CRW

| Nuclear Data File Library | $K_{eff\text{-}CRout}$ | $K_{eff\text{-}CRin}$ | ρ (%Δk/k) | CRW (%Δk/k) |
|---|---|---|---|---|
| ENDF/BVII.1 | 1.11678 ± 0.00084 | 0.93147 ± 0.00098 | 10.4568 | 17.8140373 |
| JENDL-4.0u | 1.11564 ± 0.00084 | 0.93079 ± 0.00090 | 10.4577 | 17.800970 |
| JEFF-3.2 | 1.11636 ± 0.00087 | 0.92904 ± 0.00086 | 10.7087 | 18.0611529 |

Note: # only nuclides U-235, U-238 and O-16 taken from JENDL-4.0u,
$ only nuclides U-235, U-238 and O-16 taken from JEFF-3.2

The fission cross-section of U-238 in the neutron energy region up to 1.9E4eV is no difference for JENDL-4.0u and 79.79% higher for JEFF-3.2 files, respectively, when compared to U-238 in ENDF /B-VII.1 file, as seen in Figure 5. Meanwhile, for the capture cross-sections there are relatively no significant difference between the three libraries on that neutron energy range.

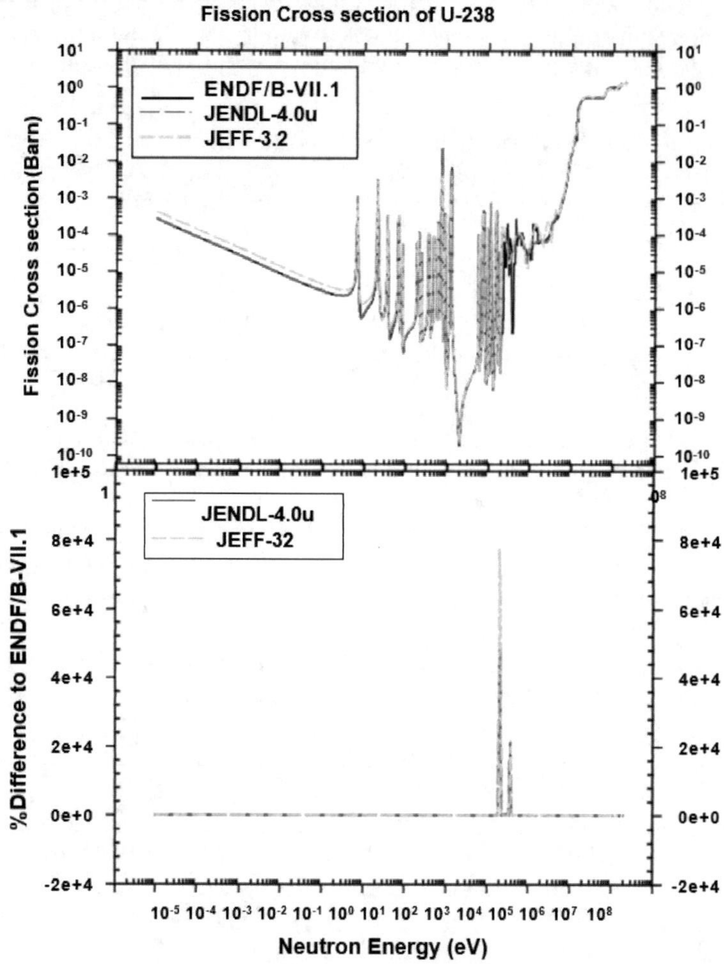


**Figure 5.** Fission cross-section of U-238 and their % difference to ENDF/B-VII.1.

For the fission cross-sections of U-235 in the thermal neutron energy region up to the resonance energy region, there are no significant differences between another nuclear data libraries, while differences begin to occur in energy regions above 475eV, as seen on Figure 6. The difference respect to ENDF / B-VII.1 file is -9.6% to 14.75% and -6.7% to 12.85% for JENDL-4.0u and JEFF-3.2 files, respectively.

As for the elastic cross-section of O-16 in the thermal neutron energy region is lower by 58.6% for JENDL-4.0u and JEFF-3.2 files, respectively, when compared to the ENDF/B-VII.1 standard reference file, while for other neutron energy regions each about 83% lower.

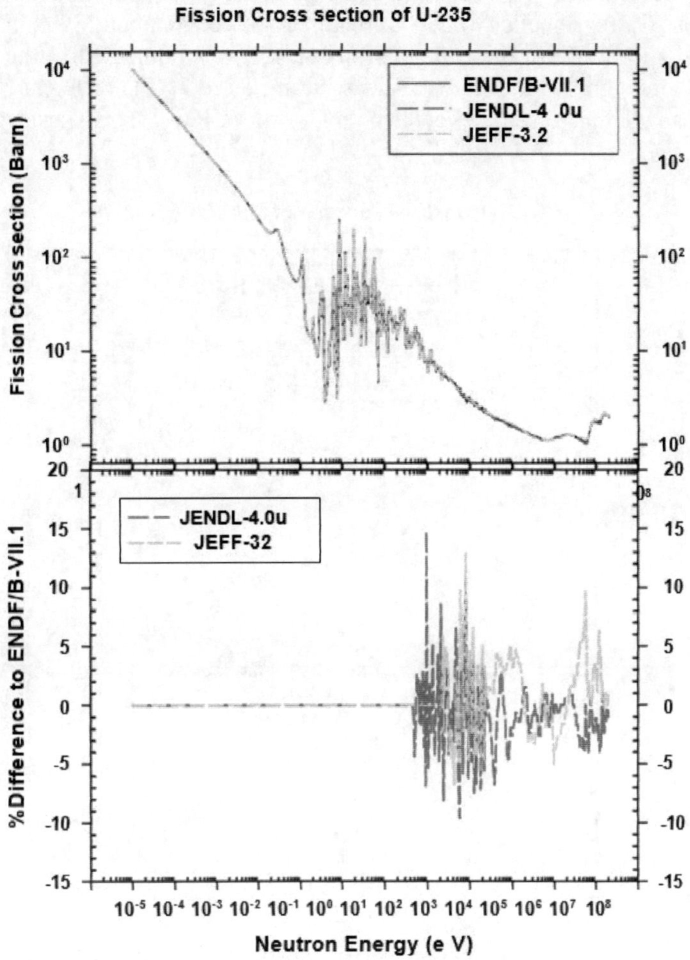


**Figure 6.** Fission cross-section of U-235 and their % difference to ENDF/B-VII.1.

So, from the above explanation can illustrate the results of calculating the value of the effective multiplication factor with the ENDF/B-VII.1 standard reference file slightly higher than the JENDL-40u and JEFF-3.2 files as listed in Table 4. Differences in nuclear data library have little impact on the control rod worth (CRW) are shown around - 0.07% to 1.39% differences.

Table 5 shows the results of the criticality and CRW calculations with nuclear data substitution, ENDF/B-VII.1 is maintained, while JENDL-4.0u and JEFF-3.2 are substituted for Carbon and Boron nuclides (B-10, B-11), and the remaining nuclides from the ENDF/B-VII.1 standard reference file.

**Table 5.** The effect of nuclides substitution of Carbon and Boron on *K*eff and CRW

| Nuclear Data File Library | $K_{eff\text{-}CRout}$ | $K_{eff\text{-}CRin}$ | ρ (%Δk/k) | CRW (%Δk/k) |
|---|---|---|---|---|
| ENDF/BVII.1 | 1.11678±0.00084 | 0.93147±0.00098 | 10.4568 | 17.8140373 |
| JENDL-4.0u | 1.11465±0.00090 | 0.92824±0.00085 | 10.4577 | 16.86827744 |
| JEFF-3.2 | 1.11885±0.00089 | 0.93202±0.00097 | 10.7087 | 17.91634908 |

Note: # only nuclides U-235, U-238 and O-16 taken from JENDL-4.0u,
$ only nuclides U-235, U-238 and O-16 taken from JEFF-3.2

Journal of Physics: Conference Series **2048** (2021) 012029 doi:10.1088/1742-6596/2048/1/012029

The change in CRW values in Table 5 that occurred in the JENDL-4.0u file is caused by the elastic cross section of the Carbon nuclide which is relatively lower by about 30% in the thermal energy region and increases to 326% in the energy of about 425 keV compared to the ENDF/B-VII.1 and JEFF-3.2 files without significant differences as seen in Figure 7. The different nuclear data libraries have a relatively small impact on the control rod worth (CRW) shown around -5.31% to 0.57% differences.

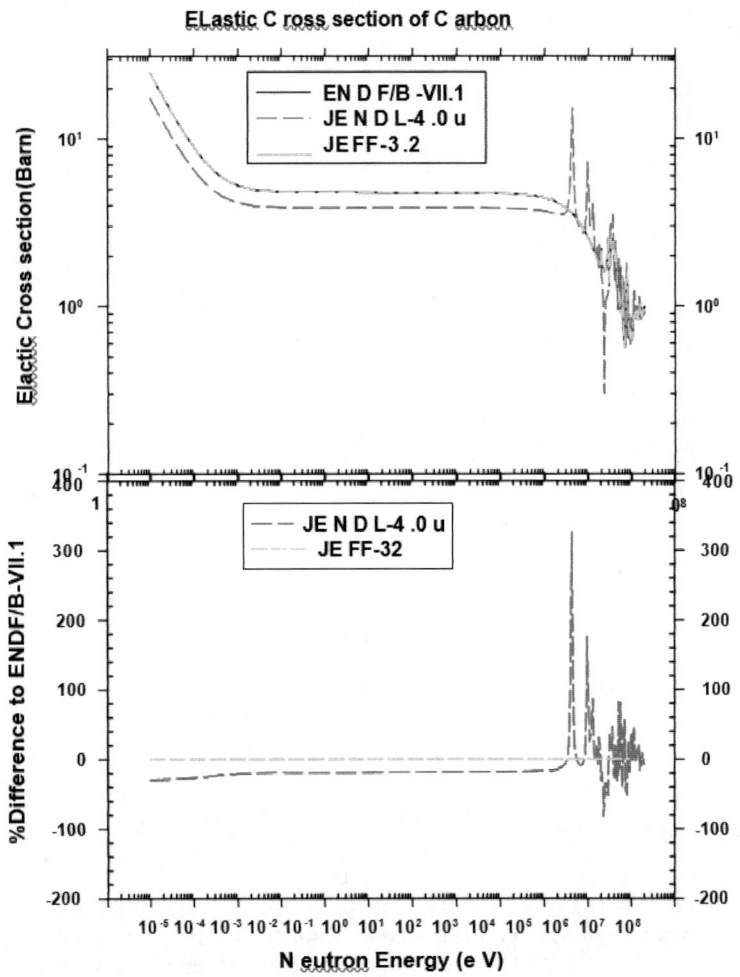


**Figure 7.** Elastic cross-section of Carbon (C-0).

The differences in *K*eff value to ENDF/B-VII.1 is 0.073-0.102% and 0.0306-0.260% for the JENDL-u and JEFF-3.2 files, respectively. So that the impact of different nuclear data libraries has little effect on differences in the calculation of the control rod worth (CRW).

So, from the above explanation it appears that the quality of the cross-section data library affects the calculation results obtained. Therefore, because the difference in the value of CRM is very small (around 1% dΔk/k) so shrewdness in selecting the right nuclear data library is needed in these calculations.

## 5. Conclusion

Accurate prediction of control rod worth is very important for the safety operation of all nuclear reactors. Investigation on the impact of different evaluated nuclear data libraries on the reactivity of control rod worth calculation on small pebble reactor has been performed. The results of the overall calculation of the integral control rod worth show that the file ENDF/B-VII.1, JENDL-40u and JEFF-3.2 give values of -17,814%dk/k, -18.0204%dk/k and - 18.0267%dk/k, respectively. The calculation results show that different nuclear data libraries have a relatively small impact on the control rod worth (CRW) on small pebble bed reactor. This result implies that some differences on result calculation caused by some cross-sections that used in CR material especially in carbon and boron nuclides.

**Acknowledgment**

We would like to express our great appreciation to KPTF-PTKRN, especially Dr. M. Hadi Kusuma for the review and improvement of this paper. The work presented in this paper was funded by the Indonesian Government through DIPA from the Center for Nuclear Reactor Technology and Safety, National Nuclear Energy Agency of Indonesia (BATAN) FY 2021.

## References

[1] W. Yuanqiang et al. 2002. Design and tests for the HTR-10 control rod system. Nuclear Engineering and Design 218 (2002) 147–154

[2] J. Shaw. 1969. Reactor Operation. Pergamon Press. Ltd., Headington Hill Hall, Oxford, First edition 1969

[3] Mohammad Rahgoshaya, OmidNoori- Kalkhoran, 2013., Calculation of control rod worth and temperature reactivity coefficient of fuel and coolant with burn-up changes for VVRS- 2 MWth nuclear reactor, Nuclear Engineering and Design. 256 (2013) 322– 331.

[4] T. Goorley et al. 2012., "Initial MCNP6 Release Overview". Journal of Nuclear Technology Volume 180, 2012.

[5] M.B. Chadwick, M. Herman, P. Oblozinský, M.E. Dunn, Y. Danon, A.C. Kahler, D.L. Smith, B. Pritychenko, G. Arbanas, R. Arcilla, R. Brewer, D.A. Brown, R. Capote, A.D. Carlson,Y.S. Cho, H. Derrien, K. Guber, G.M. Hale, S. Hoblit, S. Holloway, T.D. Johnson, T. Kawano, B.C. Kiedrowski, H. Kim, S. Kunieda, N.M. Larson, L. Leal, J.P. Lestone, R.C. Little, E.A. McCutchan, R.E. MacFarlane, M. MacInnes, C.M. Mattoon, R.D. McKnight, S.F. Mughabghab, G.P.A. Nobre, G. Palmiotti, A. Palumbo, M.T. Pigni, V.G. Pronyaev, R.O. Sayer, A.A. Sonzogni, N.C. Summers, P. Talou, I.J. Thompson, A. Trkov, R.L. Vogt, S.C. van der Marck, A. Wallner, M.C. White, D. Wiarda, P.G. Young. 2011., "ENDF/B-VII.1 Nuclear Data for Science and Technology: Cross Sections, Covariances, Fission Product Yields and Decay Data",Nucl. Data Sheets, 112, 2887-2996 (2011).

[6] K. Shibata, O. Iwamoto, T. Nakagawa, N. Iwamoto, A. Ichihara, S. Kunieda, S. Chiba, K. Furutaka, N. Otuka, T. Ohsawa, T. Murata, H. Matsunobu, A. Zukeran, S. Kamada, and J.Katakura. 2011., "JENDL-4.0: A New Library for Nuclear Science and Engineering",.J. Nucl. Sci. Technol., 48, 1 (2011).

[7] OECD/NEA Data Bank. 2014., "JEFF-3.2 Evaluated Data Library - Neutron Data". (2014)

[8] Topan Setiadipura, Syaiful Bakhri, Geni R. Sunaryo, Djarot S. Wisnusubroto, 2018., "Cooling Passive Safety Features of Reaktor Daya Eksperimental", AIP Conference Proceedings 1984, 020034. doi: https://doi.org/10.1063/1.5046618

[9] Suwoto, H Adrial, Zuhair, K Kamajaya, S Bakhri, 2019., "Analysis of Heavy Metal Loading Optimization Through Criticality Calculation on RDE", 2019. IOP Conf. Series. Journal of Physics: Conference Series. 1198 (2019) 022004.doi:10.1088/1742- 6596/1198/2/022004

[10] Ohashi H et al. 2014., "Concept on Inherent Safety in High-Temperature Gas-cooled Reactor". Transaction of the Atomic Energy Society of Japan 13(1), 17-26.

[11] Kania, M. J., Nabielek, H. and Nickel, H., 2015. "Coated Particle Fuels for High-Temperature

Reactors". Materials Science and Technology, doi: 10.1002/9783527603978.mst0449, p.1–183.

[12] Allelein H.J., Kania M. J., Nabielek H. and Verfondern K. 2014. "Thorium Fuel Performance Assessment in HTRs", Nuclear Engineering and Design 271 2014 pp.166-170.

[13] Suwoto, H. Adrial, W. Luthfi, T. Setiadipura, Zuhair. 2019. "Effect of Boron Impurity and Graphite Thermal Neutron Scattering on Criticality Calculation of Indonesian Experimental Power Reactor".AIP Conference Proceedings 2180, 020002 (2019); https://doi.org/10.1063/1.5135511

[14] Zuhair, Suwoto, Yazid PI and Pane JS. 2016. "Studi Model Benchmark MCNP6 Dalam Perhitungan Reaktivitas Batang Kendali HTR- 10". GANENDRA Majalah IPTEK Nuklir 19 (2) 2016, pp. 95-103 doi: http://dx.doi.org/10.17146/ gnd.2016.19.2.2880

[15] IAEA-TECDOC-1382, 2003. "Evaluation of high temperature gas cooled reactor performance:Benchmark analysis related to initial testing of the HTTR and HTR-10", IAEA-2003.

[16] Zuhair, Suwoto, T. Setiadipura, J.C. Kuijper, 2019. "The effects of fuel type on control rod reactivity of pebble-bed reactor", NUKLEONIKA 2019;64(4):131□138, doi: 10.2478/nuka-2019-0017.

[17] Seker, V & Colak. 2003. HTR -10 Full Core First Critically Analysis with MCNP. Nuclear Engineering and Design, Volume 222, Issues 2– 3, 263-270.

[18] J.L. Lebenhaft. 2001. *MCNP4B Modeling of Pebble-bed Reactors*. (MIT: MSNE Thesis, Massachusetts Institute of Technology), 2001.

[19] Duderstadt, J.J., Hamilton, L.J., 1976. *"Nuclear Reactor Physics"*. John Wiley &Sons,Inc., USA.

[20] MaedehYari, Ahmad Lashkari, S. FarhadMasoudi, Mirshahram Hosseinipanah, 2018. "*Three dimensional analysis of temperature effect on control rod worth in TRR".* Nuclear Engineering and Technology 50 (2018) 1266-1276

[21] N Jakiyah, Suharyana, Riyatun, and Azizul Khakim. 2014. *The Dependency of Shutdown Margin Values of the HTR-10 on Packing Fraction Absorber*, AIP Conference Proceedings **2014**, 020045 (2018); https://doi.org/10.1063/1.5054449

# Neutronics for the GEMINI+ HTGR

**J C Kuijper[1] and D Muszynski[2]**

[1]NUCLIC-Nuclear Innovation Consultancy, Iepenlaan 129, NL-1741TD Schagen, The Netherlands
phone: +31-6-4022-9728, kuijper@nuclic.nl
[2]NCBJ, National Centre for Nuclear Research, Otwock/Swierk, Poland

**Abstract.** Literally at the heart of the Euratom Horizon 2020 project GEMINI+ are the core neutronics (design) calculations. For these calculations on a relatively small (180 MWth) prismatic HTGR with cylindrical core, the 3-D monte-carlo particle transport and depletion code SERPENT version 2 (VTT, Finland) was selected, the main reasons being the flexibility and versatility of this code. This enables the modelling of all relevant details of the reactor without unnecessary approximations. A particularly useful feature of the SERPENT code is the multi-physics input capability. This allows to map a temperature field over the defined geometry, enabling the calculation of converged power and temperature distribution by means of iteration and data exchange between SERPENT and a (steady-state) thermal- hydraulics code. In this particular case the SPECTRA code (NRG, The Netherlands) was used to provide the temperature distribution. 4 to 5 iterations are sufficient to reach simultaneously converged distributions for power and temperature. The paper gives an overview of the performed analyses for the current (June 2020) design of the GEMINI+ HTGR, and results thereof. Neutronics features seem quite promising, but further improvements and therefore further investigations would be desirable.

## 1. Introduction

The Euratom Horizon 2020 project GEMINI+ [1] is aiming at the (preliminary) design of a reactor system with a net power output of 165 MWth (gross thermal power of 180 MWth including house load), hereby maximising the convergence between European and NGNP Industry Alliance HTGR designs. The GEMINI+ system is currently designed to provide steam (230 t/h at 540 °C and 13.8 MPa) to industrial end users for use in electricity production and/or process heat. The current (June 2020) state of the design is described in [2].

The GEMINI+ reactor is a relatively small (180 MW thermal power) prismatic block type reactor HTGR. The reactor components (fuel blocks, reflector blocks, compacts, coated fuel particles) are very similar to those of existing designs (General Atomics GT-MHR and MHTGR [3,4], Framatome SC-HTGR [5]), although they are fully based on information available in the open literature.

In support of the design and (thermal hydraulic) safety analysis of the GEMINI+ HTGR, reactor (core) physics (neutronics) and depletion calculations have been performed on a limited number of design versions of this reactor [6]. Some of the results will be presented in this paper.

Main characteristics of the reactor (neutronics model) are listed in Table 1. An earlier design featured 10 layers of fuel blocks in the core and slightly different placement of control rod positions in core and (radial) reflector, in the sense that the blocks containing some of the control rod channels may have been rotated, compared to the current (June 2020) 11-layer design. This modification was necessary in view of limitations to the required penetrations of the pressure vessel head [2].

Currently a *single batch loading scheme* and an operation cycle of 550 full power days is assumed. This may be replaced later by a multi-batch (typically 2 or 3) loading scheme, to improve utilization of the fuel, i.e., to increase the burn-up at final discharge. Furthermore, a single value of the enrichment is assumed. From initial studies, an enrichment of 12% in $^{235}U$ seemed to be most practical for now.

**Table 1.** Main configuration characteristics of the SERPENT model of the GEMINI+ prismatic block HTGR.

| Parameter | Value | Unit |
|---|---|---|
| Reactor/core configuration | - | - |
| # Radial rings of fuel blocks (ring around centre column is first ring) | 3 | - |
| # Fuel block columns | 25 | - |
| # Control block columns | 6 | - |
| # Axial fuel/control block layers | 11 | - |
| Distance between side faces of adjacent blocks | 0.2 | cm |
| Core height | 800 / 880<br>10 layers / 11 layers of blocks | cm |
| # Replaceable reflector rings | 2 | - |
| # Replaceable reflector columns | 54 | - |
| Bottom reflector (with coolant holes) | - | - |
| Reflector material | NBG-17 graphite [7] | |
| Reflector thickness | 160 | cm |
| Top reflector (with coolant and control rod holes) | - | - |
| Reflector material | NBG-17 graphite [7] | - |
| Reflector thickness | 120 | cm |
| Core barrel | - | - |
| Core barrel inner radius | 199.1 | cm |
| Core barrel effective outer radius | 207.1 | cm |
| Core barrel material | Alloy 800H | - |
| Core barrel height (in SERPENT neutronics model) | 1080 / 1160<br>(10 / 11 layer core) | cm |
| Reactor Pressure Vessel | - | - |
| RPV inner radius | 234.1 | cm |
| RPV outer radius | 244.05 | cm |
| RPV material | Alloy SA508 | - |
| RPV height (in SERPENT neutronics model) | 1080 / 1160<br>(10 / 11 layer core) | cm |
| Fuel block configuration | - | - |
| Block height | 80 | cm |
| Hexagon flat-to-flat distance | 36 | cm |
| Block material | NBG-17 graphite [7] | - |
| Triangular pitch | 1.9 | cm |
| # channels with fuel compacts | 216 (w/o BP)<br>210 (with BP) | - |
| Compact channel diameter | 1.27 | cm |
| # small coolant channels | 6 | - |
| Small coolant channel diameter | 1.27 | cm |
| # large coolant channels | 102 | - |
| Large coolant channel diameter | 1.6 | cm |
| Control block configuration | - | - |
| Block height | 80 | cm |
| Hexagon flat-to-flat distance | 36 | cm |
| Block material | NBG-17 graphite [7] | - |
| Triangular pitch | 1.9 | cm |
| # channels with fuel compacts | 174 (w/o BP)<br>170 (with BP) | - |
| Compact channel diameter | 1.27 | cm |
| # small coolant channels | 5 | - |
| Small coolant channel diameter | 1.27 | cm |
| # large coolant channels | 102 | - |
| Large coolant channel diameter | 1.6 | cm |
| Control rod channel diameter | 13 | cm |

N.B. The (effective) inner and outer diameter of the core barrel and the pressure vessel as stated here may slightly deviate from what is stated in [2]. This, however, does not influence the neutronic characteristics of the *core*.

Journal of Physics: Conference Series **2048** (2021) 012030 doi:10.1088/1742-6596/2048/1/012030

**Table 1 (cont.).** Main configuration characteristics of the SERPENT model of the GEMINI+ prismatic block HTGR.

| **Parameter** | **Value** | **Unit** |
|---|---|---|
| Control rod configuration (model - simplified) | - | - |
| # core rods | 6 | - |
| # reflector rods | 18 | - |
| Rod geometry | Annular | - |
| Rod length | 800 / 880 (10 layer core / 11 layer core) | cm |
| Inner radius | 3.75 | cm |
| Outer radius | 5.25 | cm |
| Absorber material | $B_4C$ | - |
| Absorber material density | 2.52 | $g/cm^3$ |
| Fuel compact configuration | - | - |
| Matrix material | C | - |
| Matrix material density | 1.75 | $g/cm^3$ |
| # coated particles per compact | 2500 *) | - |
| Compact cylinder height | 5.0 | cm |
| Compact cylinder radius | 0.625 | cm |
| Coated particle configuration | - | - |
| Kernel diameter | 500 | micron |
| Kernel material | $UO_2$ | - |
| Kernel density | 10.4 | $g/cm^3$ |
| Buffer layer thickness | 95 | micron |
| Buffer layer material | C | - |
| Buffer layer density | 1.05 | $g/cm^3$ |
| Inner PyC layer thickness | 40 | micron |
| Inner PyC material | C | - |
| Inner PyC density | 1.90 | $g/cm^3$ |
| SiC layer thickness | 35 | micron |
| SiC material | SiC | - |
| SiC density | 3.18 | $g/cm^3$ |
| Outer PyC layer thickness | 40 | micron |
| Outer PyC material | C | - |
| Outer PyC density | 1.90 | $g/cm^3$ |
| Burnable poison (BP) configuration (see Figs. 3 and 4 for locations of the burnable poison cylinders in the fuel blocks). | | |
| Height | 75.0 | cm |
| Outer radius of annular graphite cylinder | 0.625 | cm |
| Material of annular cylinder | C | - |
| Density of annular cylinder | 1.75 | $g/cm^3$ |
| Burnable poison (BP) material mixture | $B_4C$ in graphite | - |
| Fraction $f_{BP}$ of $B_4C$ in graphite | 0.0 - 1.0*) | - |
| Density of $B_4C$ in mixture | 2.52 | $g/cm^3$ |
| Density of C in mixture | 1.75 | |
| Outer radius $R_{BP}$ of BP material mixture | 0.2 - 0.525*) | cm |
| Subdivision of BP material for accurate depletion calculation - # concentric rings of equal volume | 10 | - |
| $^{10}B$ content of boron in BP | 20 (natural boron) | % |

*) The number of coated particles per compact, as well as the fuel enrichment and the parameters of the burnable poison cylinders have been/are being varied in the neutronics studies, in order to arrive at an acceptable / optimised configuration (ongoing in December 2020/January 2021).

Journal of Physics: Conference Series **2048** (2021) 012030 doi:10.1088/1742-6596/2048/1/012030

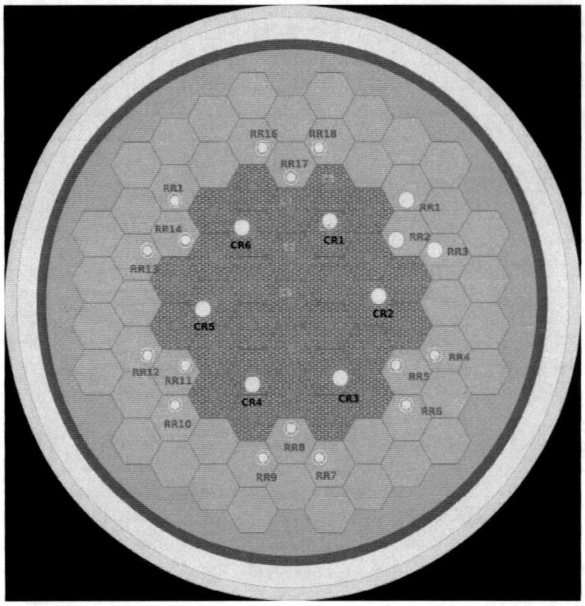


**Figure 1.** Horizonal cross section (z = 1000 cm plane; near the top of the core) of the SERPENT neutronics model for the current (June 2020) version of the GEMINI+ reactor. Control rod identifiers are given. The outer (light grey) section is the pressure vessel. Dimensions are given in Table 1. Also indicated (in green) are 5 representative (due to symmetry; for C4 this is not exact, but in rather good approximation) core columns (C1 - C5).

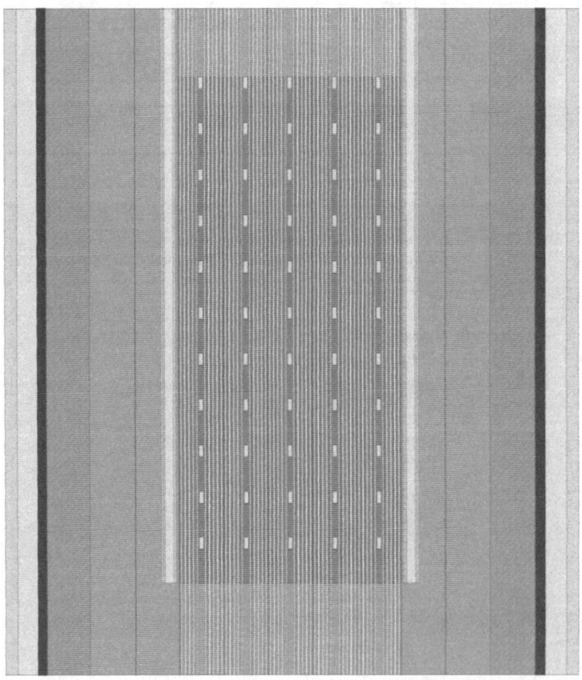

**Figure 2.** Vertical cross section (x = 0 cm plane) of the SERPENT neutronics model for the current (June 2020) version of the GEMINI+ reactor (11 layers of fuel blocks in the core). Note that the visible reflector control rods (RR8 and RR17, in green) have been fully inserted in this case. Further note that the aspect ratio shown in the drawing is not entirely realistic. Actual dimensions are given in Table 1.

## 2. The SERPENT Code

The main code employed for the core neutronics calculations is SERPENT version 2.1.31 in combination with JEFF 3.1.1 nuclear data [8]. SERPENT is a continuous energy monte carlo neutron (and photon) transport code, capable of modelling arbitrary geometry. The later includes the modelling of explicit coated particles in compacts. Integrated into the code is a detailed burn-up/depletion calculation method, featuring a semi-automatic subdivision to distinguish between cells that may initially contain the same material, but deviate during depletion due to differences in local flux (and -spectrum). Further features used in the GEMINI+ neutronics calculations are the following:

- Generation and use of explicit random particle distributions.
- Multiphysics input option.

### *2.1. Explicit coated particle modelling*

SERPENT (versions 2.1.x) has the capability to generate random spatial distributions of spheres, e.g., in a cylinder. This was used to generate the random particle positions in a stack of 15 compacts in a fuel block, e.g., 15 x 2500 = 37500 coated particles per 15 compacts. Strictly speaking, a random distribution should be generated for a single (5 cm high) compact (no coated particles crossing the outer boundary of the compact), of which 15 should be put in a stack subsequently. However, the difference in $k_{eff}$ between these two approaches is only a few pcm, so it was decided to use the simpler approach in further analyses, as described above. All compact channels of all fuel blocks are subsequently filled with the same distribution of coated particles in matrix material.

### *2.2. Multiphysics input*

SERPENT has a "multi-physics" input option. This has been used to assign different temperature to different materials in different locations in the model, without the necessity to assign different material names to materials at different temperatures. This feature has been used to import the (steady state) temperature distributions for different materials (fuel kernel, coatings, matrix material of the compacts, block graphite, etc.) as calculated by the thermal hydraulics code SPECTRA for the corresponding thermal hydraulics model [2,8,9,10].

### *2.3. Statistical uncertainties*

As SERPENT uses the (continuous energy) monte carlo method to simulate neutron (and photon) transport, all results come with a statistical uncertainty that is dependent on the number of neutrons per calculation cycles and the number of cycles per calculation for a single point in time. (Most of) the monte carlo calculations were performed using a neutron population of 100000 ("fine" mode) or 400000 ("extra fine" mode), 1000 cycles with 20 or 100 inactive cycles, using around 350 cores, and a hybrid MPI/OpenMP parallelization.

## 3. The SERPENT Neutronics Model

The current (June 2020) neutronics model with 11 layers of fuel blocks in the core is shown in Fig. 1 (horizontal cross section) and Fig. 2 (vertical cross section). Also indicated are the identifiers of the control rods in the core ("CRx") and radial reflector ("RR[x]x"), and 5 "representative" fuel columns ("C1" to "C5"). The neutronics model has been restricted to those elements that are of influence on the neutronics behaviour. Therefore, the upper and lower part of the pressure vessel (including the components within those sections) have not been included. Further information on materials and dimensions of the neutronics model is given in Table 1.

Details of the fuel blocks with and without a control rod channel is shown in Figs. 3 and 4. Note that 6 out of 216 and 4 out of 174 compact channels have been replaced by burnable poison cylinders (see below for further explanation).

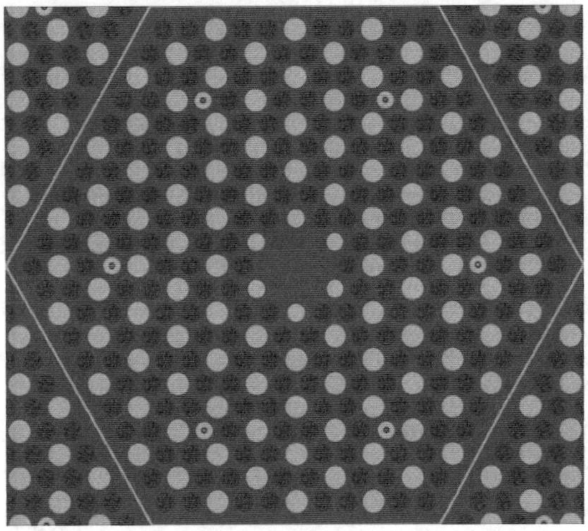

**Figure 3.** Full fuel block without control rod channel. 6 compact stacks have been replaced by burnable poison cylinders.

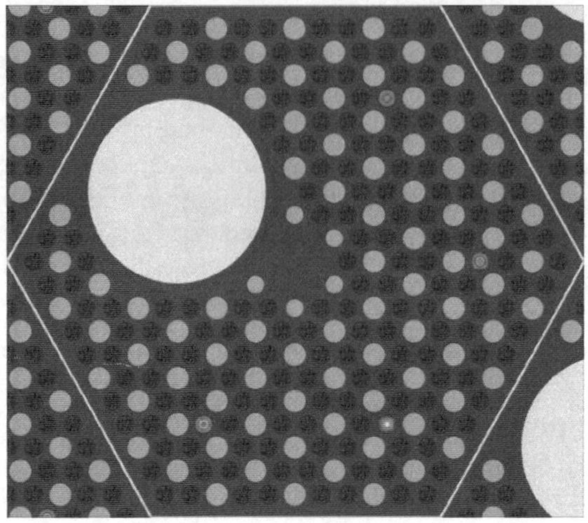

**Figure 4.** Fuel block with control rod channel. 4 compact stacks have been replaced by burnable poison cylinders.

The initial version of the reactor featured 10 layers of fuel blocks in the core, with 25 full fuel blocks and 6 fuel blocks with a control rod channel per layer. No burnable poison (BP) was used in this version, which, however, exhibited a too high (> 1600 °C) maximum fuel temperature in a Depressurised Loss of Forced Cooling (DLOFC) accident [11]. Therefore, an extra layer of fuel blocks was added in order to lower the (average) power density, increasing the total height of the core, radial reflectors, core barrel and pressure vessel by 80.0 cm [12]. This promises a great improvement (i.e., much lower) in maximum fuel temperature during DLOFC, as was indicated by transient thermal-hydraulic calculations assuming a uniform power distribution [13]. A further assumption in this DLOFC simulation was a "radially flat" power profile.

In addition, burnable poison ($B_4C$ in graphite) was introduced, as indicated in Figs. 3 and 4, for two purposes:

- To tailor the history of the (uncontrolled) $k_{eff}$ from Beginning-of-Life (BOL; start of operation; $^{135}$Xe-free) to End-of-Life (EOL; 550 full power days; equilibrium $^{135}$Xe and $^{149}$Sm). The main purpose of this is to ensure that the uncontrolled $k_{eff}$ (i.e., the value for all rods out) is within the range that can actually be compensated by the control/shutdown rods in the reflector and the core, for all operational states of the reactor. See Sections V and VI.
- To improve the (radial) power distribution over the core, as additional measure in response to the too high maximum fuel temperature in the earlier design version with 10 layers of fuel blocks in the core, without BP.

Efforts for the 2nd point are currently (August/September 2020) ongoing and have not yet been fully finalised. The aim is to flatten the (radial) power distribution (as this was the assumption in the DLOFC calculations that showed favourable characteristics with respect to peak fuel temperature [13]), or even to shift the maximum power density to the outer fuel blocks close to the radial reflector, mainly by optimising the (radial) distribution of burnable poison (and possibly the enrichment). See Section VI.

The temperature distribution over the 11-layer geometry in Hot Full Power (HFP) conditions originates from a steady state thermal hydraulics calculation by SPECTRA, assuming a "flat" radial power profile (i.e., the same axial power profile for all fuel columns) and a re-scaled 10-layer axial profile (i.e., from 10 to 11 layers) [2]. The latter originates from the iterative procedure between neutronics (SERPENT) and thermal hydraulics (SPECTRA) that was applied for the initial 10-layer configuration [10]. Only a few iterations already resulted in a converged solution for the temperature and power distribution, as is demonstrated in Fig. 5.

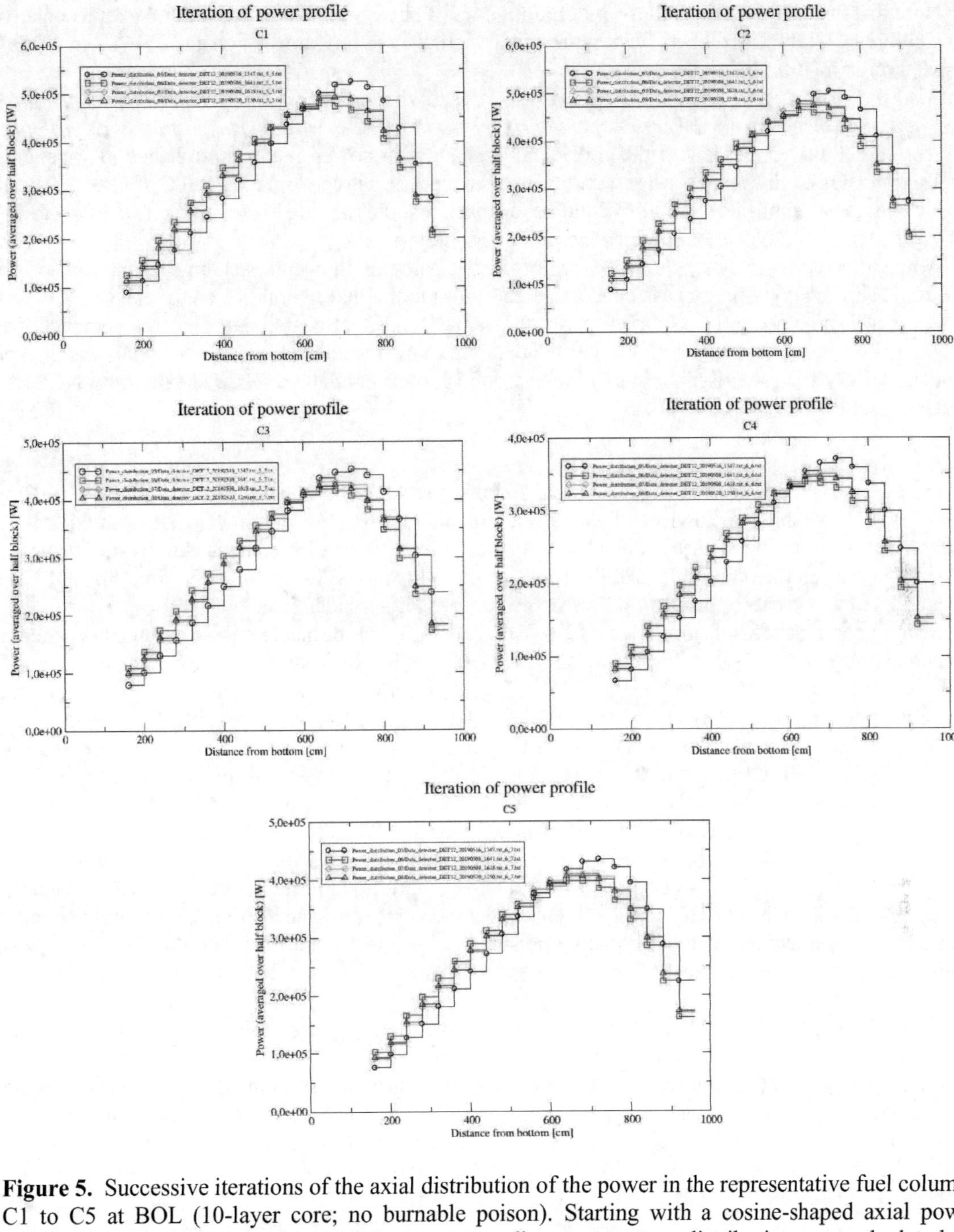


**Figure 5.** Successive iterations of the axial distribution of the power in the representative fuel columns C1 to C5 at BOL (10-layer core; no burnable poison). Starting with a cosine-shaped axial power distribution (not shown in the graphs) a corresponding temperature distribution was calculated by SPECTRA [10], based on which the power distribution for the next iteration was calculated. This was repeated 4 times, resulting in successive axial power distributions (indicated as "5" up to "8" in the graphs). Note that the power distributions of the 3rd and 4th iterations already nearly coincide, indicating convergence. Relative standard deviation of the power (per half block; half block is the meshing used for the calculation of the neutron flux and derived parameters, e.g., the power) in the results shown is 0.22 % for the peak values.

Note that the axial power profiles for iterations 3 and 4 already almost coincide for the representative fuel columns C1 to C5 (N.B. These representative fuel columns are designated "FA1" to "FA5", respectively, in [10,11]).

Also note that *this procedure was only followed at BOL* and *the resulting temperature distribution was kept unchanged during the entire operating cycle until EOL, as was envisaged from the start of the project* [1]. However, in view of the considerable changes in power distribution during the operating cycle from BOL to EOL (see further sections in this paper), this procedure may need to be revised, e.g., by introducing a simplified thermal-hydraulics feedback module running in conjunction with SERPENT, providing temperature distribution feedback for every time step.

A specific remark concerns the number of coated particles in a compact. In the majority of the neutronics calculation this was assumed to be 2500. In the thermal hydraulics analyses [10,11,12,13], however, it is assumed to be 3760. However, the actual number of coated particles in a compact does not significantly impact the maximum fuel temperature of the reactor in steady-state conditions or even in a (DLOFC - Depressurised Loss of Forced Cooling) transient. The latter was shown by NCBJ by comparing the 2 DLOFC cases [14].

## 4. $k_{eff}$ History

The search for an optimised configuration (spatial distribution of burnable poison parameters: fraction $f_{BP}$ of $B_4C$ in graphite; radius $R_{BP}$ of the cylinder containing $B_4C$ in graphite; it is assumed that all burnable poison pins in a single fuel block are identical, initially) is executed in phases. In the first phase, which focusses on the optimisation of the (uncontrolled) $k_{eff}$ history from BOL (Xe-free) to EOL, it is assumed that all burnable poison cylinders in the core are initially identical.

Several combinations of enrichment (12%, 13% and 15%) and burnable poison parameters (fraction $f_{BP}$ and cylinder radius $R_{BP}$; uniform values for all blocks in the core) have been investigated [14] and it was found that a uniform enrichment of 12%, burnable poison cylinder radius $R_{BP}$ = 0.242 cm and burnable poison density ($B_4C$ in graphite) $f_{BP}$ = 0.038 provided an acceptable behaviour of the uncontrolled (i.e. all control rods out) of $k_{eff}$ as function of time form Beginning of Life (BOL) to End of Life (EOL = 550 full power days), as is shown in Fig. 6. In this stage of the optimisation the main purpose of introducing burnable poison is to minimise $k_{eff}$ (but still with $k_{eff}$ sufficiently above 1 until EOL), so that the control and shutdown rods can be effectively used for start-up and shutdown. Ideally, $k_{eff}$ is approximately constant after reaching Xe-equilibrium (approx. 3 days) or slowly decreasing.

The $k_{eff}$ at BOL is 1.078 (Xe-free), and 1.018 (Xe-equilibrium) at EOL. This BOL-to-EOL reactivity swing is well within the reactivity range of the reflector control rods (see Section V). It should be noted that, for 12 % enrichment without burnable poison, the $k_{eff}$ (Xe-free) at BOL would have been above 1.40! A corresponding BOL-to-EOL reactivity swing of about -40% would be impossible to handle by the reflector rods.

In the 2$^{nd}$ phase of the optimisation, the objective is to improve the radial power distribution (see Section VI), by modifying the radial distribution of the burnable poison parameters, to a lesser or larger extent deviating from the uniform distribution given above, keep the enrichment at 12 %. For simplicity only 2 sets of values (of $R_{BP}$ and $f_{BP}$) were used for each of the cases: one set of values for the central fuel columns (C1 - C3) and one set for the peripheral fuel columns (C4, C5). In the search for the optimal performance, the total amount of $B_4C$ in the core (at BOL) was kept constant. Difference between central and peripheral columns was either in $f_{BP}$ or $R_{BP}$.

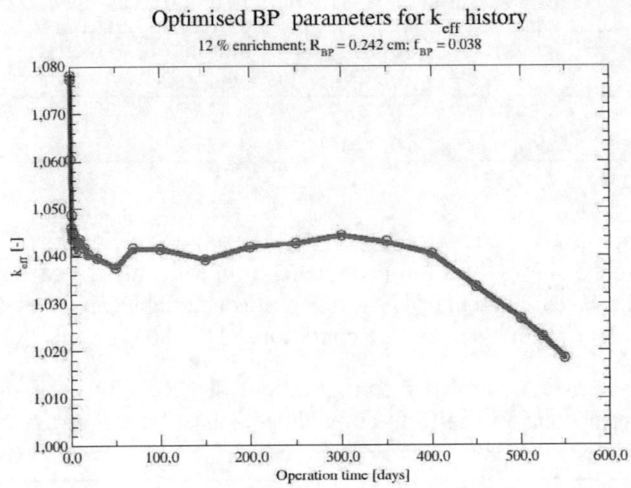


**Figure 6.** Uncontrolled (i.e. all control rods out) $k_{eff}$ versus operation time for a uniform enrichment of 12%, burnable poison cylinder radius $R_{BP}$ = 0.242 cm and burnable poison fraction ($B_4C$ in graphite) $f_{BP}$ = 0.038. Note the equilibrium reactivity worth of $^{135}$Xe is approximately -2840 pcm. $k_{eff}$ varies between 1.078 (BOL, no Xe) and 1.018 (EOL, Xe-eq.). The relative standard deviation in $k_{eff}$ is 12 to 13 pcm, which is consistent with the neutron population parameters: 100000 neutrons per cycle and 1000 cycles per point in time. In the calculation 26 non-equidistant time steps were used.

Fig. 7 shows the $k_{eff}$ history for several combinations of BP parameters for central and peripheral fuel columns. Case 202 is the case with uniform BP parameters (the same as in Fig. 6). Case 214 turned out to be the most favourable until now (September 2020) concerning the (radial) power distribution. (see Section VI), while it is also marginally superior to case 202 concerning the $k_{eff}$ history (i.e. $k_{eff}$ closer to 1.00). BP parameters for this case are given in Table 2.

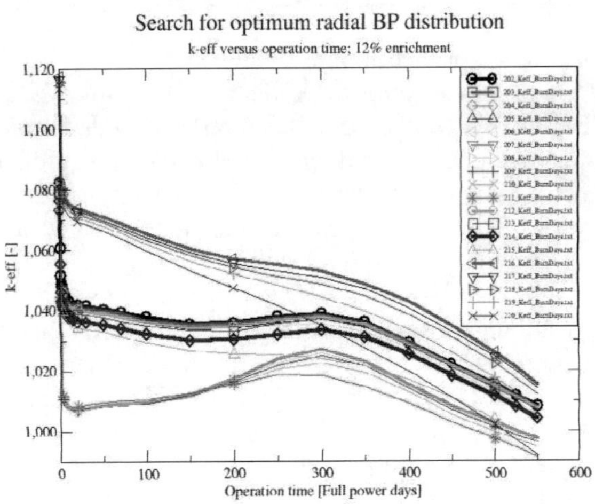


**Figure 7.** Uncontrolled $k_{eff}$ histories from calculations to improve the radial power distribution (see Section VI), by applying different burnable poison parameters for columns C1 and C2 on the one hand and C3, C4 and C5 on the other. Case 202 (bold "black circles") is the same as shown in Fig. 6 (uniform BP parameters). Case 214 (bold "purple diamonds") is the most favourable configuration so far. Neutron population parameters are the same as in Fig. 6, again yielding a relative standard deviation in $k_{eff}$ of 12 to 13 pcm.

**Table 2.** Burnable poison parameters for case 214.

| BP parameter | Columns C1, C2 | Columns C3, C4, C5 | Units |
|---|---|---|---|
| $f_{BP}$ | 0.038 | 0.038 | [-] |
| $R_{BP}$ | 0.290 | 0.227 | [cm] |

## 5. Control Rods

The reactor configuration features 6 control rods in the core and 18 (6 clusters of 3 each) in the reflector, as shown in Fig. 1. Table 3 shows the $k_{eff}$ for several control rod patterns (each rod is either fully in or fully out) for uniform initial enrichment of 12 % and uniform burnable poison parameters as in case 202, at Cold Zero Power (CZP; "room" temperature conditions: T = 300 K), BOL, Xe-free conditions.

**Table 3.** $k_{eff}$ for characteristic control rod configurations at CZP, BOL, Xe-free for 11 layers core, uniform 12 % initial enrichment and uniform burnable poison parameters (case 202).

| Rod positions | $k_{eff}$ | Remarks |
|---|---|---|
| All CR in; all RR in | 9.14812E-01 (0.012%) | CZP state is subcritical with all rods in: OK |
| All CR in; all RR out | 1.00170E+00 (0.58%) | Core rods in only are not sufficient in this configuration in CZP state: not OK (at BOL) |
| All CR in; RR1/2/3 in; RR10/11/12 in | 9.65733E-01 (0.012%) | Core rods + some reflector rods are sufficient at BOL. This could be OK, as most RR are in anyway during first days of operation (see below). |
| CR1 out; RR1, RR2, RR3 out; other rods in | 9.77099E-01 (0.012%) | Approximately 60 degr. sector free of rods, to accommodate (re-) load: OK |
| CR1 out; RR1, RR2, RR3, RR16, RR17, RR18 out; other rods in | 1.018760E+00 (0.012%) | Slightly over 60 degr. sector free of rods, to accommodate (re-load): not OK |

It is clear that the core rods alone **cannot** keep the reactor subcritical at BOL, CZP, Xe-free conditions. It is also **not** possible with only the reflector rods. However, it is possible to maintain subcriticality at BOL, CZP, Xe-free, by all core rods + 6 reflector rods inserted.

Also, it is possible to remove one core rod and the closed set of 3 reflector rods in a **60 degrees sector** of the core, while maintaining subcriticality. This is necessary for the (re-) fuelling procedure.

Similar calculations are currently (September 2020) being performed for the "radially optimised" case 214. It is expected that this will yield similar results.

At elevated temperatures (Hot Zero Power - HZP; uniform temperature T = 600K) and Hot Full Power (HFP; temperature distribution from the steady-state SPECTRA thermal hydraulics calculation) the reactivity of the core is lower, and it is very well possible to keep the reactor subcritical with reflector rods only. This is desirable as the core rods are envisaged to be fully withdrawn during operation at (full) power.

Fig. 8 shows, for case 202 with uniform initial burnable poison parameters, the $k_{eff}$ at BOL, HZP/HFP, Xe-free, as function of the number of withdrawn control rods from the reflector. *The withdrawal pattern of the reflector rods is such that more than 3 (or even more than 1) partially inserted rods are avoided, i.e., reflector rods are, as much as possible, either fully in or fully out.* The control rods in the core have been fully withdrawn, as envisaged for full power operation. Note that the total worth of the reflector rods is approximately the same for HZP and HFP, viz. 12.4 %. This is large enough to compensate the full range of uncontrolled $k_{eff}$ values indicated in Fig. 6, even in case of a Xe-free state at any time in the cycle. Similar calculations for case 214 are currently (September 2020) ongoing. Similar results are expected.

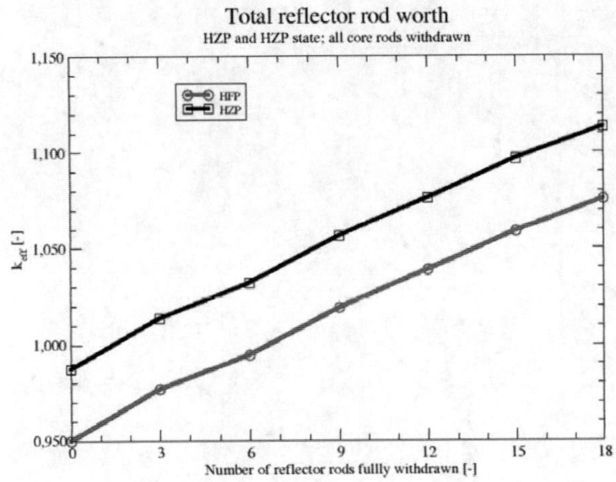


**Figure 8.** $k_{eff}$ as function of the number of withdrawn control rods in the reflector for case 202 at BOL. All control rods in the core are out. The value for all rods out at HFP corresponds to the initial value in Fig. 6. Relative standard deviation in $k_{eff}$ is 12 to 13 pcm.

In the current design of the GEMINI+ reactor, also other control rod patterns are being considered, for which, however, no neutronics analyses have been performed (yet) [2].

Also, a reserve shutdown system, in the form of small absorber spheres (approx. 6 mm diameter, containing $B_4C$) is being considered. In the current configuration these spheres are supposed to use the same channels as the core control rods. This may require a re-design of the core control rods, e.g., cruciform shape instead of annular [2]. No neutronics analyses have been performed (yet) on either one of these configurations and it is assumed that the reactivity worth of either a single channel filled with absorber spheres, or an inserted cruciform rod will have a reactivity value very similar to that of the current core control rod design.

## 6. Power and Burn-Up Distribution

As mentioned in Section III, for the DLOFC transient calculations on the current 11-layed design [13] it is assumed that the radial distribution of the power is uniform, i.e., every column of fuel block has the same axial distribution of the power (per coated particle). This leads to an acceptable behaviour (peak fuel temperature < 1600 °C) in case of DLOFC. The calculations also showed that the DLOFC behaviour is less satisfactory when the power in the central fuel columns (C1, C2) is higher than in the peripheral fuel columns (C3, C4, C5). It is expected that the behaviour will even improve further when the power maximum is "pushed" further towards the peripheral fuel columns. As mentioned earlier (Section III), the second task of burnable poison is therefore to improve the radial power distribution. Preferably the (initial) enrichment of the fuel is still uniform (12 % for the current designs).

In Fig. 9 the axial distribution of power per coated particle (average over half block) is shown for all (31) fuel columns in the core for case 202 (uniform BP parameter distribution) at BOL/Xe-free ("A"), 250 days ("B") and 525 days ("C"). The highest power per coated particle (158 mW) occurs at BOL in column C1 (820 cm). The relative standard deviation of the power in the results shown is 0.22% for the peak values. Note that there is a large spread in peak values at the same elevation (820 cm), indicating a radial power distribution that is peaking in the centre column.

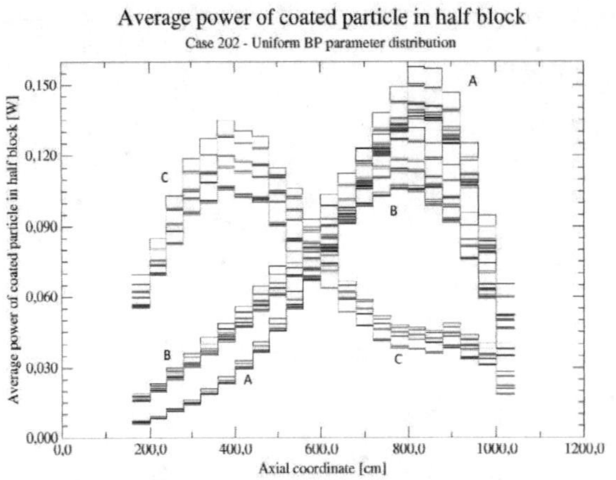


**Figure 9.** Axial distribution of power per coated particle (average over half block) for all (31) fuel columns in the core for case 202 (uniform BP parameter distribution) at BOL/Xe-free ("A"), 250 days ("B") and 525 days ("C"). The highest power per coated particle (158 mW) occurs at BOL in column C1 (820 cm). The relative standard deviation of the power in the results shown is 0.22% for the peak values.

Introducing a radial profile in the BP parameters clearly improves this situation, as is shown in Fig. 10, which shows the axial distribution of power per coated particle (average over half block) for all (31) fuel columns in the core for case 214 (radially "optimised" BP parameter distribution; Table 2) at BOL/Xe-free ("A"), 250 days ("B") and 525 days ("C"). The highest power per coated particle (145 mW) occurs at BOL ("A") in a peripheral column of type C5 (at 820 cm). Note that the lowest power per coated particle at the same elevation is 138 mW, occurring in a central column of type C2. Clearly the spread in (peak) values at the same elevation has been reduced considerably, compared to case 202, indicating a much more "radially flat" power profile. Also, the highest power does not occur in a central column, but in a peripheral column (C5-type, adjacent to the radial reflector; see Fig. 1), which is considered even more favourable.

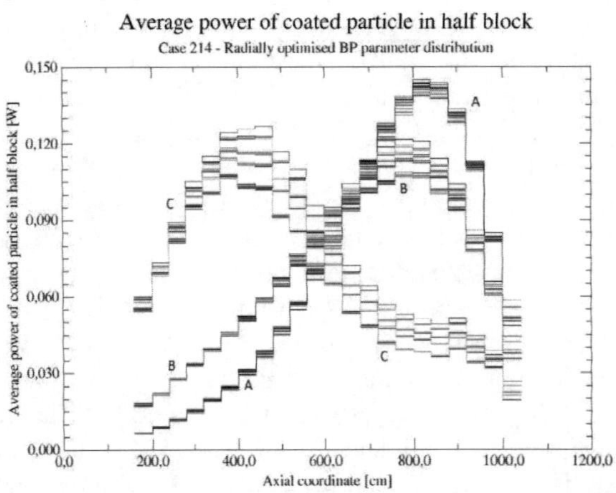


**Figure 10.** Axial distribution of power per coated particle (average over half block) for all (31) fuel columns in the core for case 214 (radially "optimised" BP parameter distribution; Table 2) at BOL/Xe-free ("A"), 250 days ("B") and 525 days ("C"). The highest power per coated particle (145 mW) occurs at BOL ("A") in a peripheral column of type C5 (820 cm). Note that the lowest power per coated particle at the same elevation is 138 mW, occurring in a central column of type C2. The relative standard deviation of the power in the results shown is 0.22% for the peak values.

The final distribution of the burn up at EOL (550 full power operation days) is the topic of Figs. 11 and 12. In the SERPENT calculations the burn up has been determined on half block level. Figs. 11 and 12 show the frequency distribution of fuel in a given burn up interval, i.e., the number of blocks containing fuel at a final burn up in the interval indicated, for cases 202 and 214, respectively. Ideally, for a single batch loading scheme all fuel should end with the same final burn up. In the frequency distribution representation this means a single burnup range (at average burn up), containing all (341) blocks. This is clearly not yet achieved in cases 202 and 214, although it can be considered slightly better for case 214 (slightly lower maximum burn up, although still far above average).

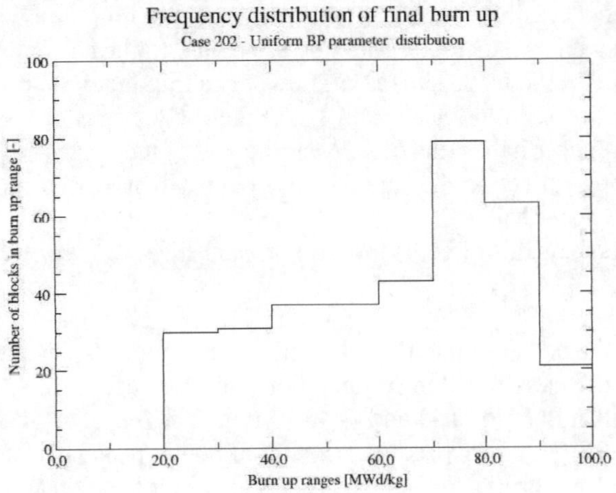


**Figure 11.** Frequency distribution of the final burn up (per block) for case 202, i.e., the number of blocks containing fuel in the indicated burn up range. The maximum burn up is 98.5 MWd/kg. The average burn up is 63.8 MWd/kg.

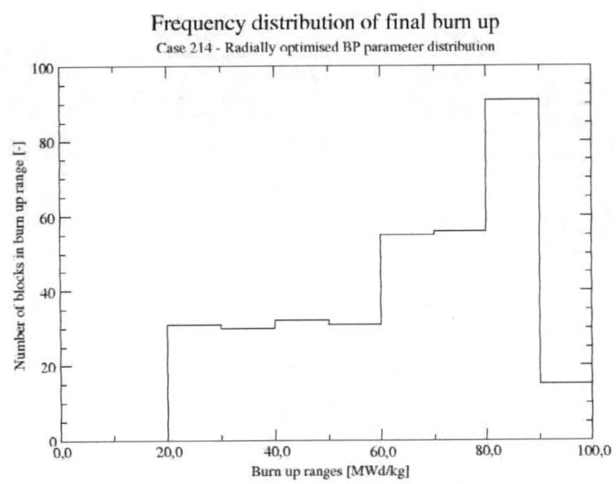


**Figure 12.** Frequency distribution of the final burn up (per block) for case 202, i.e. the number of blocks containing fuel in the indicated burn up range. The maximum burn up is 94.6 MWd/kg. The average burn up is 63.8 MWd/kg.

Further improvement can be expected from flattening the axial power profile.

A point of further discussion/investigation should be the power per coated particle (and per compact). Even for case 214 ("radially optimised" BP parameters) the maximum power per coated particle (averaged over half a block) is 145 mW at BOL. This is higher than achieved/investigated in recent TRISO fuel irradiation tests [15]. The volume of a compact is 6.136 $cm^3$. The power of a single compact filled with 2500 coated particles @ 145 mW would be 362.5 W, or 59.1 $W/cm^3$. This would also be considerably higher than achieved/investigated in those TRISO tests. Further reduction of the maximum power per particle could e.g. be achieved by increasing the number of coated particles per compact (however, see Section IX).

Another, perhaps more feasible, method of reducing the maximum power per coated particle (and per compact) would be again to flatten the axial power profile. In the current configuration, the average power per coated particle is 69.6 mW. The (axial) power peaking factor is therefore 145/69.6 = 2.08 for case 214 at BOL. As can be seen in Figs. 9 and 10, in the early stages of the cycle ("A" and "B") the power peak occurs in the upper half of the core. Near the end of the cycle ("C") a similar peak occurs in the lower half of the core, reflecting that the fuel in upper half has been mostly depleted, due to the earlier high power in the upper half.

A convenient way to show this effect is the *axial offset* $F_{AO}$:

$$F_{AO} = (P_{upper} - P_{lower}) / (P_{upper} + P_{lower})$$

In this equation $P_{upper}$ is the power in the upper half of the core and $P_{lower}$ is the power in the lower half. Fig. 13 shows the axial offset as function of operation time for cases 202 and 214. The curves nearly coincide, going from 0.58 at BOL to -0.43 and -0.45 at EOL. The presence of a power- (flux-) dependent absorber ($^{135}Xe$) just after BOL already reduces the initial power peak ($F_{AO}$ starts at 0.58 and decreases to approx. 0.45 at Xenon equilibrium, t = 3 days). This is also an indication that increasing the BP density in the upper half of the core could be effective, perhaps even without axially profiling the enrichment, in decreasing the initial power peak in the upper half at BOL, thereby also decreasing the power peak in the lower half towards EOL.

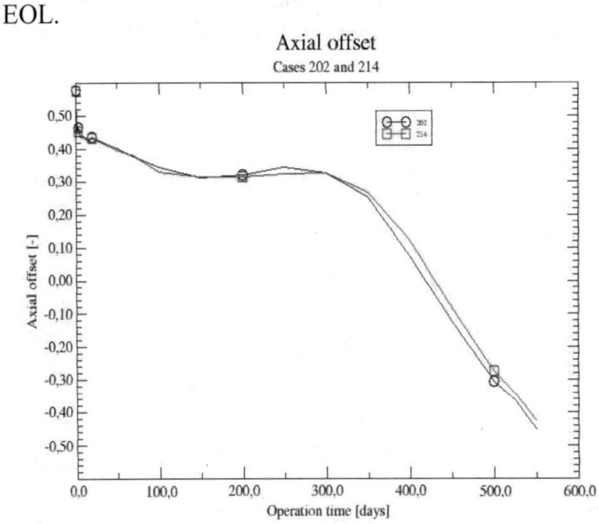


**Figure 13.** Axial offset as function of operation time for cases 202 and 214.

## 7. Temperature Coefficients

An important aspect for safe operation of any nuclear reactor are the temperature coefficients of reactivity $\alpha$. In HTGRs usually the following distinction is made:

- Fuel ("$\alpha_F$"): material in the kernel and the coating layers.
- Moderator ("$\alpha_M$"): matrix material of the compacts and the graphite of the fuel blocks constituting the core.
- Reflector ("$\alpha_R$"): graphite of top-, bottom- and radial reflectors.

The temperature coefficients of reactivity have been calculated as follows:

$$\alpha_x = [(1/k_{eff,ref}) - (1/k_{eff,x})] / \Delta T_x$$

In this equation x = F (Fuel), M (Moderator), R (Reflector) or A (all materials), and $k_{eff,ref}$ is the multiplication factor for the reference state. This concerns the reference temperature distributions at CZP (all materials at 300 K), HZP (all materials at 600 K) and HFP (temperature distribution as calculated by SPECTRA at BOL and used in the HFP calculations presented so far). $\Delta T_x$ is the (spatially uniform) increase in temperature of the materials (F, M, R, A) of interest. In the calculations $\Delta T_x$ = 30 K was used. To obtain sufficient accuracy in the calculated values, the calculations of $k_{eff,ref}$ and $k_{eff,x}$ were performed with 1000 cycles, 400000 neutrons per cycle and 100 inactive cycles. This resulted in a standard deviation of 5 pcm in the calculated values of $k_{eff}$ and, consequently, an uncertainty of 0.3 pcm/K in the calculated values of $\alpha_x$.

Table 4 shows the temperature coefficients of reactivity as calculated for the BOL, Xe-free state of case 202. For most states/configurations, the coefficients for all (F, M, R) materials are negative. However, for the HZP and HFP states, in which core rods and/or reflector rods have been withdrawn, the coefficients for the reflector are (slightly) positive. A positive coefficient of reactivity for the reflector temperature is a well-known phenomenon in HTGRs.

**Table 4.** Temperature coefficients of reactivity (fuel, moderator, reflector) for case 202, BOL (Xe-free), in pcm/K. The uncertainty in the calculated values of the temperature coefficients is 0.3 pcm/K.

| Configuration/ State | $\alpha_F$ (Fuel) | $\alpha_M$ (Moderator) | $\alpha_R$ (Reflector) | Sum | $\alpha_A$ |
|---|---|---|---|---|---|
| CZP, all rods in | -10.0 | -38.1 | -162.0 | -210.1 | -48.7 |
| HZP, all rods in | -6.8 | -4.0 | -0.8 | -21.6 | -20.2 |
| HZP, core rods in, reflector rods out | -4.6 | -10.2 | 0.4 | -14.4 | -15.1 |
| HZP, all rods out | -4.1 | -8.6 | 1.2 | -11.5 | -11.3 |
| HFP, core rods out, reflector rods in | -5.3 | -9.7 | 0.3 | -14.7 | -14.4 |
| HFP, all rods out | -3.1 | -7.4 | 1.9 | -8.6 | -9.7 |

Comparing the sum of the (F, M, R) coefficients with the coefficient for temperature change in all materials shows that the reactivity effects are reasonably linear at HZP and HFP, but strongly non-linear at CZP.

The current coefficients have been calculated for a uniform increase of 30K in temperature for the material (F, M, R, A) under consideration. To take into account the influence of localised changes in temperature on the reactivity in e.g. (transient) thermal hydraulic calculations, e.g., local **weight factors** can be used. In one-energy group approximation, and under the assumption that absorption is the dominant effect, it can be shown by first-order perturbation theory that the local neutron flux squared can be regarded as the proper weight function/weight factor for reactivity effects, caused by local variations of the effective local macroscopic absorption and fission cross sections [16]. So, in first order approximation (i.e., local variation in effective macroscopic cross section is proportional to local variation in temperature) this is also the case for the reactivity effect of local temperature variations, i.e. the local weight factor.

The results shown so far concern case 202 (uniform initial BP parameter distribution) at BOL. Calculations of temperature coefficients of reactivity are currently (September 2020) ongoing for case 202 beyond BOL and all corresponding states for case 214.

## 8. Axial Xe-Oscillations?

In the current design of the GEMINI+ HTGR the core height has been increased to 8.8 m. This has raised the concern of the possibility of occurrence of axial oscillations (axial instability) of the power, related to the changing densities of $^{135}Xe$ in the upper and lower half of the core. As a relatively simple first check, the following test was performed for case 202:

- At BOL, HFP, all core rods are out, reflector rods are 50% inserted (all reflector rod tips at 600 cm elevation), followed by full power operation for 3 days until Xe-equilibrium. This was calculated with the normal time steps, also used in the full burn up calculations. At t = 3 days, the reactor state is written to a restart file.
- At t = 3 days the calculation is continued from the restart file, with the reflector rods fully withdrawn. This calculation was done twice, with different time steps (32 time steps of 0.1 day and 2 time steps of 0.1 day, followed by 15 time steps of 0.2 days, respectively) to detect possible dependence upon the choice of the time steps.

During the entire test, the same HFP temperature profile was used, excluding thermal feedback effects.

Results of this test are shown in Fig. 14. In this figure the axial offset $F_{AO}$ is shown as function of time for the first ("black circles") and second phase ("red squares" and "green diamonds") of the test. In the first phase, all reflector rods are 50 % inserted. As the total reactor power is being kept constant at 180 MWth, the vast majority of the power is being generated in the lower half of the core, resulting in a strongly negative axial offset: -0.83 at BOL, increasing to -0.80 at Xe-equilibrium. A relatively high concentration of $^{135}Xe$ and $^{135}I$ has been built up in the lower half, where most of the power is being generated. At t = 3 days, the reflector rods are fully withdrawn. This immediately pushes the power peak to the upper half of the core, resulting in a strongly positive axial offset of 0.74. Decaying $^{135}I$ into $^{135}Xe$ in the lower half suppresses the power in the lower half further for a while, causing the axial offset to increase further to 0.78. Because of the now high power in the upper half, both $^{135}I$ and $^{135}Xe$ concentrations are increasing in the upper half, while still decreasing in the lower half, until equilibrium is reached again at t = 4.6 days, corresponding to the "usual" axial offset of the reactor at HFP near BOL, as shown in Fig. 13. Apart from the little "overshoot", immediately after withdrawal of the reflector rods, no "oscillatory" behaviour seems to occur.

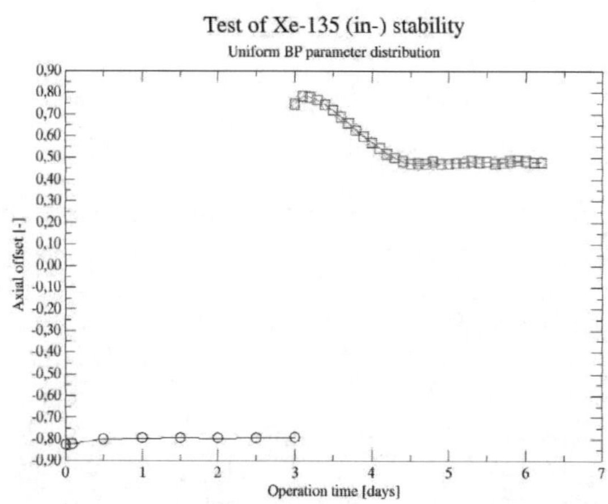


**Figure 14.** Test of axial $^{135}Xe$-related instability.

It should be noted, however, that highly positive or negative values of the axial offset mean that almost the full reactor power is generated in only half the core, resulting in even higher local power densities in coated particles and compacts. This should be avoided anyway. Therefore, it is advisable to avoid as much as possible *partially* inserted (reflector) rods during full power operation: rods should, as much as possible, be either fully in or fully out.

In the test presented here, a constant HFP temperature profile has been used, thereby excluding thermal feedback effects. It is desirable to repeat the test with full thermal feedback, also at other points in time in the cycle.

## 9. Steam Ingress

A final topic is the ability to render the reactor subcritical in case of steam ingress (HZP/HFP state only). Fig. 15 shows the influence of the steam density in the coolant on the $k_{eff}$, for 12 % enrichment and uniform BP parameters as in case 202. In case of 2500 coated particles per compact, the reactor can be kept subcritical with the core rods only with a maximum steam density of 0.09 g/cm$^3$ steam in the coolant. When both core and reflector rods can be used this is 0.15 g/cm$^3$. Higher numbers (e.g., 3000) of coated particles per compact result in a lower C/U-ratio (moderator-to-fuel ratio) in the core and a (slightly) higher reactivity increase due to steam ingress. This will not necessarily be detrimental, as some other parameters (e.g., BP parameters, fuel enrichment) may be adapted to lower the uncontrolled (all rods out) BOL $k_{eff}$.

Also note that, as can be seen in Fig. 15, the reactivity worth of the control rods decreases with increasing steam density in the core. So, in any case, measures will be necessary to limit the possible amount of steam that can enter the primary circuit.

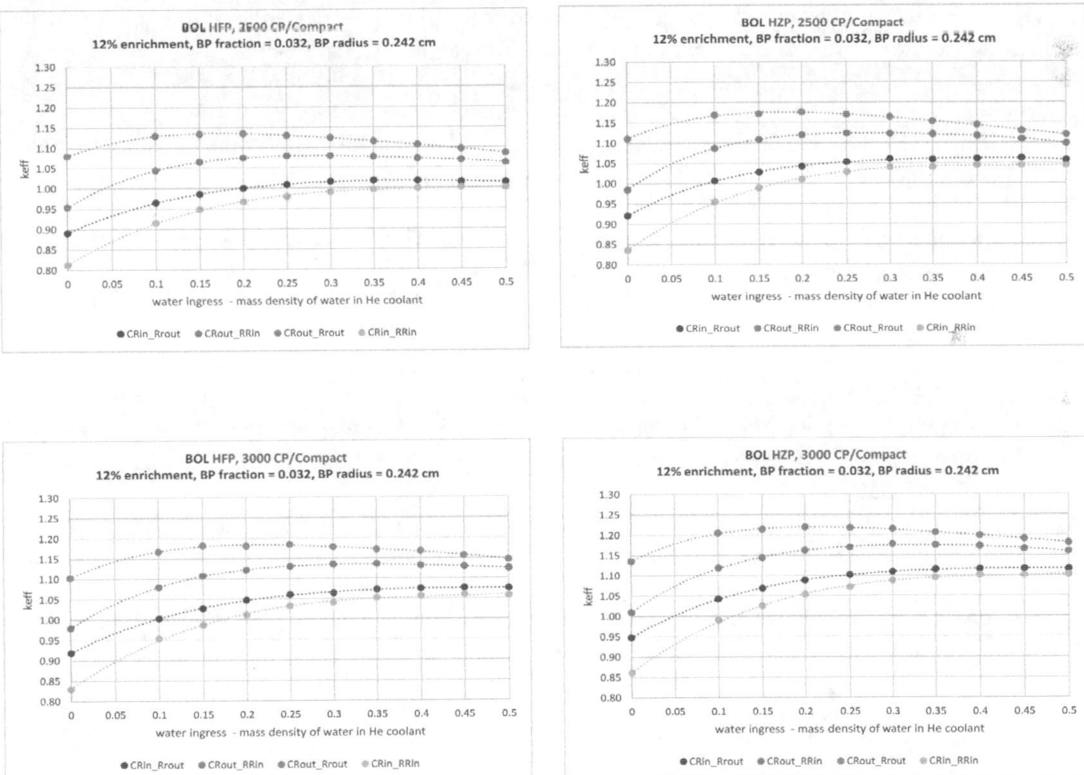


**Figure 15.** Steam ingress at BOL/HFP and HZP, for 2500 and 3000 coated particles per compact, 12 % enrichment and uniform initial BP parameter distribution as in case 202.

Similar to the calculation of the temperature reactivity coefficients, the analyses of steam ingress will also need to be done for points in time beyond BOL, also for the further optimised configurations of the BP parameter distribution.

## 10. Conclusions

Extensive neutronics calculations have been performed on the current (June 2020) design of the 180 MWth GEMINI+ HTGR. Neutronics features seem quite promising, but further improvements and therefore further investigations would be desirable, especially concerning:

- Temperature coefficients of reactivity, control rod worths, etc. beyond BOL, also for further optimised configurations of the BP parameter distribution.
- Thermal hydraulic feedback, reflecting the considerable change axial power profile during the operation cycle. In the current calculations, the temperature distribution has been kept constant throughout the operation cycle, as was initially envisaged. Adapting the temperature distribution to the actual power distribution at each point in time would be desirable.
- Further reduction of the axial power peaking, thereby reducing the maximum power per coated particle and also improving the fuel utilisation. Possible methods are axial profiling of BP parameters, axial profiling of enrichment and/or a multi-batch loading scheme.
- Increasing the number of coated particles per compact, possibly in combination with changing the enrichment and/or the BP parameter distribution.

**Acknowledgement**

This work is part of the GEMINI+ project, funded from the European Union's Horizon 2020 research and innovation programme under grant agreement No 755478.

The high precision monte carlo calculations were carried out on the HPC cluster of the Swierk Computing Centre (CIS), National Centre for Nuclear Research (NCBJ), Poland.

## References

[1] "GEMINI+ - Research and development in support of the GEMINI Initiative", Euratom Horizon 2020 project 755478, 1 September 2017 - 31 August 2020.

[2] B. Lindley, M. Davies (Jacobs), D. Hittner (LGI), M.M. Stempniewicz, E.A.R. de Geus (NRG), J. Kuijper (NUCLIC), G. Brinkmann, D. Vanvor (BriVaTech), "Final Description and Justification of the GEMINI+ System", GEMINI+ Deliverable D2.5, 30 June 2020.

[3] "GT-MHR Reactor System Design Description" – Int. GT-MHR 100002 – RE – 11.6, Rev.1, November 1997.

[4] "Preliminary Safety Information Document for the Standard MHTGR" – DOE/HTGR – 086 – 024 – Vol. 1 (1986)SC-HTGR, 1986.

[5] L. Lommers, F. Shahrokhi, J. Mayer III, F. Southworth, "AREVA Modular Steam Cycle – High Temperature Gas-Cooled Reactor Development Progress", Proc. HTR 2014, Weihai, China, 27-31 October 2014.

[6] J.C. Kuijper (NUCLIC) and D. Muszynski (NCBJ), "Core design calculations of the GEMINI+ system", GEMINI+ Deliverable D2.8 (in preparation September 2020).

[7] W. von Lensa, "NBG-17 graphite composition", private communication, 14 June 2018.

[8] Leppänen, J., et al. (2015) "The SERPENT Monte Carlo code: Status, development and applications in 2013", Ann. Nucl. Energy, 82 (2015) 142-150.

[9] "SPECTRA - Sophisticated Plant Evaluation Code for Thermal-Hydraulic Response Assessment, Version 3.61, January 2020, Volume 1 – Program Description, Volume 2 – User's Guide, Volume 3 – Verification and Validation", NRG report K6223/20.166353 MSt-200130, Arnhem, January 2020, https://www.nrg.eu/fileadmin/nrg/Documenten/Spectra-Vol1.pdf

[10] M.M. Stempniewicz, "Thermal-Hydraulic Model of the GEMINI+ HTR Plant - Safety Analysis, WP1.6", NRG report 24203/19.153415, 30 May 2019.

[11] M.M. Stempniewicz, "TH Analyses of GEMINI+ HTR Plant (8.0 m) Results of PLOFC and DLOFC Scenarios", NRG report 24203/19.153912, 30 June 2019.

[12] M.M. Stempniewicz, "GEMINI+ HTR Plant Model - Conversion from 8.000 m core to 8.800 m core", NRG report24203/19.154307 Rev. 0, 12 August 2019.

[13] M.M. Stempniewicz, "TH Analyses of GEMINI+ HTR Plant (8.8 m) - Results of PLOFC and

DLOFC Scenarios", NRG report 24203/19.154308, 20 July 2019.
[14] NCBJ to NUCLIC, Internal communication of the GEMINI+ project, 2019/2020.
[15] M. Feltus, "TRISO FUELS ", Webinar, Gen IV International Forum, 18 December 2019.
[16] H. van Dam. T.H.J.H. van der Hagen, J.E. Hoogenboom," Nuclear Reactor Physics", Lecture notes AP3341, Delft University of Technology, The Netherlands, April 2005.

# HTR-10 OTTO Cycle Depletion Simulation Using Discrete Element Method Coupled Monte Carlo

**F Putra**

Universitas Gadjah Mada, Yogyakarta, Indonesia

phone: +6283894441244, Feryantama.putra@mail.ugm.ac.id

**Abstract.** Pebble bed reactor core contains 27,000 pebbles placed in a random position. Since the pebble insertion relies on gravity, the pebble placement pattern is irregular. Discrete Element Method used to simulate the pebble interaction and pebble movement during HTR-10 operation. Even though pebbles distributed randomly, the random generation of pebble positions used in most research does not mimic the actual pebble position and pebble surface contact. The Discrete Element Method provides a realistic interpretation of the pebble position by considering the pebble surface contact and gravity force. Each pebble coordinates from the Discrete Element Method obtained to construct Monte Carlo geometry of the HTR-10 core realistically. By coupling the DEM simulation with Monte Carlo simulation, it is possible to calculate the depletion while considering the core dynamic characteristic. The OTTO recirculation depletion calculation scheme with steady 10MW power for 368 days was constructed and demonstrated in this work. The DEM coupled Monte Carlo method allow one to track and predict each depleted fuel composition. Although the flux distribution change is slight in every timestep, the relation between flux and depleted $U^{235}$ and $Xe^{135}$ composition deserves to be taken into account. The calculation model in this work is comparable with the other calculation, but the timestep adjustment is needed to provide more accurate and representative results. Flux calculation and depletion simulation performed using the OpenMC program with ENDF/B-VIII.0 cross-section data. Please refer to digital version to view graph.

## 1. Introduction

Nuclear energy is a viable option for high power baseload generation with zero carbon emission. The development of a safer and more financially competitive reactor design could stimulate the nuclear power generation industry growth for the future. For many decades to come, the Generation IV reactor will be dominating the nuclear energy market with modular reactor design and advanced operation technology aiming to answer safety and financial challenges. One of the Generation IV reactors with mature technology for power generation is High-Temperature Reactor (HTR).

HTR is a type of reactor that operates at a higher temperature than the conventional light water reactor. The most interesting HTR design is the Pebble Bed Reactor (PBR). PBR uses a discrete spherical Tristructural-Isotropic fuel element (TRISO) coated in the graphite matrix to form a spherical-shaped fuel. The reactor core was constructed with stacked graphite blocks with a cavity to contain the pebble. Due to its fuel shape, the reactor able to perform online refueling or a fuel recirculation scheme. The PBR core cooled with gases such as helium or carbon dioxide. One of the PBR is HTR-10 in which was constructed by the Institute of Nuclear Energy Technology (INET) at Tsinghua University[1].

The core of PBR fills with randomly arranged spherical fuel pebbles. The absence of a fuel placement pattern caused the neutronic simulation geometric definition hard to construct. There is two randomity considered in modelling the PBR geometry for reactor simulation or neutronic calculation. The randomity includes random placement of the TRISO element inside the fuel pebble matrix also random arrangement of the pebble inside the core. Most of the HTR-10 benchmark models employ the lattice pattern to define the double randomity of the reactor. The lattice model creates uniform packing density and less pebble-to-pebble surface contact.

In a time-dependent problem such as a calculation of depleted material, the geometrical modelling of the core needs to consider the change of pebble position every timestep. The reactor can perform online refueling by recirculating the pebble in the reactor core due to the spherical-shape fuel pebble and hopper shaped core vessel. That means, the geometric model for each simulation period needs to be updated with a different set of pebble position according to its move during that period to represent the pebble movement. Therefore, the calculation needs an infinite number of models to solve a certain length of the time-dependent problem.

Only fresh fuels are allowed to enter the reactor core in the Once-Through Then-Out recirculation scheme. The previous research employs a layer-to-layer method to model the pebble recirculation [2]. Layer-to-layer method group the pebbles with the coolant in an axial or a radial region as a cell. After a certain timestep of depletion calculation, the material of a specific cell changed with depleted material of the cell located above the specified cell for the next depletion calculation [2]. However, that method neglects three-dimensional pebble displacement and the double randomity in the PBR core.

This study will create an HTR-10 model to simulate and calculate the flux tally problem by considering its time-dependent behavior. The study demonstrated a new approach to make a very high-fidelity Monte Carlo geometry model and simulation sequence for time-dependent problems.

## 2. Model construction

### *2.1. HTR-10 Core Geometry*

The reactor model is similar to the benchmark models provided by IAEA TecDoc [1]. The detailed description of material composition data obtained from the IRPhEP report [3] which based on the IAEA technical document. There are 83 zones of reactor geometry with different compositions of carbon, boron, and coolant. Some region such as Fuel region, reflector boring, and control channel modelled resembling the description in the high-fidelity benchmark model in [1], [3]. There are 28,020 pebbles with 24,531 mixture pebbles inside the core zone at initial (t=0).

Each pebble modelled as a 3 cm radius sphere with center coordinate obtained from DEM simulation. The bottom part of the discharge tube modelled as a homogenous cell represents dummy pebbles similar to the benchmark model from IRPhEP [3]. The bottom surface of the core descends by following the lower position of the simulated pebble step. Each fuel pebble contains an exact 8,335 TRISO scattered randomly inside fuel zone. Each TRISO center point has a distance between one another same or above 1 mm.

**Table 1.** TRISO Material Properties

| | |
|---|---|
| Matrix Density | 1.73 g/cm$^3$ |
| Uranium Mass/Pebble | 5 g |
| Uranium Enrichment | 17 wt.% |
| Boron content in Kernel | 4 ppm |
| TRISO Layer | Kernel/Buffer/PyC/SiC/PyC |
| Layer Thickness (mm) | Ø=0.5/0.04/0.035/0.04/0.09 |
| Density (g/cm$^3$) | 10.4/1.1/1.9/3.18/1.9 |

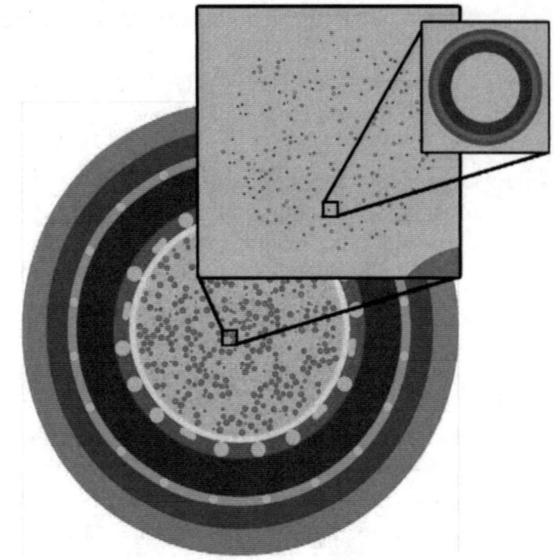

**Figure 1.** OpenMC HTR-10 model cross-section view z=0 and TRISO detail.

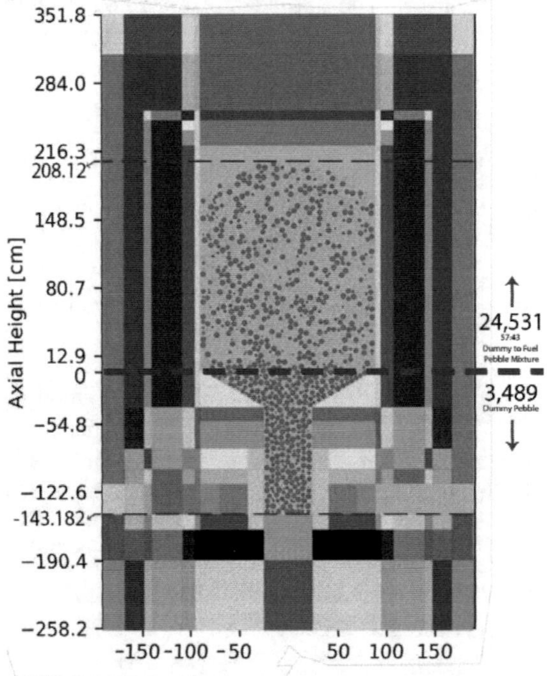


**Figure 2.** OpenMC HTR-10 model cross-section view x=0 at depletion step 0.

*2.2. DEM Simulation*

DEM simulation is used to map the center point of each pebble inside the core. Simulation performed by LAMMPS Improved for General Granular and Granular Heat Transfer Simulations (LIGGGHTS) open-source DEM code [4]. DEM simulation tracks each particle to simulate the particle contact and force balance of the particle. The force related parameter such as young modulus, friction coefficient, and Poisson ratio fed to DEM simulation. Particle to particle contact model used a linear spring and dashpot model with normal force and tangential force written as[4]:

$$F_n = -k_n \delta_n + c_n \Delta u_n \tag{1}$$

$$F_t = \min\left\{\left[\int_0^t \Delta u_t dt + c_t \Delta u_t\right], \mu F_n\right\} \tag{2}$$

Where $F_n$ is the normal force, $F_t$ is the tangential force, $k_n$ and $k_t$ are spring coefficient for normal or tangential force, $c_n$ and $c_t$ are damping coefficient for normal or tangential force, $u_n$ and $u_t$ are velocity component, $\delta_n$ is normal overlap between particle, and $\mu$ is friction coefficient. From this equation, the simulation allows overlap between particles, especially for soft particles. For solid granular such as PBR pebble in this study, the overlap created as low as possible ($\delta_n = 0.01\ mm$).

The inner core boundary modelled in STL surface mesh format. Since the user did not allow the pebble to free fall from the core boundary, the discharge tube shuts with a movable plane called 'stopper' to control slow discharge. For the initial configuration, the stopper placed at -143.182 cm level.

**Table 2.** Physical properties of pebble particle for DEM simulation.

| Parameter | Value |
|---|---|
| Radius | 3 cm |
| Density (Fuel/Dummy) | 1.857; 1.790 $g/cm^3$ |
| Young's Modulus [5] | $10^9\ Pa$ |
| Friction Coefficient [5] | 0.7 |
| Poisson Ratio [5] | 0.3 |
| Timesteps | 50 $\mu s$ |

*2.3. Monte Carlo Simulation*

Monte Carlo simulation in this study used OpenMC open-source code [6]. OpenMC code provided python Application Programming Interface (API) to ease the modelling and tally data processing. The API will automate the whole simulation methodology in this research. The simulation in this work used Evaluated Nuclear Data File (ENDF) version B-VIII.0 neutron cross-section library with ACE file format preprocessed with NJOY21 [7]. OpenMC reads HDF5 cross-section data converted from ACE file to perform the calculation [8]. This work used PWR-simplified chain for the VERA benchmark suite that includes 255 nuclides for depletion simulation [9].

Monte Carlo simulation in this work will simulate initial criticality case and full core case with various ENDF library to validate the model and compare the $k_{eff}$. Those simulations used 10,000 particles per cycle with 500 active cycles and 50 inactive cycles (5,000,000 neutron histories). Besides, Monte Carlo depletion simulation simulated 5,000 particles per cycle with 200 active cycles and 10 inactive cycles (1,000,000 neutron histories). The depletion will perform 368 days operation with 17 unequal length timestep. The integrator used for depletion simulation is high order EPC-RK4. EPC-RK4 was used due to its low relative error to exponential matrix method and low standard deviation than the Predictor-Corrector method, Exponential Linear, and CE/CM (constant extrapolation on predictor and constant midpoint on Corrector) performed by the previous research [10]. In exchange, the EPC-RK4 will simulate Monte Carlo transport four times in a timestep to solve functions order of its algorithm.

## 3. Calculation Algorithm

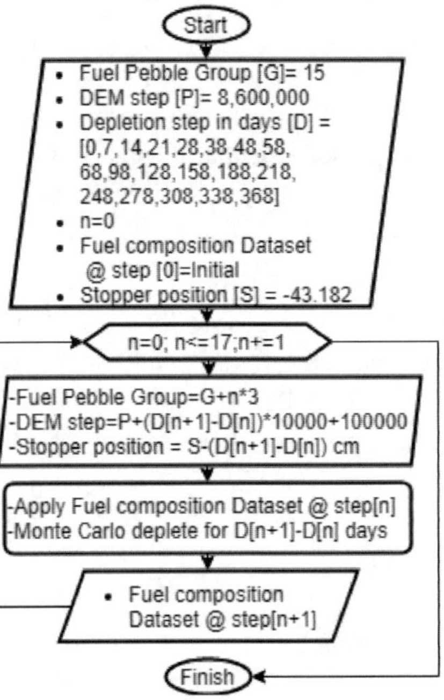


**Figure 3.** DEM coupled Monte Carlo method depletion simulation flowchart.

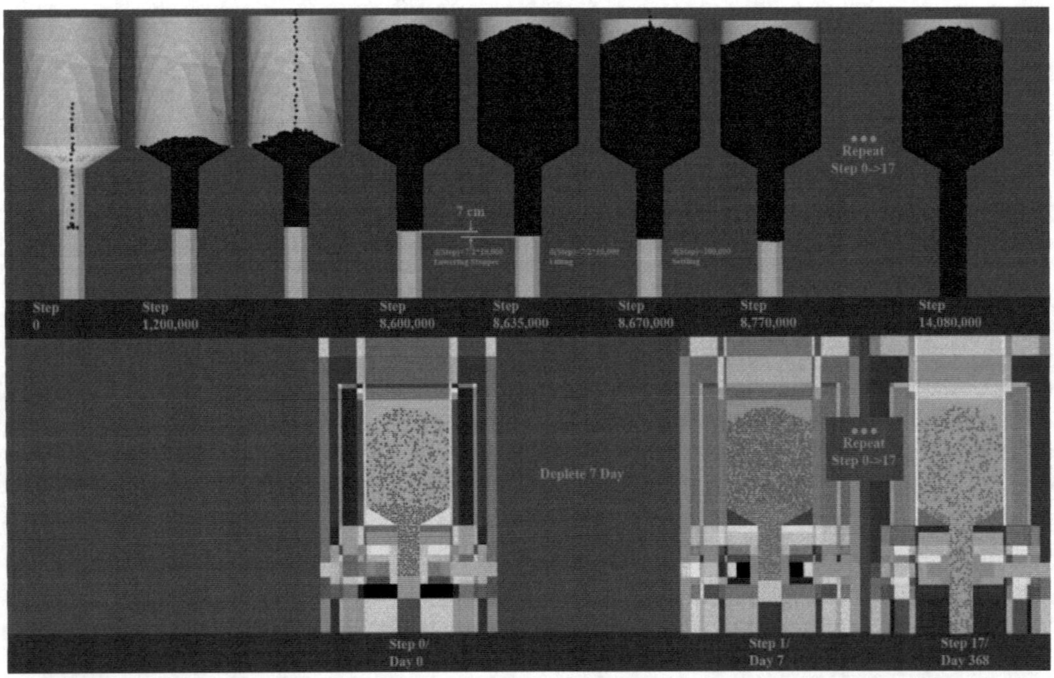


**Figure 4.** DEM simulation timestep and Monte Carlo depletion simulation step relation.

The pebble enters the reactor one by one from the 10cm diameter aperture above the reactor boundary. The total DEM timestep from the insertion of dummy pebble until all 28,020 pebbles settled ($E_k \leq 10^{-5}$ J) is 8,600,000 timestep. The stopper went down 1 cm/day of depletion timestep length to represent core height descend. Let D is a depletion time in days, then the timesteps to simulate the stopper go down is $5{,}000D$. After that, the set of unirradiated pebble inserted for the next $5{,}000D$ to compensate for the core height descend. DEM will also simulate 100,000 timesteps to make sure the pebbles are all settled. Therefore, the total timesteps performed from one depletion step to another is $10{,}000D + 100{,}000$ timesteps. The relation of DEM timesteps and Monte Carlo depletion steps shown in Figure 4.

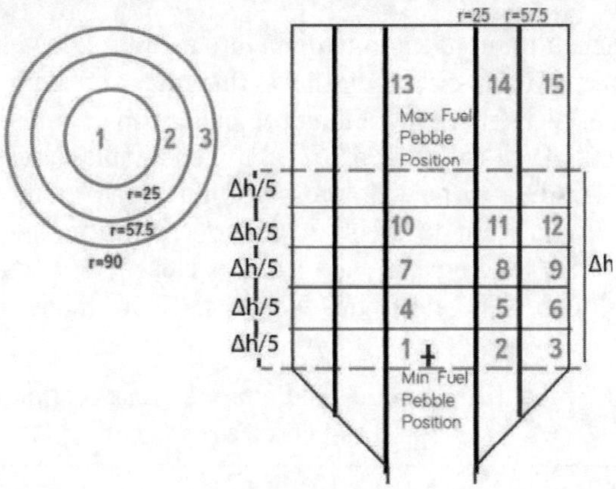


**Figure 5.** Fuel pebble grouping rule at initial depletion step.

Ideally, to perform the depletion for OTTO recirculation, each fuel pebble must be tracked individually to give an exact number of fissile materials depleted inside each fuel pebble. For simplification, the fuel pebble grouped according to its center cylindrical coordinates at timestep 0. In the initial configuration (step 0), there is 15 fuel pebble group. The fuel pebble grouping rule showed on Figure 5. Each fuel pebble in a pebble grouping has the same kernel material properties and tracked every Monte Carlo calculation step. In every step, the depletion of each pebble group accounted for the next Monte Carlo step. The newly added fuel has three groups specified by its center radial coordinate. In total, there are 66 fuel groups for 17 depletion steps ($15 + 3 \times [step]$).

**Table 3.** Pebble amount at each depletion step.

| Fuel Pebble | Total Pebble in DEM | Total Pebble in MC core | Day | Depletion Step | Active height [cm] |
|---|---|---|---|---|---|
| 13981 | 28020 | 28020 | 0 | 0 | 208.12 |
| 14006 | 28064 | 28064 | 7 | 1 | 210.97 |
| 14029 | 28106 | 28106 | 14 | 2 | 211.544 |
| 14052 | 28148 | 28148 | 21 | 3 | 212.172 |
| 14073 | 28186 | 28186 | 28 | 4 | 213.213 |
| 14100 | 28235 | 28235 | 38 | 5 | 214.161 |
| 14127 | 28284 | 28284 | 48 | 6 | 213.627 |
| 14153 | 28331 | 28331 | 58 | 7 | 212.981 |
| 14180 | 28379 | 28379 | 68 | 8 | 214.728 |
| 14305 | 28599 | 28599 | 98 | 9 | 213.998 |
| 14431 | 28821 | 28694 | 128 | 10 | 213.513 |
| 14559 | 29047 | 28659 | 158 | 11 | 214.316 |
| 14682 | 29264 | 28618 | 188 | 12 | 213.596 |
| 14810 | 29490 | 28570 | 218 | 13 | 210.829 |
| 14933 | 29706 | 28521 | 248 | 14 | 213.719 |
| 15048 | 29935 | 28488 | 278 | 15 | 212.615 |
| 15132 | 30161 | 28438 | 308 | 16 | 211.405 |
| 15192 | 30391 | 28396 | 338 | 17 | 210.875 |

The programs run on a personal computer with 16 GB of memory and 16 threaded CPU with a 3.7 GHz maximum clock speed for each CPU core.

## 4. Result

### *4.1. Multiplication Factor*

The neutron data in this calculation used room temperature at approximately 20°C. The multiplication factor from step 0 depletion and initial criticality shows that they were comparable with the other code. The initial criticality model used a similar modelling principle with the full core model. Instead of using 24,531 mixed pebbles, the initial criticality used 16,890 mixed Pebbles above level 0 cm. It appears that the model criticalities are sensitive to neutron cross-section library. Other than that, the packing of pebble inside the core gave a significant difference in reactor criticality. The full core model in this work has a maximum core height of 208.12 cm different from its closer counterpart, from [11], in which has lower core height at the full core. Therefore, this work's full core model is less packed than another model, even though the criticality is close.

**Table 4.** $K_{eff}$ comparison between different code and neutron cross-section library for initial criticality and full core case.

| Calculation | Criticality | Library |
|---|---|---|
| | **Initial Criticality** | |
| This Work | $1.01762 \pm 4.1 \times 10^{-4}$ | ENDF B-VII.0 |
| | $1.00692 \pm 4.3 \times 10^{-4}$ | ENDF B-VII.1 |
| | $1.00924 \pm 4.2 \times 10^{-4}$ | ENDF B-VIII.0 |
| IRPhEP [3] (MCNP) | $1.01190 \pm 2.1 \times 10^{-4}$ | ENDF B-VI |
| Ref. [12] (MCNP) | $1.00366 \pm 4.1 \times 10^{-4}$ | ENDF B-VII.0 |
| INL [11] (Serpent) | $1.01025 \pm 5.1 \times 10^{-5}$ | ENDF B-VI |
| | $1.00023 \pm 2.3 \times 10^{-5}$ | ENDF B-VII.1 |
| | **Full Core** | |
| This Work | $1.14467 \pm 4.0 \times 10^{-4}$ | ENDF B-VII.0 |
| | $1.13298 \pm 4.1 \times 10^{-4}$ | ENDF B-VII.1 |
| | $1.13403 \pm 4.4 \times 10^{-4}$ | ENDF B-VIII.0 |
| INL [11] (Serpent) | $1.12242 \pm 1.3 \times 10^{-4}$ | ENDF B-VII.1 26,992 Pebble |
| Iran [12] (MCNP) | 1.14545 | ENDF B-VII.0 24,705 Pebble |
| France [1] | 1.14737 | VSOP |
| China [1] | 1.1358 | VSOP |
| | 1.1381 | MCNP4A |
| Turkey [1] | 1.0941 | ENDF B-IV |
| | 1.0809 | ENDF B-V |
| USA [1] | 1.1298 | ENDF B-VI |

The $k_{eff}$ results for a different time show that the value decreased drastically only in the first step (7 days). For the rest of the time, the $k_{eff}$ decreases almost linearly. The spike or $k_{eff}$ jump happens during the addition of pebble. The $k_{eff}$ jump is barely recognizable after 38 days because fuel and dummy pebble distributed evenly in the reactor. If the simulation timestep period decreased along with lower addition each time step, the calculation should be much smoother and shows a perfect $k_{eff}$ curve without the spike.

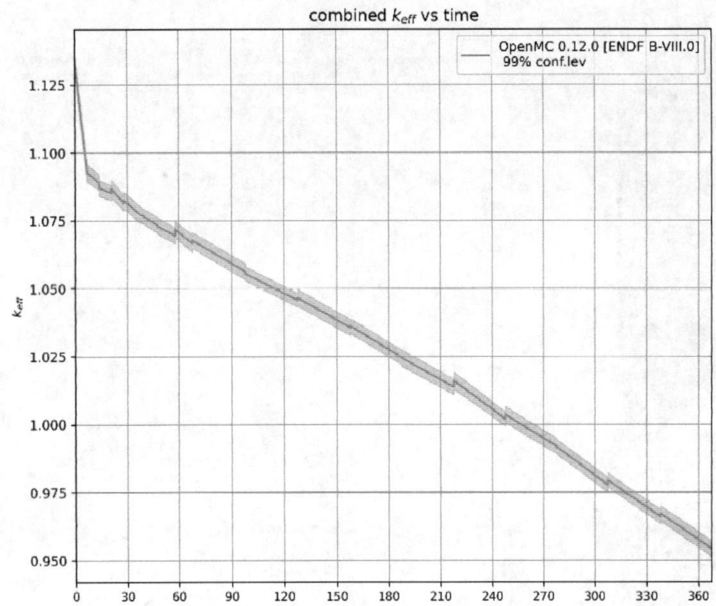


**Figure 6.** Combined $k_{eff}$ vs time in days.

The spectrum tally shows an ordinary thermal reactor spectrum with spikes at the thermal energy. Those means that the code and the library work properly to differentiate the neutron energy. However, Figure 7 does not show the multiple group cross-section used in transport simulation since this study utilizes the continuous neutron spectrum for transport simulation.

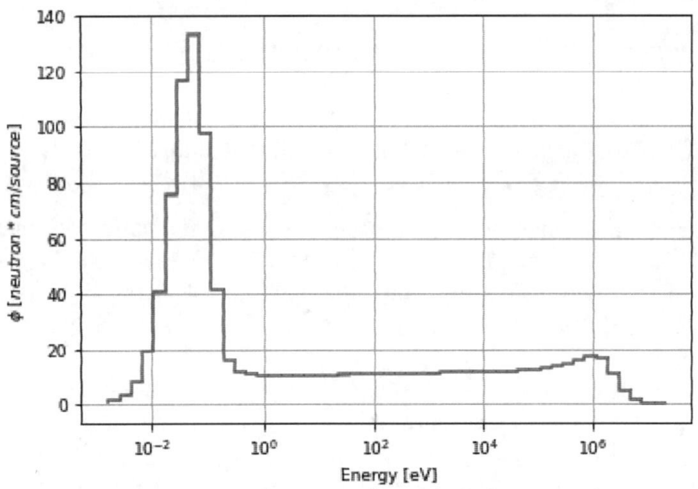


**Figure 7.** Neutron Spectrum tally with 50 log spaced energy.

### *4.2. Tally Distribution*

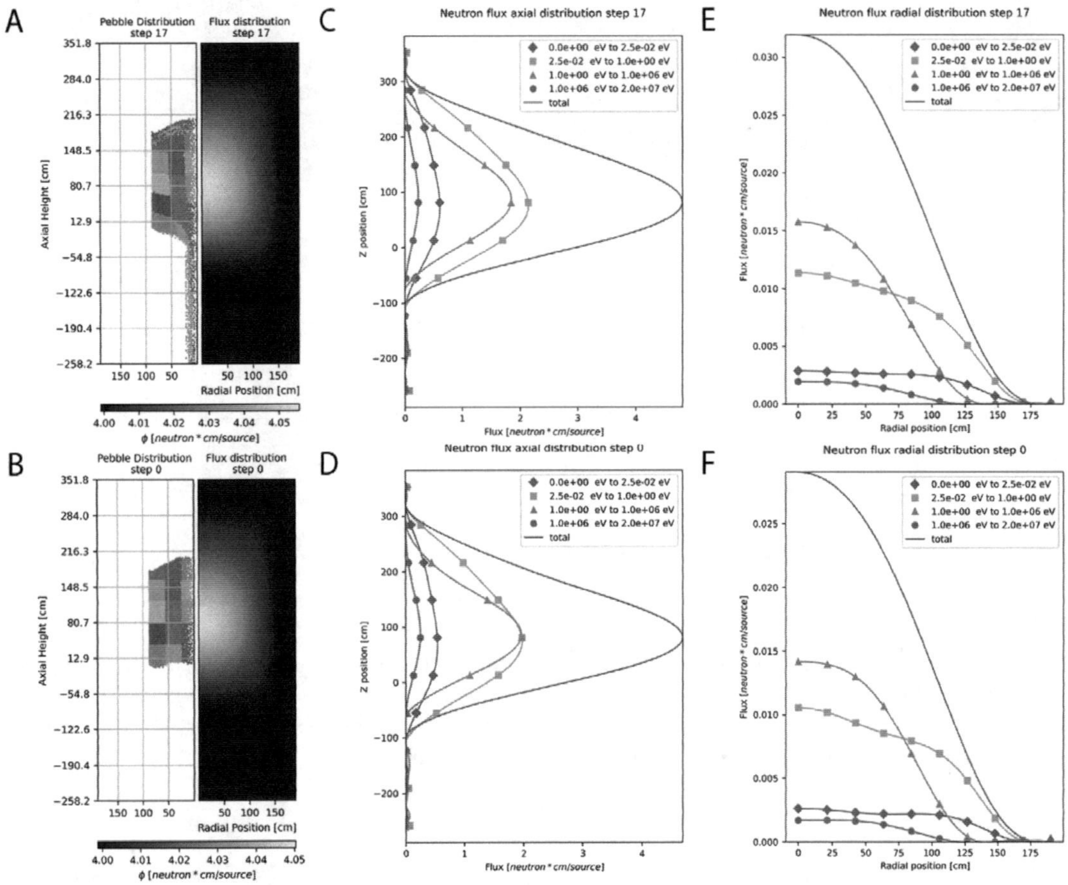


**Figure 8.** Pebble distribution and radial-axial flux distribution (A) after 338 days and (B) at initial, Axial flux distribution (C) after 338 days and (D) at initial, and Radial distribution (E) after 338 days and (F) at initial.

Tally calculation in this study utilizes the functional expansion of OpenMC, mesh tally and cell tally to score flux tally. The tally scoring used the $10^{th}$ order Legendre Polynomial for axial distribution and $10^{th}$ order Zernike Radial Polynomial for radial distribution. The score was divided into four energy spectra. Other than that, the mesh tally with $3 \times 3 \times 3\ cm^3$ size mesh was used to filter flux tally in the reactor. The cell tally also scores the flux tally for every fuel pebble.

The graph from each cylindrical dimension (Figure 8) shows a slight oscillation because of the polynomial function behavior. The distribution shows that most of the neutron is a thermal neutron and neutron between 1eV and 1MeV spectra. Because of the longer energy gap in filter 1eV to 1MeV, those energy ranges have tally distribution almost the same as thermal energy distribution. In step 0, the 1eV to 1MeV neutron spectra has a higher peak in axial distribution than the thermal neutron range.

The deviation for the tally is too small to plot and becomes unrecognized in the plot. The tally distribution concludes that the flux distribution is barely changing during recirculation. Flux normalization to units of $\frac{n}{cm^2 s}$ is necessary for further analysis.

The combination of axial-radial distribution and fuel pebble distribution shows the fuel pebble in one group may receive different flux. In detail, the fuel pebble flux visualized on Figure 10. Every color on Figure 8 (A) and (B) represent different fuel pebble group but the recirculated fuel pebble is barely visible due to its small amount. At day 338, several group-1 pebbles (center and lower group) began to exit the reactor. The fuel pebble on the discharge tube is barely perform fission due to the low flux received.

*4.3. Depletion*
The main feature of this method is the one could know the composition of each pebble or each group pebble. This method is useful for safeguard purposes to track and predict fuel pebble composition along with the operation. With the depletion analysis, the cause of flux fluctuation could be determined.

Some absorber Build-up such as $Xe^{135}$ caused the steep decrease in criticality at early operation. However, those $Xe^{135}$ jump from newly added fuel is insignificant due to the low amount of fuel pebble added. The relation between the residence time and $Xe^{135}$ densities shows that the recirculated pebbles deplete in a particular pattern. The trendline from $Xe^{135}$ composition of newly added fuel to residence time fit with an exponential curve that almost linear. The $Xe^{135}$ on a group-1 fuel pebble steeply decrease after 158 days due to lesser flux received by those fuel pebble in discharge tube. In the end, the $Xe^{135}$ concentration became steady after those pebbles exits the core.

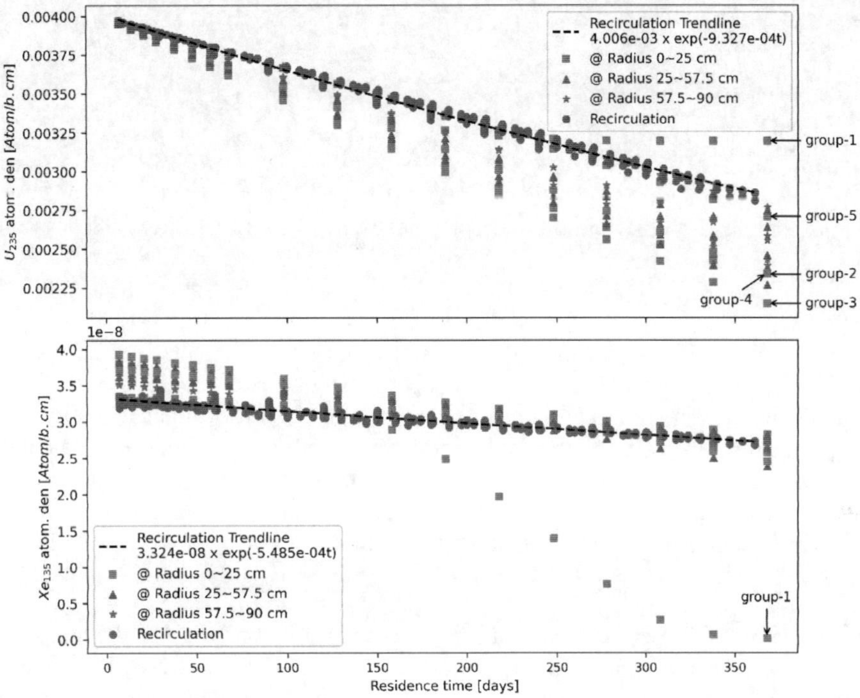


**Figure 9.** $U^{235}$ and $Xe^{135}$ atom density in fuel pebble vs residence time.

The same phenomenon also happens with $U^{235}$ nuclide. The center group deplete faster than the outer radial group due to concentrated flux at the core center. Different from $Xe^{135}$ profile, the $U^{235}$ composition to residence time profile for the initial loading fuel pebbles widen. At day 248, the $U^{235}$ composition in group-1 fuel pebble begins to steady until it exits the core. Similar to $Xe^{135}$, the $U^{235}$ composition of newly added fuel creates an exponential trendline.

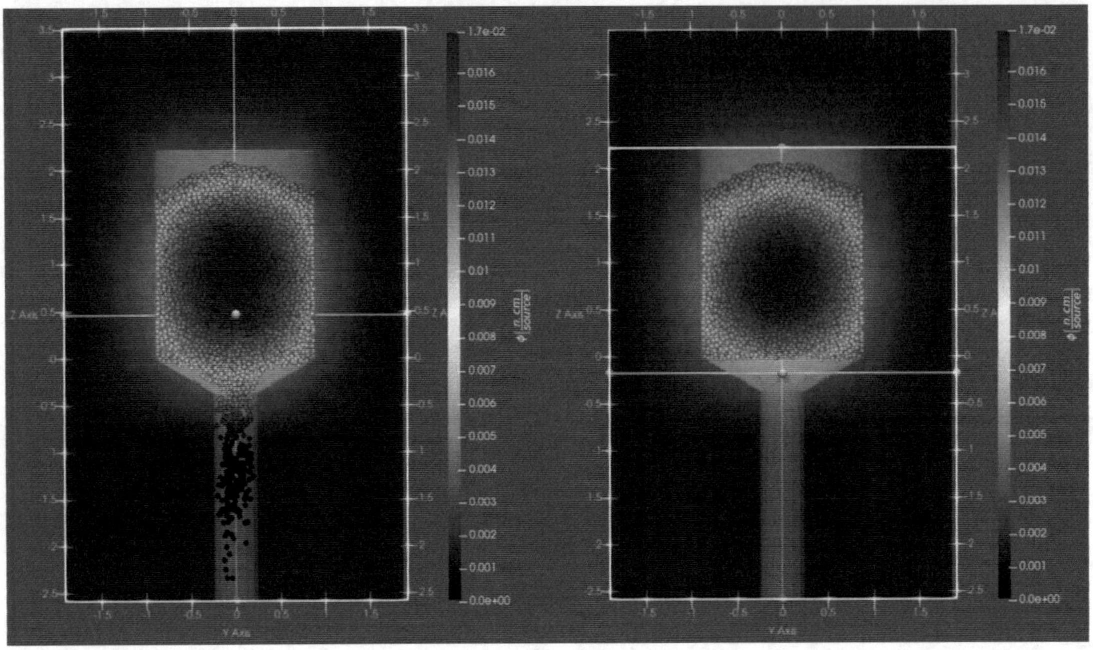


**Figure 10.** Fuel Pebble flux distribution and core mesh tally flux (left) after 338 days and (right) at initial.

## 5. Conclusion

The method of coupling DEM with Monte Carlo simulation could create realistic geometry of HTR10. With the methodology provided in this work, one could investigate each pebble composition by grouping them and tracking its movement along with the operation. The result of this calculation is comparable with a similar modelling method or other older modelling method. However, this calculation method needs more sensitivity analysis on DEM parameter to create a comparable model with the other benchmark. It is also necessary to perform a longer depletion simulation to give a more representative relation between fuel pebble residence time and nuclide composition.

**Acknowledgments**

This paper and the research behind it would not have been possible without the support our faculty member and referees. Special thanks to Dr. Alexander Agung (Head of DNEEP, Universitas Gadjah Mada) for allowing me to run the OpenMC simulation in our department server and for his useful suggestions.

## References

[1] IAEA, Evaluation of high temperature gas cooled reactor performance: Benchmark analysis related to initial testing of HTTR and HTR-10, IAEA TecDoc-1382, no. November. 2003.

[2] S. Wu, J. Peir, and J. H. Liang, "Burnup Computation for HTR-10 Using Layer-to-Layer Movement," in Proceedings of the 21st International Conference on Nuclear Engineering, 2013, no. January 2017, pp. ICONE21-16485.

[3] W. K. Terry, L. M. Montierth, J. J. Cogliati, A. M. Ougouag, J. B. Briggs, L. M. Montierth, H. D. Gougar, and V. F. Dean, "EVALUATION OF THE INITIAL CRITICAL CONFIGURATION OF THE HTR-10 PEBBLE-BED REACTOR NEA/NSC/DOC(2006)1," 2006.

[4] C. Kloss and C. Goniva, "LIGGGHTS - OPEN SOURCE DISCRETE ELEMENT SIMULATIONS OF GRANULAR MATERIALS BASED ON LAMMPS," Mater. Fabr. Prop. Charact. Model., vol. 2, pp. 781–788, 2011.

[5] Y. Li and W. Ji, "Pebble Flow and Coolant Flow Analysis Based on a Fully Coupled Multi-

Physics Model Pebble Flow and Coolant Flow Analysis Based on a Fully Coupled Multiphysics Model," Nucl. Sci. Eng., vol. 173, no. November, pp. 150–162, 2013.

[6] P. K. Romano, N. E. Horelik, B. R. Herman, A. G. Nelson, B. Forget, and K. Smith, "OpenMC : A state-of-the-art Monte Carlo code for research and development," Ann. Nucl. Energy, 2014.

[7] D. A. Brown, M. B. Chadwick, R. Capote, A. C. Kahler, A. Trkov, M. W. Herman, A. A. Sonzogni, Y. Danon, A. D. Carlson, M. Dunn, D. L. Smith, G. M. Hale, G. Arbanas, R. Arcilla, C. R. Bates, B. Beck, B. Becker, F. Brown, R. J. Casperson, J. Conlin, D. E. Cullen, M. Descalle, R. Firestone, T. Gaines, K. H. Guber, A. I. Hawari, J. Holmes, T. D. Johnson, T. Kawano, B. C. Kiedrowski, A. J. Koning, S. Kopecky, and L. Leal, "ENDF / B-VIII . 0 : The 8 th Major Release of the Nuclear Reaction Data Library with CIELO-project Cross Sections , New Standards and Thermal Scattering Data," Nucl. Data Sheets, vol. 148, pp. 1–142, 2018.

[8] P. Romano and S. Harper, "Nuclear data processing capabilities in OpenMC," EPJ Web Conf., vol. 06011, no. ND2016, pp. 2–5, 2017.

[9] K. S. Kim, "Specification for the VERA Depletion Benchmark Suite," 2015.

[10] C. Josey, B. Forget, and K. Smith, "High Order Methods for the Integration of the Bateman Equations and Other Problems of the Form of y = F ( y , t ) y," J. Comput. Phys., no. August, 2017.

[11] J. Ortensi, S. Schunert, Y. Wang, and V. Labour, "Benchmark Analysis of the HTR-10 with the MAMMOTH Reactor Physics Application," Idaho, 2018.

[12] A. Abedi and N. Vosoughi, "Neutronic simulation of a pebble bed reactor considering its double heterogeneous nature," Nucl. Eng. Des., vol. 253, pp. 277–284, 2012.

Journal of Physics: Conference Series **2048** (2021) 012032 doi:10.1088/1742-6596/2048/1/012032

# Influence of Coiling Direction of Helical Tube Bundles on the Thermal-Hydraulics of the HTGR Steam Generator

**Weikai Gao[1,2], Xiaoyang Xie[1], Xiaowei Li[1,*], Xinxin Wu[1]**

[1]*Key Laboratory of Advanced Reactor Engineering and Safety of Ministry of Education, Collaborative Innovation Center of Advanced Nuclear Energy Technology, Institute of Nuclear and New Energy Technology, Tsinghua University, Beijing 100084, PR China*
[2]*China Academy of Launch Vehicle Technology, Beijing 100076, PR China*

*lixiaowei@tsinghua.edu.cn

**Abstract.** Helical tube bundles were usually adopted in the steam generators (SGs) or intermediate heat exchangers (IHXs) of high temperature gas-cooled reactors (HTGRs). Heat transfer tubes in neighboring tube layers can be coiled in the same direction or in the opposite direction. The coiling direction has influences on the thermal-hydraulic performances of the SGs or IHXs. The cross flow convection over helical tube bundles with neighboring tube layers having the same coiled direction and opposite coiled direction were numerically investigated. Reynolds stress model with standard wall functions was used for the turbulence modeling. For a helical tube bundle with neighboring layers coiled in the same direction (parallel tube layers), the tangential velocity along the coiled circumferential direction could be observed obviously. For a helical tube bundle with neighboring layers coiled in the opposite direction (crossed tube layers), there is no average tangential velocity of the whole flow filed. And the streamlines of the fluid are very complex. The flow resistances and heat transfer coefficients over helical tube bundle with parallel tube layers and crossed tube layers were compared. Although the heat transfer over helical tube bundles with crossed tube layers was 9.39% smaller than that with parallel tube layers, the pressure drop over tube bundle with crossed tube layers was much smaller compared with those with parallel tube layers.

## 1. Introduction

Steam generator (SG) is the most important heat transfer equipment for High Temperature Gas-cooled Reactor (HTGR) [1, 2]. Helical tube bundles are usually adopted in the SG to increase the heat transfer area and improve the compactness due to the low heat transfer coefficient in the gas side. As the SG adopts once through flow pattern, its heat capacity is very small. The once through steam generator (OTSG) is sensitive to thermal hydraulic parameter fluctuation and geometric deviations [3]. Analysis of the HTR-PM OTSG shows that the flow and heat transfer characteristics in the primary side have more influences on its overall thermal hydraulic performance [4]. The basic flow pattern in the primary side of the SG is turbulent cross flow over helical tube bundles. The geometrical parameters such as longitudinal tube pitches, transverse tube pitches and tube diameter, will influence the cross flow and heat transfer characteristics over tube bundles. 1D and 2D tube and shell side coupled methods were proposed by Li et al. for HTGR OTSG [5]. The overall thermal performance of HTR-PM OTSG was simulated using a 1D method. The thermal non-uniformity or thermal deviations caused by the geometrical and thermal hydraulic deviations were analyzed using a 2D method. It is shown that a 1% change of secondary side water flow rate of a certain layer of tubes will result in a 5-6°C variation of the outlet steam temperature of this layer of tubes. A helical diameter variation of 1 mm will result in a 6-7°C variation of the outlet steam temperature. An inlet helium temperature profile with a 10°C variance will result in a 2°C variation of the outlet steam temperature.

The influences of the bounding walls on the cross flow and heat transfer characteristics were numerically investigated using CFD method [6]. It is found that the wall effects depress turbulence intensities of the flow in the near wall flow passages. So the heat transfer coefficients of the near wall tubes are 10% lower than those of the tubes in the middle of the bundle. The influence of fabrication tolerance on the cross flow and heat transfer characteristics over tube bundles in the HTR-PM OTSG was numerically investigated using the 2D tube and shell side coupled method and the 2D URANS method [4]. It is found that a fabrication tolerance of 0.5 mm in helical diameter will result in 1.4% pressure resistance variation and 0.7% flow rate variation among the 19 units. And it will induce about 5°C steam temperature variance among the 5 layers of tubes. The influence of the of helical tube bundles on the thermal hydraulic performance of the helical tube bundles was numerically investigated. The turbulent cross flow and heat transfer characteristics over medium scale and large scale helical tube bundles were compared [7]. It is found that the temperature non-uniformity in the large scale helical tube bundles is larger than that in the medium scale helical tube bundles.

There are two types of coiling directions of helical tube bundles in the commonly used steam generators. Heat transfer tubes on neighboring tube layers can be coiled in the same direction or in the opposite direction. The coiling direction has influences on the thermal-hydraulic performances of the SGs or IHXs. The angles between the tube axes of helical tubes and the plane perpendicular to the fluid flow directions, which are called the flow attack angle or the yaw angle of the tubes, also affects the cross flow and heat transfer characteristics over helical tube bundles. For example, the IHX of High-temperature Engineering Test Reactor (HTTR) adopted helical tube bundles with neighboring tube layers coiled in the same direction [8]. The overall flow resistance, heat transfer characteristics and flow induced vibrations was experimentally studied. The helix angle of the HTTR IHX is 12°. It is found that the flow resistance and heat transfer coefficient were both smaller than those calculated using the experimental correlations. HTR-PM SG adopted helical tube bundles with neighboring layers coiled in the opposite direction. The helix angle of HTR-PM SG is about 7°.

It was found that the flow resistance and Nusselt number measured in the experiment were smaller than that calculated using the experimental correlations [9]. Groehn [10] experimentally studied the influence of the yaw angle on heat transfer and pressure drop of straight tube bundles in the heat exchangers. The yaw angle of the tubes varied between 15° and 90° ($15° \leq \varphi \leq 90°$). And Reynolds number varied between $2\times10^3$ and $10^5$ ($2\times10^3 \leq Re \leq 10^5$). It was found that the correlations for flow attack angle of 90° could be applied to predict the heat transfer coefficient of yawed tube banks if the velocity is corrected for calculating the Reynolds number. However, it is not applicable to predict the hydraulic resistance.

Groehn [11] experimentally studied the flow and heat transfer characteristics over yawed tube banks with neighboring layers having opposite sense of inclination. Moreover, a full-scale test of a helical-type heat exchanger has been done to verify the fundamental research. It was found that opposite-sense inclination of neighboring tube layers of inline tube banks leads to a small reduction of the heat transfer coefficient while the hydraulic resistance decreases substantially. The opposite sense inclination becomes more evident with smaller transverse tube pitches. It was also shown that the results from the investigations of inclined straight tube banks are transferable to helical coiled tube bundles.

Due to the high compactness and sensitivity of HTR-PM SG, the turbulent cross flow and heat transfer characteristics over helical tube bundles with different coiling direction should be studied in more detail. Because of the complexness of the geometry of the helical tube bundle and the huge computational resources required for the simulation, only the overall flow characteristics over helical tube bundles was simulated. The detailed flow and heat transfer was simulated using the geometry of straight tube bundle with inclination. It requires less computational resources and more accurate models can be used. Then the influences of coiling direction on the cross flow and heat transfer characteristics over tube bundles was studied.

## 2. Numerical methods

### *2.1. Geometric model*

The geometric models of helical tube bundles were shown in Figure 1 and Figure 2. They were three-dimensional wall bounded helical tube bundles with 20 rows of tubes in the axial direction (stream wise direction) and 5 layers of tubes in the radial direction (transverse direction). The geometric model of helical tube bundles coiled in the same direction was shown in Figure 1. The geometric model of the 1st and 2nd tube layers of helical tube bundles coiled in the opposite direction was shown in Figure 2(a). The geometric model of the 3rd, 4th and 5th tube layers was shown in Figure 2(b). Layer No.1 and layer No.5 tubes were adjacent to the inner wall and outer wall. There were 5, 6, 7, 8, 9 rows of tubes in layer No. 1, 2, 3, 4, 5, respectively. The structure of the helical tube bundles was very complex. In order to make it clearly understood, only part of the helical tubes in each layer of the tube bundles was shown in the figures. The tube diameter was 19 mm. The stream wise tube pitch was 25 mm, and the transverse tube pitch was 30 mm. The helix angle was 7.3°.

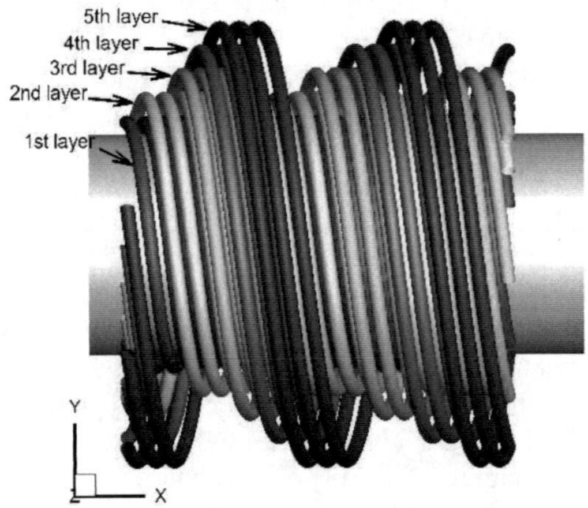


**Figure 1.** Geometric model of helical tube bundles coiled in the same direction

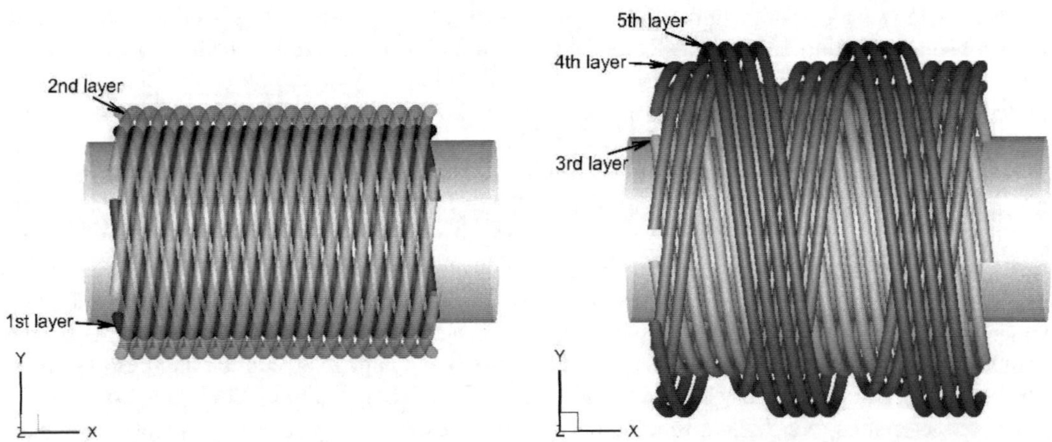


(a). 1st and 2nd tube layers (b). 3rd, 4th and 5th tube layers

**Figure 2.** Geometric model of helical tube bundles coiled in the opposite direction

The geometric models of the straight tube bundles were shown in Figure 3. The tube bundles were in similar arrangements as the helical tube bundles. There were 5 layers of tubes in the transverse direction and 8 rows of tubes in the stream wise direction. The tube diameter was 19 mm. The stream wise tube pitch was 25 mm, and the transverse tube pitch was 30 mm. The yawed angle was 7.3°.

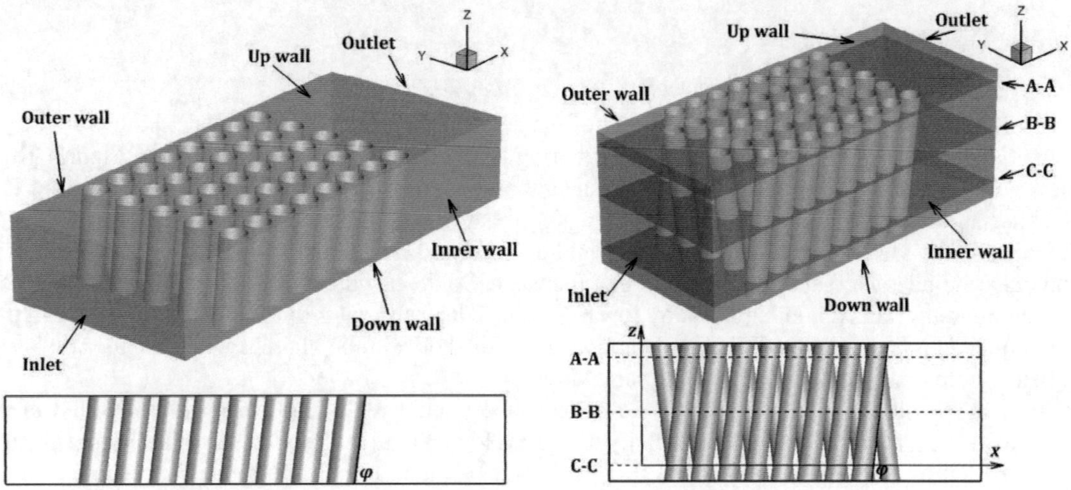


(a). Tube bundle with parallel tube layers (b). Tube bundle with crossed tube layers

**Figure 3.** Geometric model of straight tube bundles with inclination

### *2.2. Governing equations and boundary conditions*

Unstructured grid was generated for the computational domain of helical tube bundles. The total element number of the tube bundle with neighboring layers coiled in the opposite direction was 18,079,231. The total element number of the tube bundle with neighboring layers coiled in the same direction was 18,146,556. Structured grid was generated for the computational domain of straight tube bundles with inclination. The total element number of tube bundle with parallel tube layers was 18,709,600. The total element number of tube bundle with crossed tube layers was 51,443,136.

Velocity inlet boundary condition was set for the inlet. The outlet was fully developed boundary condition. Adiabatic and non-slip wall boundary conditions were used for the inner wall and outer wall. Constant temperature and non-slip wall boundary conditions were set for the tube walls. The tube wall temperature was 953.15 K. The working fluid was helium with constant properties. The physical properties of helium are shown in Table 1. The inlet velocity of the helical tube bundles is 7.134 m/s. The operating pressure is 7 MPa.

**Table 1.** Physical properties of helium

| Properties | Units | Value |
|---|---|---|
| Density [$\rho$] | kg/m$^3$ | 3.46 |
| Heat capacity [$c_p$] | J/(kg·K) | 5189.67 |
| Thermal conductivity [$\lambda$] | W/(m·K) | 0.36 |
| Viscosity [$\mu$] | kg/(m·s) | 4.51E-05 |

The governing equations were the time-dependent three-dimensional Reynolds Averaged Navier-Stokes equations and the energy equation. Li et al.[6] numerically investigated the turbulent cross flow and heat transfer in a wall bounded tube bundle. Standard $k$-$\varepsilon$ model, SST $k$-$\omega$ model and Reynolds stress model were used for the simulation. It was found that both standard $k$-$\varepsilon$ model and Reynolds stress model showed good agreements with the experiments. Thus, Reynolds stress model was used for the turbulence modeling in this paper. Standard wall function was used for the near wall treatment of helical tube bundles. And enhanced wall treatment was used for the near wall treatment of straight tube bundles. The governing equations were solved using the commercial CFD software ANSYS Fluent. Velocity-pressure coupling was treated with the SIMPLEC algorithm. The convection terms were discretized with the QUICK scheme. The time step is 0.0001 s

## 3. Results and discussion

### *3.1. Overall flow characteristics over helical tube bundles*

Figure 4 shows the transient velocity contour of the helical tube bundle on z=0 plane. Figure 4(a) is the velocity contour of the tube bundle with neighboring layers coiled in the same direction. Figure 4(b) is the velocity contour of the tube bundle with neighboring layers coiled in the opposite direction. It is shown that the fluid in the tube bundle sways as it passes the tube bundles. The turbulent wakes after the tubes swing towards upper right or lower right or backward. The bounding walls (inner cylinder wall and outer cylinder wall) suppress the swing of the wake. So the turbulent wakes after the tubes adjacent to the bounding walls could hardly sway towards them. The transient periodic zigzag flow appeared in wall bounded inline tube bundles was also observed in the helical tube bundles with neighboring layers coiled in both opposite direction and the same direction,

It is shown that the wake swing in the helical tube bundle with neighboring layers coiled in the opposite direction has no obvious periodicity compared to that in the tube bundles with neighboring tube layers coiled in the same direction and that in the straight tube bundle. It is mainly because that the velocity components along the tube axis influences the main flow and the vortex shedding. For the helical tube bundle with neighboring tube layers coiled in the same direction, the tube arrangements in different cross section along the circumferential direction are the same. The maximum velocity in these cross sections are equal. The velocity components along the tube axis have the same influence on the vortex shedding. For the helical tube bundle with neighboring tube layers coiled in the opposite direction, the tube arrangements in different cross section along the circumferential direction are different. The flow passages in these sections are slightly different. The maximum velocities in the different cross sections are not equal. The velocity components along the tube axis have different influences on different tubes. Thus, the wake swing in tube bundle with crossed tube layers are not periodic.

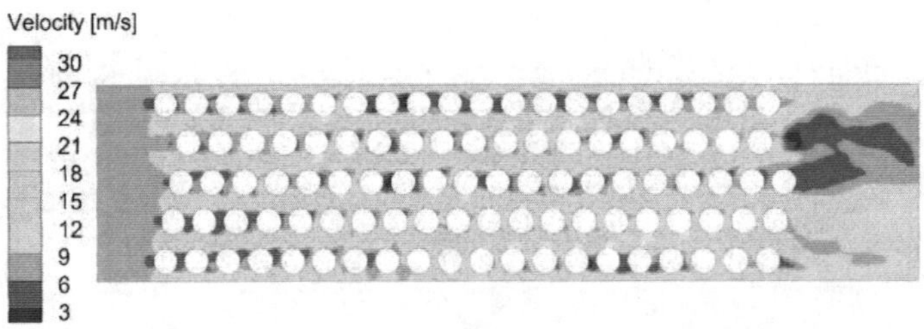


(a). Helical tube bundle coiled in the same direction

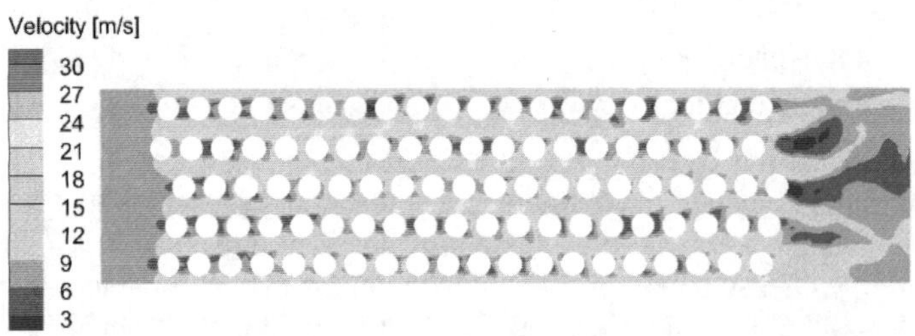


(b). Helical tube bundle coiled in the opposite direction

**Figure 4.** Transient velocity contour

The circumferential velocity contours of the helical tube bundles are shown in Figure 5. The cross section shown in Figure 5 is illustrated in Figure 8 and Figure 9. Figure 5(a) shows the circumferential velocity in helical tube bundles with neighboring layers coiled in the same direction. It is shown that the circumferential velocities of all tube layers in the upper section are negative. And the circumferential velocities of all tube layers in the lower section are positive. Thus, due to the same coiling direction of the helical tubes, the direction of the circumferential velocities in different tube layers are all the same. Figure 5(b) shows the circumferential velocity in helical tube bundles with neighboring layers coiled in the opposite direction. It is shown that the circumferential velocities near the 1st, 3rd and 5th tube layers in the upper section are negative. However, the circumferential velocities near the 2nd and 4th tube layers are positive. Similarly, the circumferential velocities near the 1st, 3rd and 5th tube layers in the lower section in Figure 5(b) are positive. The circumferential velocities near the 2nd and 4th tube layers are negative. Thus, due to the opposite coiling direction of the helical tubes, the direction of the circumferential velocities in different tube layers are different.

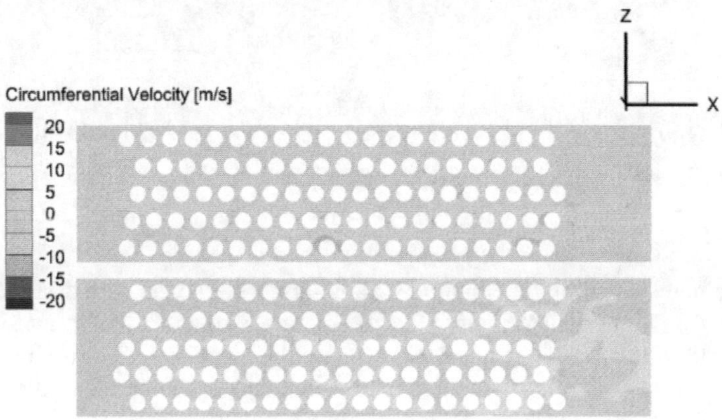


(a). Helical tube bundle coiled in the same direction

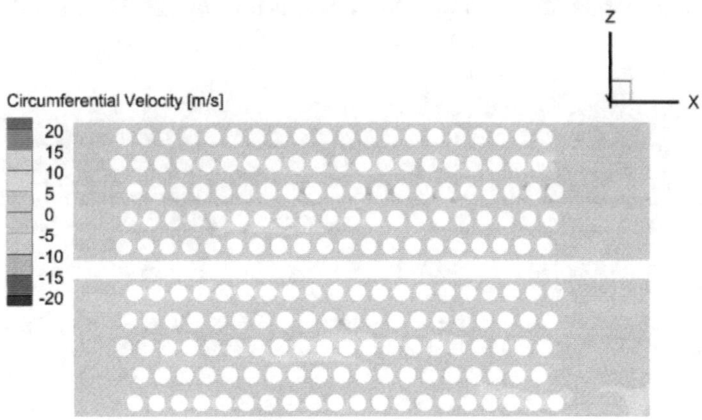


(b). Helical tube bundle coiled in the opposite direction

**Figure 5.** Circumferential velocity contour

The transient velocity vector in tube bundle with neighboring layers coiled in the same direction is shown in Figure 6. The overall velocity field of section x=0.275 m is shown in Figure 6(a). The detailed velocity field of the local area marked by the red box in Figure 6(a) is shown in Figure 6(b). It is shown that almost all the velocity vector on the cross-section are in the same direction. For a helical tube bundle with neighboring layers coiled in the same direction, the tangential velocity along the coiled circumferential direction could be obviously observed.

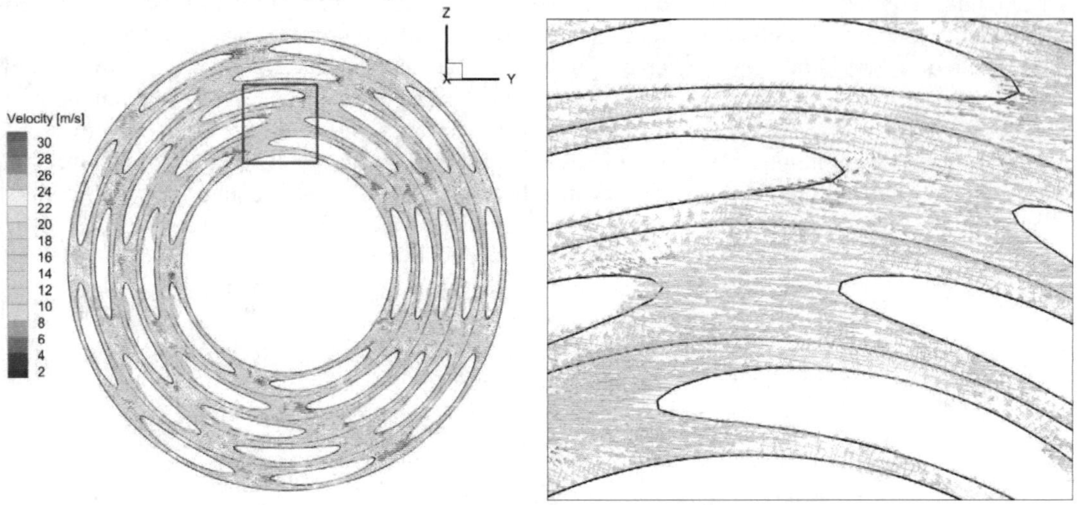


(a). Overall velocity field (b). Detailed velocity field

**Figure 6.** Transient velocity vector of helical tube bundle with neighboring layers coiled in the same direction

The transient velocity vector in tube bundle with neighboring layers coiled in the opposite direction is shown in Figure 7. The overall velocity field of section x=0.275 m is shown in Figure 7(a). The detailed velocity field of the local area marked by the red box in Figure 7(a) is shown in Figure 7(b). It is shown that the velocity vector in the neighboring layers are in the opposite direction. For example, the flow direction of the fluid in different radial position of the 2nd flow passage (the flow passage between the 1st tube layer and the 2nd tube layer) is different. The fluid near the 1st tube layer flow towards upper left and the fluid near the 2nd tube layer flow towards lower right. The fluid flow is more complex than that in the cross section of tube bundle with neighboring layers coiled in the same direction. And there is no average tangential velocity of the whole flow filed.

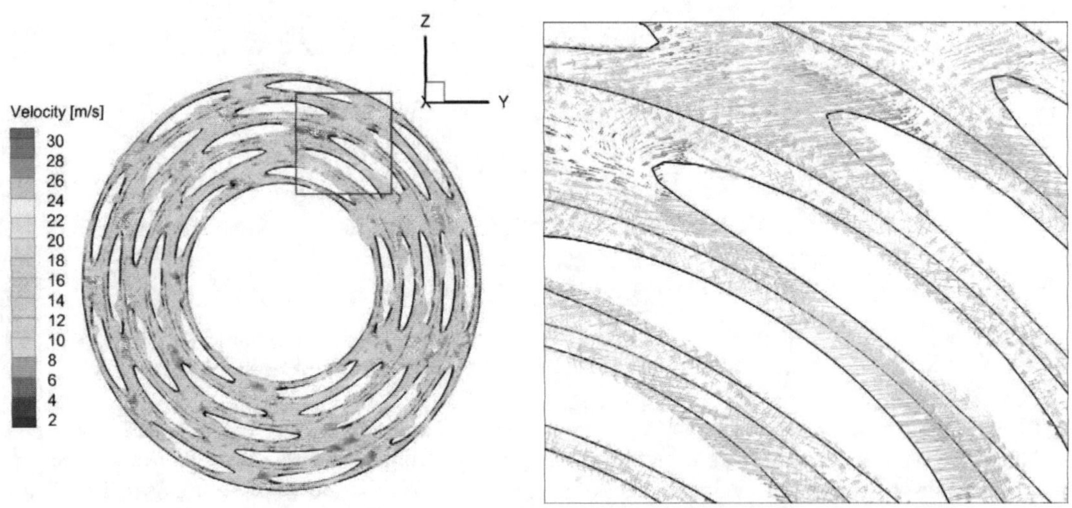


(a). Overall velocity field (b). Detailed velocity field

**Figure 7.** Transient velocity vector of helical tube bundle with neighboring layers coiled in the opposite direction

The circumferential velocity and streamlines of the cross section of helical tube bundle with neighboring layers coiled in the same direction is shown in Figure 8. The helical tubes were coiled in the same direction and the attack angles of the tubes in the neighboring tube layers were all 7.3°. Therefore, the directions of the circumferential velocity are all the same. As a result, the streamlines in the tube bundle bends along the coiling direction of the helical tubes. And the tangential velocity along the coiled circumferential direction could be obviously observed. The main fluid flows in a helical direction in tube bundles with neighboring layers coiled in the same direction.

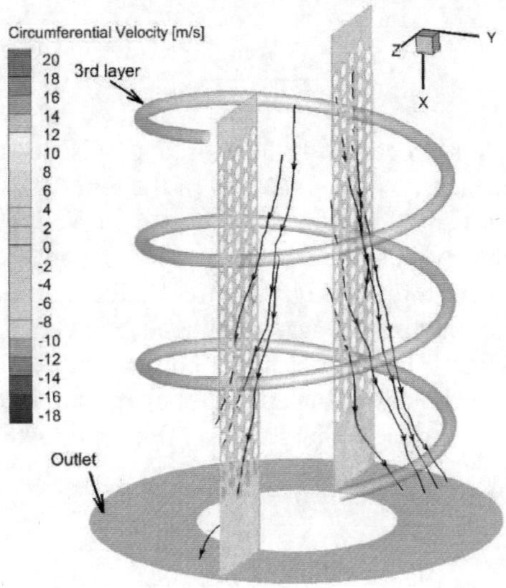


**Figure 8.** Circumferential velocity contour and streamlines in tube bundle with neighboring layers coiled in the same direction

The circumferential velocity and streamlines of the cross section of helical tube bundle with neighboring layers coiled in the opposite direction is shown in Figure 9. The absolute value of the attack angle of the neighboring tube layers is equal. But one is +7.3° and the other is -7.3°. Therefore, the direction of the circumferential velocity in different tube layers is opposite. As a result, the streamline shown in Figure 9 are almost in the same cross section, and a certain degree of circumferential bending occurs. This will make the thermal mixing in the tube bundle with neighboring layers coiled in the opposite direction better than that in the tube bundle with neighboring layers coiled in the same direction.

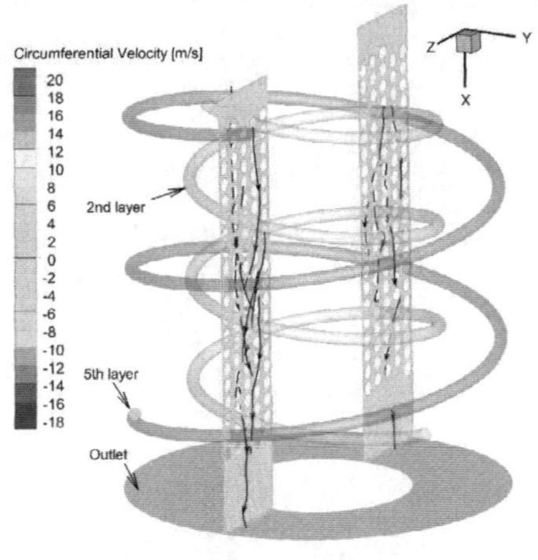


**Figure 9.** Circumferential velocity contour and streamlines in tube bundle with neighboring layers coiled in the opposite direction

### *3.2. Time-averaged flow characteristics in straight tube bundles*

The turbulent cross flow over tube bundles is periodic. The transient flow and heat transfer characteristics are extracted from the data files of each time step. Then the time averaged flow and heat transfer characteristics are obtained by averaging the transient flow and heat transfer characteristics for several periods.

Figure 10 shows the drag coefficient of the tube bundles with parallel tube layers and crossed tube layers. The horizontal coordinates are the row numbers of the tubes. The drag coefficient of the tube is calculated using Eq.(1).

$$C_d = \frac{F_{p,x} + F_{v,x}}{0.5\rho u_\infty^2 dH} \tag{1}$$

where $F_{p,x}$ is the $x$ direction pressure force, $F_{v,x}$ is the $x$ direction viscous force. The forces are calculated by integrating along the wall surfaces. $d$ is the diameter of the tube; $H$ is the length of the tube.

It is found that the drag coefficient of the tube bundle with crossed tube layers is smaller than that of the tube bundle with parallel tube layers in the fully developed region. The drag coefficients of the tubes near the inlet and outlet, which are influenced by the inlet effect and outlet effect, are neglected. The averaged drag coefficient of the tube bundle was calculated by averaging the drag coefficients of the tubes in the fully developed region. The averaged drag coefficients were shown in Table 2. It is found that the drag coefficient of the tube bundle with parallel tube layers is 15.62% larger than that of the tube bundle with crossed tube layers. The opposite inclination effect will lower the flow resistance of the tube bundles.

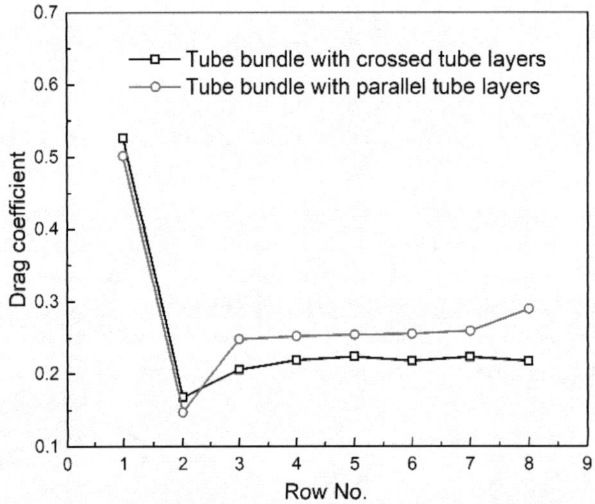


**Figure 10.** Drag coefficient of straight tube bundles

**Table 2.** Time-averaged flow resistance coefficient

| | Drag coefficient | Difference |
|---|---|---|
| Tube bundle with crossed tube layers | 0.2209 | - |
| Tube bundle with parallel tube layers | 0.2554 | 15.62% |

### *3.3. Time-averaged heat transfer characteristics in straight tube bundles*

Figure 11 shows the Nusselt number of the tube bundles with crossed tube layers and parallel tube layers. The horizontal coordinates are the row numbers of the tubes. It is found that the Nusselt number in the inlet region increases along the flow direction. The Nusselt number of the tube bundle with crossed tube layers is smaller than that of the tube bundle with parallel tube layers in the fully developed region. The Nusselt numbers of the tubes near the inlet and outlet, which are influenced by the inlet effect and outlet effect, are neglected. The averaged Nusselt number of the tube bundle is calculated by averaging the Nusselt number of the tubes in the fully developed region. The averaged Nusselt number are shown in Table 3. The Nusselt number of the tube bundles with parallel tube layers in the fully developed region is 9.39% larger than that of the Nusselt number of the tube bundles with crossed tube layers. The opposite inclination effect will lower the heat transfer of the tube bundles.

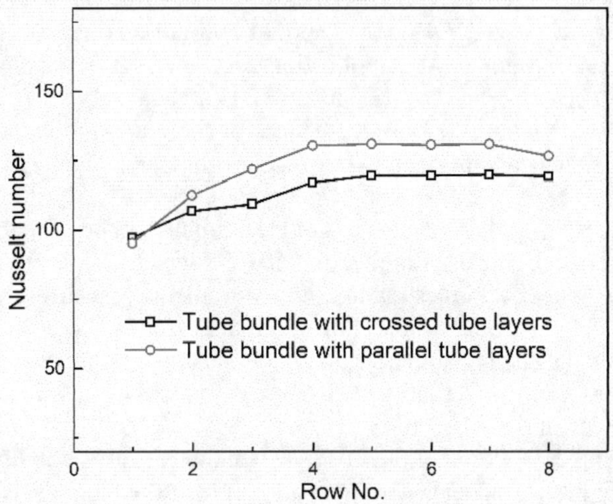


**Figure 11**. Nusselt number of straight tube bundles

**Table 3.** Time-averaged flow resistance coefficient

| | Nusselt number | Difference |
|---|---|---|
| Tube bundle with crossed tube layers | 119.56 | - |
| Tube bundle with parallel tube layers | 130.79 | 9.39% |

## 4.Conclusions

The overall flow characteristics over helical tube bundles with neighboring layers coiled in the same direction and opposite direction were simulated. The detailed flow and heat transfer characteristics over straight tube bundles with parallel tube layers and crossed tube layers were numerically investigated. The influences of coiling direction on the cross flow and heat transfer characteristics over tube bundles was studied. The main conclusions are:

1. For a helical tube bundle with neighboring layers coiled in the same direction, the tangential velocity along the coiled circumferential direction could be observed obviously.
2. For a helical tube bundle with neighboring layers coiled in the opposite direction, there is no average tangential velocity of the whole flow filed. However, the steam lines or flow paths of the fluid are very complex, this may enhance the thermal mixing among different tube layers of the helical tube bundles.
3. The heat transfer over tube bundles with crossed tube layers is 9.39% smaller than that with parallel tube layers, the pressure drop over tube bundles with crossed tube layers is 15.62% smaller than that with parallel tube layers.

## Acknowledgments

This work was financially supported by the National Natural Science Foundation of China (51576103) and the National S&T Major Project (Grant No. ZX06901)

## References

[1] Z. Zhang, Y. Dong, F. Li, Z. Zhang, H. Wang, X. Huang, H. Li, B. Liu, X. Wu, H. Wang, X. Diao, H. Zhang, J. Wang, The Shandong Shidao Bay 200 MWe high-temperature gas-cooled reactor pebble-bed module (HTR-PM) demonstration power plant: an engineering and technological innovation, Engineering, 2(1) (2016) 112-118.

[2] Z. Zhang, Z. Wu, D. Wang, Y. Xu, Y. Sun, F. Li, Y. Dong, Current status and technical description of Chinese 2 x 250 MWth HTR-PM demonstration plant, Nuclear Engineering and Design, 239(7) (2009) 1212-1219.

[3] X. Li, X. Wu, X. Luo, J. Zhao, Y. Zhang, Thermal hydraulic issues of HTGR helical tube once through steam generator: Methods and applications, in: The 8th International Topical Meeting on High Temperature Reactor Technology (HTR 2016), Las Vegas, NV, 2016.

[4] W. Gao, X. Li, X. Wu, J. Zhao, X. Luo, Influences of fabrication tolerance on thermal hydraulic performance of HTGR helical tube once through steam generator, Nuclear Engineering and Design, 363 (2020) 110665.

[5] X. Li, W. Gao, Y. Su, X. Wu, Thermal analysis of HTGR helical tube once through steam generators using 1D and 2D methods, Nuclear Engineering and Design, 355 (2019) 110352.

[6] X. Li, X. Wu, S. He, Numerical investigation of the turbulent cross flow and heat transfer in a wall bounded tube bundle, International Journal of Thermal Sciences, 75 (2014) 127-139.

[7] W. Gao, X. Li, X. Wu, L. Zhang, Numerical study on the temperature non-uniformity in large scale helical tube bundles, in: International Congress on Advances in Nuclear Power Plants (ICAPP2019), Juan-les-pins, 2019.

[8] Y. Inagaki, H. Koiso, H. Takumi, I. Ioka, Y. Miyamoto, Thermal hydraulic study on a high-temperature gas–gas heat exchanger with helically coiled tube bundles, Nuclear Engineering and Design, 185(2) (1998) 141-151.

[9] W. Gao, X. Li, X. Wu, J. Zhao, Y. Zhang, X. Luo, Cross flow and heat transfer characteristics of tube bundles with neighboring layers having opposite sense inclination, in: 2018 International Congress on Advances in Nuclear Power Plants (ICAPP18), Charlotte, NC, 2018.

[10] H.G. Groehn, Influence of the yaw angle on heat transfer and pressure drop of tube bundle heat exchangers, Heat Transfer, 6 (1982) 203-209.

[11] H.G. Groehn, Thermal-hydraulics of helical-type helium/helium intermediate heat exchangers (IHX) for nuclear process heat applications of high-temperature gas-cooled reactors (HTR) — fundamental research and large-scale tests, Nuclear Engineering and Design, 126(2) (1991) 285-290.

# Developing a Design Optimization Methodology for the Thermal-Hydraulic Evaluation for a High Temperature Reactor During a DLOCA

**Seddon Atkinson [1,2], Ander Gray [1], Edoardo Patelli [1,2,3]**

[1] *The University of Liverpool*
*University in Liverpool School of Engineering, Harrison Hughes Building L3 5RF, Liverpool, United Kingdom*
[2] *National Nuclear Laboratory*
*National Nuclear Laboratory, Chadwick House, Birchwood Park, Warrington, WA3 6AE, United Kingdom*
[3] *Civil & Environmental Engineering, University of Strathclyde, Glasgow, G1 1XJ, United Kingdom*

Seddon.Atkinson@Liverpool.ac.uk

Abstract. Methods of implementing uncertainty within nuclear reactor modelling have traditionally been achieved via worst case scenario uncertainty quantification. This article investigates how this practice can be expanded to provide data on the driving factors behind the temperatures experienced during accident conditions via a global sensitivity analysis. The second part of the article investigates how a stochastic optimization technique can be included within the design process to provide the most cost-effective core geometry which meets the temperature constraints of the fuel and the reactor pressure vessel. The third study investigates the impact of how uncertainty reduction can be used in combination with the stochastic optimization technique to provide further design optimization.

## 1. Introduction

Historically, nuclear energy systems have been designed by government sponsored research establishments which enabled the country to gain a lead within the nuclear market. As the technology matured, mainly through light water reactors, the export potential has been significant, and this has created highly skilled jobs and export potential. Several countries, such as the UK and France have privatized (and partially privatized) these assets, which has led to companies which are commonly seen today such as Westinghouse [1] and EDF energy. Today, due to the availability to nuclear design tools and a highly skilled labor market, nuclear designs are now open to small startups which are trying to revolutionize the future of nuclear reactors through Generation IV designs and Small Modular Reactors (SMRs) [2], [3].

With a generation of design engineers embracing the freedom of new ideas and new modeling methods, this provides the opportunity to change the way which the design process is implemented. One exciting area of new development is the use of design sensitivity and optimization tools. From a regulatory perspective it is a requirement for the designer to provide evidence that under all circumstances the reactor is safe to operate. This is historically achieved through a "Worst case scenario" approach, where conservative design variables are chosen to represent the worst case physically possible. This method is particularly attractive as it is easy to implement, and the computational power is low as only a minimal number of simulations are required.

As nuclear systems are complicated, the variables within the system are often not independent of one another. This means that the prediction of worse case scenarios becomes challenging and new methods of identifying the impacts of changes on the system are required. As modern computational power has developed, uncertainty and optimization tools are being developed to support these engineering requirements as this will improve the design process. As nuclear energy develops, these tools should be used to enhance the safety of nuclear systems and minimize the cost.

This article aims to provide modern uncertainty and design optimization tools on the High Temperature Engineering Test Reactor (HTTR) [4] which is owned and operated by Japan Atomic Energy Agency (JAEA). The optimization process occurs when simulating a Depressurize Forced Loss of Coolant Accident (DLOCA). Within this accident scenario, there are two key factors, the maximum fuel temperature and the maximum Reactor Pressure Vessel (RPV). The maximum fuel temperature is based upon the TRi-structural ISOtropic (TRISO) fuels design limit, where the structural integrity of the silicon carbide layer starts to deteriorate at ~1600 °C, therefore, JAEA have a maximum fuel temperature design limit of 1495 °C [5]. The maximum RPV temperature is determined by the type of steel used within the design, if breached, the steel will start graphitizing and the structural integrity of the steel is reduced. The RPV is made of SUS304 steel which has a design limit of 550 °C [5]. The maximum fuel and RPV temperature occur at opposing conditions, where the minimal thermal conductivity of the core provides the highest fuel temperature and conversely for the maximum RPV temperature.

This article takes the form of providing a 1D heat transfer model of the HTTR where a code to code comparison between JAEA's heat transfer software TAC-NC [6] is undertaken. After this a sensitivity analysis is performed with regards to the design variables of the reactor. Following this, a design optimization procedure is undertaken using genetic algorithm to determine the optimum design geometry based upon minimizing the cost of the design while maintaining the safety-based temperature constraints. The final study combines the sensitivity study with the optimization procedure as an uncertainty reduction optimization study is performed.

## 2. DLOCA in the high temperature engineering test reactor

High temperature reactors are renowned for their passive safety features which have been well documented. One such source of this information is the HTTR, where a DLOCA was performed at 9MWth. Prior to this, JAEA had modelled the DLOCA scenario using their code suite to determine the maximum temperatures experienced. Within open literature, JAEA have published a full power DLOCA to provide the maximum fuel and RPV temperature at day 660 and day zero of the HTTRs operation [5] (beginning of life and end of life). This work aims to reproduce these results by providing a similar analysis by producing a 1D heat transfer model for the HTTR in Matlab. This is achieved by creating models representing the conditions of the HTTR at these dates using the engineering first principles in TAC2D [7], TAC-NC's predecessor.

### *2.1. Model description*

Within JAEA's model a worst-case approach has been taken towards the parameters of both the maximum fuel and RPV temperature. The HTTR is shown in Figure 1 where the heat transfer problem occurs from the center of the core outwards towards the exterior. At the exterior the HTTR's auxiliary cooling system provides the boundary condition of 90 °C immediately after the accident. Up until the point of the boundary, the heat transfer across the core is calculated by radiation and conduction through each material and a 1 mm gap between each component.

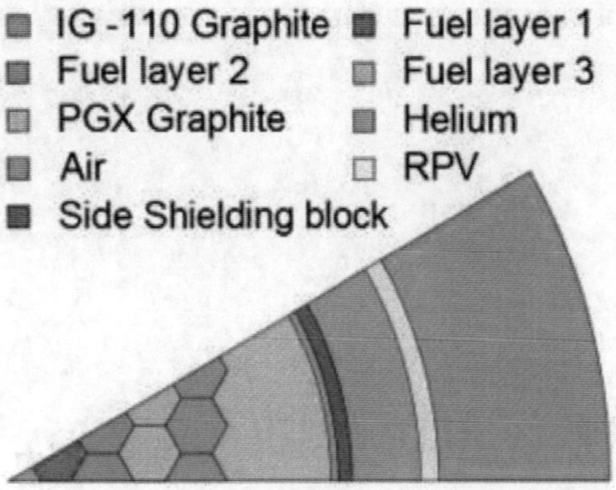


**Figure 1.** HTTR radial representation of the materials across the core. Within the modelling procedure the hexagonal shapes are approximated by using equal volume cylinders to provide a length for the heat transfer path.

The model provides the heat transfer methods shown in eq 1-3.

$$Q_{conduction} = \frac{2\,\pi\,R_i\,H\,K(T_i - T_o)}{\Delta g} \tag{1}$$

$$Q_{convection} = 2\,\pi\,R_i\,H\,h_{coff}\,(T_i - T_o) \tag{2}$$

$$Q_{radiation} = \frac{2\,\pi\,R_i\,H\,\sigma\,(T_i^{\,4} - T_o^{\,4})}{\frac{1}{\epsilon_i} + \left(\frac{1}{\epsilon_o} - 1\right)\left(\frac{R_i}{R_o}\right)} \tag{3}$$

Where subscripts i and o represent inside and outside of the gap areas surfaces, H represents the height of the section, σ the Boltzmann constant, T as temperature, R as radius, $\Delta g$ as gap length, $h_{coff}$ as the heat transfer coefficient.

Following on from these equations TAC2D provides the following formula to determine the surface temperatures between gaps as follows.

$$T_i = B(To_V - T_o) + Ti_V \tag{4}$$

$$T_o = \frac{To_V(NB + 1) + NTi_V}{NB + 1 + N} \tag{5}$$

Where B and N are defined in eq. 6 & 7, and K represents the thermal conductivity of the material.

$$B = \frac{K_o A_o L_i}{K_i A_i L_o} \tag{6}$$

$$N = \frac{K_g A_g L_o}{K_o A_o \Delta g}\left(1 \frac{\sigma \Delta g (T_i^{\,2} + T_o^{\,2})(T_i + T_o)}{K_g\left(\frac{1}{\epsilon_i} + \frac{1}{\epsilon_o} - 1\right)}\right) \tag{7}$$

To emphasize the different conditions of the thermal conductivities of some of the materials, the fuel layers thermal conductivity at day zero and day 660 is shown in Figure 2.

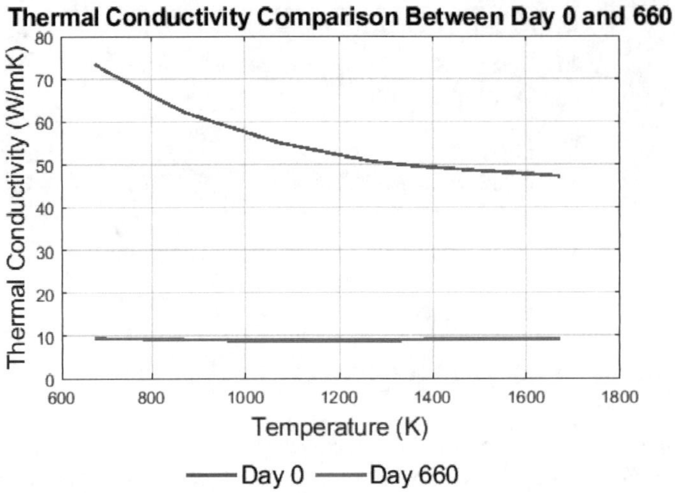


**Figure 2.** Thermal conductivity of the fuel layers at day zero and day 660

The thermal conductivities in Figure 2 are based upon worse case scenarios, where a 20% safety margin has been added to each case [5]. The significant reduction in the thermal conductivity provides a restricted heat transfer path across the gemometry and therefore provides the higher maximum fuel temperatures experienced. The power profiles at the different time periods for the fuel layers are shown in Table 1.

**Table 1.** Power fractions for the fuel blocks at day zero and day 660

| | | Fraction of the total power | | |
|---|---|---|---|---|
| | Day | Layer 1 | Layer 2 | Layer 3 |
| Power block 1 (top) | 0 | 0.0319 | 0.0331 | 0.0967 |
| | 660 | 0.0458 | 0.0467 | 0.1313 |
| Power block 2 | 0 | 0.0605 | 0.0623 | 0.1702 |
| | 660 | 0.0584 | 0.0606 | 0.1647 |
| Power block 3 | 0 | 0.0607 | 0.0570 | 0.1586 |
| | 660 | 0.0492 | 0.0510 | 0.1368 |
| Power block 4 | 0 | 0.0331 | 0.0343 | 0.0959 |
| | 660 | 0.0332 | 0.0332 | 0.0873 |
| Power block 5 | 0 | 0.0214 | 0.0222 | 0.0622 |
| | 660 | 0.0222 | 0.0222 | 0.0577 |

### *2.2. Model validation*

To validate the model a code-to-code comparison is produced between TAC-NC and the model produced during the worst-case accident faults. As these faults occur at different times, the maximum temperatures experienced are shown in Figure 3 & 4.

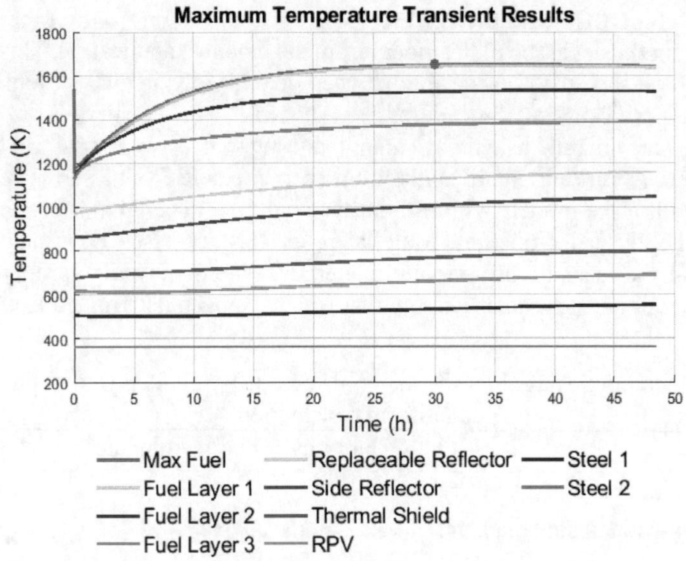


**Figure 3.** Maximum fuel temperature of the model compared to JAEA's value which is represented as a red dot.

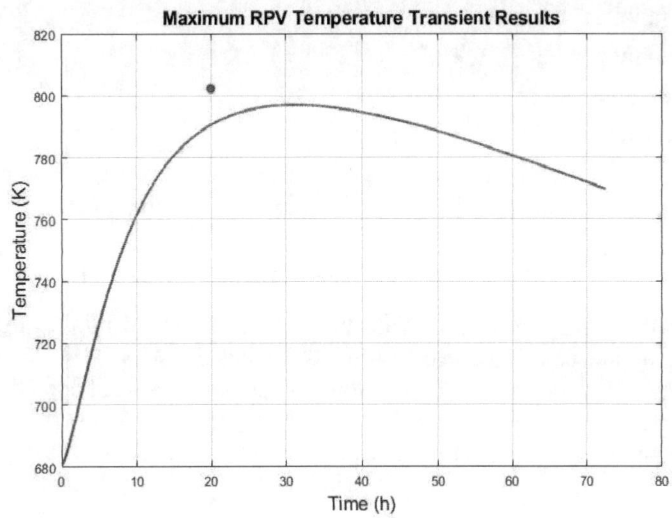


**Figure 4.** Maximum RPV temperature of the model compared to JAEA's value which is represented as a red dot.

Figure 3 provides a full temperature evaluation of each material. The model can accurately represent the maximum fuel temperature during the transient, with the maximum discrepancy being 10 K. From Figure 4, there are some slight deviations from TAC-NC which is caused by the lack of natural circulation used within the model provided in this work which means that immediately after the transient the coolant within the fuel blocks is circulated to the RPV, causing a slightly quicker heat up of the RPV.

As a conclusion, the model can produce similar results to TAC-NC under the worst-case assumptions.

## 3. Sensitivity study of a DLOCA in the HTTR

Uncertainty arises from the deviation of the model from the practical application. This can occur through various means and these should all be considered when quantifying the total system uncertainty as this can have an impact on critical safety procedures.

The nuclear industry invests heavily in manufacturing processes to reduce the uncertainty of components or materials varying significantly from their predicted value; however, uncertainty will always be present within the model. Within this case study the uncertainties are grouped as material properties and thermophysical properties. Material properties are based upon machine tolerances of parameters, such as the density of graphite materials. Thermophysical properties represent the uncertainty of the thermophysical data. These unknowns have been determined from the literature and are depicted in Tables 2 & 3.

**Table 2.** Uncertainties used for the materials case [8] [5] which were represented as a uniform distribution.

| Part | Nominal value | Tolerance | Units |
|---|---|---|---|
| Fuel compact inside diameter | 10 | 0.1 | mm |
| Fuel compact outside diameter | 26 | 0.1 | mm |
| Graphite sleeve inside diameter | 26.25 | 0.1 | mm |
| Coolant channel inside diameter | 34 | 0.1 | mm |
| Coolant channel outside diameter | 41 | 0.1 | mm |
| IG110 graphite | 1.75 | 0.04 | g/cm$^3$ |
| PGX graphite | 1.73 | 0.04 | g/cm$^3$ |
| Initial helium pressure | 40 | 3.50% | Bar |
| Inlet temperature | 395 | 14 | °C |
| Gap width | 1 | 100% | mm |
| Emissivity graphite | 0.8 | 25% | n.a. |
| Emissivity steel | 0.8 | 25% | n.a. |

It should be noted that JAEA does not provide any uncertainty data within regards to the volumetric heat capacity of the graphite, so this has been artificially included.

A global sensitivity analysis aims to determine the output variance based upon the input uncertainty; this is particularly useful within the design process as this method can highlight the most affective design parameters on certain input conditions. The global sensitivity analysis chosen was Sobol' indices ($S_i$) [9] which is a ratio of the conditional expectance of the input parameter over the total variance of the output Var(Y) as shown in eq. 8.

$$S_i = \frac{Var_{X_{\sim i}}\left(E_{X_{\sim i}}(Y|X_i)\right)}{Var(Y)} \tag{8}$$

Where ~i means the expected values are calculated for all other variables except i. One of the benefits of this method comes from the ability to include combinations of each input parameter, to determine the total index ($T_i$) and thus determine the combined effect.

$$T_i = 1 - \frac{Var_{X_{\sim i}}\left(E_{X_i}(Y \mid X_{\sim i})\right)}{Var(Y)} \tag{9}$$

The test used OpenCossan's [10] Monte Carlo simulation to determine the output variances for each of the input variables and OpenCossan calculated Sobol's indices and the total index. The Monte Carlo simulation used 290K samples.

**Table 3.** Uncertainties for the thermophysical properties [5] which were represented as a uniform distribution. Where ∝ means proportional to.

| Uncertainties | Nominal value | Uncertainty (%) | Unit |
|---|---|---|---|
| Reactor power | 30 | 2.50% | MWth |
| Thermal conductivity fuel layers | ∝ Temperature | 20% | W/mK |
| Specific heat capacity fuel layers | ∝ Temperature | 10% | J/m$^3$K |
| Thermal conductivity RR | ∝ Temperature | 20% | W/mK |
| Specific heat capacity RR | ∝ Temperature | 10% | J/m$^3$K |
| Thermal conductivity SR | ∝ Temperature | 20% | W/mK |
| Specific heat capacity PR | ∝ Temperature | 10% | J/m$^3$K |

### *3.1. Results of the sensitivity analysis of the HTTR*

The sensitivity analysis was performed to determine the parameters which have the highest impact on the maximum fuel and RPV temperatures. Within this analysis a single simulation was performed, which provided Sobol's indices for each parameter, which provides the individual contribution for each parameter. It was determined that the total index variance was almost identical to the first index and therefore the combined interactions between uncertainty are not a dominant factor for the sensitivity of the system. If these indices were significantly different, the total index would be the most suitable to use.

For clarity, these are displayed in two graphs but represent the first indices of the maximum fuel and RPV temperature. From Figure 5, the manufacturing tolerances provide very little impact on the maximum temperatures experienced. The highest impact parameter is the emissivity of steel is the largest driving factor for the RPV temperature, this is because the heat leaving the RPV to the outside steel is determined nearly independently through radiation.

From Figure 6, the thermal conductivities are, as expected, the main contributors for the maximum fuel temperatures.

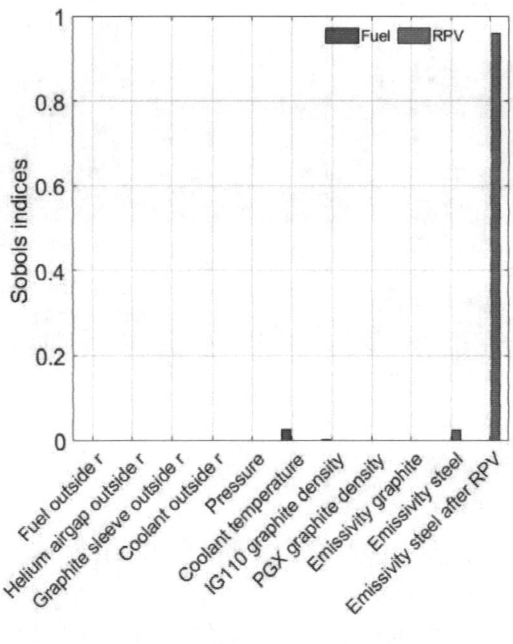


**Figure 5.** Materials Sobol's indices during the DLOCA for the maximum fuel and RPV temperatures. Where r denotes the radius.

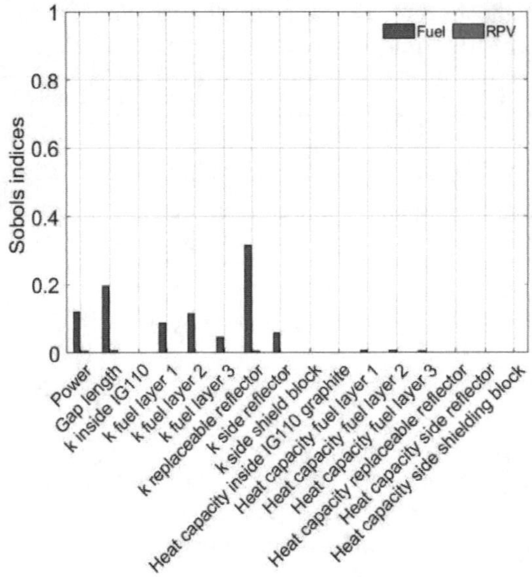


**Figure 6.** Thermophysical Sobol's indices during the DLOCA for the maximum fuel and RPV temperatures. Where k denotes the thermal conductivity.

## 4. Optimization procedures for the HTTR Geometry during a DLOCA

With modern techniques it is possible to reduce the overall cost of the design based upon automated stochastic global optimization methods such as Genetic Algorithm (GA) [11]. GA is an artificial learning technique which follows the process of Figure 7. The initial population is a coarse range of the input parameters, these are then evaluated to determine the best "score" based on the object function, in the case cost and any selection which does not meet the constraints is discarded. The highest scoring designs have their design variables crossed between other high scoring selections; this allows for GA to determine the highest impact parameters on the object function. After the crossover, the design variables can mutate, providing a finer range of the design variables until the optimum solution is found.

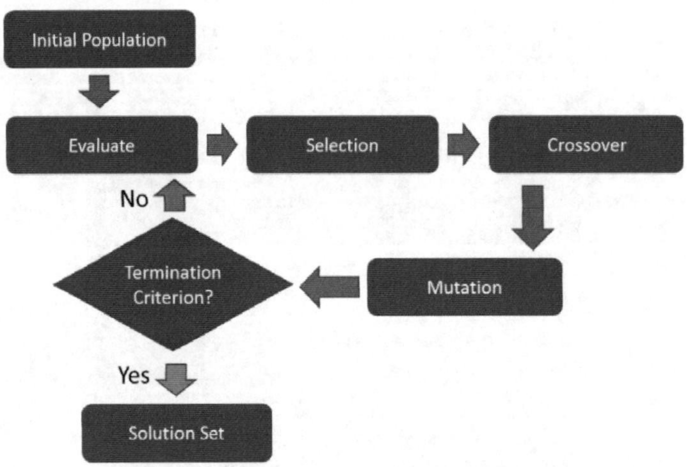


**Figure 7.** Genetic Algorithm solver flowchart

The design variables which are edited relate to the size of the reactor, with the aim of finding the optimal radial geometry. The variables, a, X2, X3 and X4 are shown in Figure 8 and eq. 9.

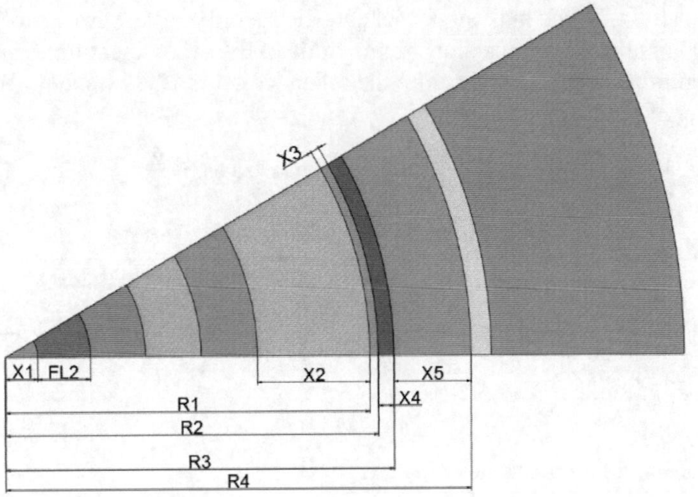


**Figure 8.** HTTR design variables X2, X3 and X4 highlighted.

Each of the fuel layers and replaceable reflector use of the same value of a, this is to retain the hexagonal lattice withing prismatic HTR cores. The value of X1 is determined via eq. 10.

$$\sqrt{\frac{3\sqrt{3}}{2\pi}a^2} = X1 \tag{10}$$

X2 represents the replaceable reflector width and with X3 being the inside helium channel. To retain the same inlet flowrate, the volume of helium is kept the same, so X5 increases in size proportionally to the design variable X3. X4 is the thickness of the side shielding block. The nominal values of these parameters and the upper and lower bounds for GA can be found in Table 4. The uncertainty within the model uses the worst-case scenario method for each of the parameters presented within Table 2 and Table 3 which was determined by performing a local sensitivity analysis using a one-at-a-time (OAT) technique to determine if the maximum or minimum value should be used for the worse case analysis.

The cost of the reactor must be estimated based upon realistic material costs as shown in Table 5 which have been obtained from a recent report on the U-Battery, a similar HTR reactor type [12]. The graphite in the HTTR uses IG110 graphite, which is purified, this increases the cost compared to the PGX graphite. The steel within this case represents the cost of RPV steel, which is significantly higher due to maintenance and fabrication costs. The cost of the core is based upon open literature with the materials of each section shown in Table 6 it should be noted that this excludes fuel, licensing and manufacturing costs which are assumed to be uniform for all designs.

**Table 4.** Arbitrary Design variables used for GA

| Part | Variable | Nominal (cm) | Lower bound (cm) | Upper bound (cm) |
|---|---|---|---|---|
| Fuel block | a | 20.78 | 18.70 | 22.86 |
| Side reflector | X2 | 66.5 | 33.25 | 99.75 |
| Helium gap | X3 | 5 | 2.5 | 7.5 |
| Side shielding block | X4 | 9.3 | 4.65 | 13.95 |

The design variables for GA were selected to provide an input range for the GA and therefore these do not consider external factors which might be considered within the design phase such as radiation damage.

Journal of Physics: Conference Series **2048** (2021) 012033 doi:10.1088/1742-6596/2048/1/012033

The limiting constrains of the maximum fuel and RPV temperature were set to 1495 °C and 550 °C respectively as to maintain the original constraints from JAEA. The object function of GA as shown in eq. 11 aimed to minimize the design cost with the tolerance set is $10^{-5}$ with a maximum amount of 200 iterations for convergence.

$$Min = Cost_{IG110} + Cost_{PGX} + Cost_{RPV\ steel} + Cost_{SSB} \tag{11}$$

**Table 5.** Costs of materials used in GA

| Material | Cost $/Kg | Original design costs (M$) |
|---|---|---|
| IG110 graphite | 77 | 1.76 |
| PGX graphite | 53 | 5.52 |
| RPV Steel | 42 | 13.85 |
| Side shielding block steel | 35 | 1.08 |

The overall nominal cost of core is $22.22 M. The smallest core will result in the cheapest core, however, as the core size shrinks, the RPV temperature increases and GA will have to find the optimal size at the minimal cost.

**Table 6.** Geometry material descriptions and the nominal geometry on the HTTR

| Part | Material | Installed dimensions | |
|---|---|---|---|
| | | Inside | Outside |
| Central graphite block | IG110 graphite | n.a. | 0.191 |
| Fuel layers | IG110 graphite | 0.191 | 1.156 |
| Replaceable reflector | IG110 graphite | 1.156 | 1.485 |
| Side reflector | PGX graphite | 1.485 | 2.15 |
| Side shielding block | Steel/PGX 0.47/0.53 | 2.2 | 2.293 |
| Steel | Steel | 2.75 | 2.872 |

### *4.1. Results of the optimization analysis of the HTTR*

GA was provided with the boundaries in Table 4 and was tasked with determining the optimal geometry (lowest cost) yet remains within the constraints of the maximum temperatures of 1495 °C and 550 °C. The determined design is shown in Figure 9.

From Figure 9 the optimal solution for the geometry of the HTTR. GA has used a combination of reducing a and X2 to provide the main volume reduction of the core and thus saving per unit. The helium thickness (X3) is reduced to help reduce the cost of the expensive thermal shield (X4) where this volume has been minimalized. The overall cost of GA's design is $18.02 M, which is a 18.9% cost reduction over the original design. To convert the cylindrical geometry back to the hexagonal form, the total volume of the hexagonal region would be divided equally amongst the hexagons to provide the area of a single hexagon.

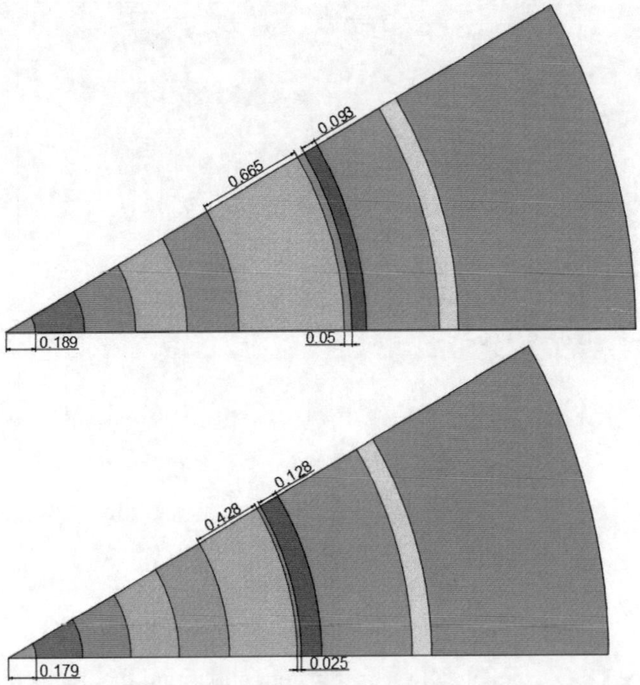


**Figure 9.** Top; The original HTTR geometry. Bottom; GA's optimized geometry.
All geometry in meters.

To be assured that this new design meets the safety criteria the new DLOCA temperature profiles are provided within Figure 10 and Figure 11. It should be noted that the limiting factor within this design is the maximum RPV temperature.

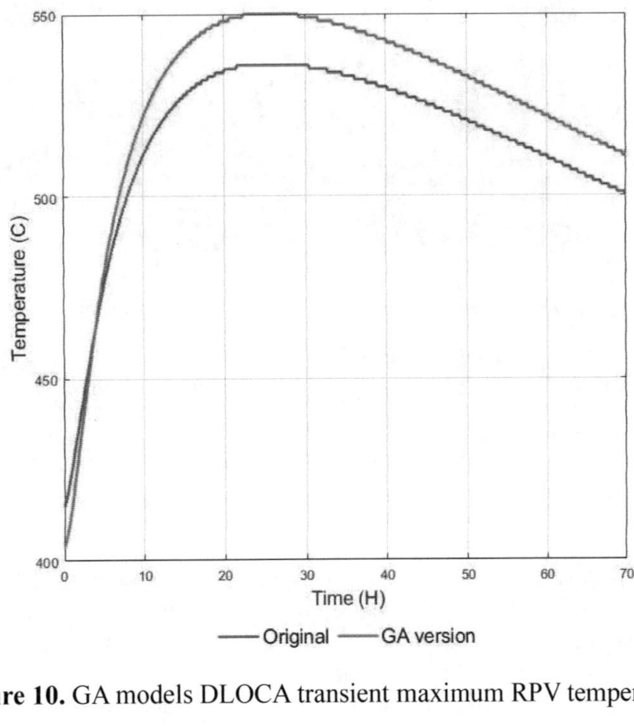


**Figure 10.** GA models DLOCA transient maximum RPV temperature.

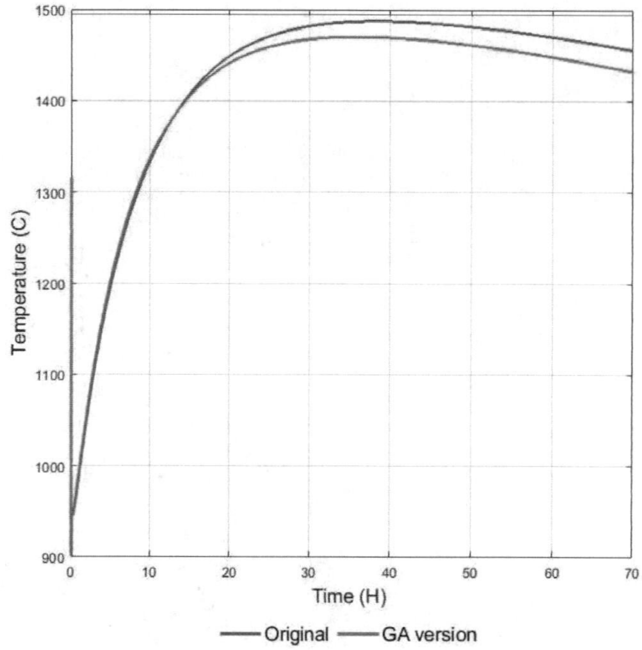


**Figure 11.** GA models DLOCA transient maximum fuel temperature.

GA has found a reduced cost design based upon the original design criterion which can meet the exact design constraints of set by JAEA. The process of using GA is relatively simple, due to the software being easy to use in parallel which makes this optimization technique easily applicable to the design of reactors, without the requirement for large amounts of computational time.

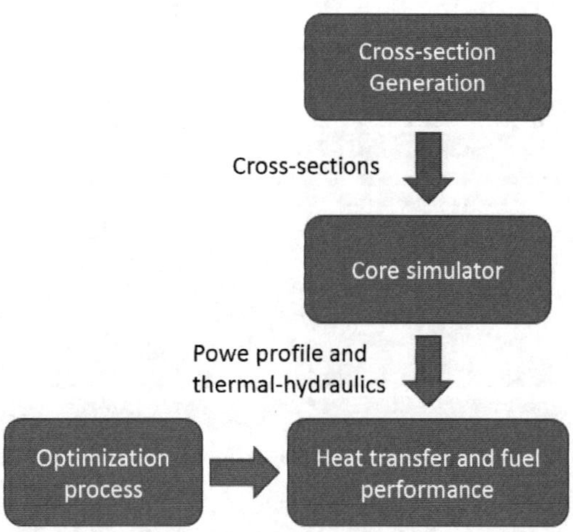


**Figure 12.** Current modelling methodology.

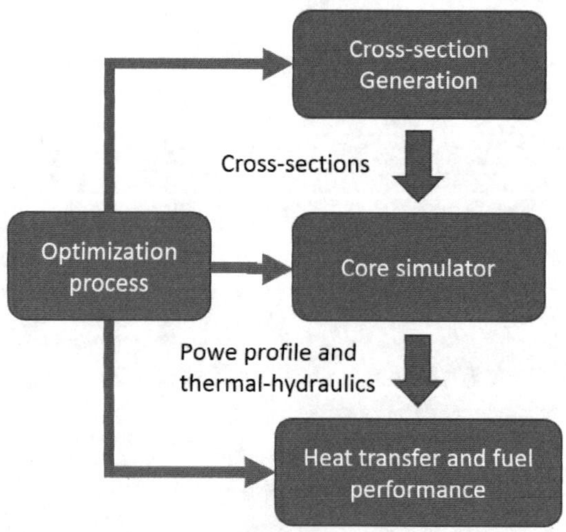


**Figure 13.** New proposed modelling methodology.

It should be noted that this study is limited, as the changes in the geometrical parameters of the design will have an impact into the performance of the design. This section has highlighted that GA can be used as a powerful tool within the design phase, however, to achieve a full system understanding of the new design, this must be incorporated within the modelling structure of reactors shown in Figure 12. To accomplish this, uncertainty and optimization tools are regularly used as methods of coupling software together, as in the case of OpenCossan. To achieve this, OpenCossan would need to be linked to other design software in parallel, as depicted by Figure 13. The drawbacks of this method would be incurred due to the computational power required; however, this can easily be managed by only running each software for high scoring designs.

## 5. Uncertainty reduction opimization procedures for the HTTR during a DLOCA

Section IV identified that GA can provide a design at a lower cost, however, this new design is limited by the maximum temperature of the RPV. To further refine these techniques, an uncertainty reduction study has been performed, where the global sensitivity analysis determined the highest impact parameter on the maximum RPV temperature is the emissivity of the steel proceeding the RPV. The steel proceeding the RPV is important as the distance between the RPV and the containment vessel is large and the conducting medium is air, which means most of the heat transfer is provided by radiation. JAEA models this emissivity as a conservative 0.6 during the worst-case scenario modelling of a DLOCA for the RPV temperature. There are methods to increase this emissivity, such as painting the containment building with a matt black paint or changing the material to provide a higher emissivity. This next study aimed to determine if the overall costs of the design could be reduced by reducing the uncertainty of this material.

### *5.1. Results of the reduced uncertainty optimization of the HTTR*

GA was once again used for a gradually reduced uncertainty of the emissivity proceeding the RPV. The results of the impact on the total cost are depicted in Figure 14.

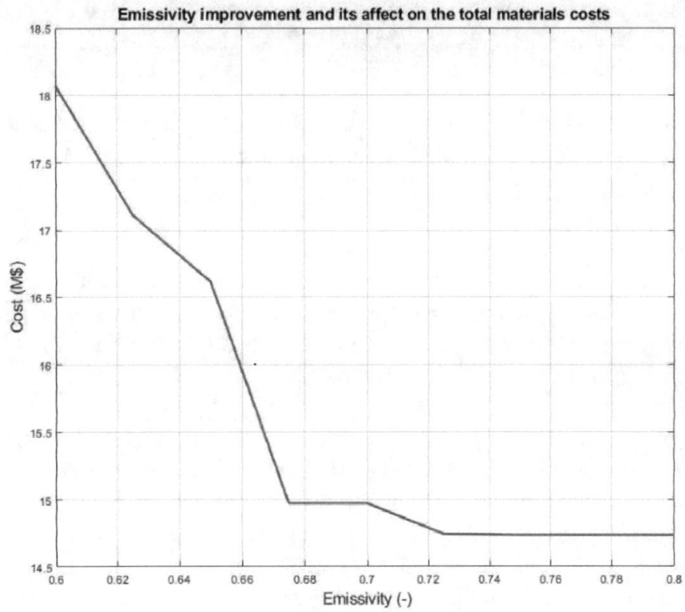


**Figure 14.** Design costs as the emissivity of the steel proceeding the RPV is reduced

From Figure 14, GA has identified that the design costs can be reduced to 14.75 M$ with an emissivity of 0.72 at which point any further reduction sees no benefit. This represents a further 18% cost reduction from the optimal design within section IV. This was an interesting study as GA not only predicted an optimal design, but also provided a target emissivity for the design which is useful for the design process. For completeness, the optimal geometry model geometry for the lowest cost design with reduced uncertainty is shown in Figure 15.

This study can be continued further for other design parameters; however, this is beyond the scope for this article. It should be noted that GA requires a new simulation for each value of the emissivity used, this is more computationally expensive than the method used within section IV, so, these simulations work well alongside the global sensitivity analysis.

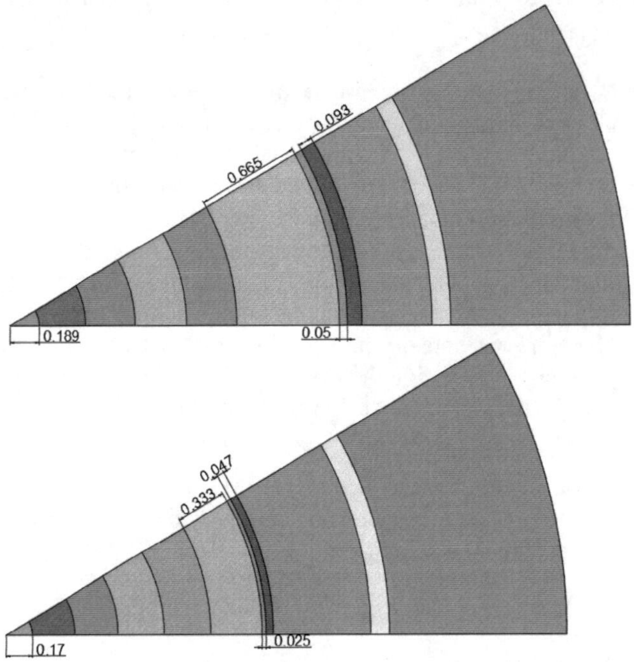


**Figure 15.** Top; Original model dimensions. Bottom; Optimal cost with increased emissivity of the RPV steel geometry

## 6. Conclusion

This article aimed to provide a methodology to incorporate design uncertainty and optimization software for the design of high temperature reactors with an aim of reducing the capital costs. This was initially achieved via a global sensitivity analysis which provided a method of identifying the highest impact parameters for the maximum temperatures experienced. This study provided the impact of each of the parameters, thus enabling for further insight into the design process.

The second study investigated how GA can be used to determine the optimal geometrical parameters of the design. This process enabled a smaller design to be obtained, which came in at a reduced cost yet remained below the safety-imposed design constrains. This study highlighted that this methodology works well, however, there are limitations as a full system approach should be used to understand the impact of the new chosen design. A method to implement this by using an interlinked system has been developed, however, this would require further work to determine the true potential of this software and the drawbacks with regards to computational requirements.

The third analysis combined the results from the sensitivity study and the GA to provide an uncertainty reduction investigation with regards to the emissivity of the steel proceeding the RPV. This was a very useful study as this highlighted that GA can also provide methods to optimize the material choice with defined targets to meet with regards to material properties.

This work has highlighted the benefits of including uncertainty and optimization software within the design process. This can be a powerful tool for HTR design manufacturers to optimize the design and provide vital safety specific data for regulatory approval. The practicality of such a software depends on the speed at which the relevant calculations can be performed, so this approach might not be beneficial for high fidelity methods due to the computational requirements. From a practical perspective, these methods could easily be applied for design refinement using the current approach, however, this is likely to be an interesting topic within the future, with long term benefits for all reactor designs.

**Acknowledgements**
The author would like to that JAEA where the heat transfer software was developed during a secondment to their HTGR group. This secondment was funded via the University of Liverpool's Early Careers Researchers and Returners Fund.

**References**
[1] Christopher Rhodes, "Privatisation - House of Commons," 2014.
[2] Seaborg Technologies, "Seaborg Technologies," 2015. [Online]. Available: https://www.seaborg.co/. [Accessed: 03-Jan-2020].
[3] Moltex Energy, "Clean Energy Through Safe Nuclear Reactors - Moltex Energy." [Online]. Available: https://www.moltexenergy.com/. [Accessed: 03-Jan-2020].
[4] S. Saito, T. Tanaka, and Y. Sudo, "Present status of the High Temperature Engineering Test Reactor (HTTR)," *Nucl. Eng. Des.*, vol. 132, no. 1, pp. 85–93, 1991.
[5] H. I. K.Kunitomi, S.Nakagawa, "Thermal Transient Analysis during a depressurization Accident in the High Temperature Engineering Test Reactor," Oaria, 1991.
[6] M. H. K.Kunitomi, S.Nakagawa, K.Suzuki, H.Wada, "Two-dimentional Thermal Analysis Code 'TAC-NC' for HTTR and its Verification," 1989.
[7] J. P. S.Clarke, "TAC2D A GENERAL PURPOSE TWO-DIMENTIONAL HEAT TRANSFER COMPUTER CODE," 1969.
[8] J. D. Bess, B. H. Dolphin, F. Core, and J. D. Bess, "Evaluation of the Start- Up Core Physics Tests at Japan's High Temperature Engineering Test Reactor (Fully- Loaded Core)," 2009. [Online]. Available: https://inldigitallibrary.inl.gov/sites/sti/sti/4215157.pdf. [Accessed: 24-Oct-2019].
[9] I. M. Sobol, "On sensitivity estimation for nonlinear mathematical models," *Matem. Mod*, vol. 8, no. 2, pp. 33–165, 1990.
[10] E. Patelli, M. Broggi, M. De Angelis, and M. Beer, "OpenCossan: An Efficient Open Tool for Dealing with Epistemic and Aleatory Uncertainties," *Vulnerability, Uncertainty, Risk Quantif. Mitigation, Manag. - Proc. 2nd Int. Conf. Vulnerability Risk Anal. Manag. ICVRAM 2014 6th Int. Symp. Uncertain. Model. a*, no. July, pp. 2564–2573, 2014.
[11] J. S. Arora, "Genetic Algorithms for Optimum Design," *Introd. to Optim. Des.*, pp. 643–655, 2012.
[12] M. Ding, J. L. Kloosterman, T. Kooijman, and R. Linssen, "Design of a U-Battery ®," 2011. [Online]. Available: http://www.janleenkloosterman.nl/reports/ubattery_final_201111.pdf. [Accessed: 11-May-2018].

# Simulation System for PeLUIt 150 MW Nuclear Reactor by using vPower

**M Yunus[1*], A A Budiman[1], S Zhe[2*], Kiswanta[1], W Chunlin[2], M Subekti[1], S Bakhri[1], and S Jun[2]**

[1] *Centre for Nuclear Reactor Technology and Safety – National Nuclear Energy Agency Puspiptek Area Building No. 80, Serpong, South Tangerang, Indonesia 15310*
[2] *Institute of Nuclear and New Energy Technology, Tsinghua University, Beijing 100084, China.*

Email: muhammad-yunus@batan.go.id and suiz@tsinghua.edu.cn

**Abstract.** In developing the PeLUIt 150 MW nuclear power plant based on the High Temperature Gas-cooled Reactor (HTGR) technology, with the helium-coolant and output thermal power of 150 MW, the PeLUIt simulator is also developed for training the operators and educating other technical personnel. Referred to the balance of plant (BOP) design of the PeLUIt, the simulator utilized the vPower simulation platform to simulate the secondary loop for power generation with a water-steam Rankine cycle. The paper focuses on developing the secondary loop's main components: steam generator, steam turbine, condenser, deaerator, and feedwater pump. The reactor module in the primary loop is simplified as a heat source with 150 MW output. The steam generator that connects the primary and secondary loops is modeled with the heat exchanger module by transferring heat from helium to water/steam. Meanwhile, pressure and flow parameters can also be simulated for both helium and water/steam flows in steady-state and transient operating conditions. The steady-state simulation results are almost the same as the design data. The differences in the main steam temperature, feedwater pressure, and feedwater temperature, are 0.03%, 0.53%, and 0.02%, respectively. Meanwhile, the transient condition carried out in the loss of coolant accident showed a decrease in flowrate of 43.31 kg/s and an increase in temperature of feedwater and main-steam of 52.32 and 15.38 °C, respectively. In addition, there was a pressure drop of around 10.37 (feedwater) and 10.16 MPa (main-steam).

## 1. Introduction

Related to the development of *Pembangkit Listrik dan Uap untuk Industri 150 MW* or referred to PeLUIt 150 MW Nuclear Reactor based on High-Temperature Gas-cooled Reactor, one of the things that need to be prepared is the development of a nuclear reactor simulator. Nuclear reactor simulators are needed as a means of education and training for operators of the nuclear reactor. Training with this simulator is essential to improve the safety of nuclear reactor operations. Therefore, as part of developing large-scale nuclear reactors and SMRs design in Indonesia, it is necessary to develop a nuclear reactor simulator design in preparing human resources as a nuclear power plant operator.

Development of nuclear reactor simulators has been carried out both for PWR type reactors that operate a lot around the world as well as some advanced reactor designs such as High-Temperature Gas-cooled Reactors (HTGR) and Lead-cooled Fast Reactors (LFR) [1]–[8]. Various platforms or software are used for the development of nuclear reactor simulator designs, such as the merger between RELAP5 and LabVIEW [9], the use of SAS4A / SASSYS-1 and SIMULINK safety analysis codes in modeling the LFR reactor core simulator [1], and THERMIX / BLAST and the vPower used in the HTR-PM simulator [4]. Compared with various software for simulators, vPower is a simulation platform based on power generation, object-oriented components or modules, and an easy-to-use graphical interface.

In this research, a nuclear reactor simulator system will be developed by using the vPower platform. vPower is a new generation of simulation software that supports various power generation systems, including nuclear power plants. The vPower system covers developing simulation systems, including simulator design, modeling, testing, training, operations, and maintenance. The vPower platform library provides various thermohydraulic, control, and electrical-related modules that can meet various power plants' simulation requirements. vPower is also able to do modeling accurately with mathematical modeling, which includes the equilibrium of mass, momentum, and energy. In addition, vPower provides graphical configuration-based modeling, network communication, and database management in real-time and others [4].

This research focuses on developing simulators for modeling secondary cooling systems, including major components such as steam generators, steam turbines, condensers, deaerators, and water pumps. The development of this secondary system is based on the BOP from the design of a nuclear reactor. As for modeling on primary systems, nuclear reactors are modeled as a simple module of heat generation. The modeling will simulate nuclear reactors' conditions in full operation and transient conditions such as the Loss of Cooling Accident (LOCA) accident.

## 2. Design of PeLUIt 150 MWt Nuclear Reactor Simulator

### *2.1. Balance of Plant of PeLUIt 150 MW Nuclear Reactor*

Development for the 150 MWt Nuclear Power Plant Simulator is focused on the secondary system of conceptual design that was previously simulated using ChemCAD software. The parameters obtained from the design will then be simulated using the vPower simulation platform. The nuclear reactor's main components consist of reactor vessels, blowers, steam generators, steam turbines, pumps, condensers, cooling towers, and deaerators. General installation data from a 150 MWT nuclear reactor is shown in Table 1 and power conversion system data is shown in Figure 1.

**Table 1.** The main parameters of PeLUIt reactor

| Reactor parameter | |
|---|---|
| Thermal power (MW) | 150 |
| Helium inlet/outlet temperature (°C/°C) | 250/700 |
| Helium pressure (MPa) | 7 |
| Helium mass flowrate at full power (kg/s) | 96 |

As shown in Figure 1, this simulator's design is divided into 2 main systems 2, namely the primary and secondary systems, where the secondary circuit is further divided into 4 schemes. In the primary circuit consisting of a reactor as a heat generator, a blower as a regulator of helium flow and a steam generator as a steam generator used to drive a turbine. The secondary system is divided into 4 schemes. Each scheme represents the secondary system's main components, including the turbine, condenser, deaerator, and steam generator components. In this secondary system, water is converted into steam in the steam generator and flows to the turbine that is connected to an electric generator. In addition to converting water to steam, steam generators also function as heat exchangers between the primary and secondary systems.

### *2.2. Modelling of Secondary Loop System*

The simulation modules developed in the secondary system of the 150 MWt nuclear power plant design use modules contained in the vPower simulation platform [5]. In general, the secondary system's main components include main-steam flow system, cooling water circulation system, condensate water flow system, and feed water flow system.

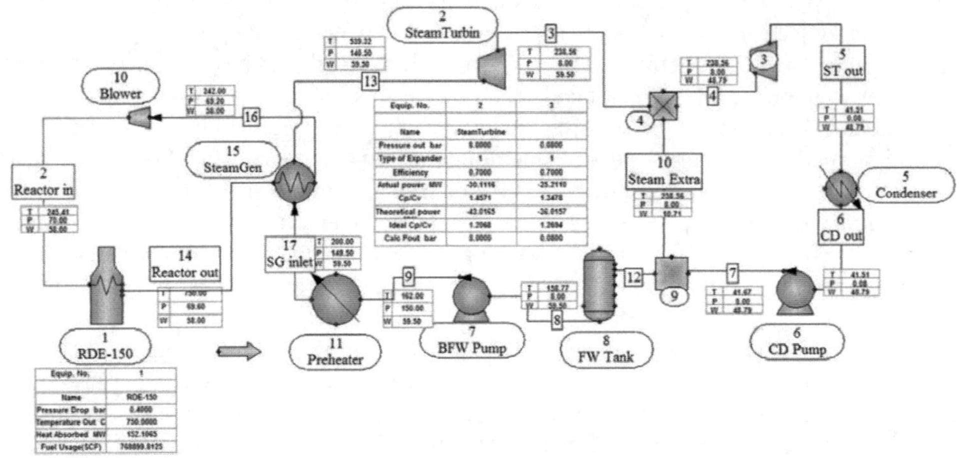


**Figure 1.** Balance of Plant of PeLUIt 150 MW Nuclear Reactor

In this modeling and simulation with vPower, there are 2 parts, namely solving the thermal fluid network equation and simulating the main components of the system. The thermal fluid network is an essential part of a power plant simulation. In this platform, the components in the thermal fluid network include Node: the intersection of two or more branches where pressure is an unknown parameter that must be resolved in a fluid network, Branch: A channel of the direct flow of fluid, where the mass flux is an unknown parameter, boundary: a special node where pressure is applied, and Branch equipment: components of the branch such as pumps, valves, and others.

The model of the thermal fluid network can be explained as follows:

*The fluid models on a node:*

$$\frac{d(\rho V)}{dt} = \sum_{i=1}^{m} w_i - \sum_{j=1}^{n-m} w_{m+lj} + w_{LE} + w_{LL} \tag{1}$$

where,

$\rho$ = density of the node
$V$ = volume of the node
$n$ = number of nodes that connect with the node
$m$ = number of upstream nodes
$w$ = mass flux of the upstream or downstream branch
$w_{LE}$ = leakage mass flux into the node
$w_{LL}$ = leakage mass flux out of the node;

*The fluid model on a branch:*

$$p_1 - p_2 + f(w) + \rho g \Delta z = \frac{1}{\rho C_v^2} |w| w \tag{2}$$

where,

$p_1$, $p_2$ = pressure of the upstream node and the downstream node, respectively
f(w) = increased pressure of the pump equipment
$w$ = mass flux of the branch
$\rho$ = density of the upstream node
$Cv$ = flow resistant factor of the branch;

*The thermal energy conservation model of the node*

$$M\frac{dh}{dt} = \sum_{i=1}^{m} w_i h_i - \sum_{j=1}^{n-m} w_{m+j} h_{m+j} + Q \tag{3}$$

where,

$M$ = mass of the node
$h$ = enthalpy of the flow
$Q$ = heat transfer to the node.

## 3. Methodology

This simulation is carried out under normal conditions at full power operation and transient under conditions of loss of the cooling system or loss-of -feedwater (LOFW) accident. From the secondary system scheme, there are modules of the primary and supporting components, including steam turbine with high-pressure and low-pressure, deaerator, condenser, feed water pump, check and single valve, vacuum pump, and components of a convection system on a steam generator as shown in Figure 2. Under normal conditions, the simulation results with vPower will be verified with BOP data (as shown in Figure 1) to see the level of accuracy of the simulator system that has been made. In general, the simulation results on the 150 MWt nuclear power plant simulator that will be verified are the power conversion system data. Under normal conditions, the reactor design shows that the flow rate of steam on the secondary system is 59.5 kg/s with pressure at SG inlet about 14.9 MPa and SG outlets 14 MPa. Likewise, in the LOFW condition simulation, the energy conversion system data will be further analyzed when the primary and secondary cooling systems.

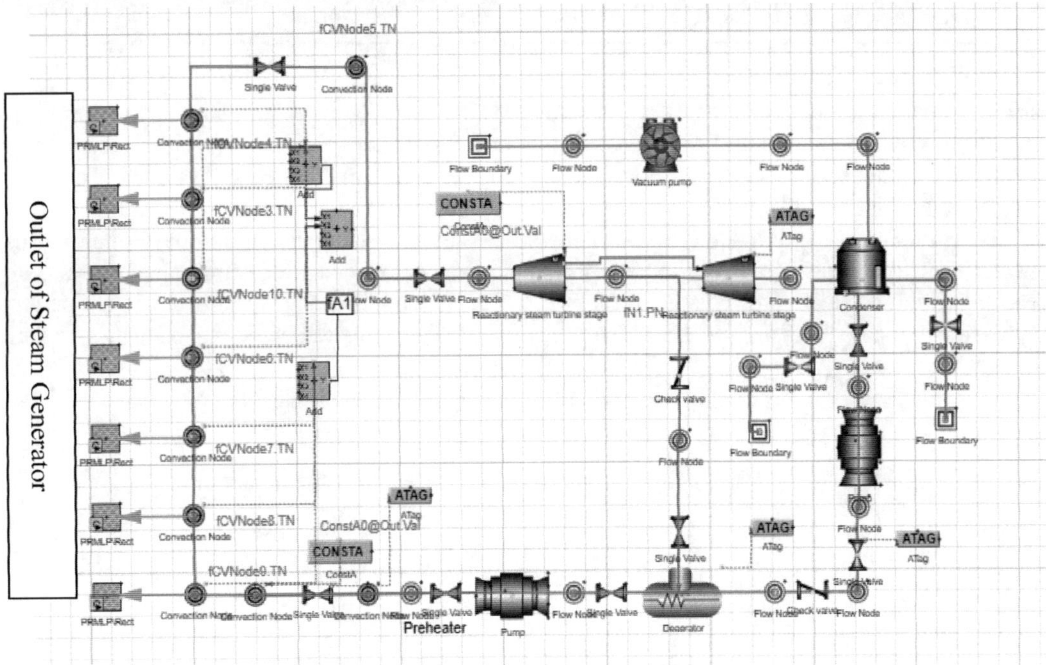


**Figure 2.** Secondary loop system of PeLUIt 150 MW Nuclear Reactor.

## 4. Result and Analysis

### *4.1. Simulation of Steady States with 100% Rated Power*

The simulation results on the PeLUIt 150 MWt Nuclear Reactor carried out at full power are shown in Table 2. The parameters shown in Table 2 are a comparison between the simulation results and the design value. This research focuses on the secondary system so that the data obtained is also a part of the steam generator connected to the secondary system. The power of the reactor is set such that the parameters obtained from the simulator approach the design value. As shown in Table 2, the relative error between the simulation value and the design values is not more than 2% which means the design is reliable [4][5].

**Table 2.** Comparison between simulation results and design data.

| Parameters | Design | Simulation | Relative Error |
|---|---|---|---|
| Working fluid | (superheated) Steam | (superheated) Steam | |
| Main Steam flowrate (Kg/s) | 59.50 | 59.50 | 0.00% |
| Main Steam Pressure (MPa) | 14.05 | 14.05 | 0.00% |
| Main Steam Temperature (°C) | 539.32 | 539.18 | 0.03% |
| Feedwater Flowrate (Kg/s) | 59.5 | 59.5 | 0.00% |
| Feedwater Pressure (SG inlet) (MPa) | 14.95 | 14.87 | 0.53% |
| Feedwater temperature (°C) | 200 | 200.04 | 0.02% |

### *4.2. LOFW Accident Scenario*

Besides steady-state conditions, the PeLUIt 150 MWt Nuclear Reactor Simulator is also applied to simulate transient conditions and accidents. In this part, the loss of feedwater accident scenario was simulated which the secondary system loses the cooling flow system. This loss of coolant is caused by pump damage which results in a decrease in pump performance. The scenario is started from full power condition as the initial condition and followed the process of decreasing the pump's performance causes the water flow to decrease gradually. A decrease in feedwater flow occurs for almost 150 seconds until it reaches saturation flow. This change in feedwater flow results in changes in flow rate, temperature, and pressure of main-steam. Figure 3-5 shows the curve of dynamic parameter changes in the simulation process.

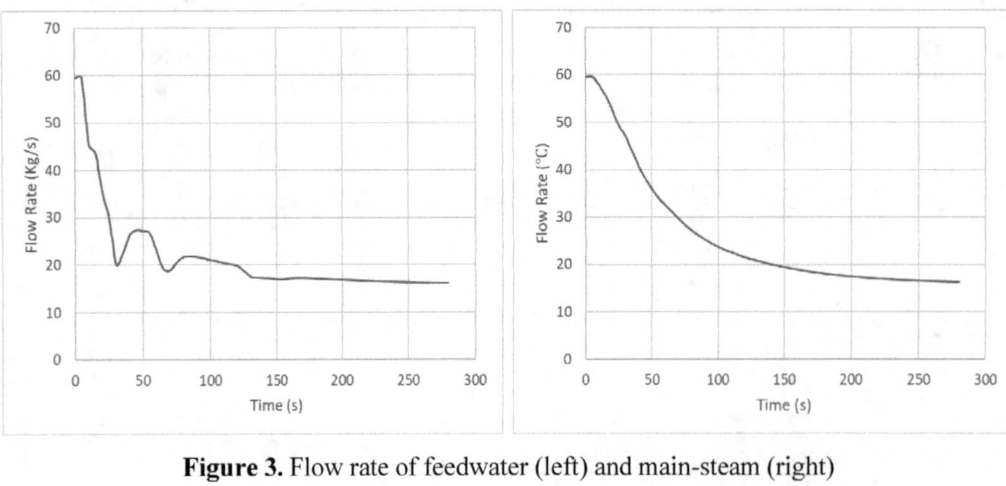


**Figure 3.** Flow rate of feedwater (left) and main-steam (right)

Journal of Physics: Conference Series **2048** (2021) 012034 doi:10.1088/1742-6596/2048/1/012034

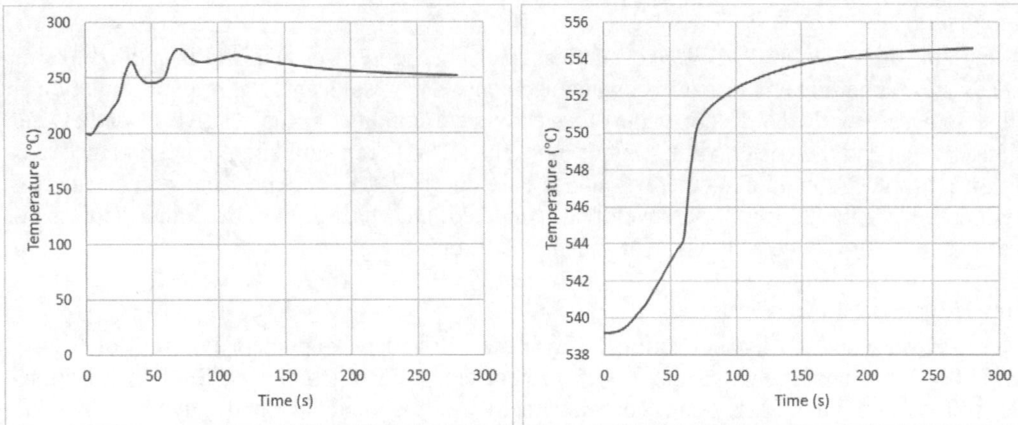


**Figure 4.** Temperature of feedwater (left) and main-steam (right)

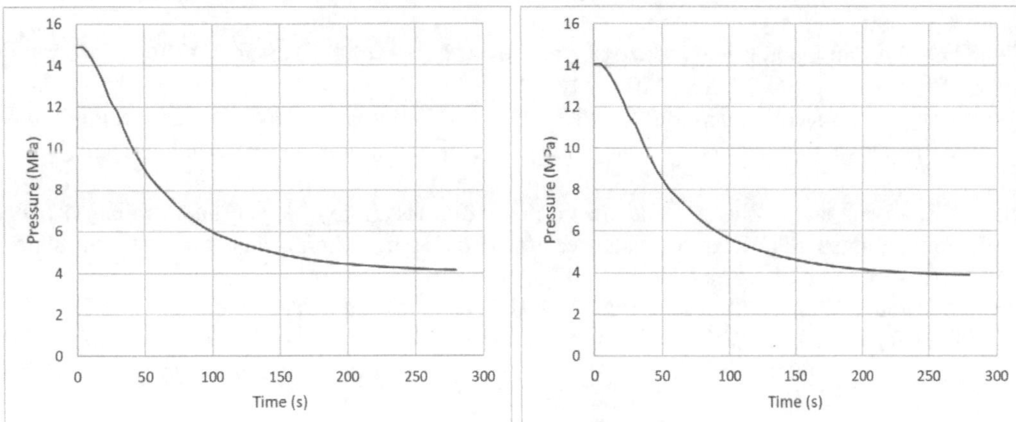


**Figure 5.** The pressure of feedwater (left) and main-steam (right)

Figure 3 shows the change in the flow of feedwater and main-steam. When the pump fails, resulting in a decrease in flow in the feedwater as shown in Figure 3 (left), it causes the flow to decrease from 59.5 Kg/s to around 16.19 Kg/s. The decline in feedwater flow rapidly occurred at 30 s, and after that, it began to saturate up to 150 s. In this simulation, even though there was a pump failure, up to 280 s, the feedwater's residual flow did not stop quickly. Meanwhile, the decrease in the feedwater flow causes a decrease in the steam flow, which takes place gradually to form an exponential curve pattern. Up to 280 s, the steam generator's main-steam flow is almost the same as the feedwater flow. The difference in flow between main-steam and feedwater after the accident was minimal, around 0.13 s.

Meanwhile, the decrease of feedwater flow increases the feedwater temperature, i.e., about 52.32 °C, followed by an increase in main-steam temperature, around 15.38°C given in Figure 4. The decrease in flow in feedwater which is very significant at 100 s, results in a significant increase in temperature. After that, the temperature begins to saturate after the process is running 150 s.

Figure 5 shows the pressure change during the LOFW process. From this figure, it can be seen that there is a pattern of changes in pressure that is almost the same between feedwater and main-steam gradually. In feedwater, there was a decrease in pressure from 14.87 MPa to 4.14 MPa. Meanwhile, main-steam decreased from 14.05 MPa to 3.89 MPa. However, the overall data cannot be further verified because there is no supporting experimental data.

## 5. Conclusion

The Simulator of PeLUIt 150 MWt Nuclear Reactor using the vPower platform is applied to simulate the steady state condition and loss of feedwater accidents. The results analysis of this simulation shows that that is agreed with the design value. In steady-state conditions, the relative error between the simulation value and the design values is not more than 2%. It can simulate normal and also accident conditions. In LOCA condition, there is a decrease in flow rate and pressure and an increase in temperature. This simulator will be developed, validated, and verified with the other data of PeLUIt nuclear reactor design, especially in any accident condition.

## Acknowledgement

This research is supported by the National Key Research and Development Program of China (No. 2017YFE0102100) and INSINAS 2020 with project entitle "Pengembangan Simulator Engineering PLTN 150 MWatt Tipe Classroom. The flow network was modelled and solved on the vPower simulation platform developed by Beijing Neowise Technology Co. Ltd, China.

## References

[1] Shahzad M A Qin L and Imam S S, 2018 Analysis of lead-cooled fast reactor using a core simulator *Prog. Nucl. Energy* **104**, March p. 229–241.
[2] Xu P Wang J Yang M Wang W Bai Y and Song Y, 2017 Analysis of operator support method based on intelligent dynamic interlock in lead-cooled fast reactor simulator *Ann. Nucl. Energy* **99** p. 279–282.
[3] Sun P Zhao H Liao L Zhang J and Su G, 2017 Control system design and validation platform development for small pressurized water reactors (SPWR) by coupling an engineering simulator and MATLAB/Simulink *Ann. Nucl. Energy* **102** p. 309–316.
[4] Tang Y Zhou Y Zhou Z Shi L and Tang Y, 2017 Development and Application of an Engineering Simulator for HTR-PM Using THERMIX / BLAST and vPower Development and Application of an Engineering Simulator for HTR-PM Using THERMIX / BLAST and vPower *Nucl. Technol.* **00**, 00 p. 1–18.
[5] Vpower H B, 2012 Energy Procedia Simulation for the Secondary Loop of the Chinese 200Mwe 1.
[6] Zubair M Ababneh A and Ishag A, 2017 Station black out concurrent with PORV failure using a Generic Pressurized Water Reactor simulator *Ann. Nucl. Energy* **110** p. 1081–1090.
[7] Zhe S Jun S Chunlin W and Yuanle M, 2014 The engineering simulation system for HTR-PM *Nucl. Eng. Des.* **271** p. 479–486.
[8] Jun-san W Yu-ding W Shu-yong Z Rui-zhong C A I and Jian-ting C A O, 2014 The HTR-PM Plant Full Scope Training Simulator.
[9] Kim K D and Rizwan-uddin, 2007 A web-based nuclear simulator using RELAP5 and LabVIEW *Nucl. Eng. Des.* **237**, 11 p. 1185–1194.

Journal of Physics: Conference Series **2048** (2021) 012035 doi:10.1088/1742-6596/2048/1/012035

# Preliminary Study on HTR-10 Operating in Higher Outlet Temperature

**Zheng Yanhua*, Xia Bing, Chen Zhipeng, Zhang Han, Sun Jun**

*Institute of Nuclear and New Energy Technology, Collaborative Innovation Center of Advanced Nuclear Energy Technology, Key Laboratory of Advanced Reactor Engineering and Safety of Ministry of Education*

Tsinghua University, Beijing, 100084, China phone: +86-10-62782953,

Coresponding author's e-mail : zhengyh@mail.tsinghua.edu.cn

**Abstract.** High Temperature Gas-cooled Reactor (HTGR), which has well-known safety features and high temperature heat supply capability, is expected to be widely used for heat supply and technology heat utilization including the hydrogen production, and so contributing to the reduction of carbon dioxide emissions in various sectors. The 10 MW High Temperature gas-cooled test Reactor (HTR-10) had been constructed and operated in China as a pilot plant to demonstrate the inherent safety features of the modular HTGR. The first criticality of HTR-10 at air condition was realized on December 1, 2000, and the full power operation for 72 h on January 29, 2003. Supported by Chinese National S&T Major Project, HTGR for hydrogen production are now being studied. The physical and thermal hydraulic design to raise the outlet helium temperature of the HTR-10 reactor core from 700 ºC to 850~1000 ºC is carried out. In this paper, the preliminary thermal hydraulic design of the HTR- 10 with the outlet helium temperature of 950 ºC (HTR-10H) is introduced. The power density distribution, the fuel temperature distribution and the reactor pressure vessel (RPV) temperature are studied to identify what need to be focused on next. Besides, the typical DLOFC accident has been studied to evaluate the safety feature of the HTR-10 operating under higher core temperature and outlet temperature. The preliminary results show that, operated at the higher outlet helium temperature, the original acceptance criteria for HTR-10 will be challenged. In the future, the design optimization, as well as the possible modification of these acceptance criteria, which were set more than two decades ago, should be studied based on the current knowledge of the fuel element properties and structure material properties.

## 1. Introduction

High Temperature Gas-cooled Reactor (HTGR) with higher outlet temperature from 700 ºC to 800~1000 ºC is expected to be widely used for heat supply and technology heat utilization including the hydrogen production, steelmaking, seawater desalination, thermal recovery of heavy oil, coal liquefaction and gasification. Further popularization and application of the HTGR technology with well- known safety features can greatly contribute to reducing carbon dioxide emissions.

The 10 MW High Temperature gas-cooled test Reactor (HTR-10) had been constructed and operated in China as a pilot plant to demonstrate the inherent safety features of the modular HTGR [1, 2]. The primary circuit of the HTR-10 is shown in Figure 1, while the main parameters are listed in Table 1.

Supported by Chinese National S&T Major Project and National Key R&D Program of China, some research on HTGR, including the operation of HTR-10 in higher outlet helium temperature, combination of HTGR technology and hydrogen production, design of intermediate heat exchanger for HTR-10, and so on, are carried out in the Institute of Nuclear and New Energy Technology (INET), Tsinghua University, China.

The reactor core of the HTR-10 is a packed bed of 27,000 spherical fuel elements. The on-line charge and discharge of the fuel elements have been successfully demonstrated in the HTR-10. The heavy- metal loading per fuel element is 5g and the enrichment of fresh fuel element is 17%. In the equilibrium state, each fuel element may reach the target burn-up and then be discharged after 5 passes through the reactor core.

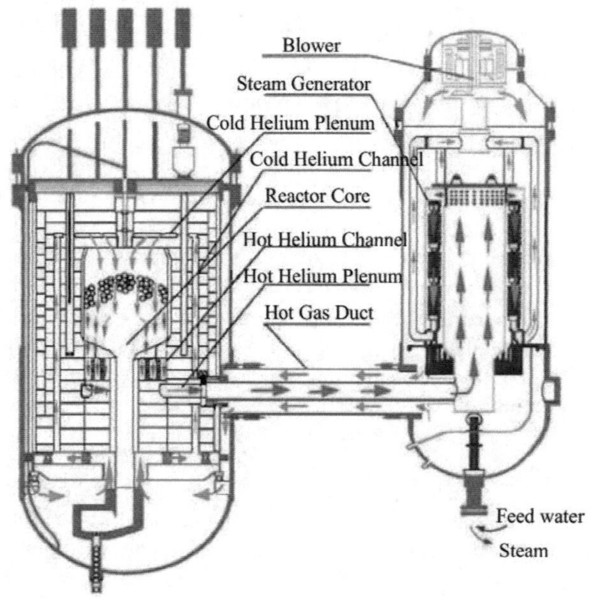


**Figure 1.** Cross section of the HTR-10 primary circuit.

**Table 1.** Main design parameters of the HTR-10.

| Parameter | Unit | Value |
|---|---|---|
| Thermal power | MW | 10 |
| Reactor core diameter | cm | 180 |
| Reactor core height | cm | 197 |
| Primary helium pressure | MPa | 3 |
| Inlet/outlet helium temperature | °C | 250/750 |
| Helium flow rate | kg/s | 4.32 |
| Number of fuel elements | - | 27,000 |
| Average discharge burn-up | GWd/tHM | 80 |
| Feed water temperature | °C | 104 |
| Steam pressure | MPa | 4 |
| Steam temperature | °C | 440 |
| Steam flow rate | kg/s | 3.47 |

Based on the structure design and fuel cycle design of the 10 MW High Temperature gas-cooled test Reactor (HTR-10), a preliminary thermal hydraulic design with the outlet helium temperature of 950 °C (below is called HTR-10H) is introduced in this paper. The power density distribution, the fuel temperature distribution and the reactor pressure vessel (RPV) temperature are also presented. Besides, the Depressurized Loss of Forced Cooling (DLOFC) accident has been analyzed to study the maximal fuel temperature.

This preliminary study mainly focuses on the primary circuit. The primary helium pressure and the inlet helium temperature are same as those shown in table 1. To reach a higher outlet helium temperature of 950 °C, the mass flow rate of the coolant decreases to about 2.74 kg/s.

## 2. Thermal Hydraulic Parameters of the Equilibrium Core

The physical design and thermal hydraulic design of the HTR-10H operating in higher outlet helium temperature of 950 °C are carried out the V.S.O.P. code [3] and TINTE code [4]. The two-dimensional flow model of TINTE code is shown in Figure2.

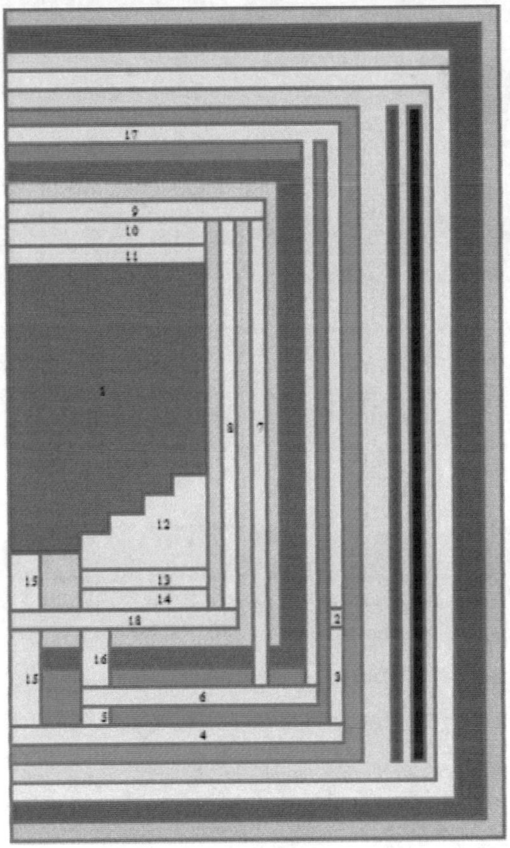

Fluid area

1: core; 2: core inlet cavity; 3: core inlet channel; 4: RPV bottom cavity; 5: RPV bottom flow passage; 6: core bottom cavity; 7: coolant channel; 8: control rod channel; 9: cold helium plenum; 10: top reflector flow passage; 11: core top cavity; 12, 13: bottom reflector flow passage; 14: plenum in bottom reflector; 15: discharging tube; 16: bypass flow; 17: helium gap; 18: hot helium plenum

Solid area

: graphite reflector; : carbon brick; : metal internals and core vessel (CV); : RPV; : air gap; : metallic plate; : water cooling panel; : thermal insulation; : concrete wall; : air boundary.

**Figure 2.** Flow model of TINTE for the HTR-10H

Figure 3 shows the power density distribution of the HTR-10H (R=0 means the center of the core. H=0 means the top of the core, while H=217 means the bottom of the core). Maximal power density is about graphite reflector and carbon brick is also considered. It also can be seen that, based on the HTR-10 structure design, fuel design and fuel cycle design, the power density distribution seems flatter when it operated in higher outlet temperature.

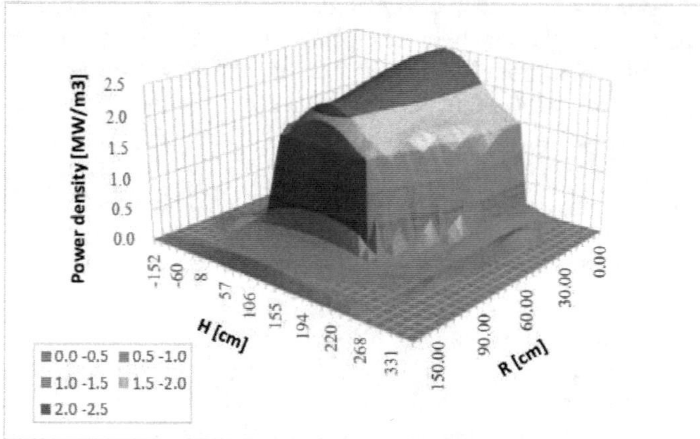


**Figure 3.** Power density of the HTR-10H.

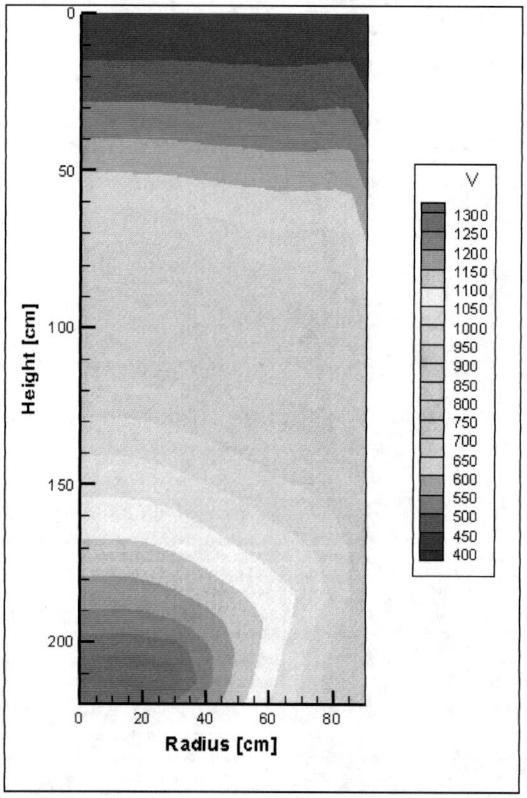


**Figure 4.** Solid temperature distribution of the HTR- 10H.

Figure 4 shows the solid temperature, which means the fuel surface temperature within the core area (as shown in the Figure 2). The maximal fuel surface temperature and fuel center temperature at the bottom of the core are about 1290 °C and 1390 °C respectively, much higher than those of HTR-10. It can be explained as below: 1) The flatter power density distribution, in other words, the higher power density at the reactor bottom, will cause the higher temperature difference between the fuel center and fuel surface. 2) With the same power and same inlet helium temperature, to reach the higher outlet helium temperature, much lower mass flow rate of the coolant is adopted, which results in a weaker heat transfer between the fuel elements and gas. 3) In HTGR, there exists leakage flow, also called bypass flow, through the tiny gaps between the graphite blocks. Due to the lower coolant flow rate, as well as this bypass flow, the radial temperature deviation at the core outlet is also larger.

Figure 5 shows the temperature distribution along the side of the RPV. Maximal temperature appears at about the center of the pebble bed core. With the higher fuel temperature, the temperatures of the RPV of the HTR-10H are also higher than those of the HTR-10.

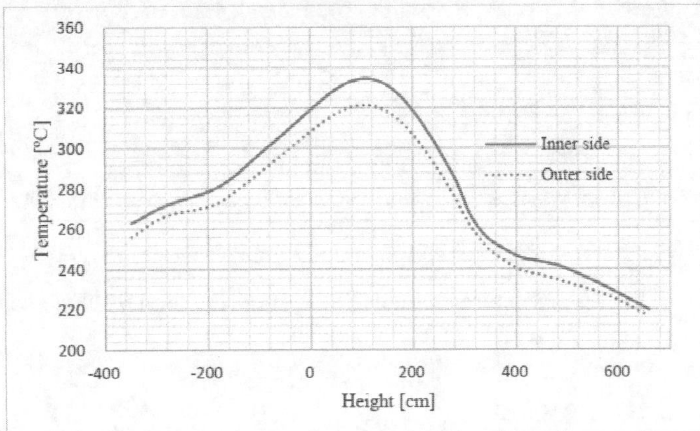


**Figure 5.** RPV temperature distribution of the HTR- 10H

As the first test HTGR in China established more than two decades ago, to ensure the fission product retention capacity of the coated particles in the fuel element, the temperature limitation of the fuel element of the HTR-10 during normal operation and all Design Basis Accidents (DBAs) is set as 1230 °C. The temperature limitations of RPV during normal operation and DBAs are 320 °C and 375 °C respectively. All these acceptance criteria were set very conservatively with large margins, compared to those of the AVR (Arbeitsgemeinschaft Versuchsreaktor) in German and the later 200 MWe Pebble-bed Modular High Temperature gas-cooled Reactor (HTR-PM) in China. For example, the fuel temperature limitation for the HTR-PM in all DBAs is 1620 °C, while the RPV temperature limitations during normal operation and DBAs are 350 °C and 425 °C respectively.

Therefore, based on the further understanding of the fuel element properties and structure material properties, the acceptance criteria for HTR-10H should be reconsidered and reasonable modification is expected.

Although the coated particles in the fuel element have excellent fission product retention capacity, the higher fuel temperature during the normal operation will result in a slight increase in radioactivity in the primary coolant. Besides, the higher fuel temperature and RPV temperature may reduce the margin for the accident conditions. Therefore, further design optimization should also be considered.

## 3. DLOFC Accident Analysis

Based on this preliminary thermal hydraulic design, the DLOFC accident is analyzed with the TINTE code.

It is conservatively assumed that the reactor loses all the primary coolant instantaneously and all the decay heat are carried out on via the heat conduction and thermal radiation. Another conservatively assumption is that when accident happens the reactor is operated at the 102% rated power, and after reactor shutdown the decay heat is also 102% of the normal value. Figure 6 shows the maximal and average fuel temperatures during the accident.

Due to the low nuclear power (10 MW) and power density (~2 MW/m$^3$), and also due to the large heat capacity of the graphite reflector and carbon brick, in accident condition, after reactor shutdown, the decay heat can be transferred to the reactor cavity and finally to the environment quickly. As the Figure 6 shows, the maximal fuel temperature, as well as the average fuel temperature will decrease continuously.

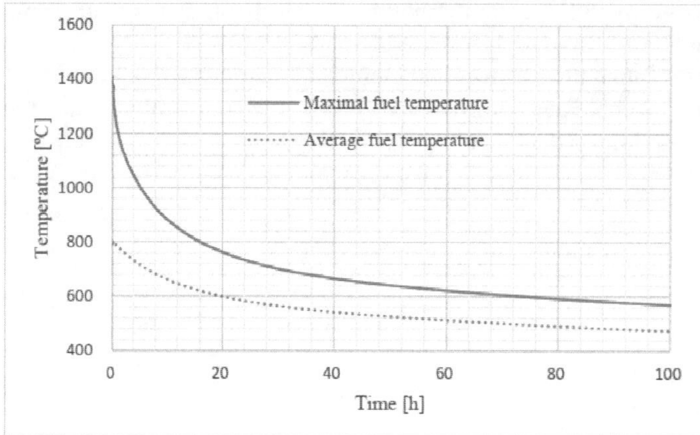


**Figure 6.** Fuel temperature of the HTR-10H during the DLOFC accident.

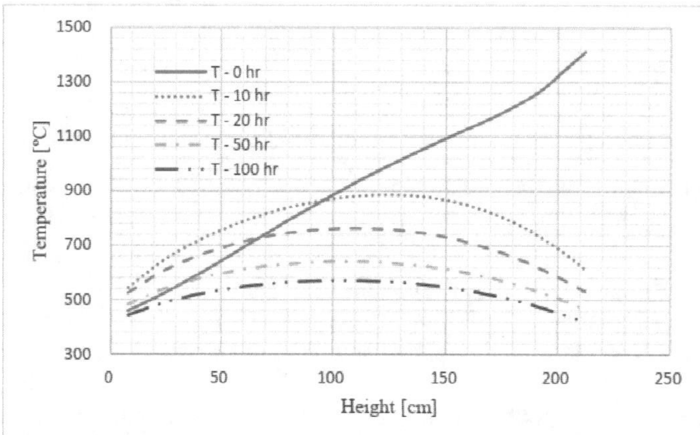


**Figure 7.** Fuel temperature of the HTR-10H during the DLOFC accident.

Figure 7 shows the center temperature of the fuel elements at the reactor center. It can be seen that, after reactor shutdown, the fuel temperatures of the lower part of the core will decrease quickly, while there exists little increase for the fuel temperatures of the upper part of the core.

But the RPV temperature will increase after the accident happen, because the decay heat transferred from the core to the RPV continuously, as shown in Figure 8. In the Figure 9, temperatures of the inner side and outer side of the RPV 25 hrs. after the accident happens, when the maximal fuel temperature of the RPV reaches the peak value, are shown.

With the decrease of the decay heat, as well as the increase of the heat transferred by the reactor cavity cooling system (RCCS), the RPV temperature will begin to decrease about 20 to 30 hrs. after the accident happens. Figure 10 shows the changes of the decay heat and the heat transferred by the RCCS during the accident.

The calculation results show that, during the DLOFC accident, the maximal fuel temperature and maximal RPV temperature will not exceed the temperature limitation for the HTR-PM (namely 1620 °C for fuel element and 425 °C for RPV). But they do exceed the conservative temperature limitation for the HTR-10.

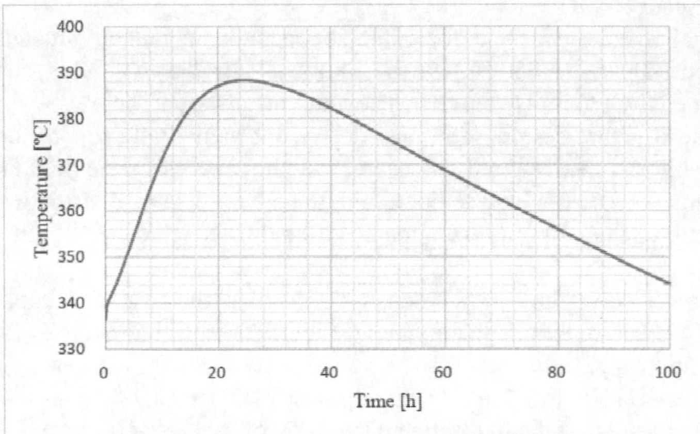


**Figure 8.** Maximal RPV temperature of the HTR-10H during the DLOFC accident.

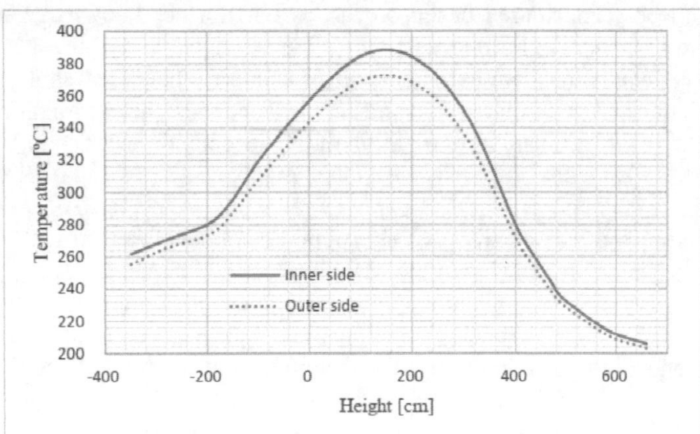


**Figure 9.** RPV temperature distribution 25 hrs. after the accident happens.

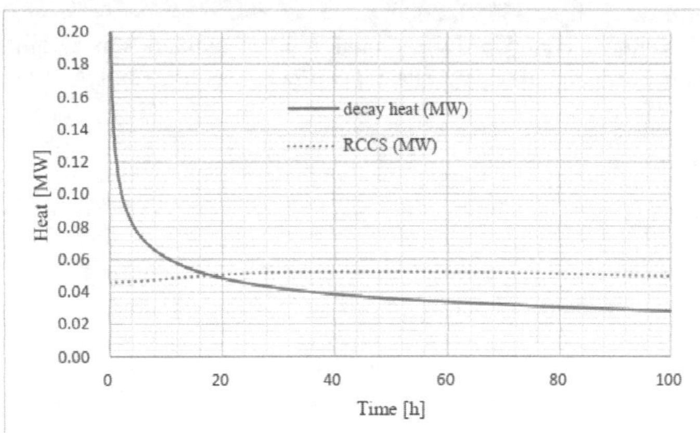


**Figure 10.** Decay heat and RCCS heat load during the DLOFC accident.

## 4. Conclusion and Future Work

A preliminary thermal hydraulic design for HTR-10 operated in higher outlet helium temperature increased from current 700 °C to 950 °C) in the future is introduced in this paper. Based on this preliminary design, the DLOFC is also studied. The main results are as below:

1. With the same structure design, same fuel design and same fuel cycle design, the higher outlet helium temperature is realized only by decreasing the mass flow rate of the helium.
2. Operated in higher outlet helium temperature, the power density distribution seems flatter. The fuel temperature, the structure temperature and the RPV temperature have increased considerably.
3. Due to the lower power and power density, as well as the large heat capacity of the graphite reflector and the carbon brick, during the DLOFC accident, the maximal fuel temperature will decrease continuously.
4. As the first test HTGR in China designed and established more than two decades ago, the temperature limitations of the fuel element and RPV of the HTR-10 were set very conservatively. Analysis results show that, both in normal operation and accident condition, the acceptance criteria of fuel element and RPV designed for the HTR-10 would be exceeded. The acceptance criteria should be reconsidered based on the current further knowledge of the fuel element properties and RPV material properties.

According to above results, further design optimization and further research need to be carried out, including the in-depth thermal hydraulic design and accident analysis, the optimization of the fuel design or fuel cycle mode, the revaluation and modification of the acceptance criteria, and so on.

**Acknowledgements**

This paper is supported by the National Key R&D Program of China (Grant No. 2018YFB1900501) and Chinese National S&T Major Project (Grant No. ZX06902013)

## References

[1] Zongxin Wu, Dengcai Lin, Daxin Zhong. The design features of the HTR-10, Nuclear Engineering and Design, v218, p.25, 2002.

[2] Yuanhui Xu, Kaifen Zuo. Overview of the 10 MW high temperature gas cooled reactor – test module project, Nuclear Engineering and Design, v218, p.13, 2002.

[3] H. J. Rütten, K. A. Haas, H. Brockmann, W. Scherer. V.S.O.P. (99/05) computer code system, Forschungszentrum Jülich, Jül-4189, 2005.

[4] H. Gerwin, W. Schere. The two-dimensional reactor dynamics programme TINTE (part 3: programme architecture and user's manual), Forschungszentrum Jülich, 2001.

Journal of Physics: Conference Series **2048** (2021) 012036 doi:10.1088/1742-6596/2048/1/012036

# Simulation of Steam Generator Tube Rupture on the Experimental Power Reactor (RDE)

**A. S. Ekariansyah, M. Subekti**[1]

*Center for Nuclear Reactor Technology and Safety - BATAN,*
*Puspiptek Area, Setu, South Tangerang, 15310, Indonesia phone: +62-21-7560912,*
*andi_se@batan.go.id*
*[1]Center for Nuclear Reactor Technology and Safety - BATAN, Puspiptek Area, Setu, South Tangerang, 15310, Indonesia*

**Abstract.**As an effort to introduce nuclear power plant in Indonesia, Indonesia's National Atomic Energy Agency (BATAN) has been developing the small sized pebble- bed reactor of high temperature gas-cooled reactor (HTGR) technology since 2015. The 10 MWt Experimental Power Reactor (*Reaktor Daya Eksperimental* / RDE) was designed based on the HTR-10 design and is entering the drafting process of detail design document involving a number of calculations, experiment activities and simulations. One of research activities to verify the safety of the RDE design is by performing simulations using RELAP5 thermal hydraulic code starting from the development of RDE model for steady-state condition. One initial event classified in the safety analysis report is the steam generator tube rupture, which is simulated in this paper. The purpose of the simulation is to analyze, how accurate is the available RDE model to predict changes in the thermal behavior, particularly in the primary system. The results of two simulated cases by assuming two helical tubes ruptures, with and without safety system actuations show that the transients of pebble temperatures in the core are still under safety limit of the TRISO pebble fuel of 1230 °C. Both cases also indicate the importance of the pressure limitation devices in the primary system to control the increase of the primary pressure during the event into the allowable operating value. Other issues are still open to address such as the heat sink in the reflector model for the pebble temperature behavior, core positive reactivity due to the water-steam increase and the operation of the steam generator discharge system to mitigate the event. In general, the RELAP5 code is able to simulate the particular event, even the time sequences are different if compared with the THERMIX code.

## 1. Introduction

One of High Temperature Gas Reactor (HTGR) type, which is still under construction in 2020, is the pebble bed core HTGR or Pebble Bed Reactor (PBR). That HTGR type is named as HTR-PM located in the Shidaowan site of China, which features two small reactors and a turbine [1]. Each HTR-PM reactor refers to the HTR-10 design with lower thermal power as a prototype of the PBR development since 2000 [2]. The PBR has been also selected as the one of national programs to support the National Medium-Term Development Plant in year 2015 – 2019 by starting a development of *Reaktor Daya Eksperimental* (RDE) or Experimental Power Reactor (EPR) program in 2015, conducted by the Indonesia National Nuclear Energy Agency (BATAN). Since 2018, the development of RDE has been entering the drafting process of detail design document involving a number of calculations, experiment activities and simulations [3].

One of contents of the detail design document is the descriptions of safety analysis during the operation of RDE. Referring to the HTR-10 safety analysis process, a number of simulations had been carried out to justify the safety design of the plant. For instance, Gao Zuying et al. described thermal hydraulic transient analysis using the PBR analysis software THERMIX of four typical accidents to demonstrate the HTR-10 safety features [4]. In case of RDE design development, several thermal hydraulic analyses have also been carried out using different approach and tools due to the limitation of code owned by BATAN. One safety analysis of the RDE was related to the function of the passive safety features in the worst accident scenario performed using PEBBED code [3]. Another particular research was performed using the RELAP5 code, which is a thermal hydraulic simulation software for the light water reactor having capability to model the pebble bed and gas properties of HTGR [5]. On that case, the RDE model was developed for steady-state condition as the basis for accident simulation, in which its modelling methodology using RELAP5 referred to that of the HTR-10 [6].

Since the basis of the RDE model is available, a selected transient analysis can be performed as described in this paper. According to the initial events classified in the HTR-10 [4], a steam generator tube rupture is selected to be simulated using RELAP5. The purpose of the simulation is to analyze, how accurate is the RELAP5 model of RDE to predict changes in the thermal behavior, particularly in the primary system. As comparisons, the similar event is used as reference calculated by THERMIX code [4]. The RELAP5 code to be used is the SCDAP/Mod 3.4 version owned by BATAN.

## 2. RDE Modelling for Steady-State Condition

The most important part of the RDE is the core, in which the fuel elements are in form of pebble bed. The pebbles are modelled using the spherical heat structure provided by the RELAP5 code. The total number of the pebbles are calculated by considering the core volume, pebble volume, and the void fraction to approach 27,000 pebbles by design. The core section is divided into 10 segments axially and 6 core channels radially to accommodate the power distribution determined by neutronic analysis. For this analysis, power density distributions for once- through-then-out (OTTO) refueling mode were used, which were calculated using GAVROSH code [5] with 10 MW thermal power. The helium flow inside the reactor vessel will be directed along the annulus structures inside the vessel starting from cold helium pipe, into the side annulus, cold helium plenum, cold helium channels, upper helium plenum and the core channels. From there the heated helium gas enters the fuel discharging tube and hot helium channels to be collected in the middle hot helium plenum before flowing to the outer hot helium plenum and finally to the hot helium pipe.

The reactor part of the RDE model is important to define the heat source inside the helium gas in the primary system into the steam generating part of the RDE. The RDE steam generator has multiple-layer of 49 tubes of helical form. The helical steam generator of RDE was modelled by first assuming the multiple- layer of helical tubes as a straight tube with the flow area calculated from all 49 helical tubes. The tubes are designed to generate superheated steam of 520 °C with 6 MPa pressure from the feedwater of 145 °C and 3.45 kg/sec mass flow inside the tubes, which is pumped by the secondary pump from the lower part of steam generator up to the steam lines.

Figure 1 illustrates the result of integration of the RDE reactor and its helical steam generator by the co- axial cold and hot gas duct and the blower component. In the model, the hot gas duct (P-400) directs the hot gas helium from the reactor to the upper part of the helical steam generator before entering the outer surface of the helical-coiled tubes (P-440) inside a shell, in which the heat is transferred into the feedwater inside the helical tubes (P-670). The cold gas helium is then directed into the gap between the steam generator vessel and the shroud (P- 460) before entering the suction part of the blower and discharged into the cold gas duct (P-300).

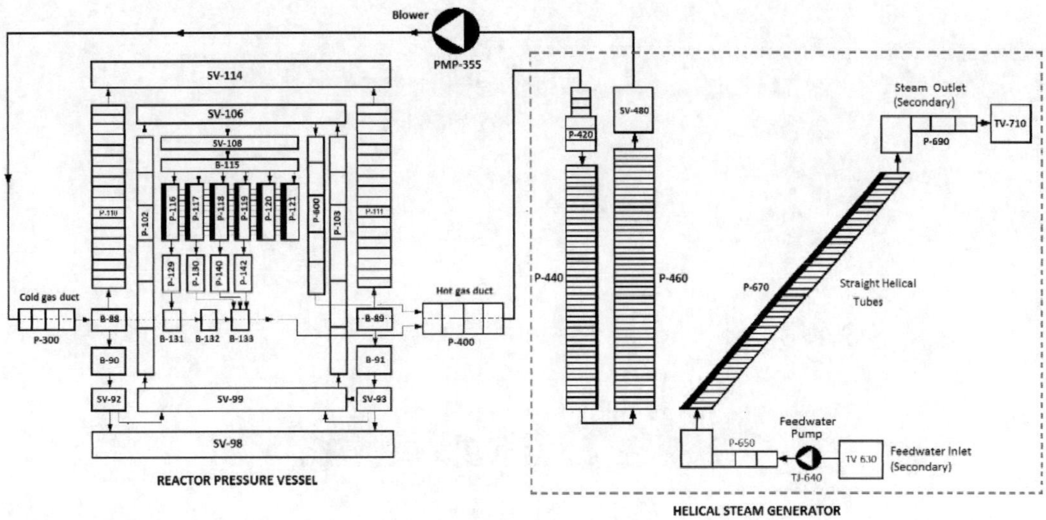


**Figure 1.** The integrated model of RDE reactor part and helical-coiled steam generator developed by RELAP5 code

## 3. Modelling of Steam Generator Tube Rupture

In this analysis, it is assumed that two helical tubes ruptures, which is the severest case in the event of steam generator leakages [4]. In the RELAP5 model, the leakages are modelled using the Valve component with the flow area of two tubes (21 mm inner diameter for each tube) connecting one segment of the tube component (P-670) and the other segment of the helium shell (P-440). The valve will be set to open about five seconds after achieving the steady- state calculation. For the first simulation, the event is followed by the no active actions of the reactor safety systems, which are no scram, no steam generator isolation and emptying and no control on the blower [7]. Operating thermal parameter to be analyzed are transients of primary pressure, pebble temperature, core power, and coolant temperature.

## 4. Results and Discussion

The steady-state calculation is basically similar to the analysis in the previous study related to the nuclear steam supply system of the RDE model [8]. Several modifications have been made since then to improve the steady-state results after 50,000 second calculation in the RELAP5.

Figure 2 shows the initiating tube ruptures in which water inside tubes enters the primary system filled with hot helium. Following the event, the blower still operates normally, the reactor protection system (RPS) is assumed to fail, and there is no isolation of the secondary system. This event causes the increase of the primary pressure as the inventory of the secondary system with the higher pressure entering the primary system. The water ingress will increase the moisture content of the helium as indicated in the non-condensable gas mass fraction in the RELAP5 output in which its value drops over the simulation time from 0.8 to 0.02 in average.

The effect of the water ingress in the helium gas will be visible in the core cooling, in which the heat transfer capability of the steam generator decreases as shown in Figure 3. The cold helium temperature will gradually increase, whereas the core heat cannot be absorbed properly by the helium coolant, which affects the pebble temperature. In the figure, only one segment of the pebble temperature in the middle core with the highest increase is showed. The peak of the pebble temperature is still below the safety criteria of the TRISO pebble temperature of 1230 °C [9], since the fuel temperature reactivity coefficient (FTC) is included in the input data to ensure the safety of the reactor. The FTC value for the equilibrium core adopts the HTR-10 calculation, which is – (minus) 2.55 pcm / °C [4].

The effect of the negative FTC can be seen on the core power oscillations along the time, which is in parallel with the change of the fuel pebble temperature.

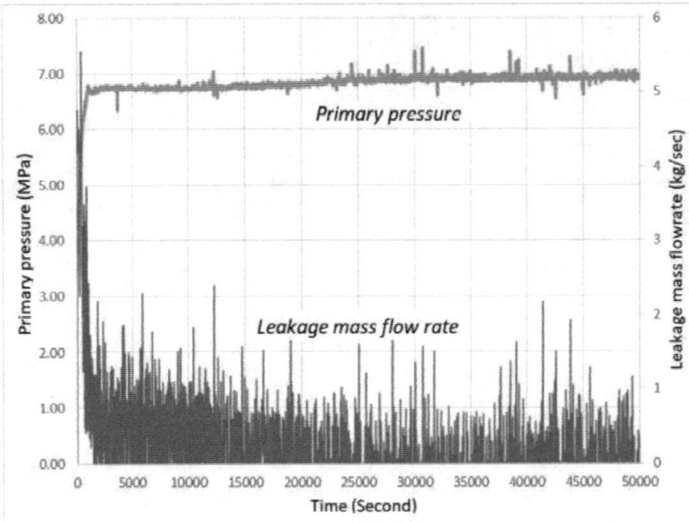


**Figure 2.** Tube rupture mass flowrate and transient of primary pressure (no safety system actuations)

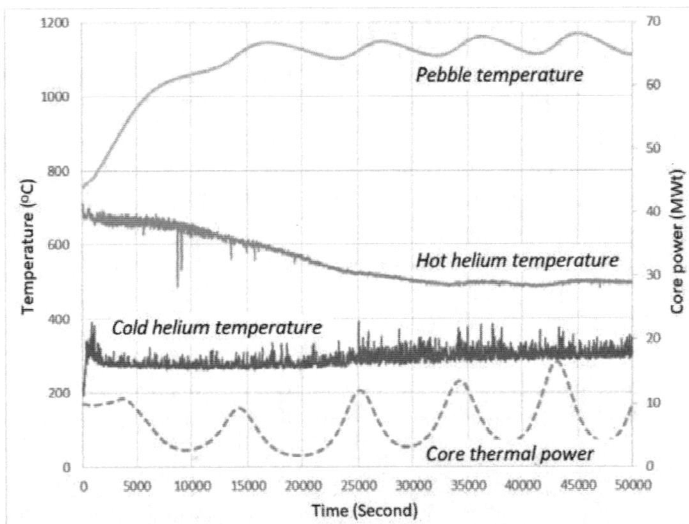


**Figure 3.** Transient of pebble, cold and hot helium temperature and core power (no safety system actuations)

The second case of simulation is performed by considering the actions of the reactor safety systems, which are the RPS to shut down the reactor, stopping the blower operation, and isolation of the secondary system. In this case, the actions to stop the blower and isolation of the secondary system are assumed to occur simultaneously 20 seconds after the tube break initiation followed by the shutting down the reactor 5 seconds later. Figure 4 shows the transient of the primary pressure and the leakage mass flow rate about 5000 seconds after the event. The differences with the Figure 2 are that increase of the primary pressure is not so high since the secondary system has been isolated so that the pressures on both systems are in balance. That pressure condition also causes the leakage rate from the secondary system to be terminated immediately. Figure 5 shows the transient of the pebble temperature and helium temperature for the particular case. The pebble temperature with highest increase is depicted for the 5$^{th}$ segment in the middle core, in which the values are decreasingly still below the limit. All other transients in the temperature are contributed from the shutdown of the reactor power and the heat transfer into the reflector around the core.

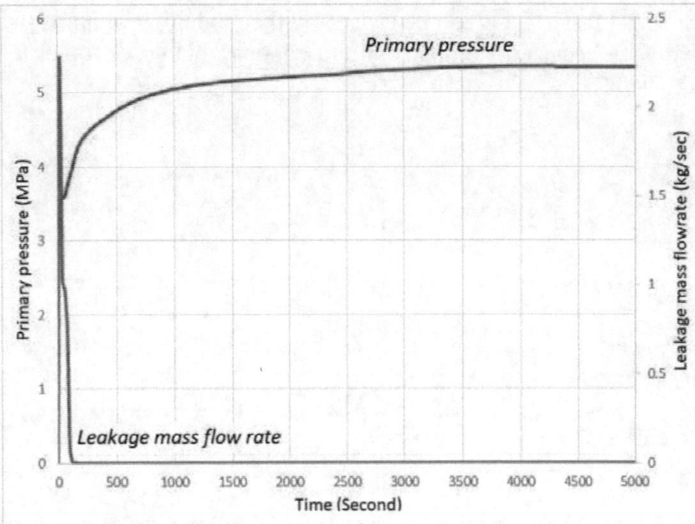


**Figure 4.** Tube rupture mass flowrate and transient of primary pressure (with safety system actuations)

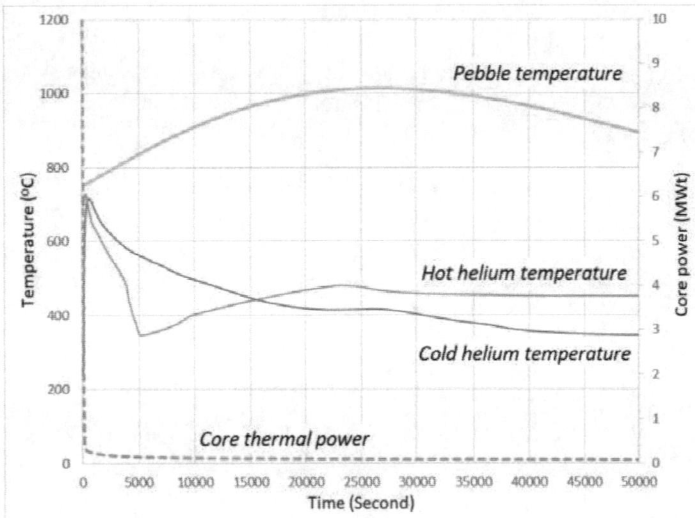


**Figure 5.** Transient of pebble, cold and hot helium temperature and core power (with safety system actuations)

Both cases of with and without safety system actuations result in the increase of the primary pressure above the operating parameter. Even the pebble temperatures are below the limit, the high primary pressure should be prevented, as in the HTR- 10 design, by the operation of the primary safety valve [4]. By considering the pressure relief, the simulation results between the RELAP5 code calculation in this work and the THERMIX code [4] can be compared each other. In the RDE preliminary safety analysis report, that action is accomplished by the use of the pressure limiting valve to open at 4.2 MPa and close at 3.2 MPa of primary pressure. Figure 6 shows the result of the limiting valve model as the primary pressure increases after the tube leakage. It shows that the helium inventory inside the reactor vessel can be released so that the primary pressure become controlled in the safe value. The comparison with the HTR-10 simulation is shown in Figure 7 for the similar parameter. Other parameter such as core hot and cold helium temperature are not available for comparison. In that figure, the decrease of the primary pressure of HTR-10 has basically similar trend with the lower pressure limiting value. For the pebble temperature however, the decrease of HTR-10 is sharper than of RDE model. Its achievement into the stable low value occurs also faster. This can be caused by the modelling of air as the ultimate heat sink in the RDE reflector model, because two different non-condensable gases (other than Helium) are not possible in RELAP5.

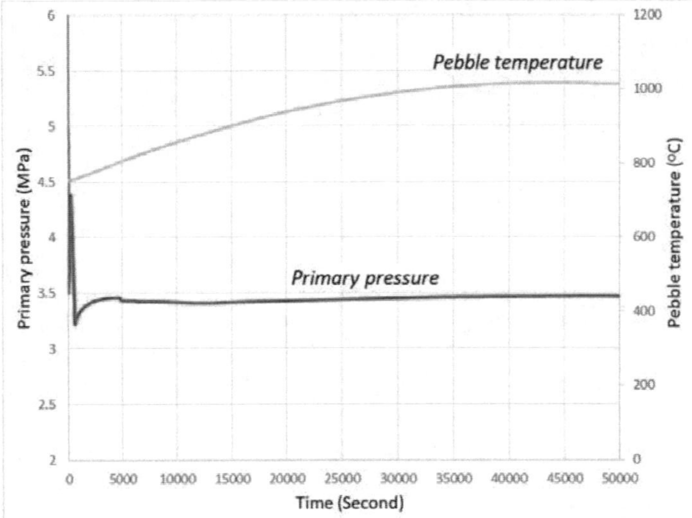


**Figure 6.** Transient of pebble temperature and primary pressure (with safety system actuations and pressure relief)

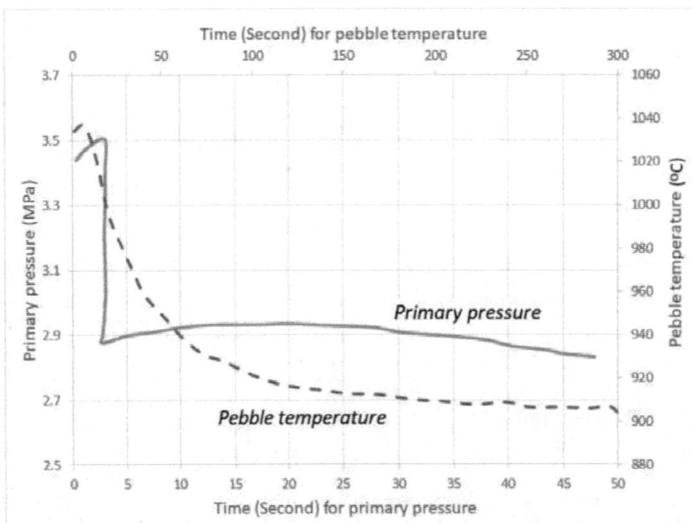


**Figure 7.** Transient of pebble temperature and primary pressure (with safety system actuations and pressure relief) of HTR-10 using THERMIX [4]

Overall, the simulation of the tube rupture in the RDE model has been successfully performed using the RELAP5 thermal hydraulic code. There are still other researches to be done such as the issues with the heat sink in the reflector model, which affects the pebble temperature behavior, core positive reactivity due to the water-steam increase in the core [4, 7] and the operation of the steam generator discharge system to mitigate the event [10].

## 5. Conclusion

Simulation of the steam generator helical-tube rupture of the RDE using RELAP5 code has showed calculation results according to the safety limits based on available RDE model. From two simulated cases, with and without safety system actuations, the pebble temperatures in the core are still under safety limit of the TRISO fuel. Both cases also indicate the importance of the pressure limitation devices in the primary system to control the increase of the primary pressure during the event into the allowable design value. Other issues are still open to address such as the heat sink in the reflector model for the pebble temperature behavior, effect on the core power from the positive reactivity due to the water-steam increase and the operation of the steam generator discharge system to mitigate the event. In general, the RELAP5 code is able to simulate the particular event even the time sequences are different if compared with the THERMIX code.

## Acknowledgement

The author is very grateful to the INSINAS Flagship program of the year 2018 to 2019 for financing the research and also to the Center for Nuclear Reactor Technology and Safety (PTKRN) of BATAN for the support technically and financially.

## References

[1] Z. Zhang, Y. Dong, F. Li, Z. Zhang, H. Wang, X. Huang, H. Li, B. Liu, X. Wu, H. Wang, X. Diao, H. Zhang, J. Wang, The Shandong Shidao Bay200 MWe High-Temperature Gas-Cooled Reactor Pebble-Bed Module (HTR-PM) Demonstration Power Plant: An Engineering and Technological Innovation, Engineering, v2, p.112, 2016.

[2] Y. Xu, S. Hu, S. Yu, High temperature reactor development in China, Progress in Nuclear Energy, v47, p. 260, 2005.

[3] T. Setiadipura, S. Bakhri, G. R. Sunaryo, D. S. Wisnusubroto, Cooling passive safety features of Reaktor Daya Eksperimental, AIP Conference Proceedings 1984, 020034 (2018).

[4] Z. Gao, L. Shi, Thermal hydraulic transient analysis of the HTR-10, Nuclear Engineering and Design, v218, p. 65, 2002.

[5] A.S. Ekariansyah, M. Subekti, S. Widodo, H. Tjahjono, Susyadi, P.I. Wahyono, A. Budianto, Development of Experimental Power Reactor (EPR) Model For Safety Analysis Using RELAP5, Tri Dasa Mega, v21, p. 51, 2019.

[6] M.E. Scari, A. L. Costa, C. Pereira, C. E. Velasquez, M.A.F. Veloso, HTR steady state and transient thermal analyses, International Journal of Hydrogen Energy, v41, p. 7192, 2016.

[7] Z. Zhang, Y. Dong, Assessment of Water Ingress Accidents in a Modular High-Temperature Gas-Cooled Reactor, Nuclear Technology, v149, p. 253, 2005.

[8] S. Ekariansyah, M. Subekti, S. Widodo, Simulation of nuclear steam supply system of experimental power reactor, AIP Conference Proceedings 2180, 020008 (2019).

[9] F. Chen, Y. Dong, Y. Zheng, L. Shi, Z. Zhang, Benchmark Calculation for the Steady-State Temperature Distribution of the HTR-10 under Full-Power Operation, Journal of Nuclear Science and Technology, v46, p. 572, 2009.

[10] J. Dong, J. Fu, Stress and seismic calculation of HTR-10 SG accident discharge system, Proc. HTR-2002, Petten, Netherland, 22 – 24 April 2002.

# Experimental Study on the Residual Heat Removal System in HTR-10

**Jing Li, Liqiang Wei, Yanhua Zheng, Tao Ma, Xiaoming Chen, Feng Xie*, Haitao Wang**

*Institute of Nuclear and New Energy Technology, Collaborative Innovation Centre of Advanced Nuclear Energy Technology, Key Laboratory of Advanced Reactor Engineering and Safety of Ministry of Education, Tsinghua University, Beijing, 100084, China*

*Corresponding author: fxie@tsinghua.edu.cn

**Abstract** – *The 10MW high temperature gas-cooled reactor (HTR-10) is a modular pebble-bed type reactor, of which the inlet and outlet helium temperature are 250 and 700 ℃, respectively. It reached to its first criticality in December, 2000, and operated for nearly twenty years successfully. Currently, HTR-10 is the only pebble-bed type high temperature gas-cooled reactor that can operate in the world. To verify the natural circulation operating characteristics and safety features of the passive residual heat removal system, a series of experimental studies have been performed under different operation conditions of HTR-10, which include the performance tests of the passive residual heat removal system under various reactor operating power, different ambient temperature and single loop run mode. According to the data collation and result analysis, it shows that the performance of the residual heat removal system in HTR-10 meets the design and safety requirements.*

## 1. Introduction

The 10MW high temperature gas-cooled reactor (HTR-10) is a modular pebble-bed type reactor with passive safety characteristics. It is the first high temperature gas-cooled reactor with independent intellectual property rights which was designed, built and operated in China. The HTR-10 adopts graphite spheres containing ceramic tri-structural coated particles, high temperature resistant graphite, and helium as fuel elements, core structural material, and primary coolant. The rated thermal power of the reactor is 10 MW, the primary operating pressure is 3.0 MPa, and the core outlet temperature of helium is 700 °C [1].

The first tank of concrete of HTR-10 was poured on June 14, 1995, the cold commissioning was finished in November, 2000, and the first criticality was reached on December 1, 2000. In January, 2003, the 72 hours of full power operation and acceptance test of grid-connected power generation were completed. Since then, relevant safety and high-power operation tests have been performed successively until July 2007. All parameters were fully reached the design target, indicating that China has mastered a series of core technologies and design technologies for the HTGR, as well as system integration technologies for the research, development, design, processing and construction of new reactors [2].

The residual heat removal system is one of the important guarantees and embodiment of the inherent safety of HTR-10. It adopts the idea of passive design which relies on the radiation, heat conduction and natural convection to carry out the heat. After shutdown of the reactor, it can continue to run without any operation [3-7]. In this paper, we introduce a series of experimental studies which have been performed under different operation conditions of HTR-10 to verify the natural circulation operating characteristics and safety features of the passive residual heat removal system.

## 2. Residual Heat Remove System of HTR-10

During normal operation of the HTR-10 reactor, the residual heat removal system performs the cooling functions of the pressure vessel support and reactor compartment. During normal shutdown, especially after the accident shutdown, it takes the function of residual heat removal [8-12]. The reactor residual heat is carried out of the reactor compartment, which can ensure that the temperature of the reactor internals and pressure vessels are lower than the specified limits. The HTR-10 residual heat removal system includes two independent loops, each with a design capacity of 134 kW. One loop of operation can meet the requirement of residual heat removal. As described in Figure 1, the system is composed of water cooling wall, expansion tank, air cooler, connecting pipe and air cooler.

The residual heat of the reactor is carried out through two natural circulation loops. The heat transferred by radiation and natural convection from the pressure vessel and compartment was absorbed to heat the cooling water in the water cooling wall. The cooling water increases in temperature and decreases in density, thus flows upward along the hot water pipe to the air cooler driven by buoyancy lift. After cooling water is cooled in the air cooler, it flows back to the water cooling wall along the cold-water pipe due to gravity, and continues to absorb heat to form a natural circulation in the water. Ambient air enters from the bottom of the air-cooling tower by lifting force. After heating by the air cooler, the temperature increases and the density decreases, and then the air is discharged through the upper outlet of the air-cooling tower into the final heat sink–atmosphere.

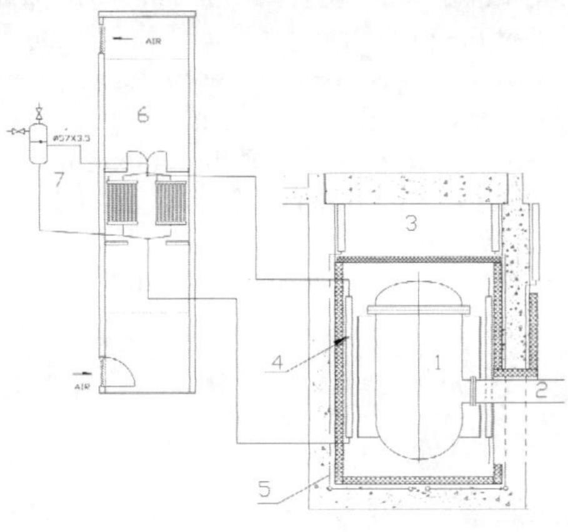


1. Reactor Vessel
2. Hot Gas Duct
3. Reactor Cavity
4. Water Cooling Wall
5. Concrete Vessel
6. Air Cooler
7. 7. Expansion Tank

**Figure 1.** Residual heat removal system of HTR-10.

## 3. Thermal Hydraulic Calculation and Experimental Studies

### *3.1. Thermal hydraulic calculation*

The design of residual heat removal system of HTR-10 is on the basis of thermal hydraulic calculation. The whole heat transfer process was calculated during the system design. In the calculation, it is assumed that the pressure vessel wall and the water cooling wall are two concentric cylinders of finite length, and the ratio between the annular space from the pressure vessel to the water cooling wall and the pressure vessel height is only approximately 0.058. Therefore, the convection heat transfer can be estimated according to the natural convection in the finite space.

The radiative heat transfer calculation formula can be expressed as follows:

$$Q = \varepsilon_n C_0 F_1 \left[ \left( \frac{T_1}{100} \right)^4 - \left( \frac{T_2}{100} \right)^4 \right] \quad (1)$$

$$\varepsilon_n = \frac{1}{\frac{1}{\varepsilon_1} + \frac{F_1}{F_2}\left( \frac{1}{\varepsilon_2} - 1 \right)} \quad (2)$$

Where, $\varepsilon_1$ is the blackness coefficient of the pressure vessel wall, $\varepsilon_2$ is the blackness coefficient of the water cooling wall, $C_0$ is the absolute blackness coefficient, $F_1$ is the outer wall area of the pressure vessel, $F_2$ is the surface area of the water cooling wall, $T_1$ is the outer wall temperature of the pressure vessel, $T_2$ is the surface temperature of the water cooling wall.

The calculation formula of the convective heat transfer can be expressed as follows:

$$Q = \frac{F\lambda_e}{\delta}(t_1 - t_2) \quad (3)$$

$$G_r = \frac{9.81 \times \delta^3 \times \frac{1}{\beta} \times (t_1 - t_2)}{\nu^2} \quad (4)$$

$$\varepsilon_K = \frac{\lambda_e}{\lambda} = 0.4(G_r \cdot P_r)^{0.2} \quad (5)$$

Where, $F$is the surface area of the pressure vessel wall, $\delta$is the annular space, $\lambda_e$is the equivalent thermal conductivity, $t_1$is the wall temperature of the pressure vessel, $t_2$is the temperature of the water cooling wall, $\beta$is the gas expansion coefficient, $\nu$ is the gas viscosity, and$P_r$ is the Prandtl number.

Assuming that the temperature of the pressure vessel wall is 234 °C and the temperature of the water cooling wall is 80 °C, the thermal hydraulic calculation shows that the radiant heat transfer from the wall of the pressure vessel to the water cooling wall is approximately 214 kW, and the natural convection on the wall of the pressure vessel can generate a heat of 17.2 kW.

The air cooler heat dissipation and the air cooling tower heat load formulas can be expressed as follows:

$$Q_2 = K \cdot F \cdot \Delta T \quad (6)$$

$$Q_1 = G \cdot C_P \cdot \Delta T \quad (7)$$

According to the above formulas, the heat transfer power is calculated to be approximately 135 kW, which can meet the requirement of heat transfer power of 134 kW designed for the residual heat removal system.

### *3.2. Performance verification tests under different operating power of reactor*

As shown in Fig 2, performance tests for the residual heat removal system under different operating power of the HTR-10 reactor were performed. The variation trends of operating parameters related to the residual heat removal system from reactor start-up, power increase, stable operation to the emergency shutdown were recorded, which mainly include the nuclear power, main feed water flow, the wall temperature of the pressure vessel, the inlet and outlet water temperature of the water cooling wall, and the inlet and outlet air temperature of the air cooler.

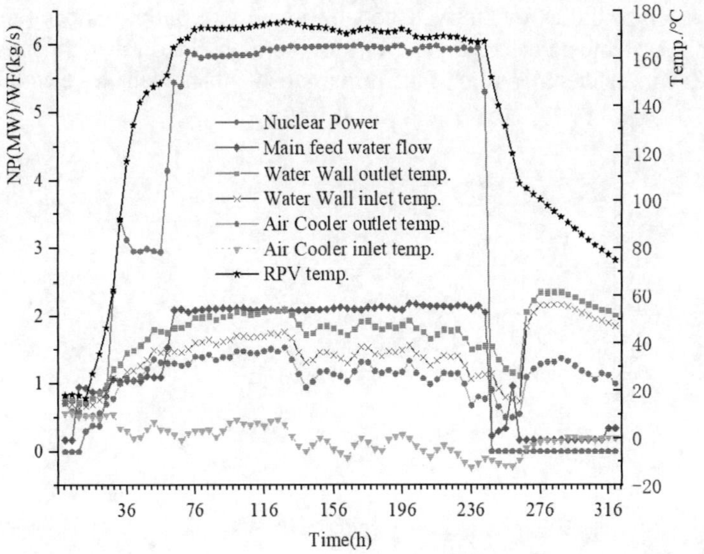


**Figure 2.** Parameter curves of the residual heat removal system under different operating conditions

From the variation of the parameter curves of the residual heat removal system at different operating powers of HTR-10, it can be seen:

(1) The reactor power and the wall temperature of the pressure vessel rise rapidly in the start-up process of the reactor. However, due to certain heat capacity of the heat transfer materials and working medium, the parameter change of residual heat removal system is delayed behind those of the reactor power and the wall temperature of the pressure vessel. With the increase of the temperature of the outer wall of the pressure vessel, the driving forces of radiation and convective heat transfer to the water cooling wall are correspondingly increased, and more heat is absorbed by the cooling water in the residual heat removal system. Therefore, the driving force of buoyancy is increased, the flow rate is increased, and the carrying heat is also gradually increased.

(2) During the stable operation of the reactor, the operating parameters of the residual heat removal system fluctuate with the change of the ambient temperature at the inlet of the air cooler. The temperature difference between the inlet and outlet of the water cooling wall is maintained at approximately 10 °C and the residual heat load is approximately 100 kW. The water temperature at the outlet of the water cooling wall is far below the boiling point of 100 °C, which meets the requirements of stable operation.

(3) The reactor power drops rapidly after the emergency shutdown of the reactor. However, due to the certain heat capacity of heat transfer materials and working mediums, the change of the parameters of the residual heat removal system is delayed behind significantly and is closely related to the in-reactor cooling. When the reactor is cooled inside, the wall temperature of the pressure vessel and the parameters of the residual heat removal system decrease obviously. While when the in-reactor cooling is lost, the wall temperature of the pressure vessel decreases slowly, and the inlet and outlet temperature of the water cooling wall and outlet temperature of the air cooler increase rapidly.

### *3.3. Effects of different ambient temperatures on the performance of residual heat removal system*

As shown in Figure 3, the changes of relevant performance parameters of the residual heat removal system at different ambient temperatures under the steady-state operating conditions of the reactor are presented. The lowest and highest ambient temperatures are approximately -12.7 °C and 36.4 °C, and the inlet and outlet temperatures of the water cooling wall and outlet temperature of the air cooler increase as the ambient temperature changes from low to high. The wall temperature of the pressure vessel only changes with the temperature of the primary coolant and behaves a certain lag.

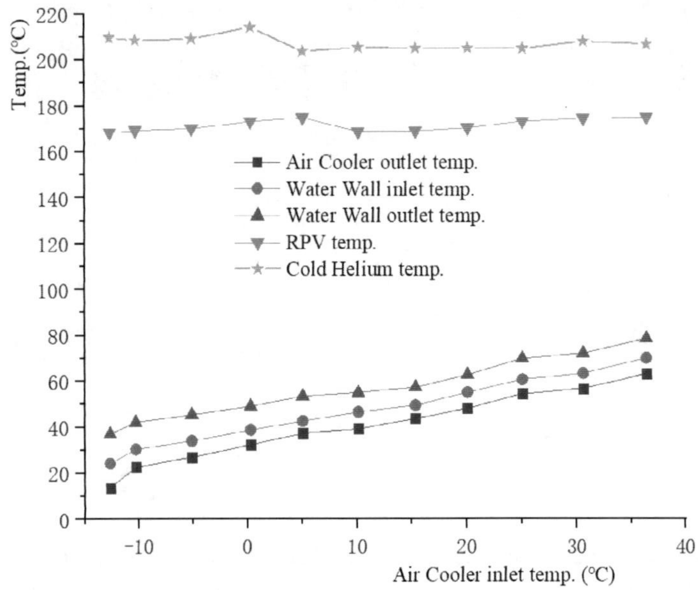


**Figure 3.** Parameter curves of residual heat removal system at different ambient temperatures.

Based on the parameter curves of residual heat removal system under different ambient temperatures, the ambient temperature has a great influence on the inlet and outlet temperatures of the water cooling wall and outlet temperature of the air cooler. The low ambient temperature is more conducive to the operation of the residual heat removal system. However, it should be noted that the opening of cooling air valve should be adjusted timely in the startup and shutdown of the reactor to prevent the abnormal freezing blocking in the water cooling wall caused by the excessively low ambient temperature. When the maximum ambient temperature is reached, the outlet temperature of the water cooling wall of the residual heat removal system is approximately 80 °C. There is a large margin from the normal boiling point of 100 °C, so it can meet the requirements of safe operation.

### *3.4. Single loop run test*

The single loop run test was carried out at 3MW stable power operation of the reactor during the time interval from 8h to 14h, in order to verify the passive residual heat removal ability of single loop run when one of the two loops of residual heat removal system fails. The two loops are denoted as #1 and #2, respectively. The test was carried out by artificially closing the inlet and outlet damper of #1 air cooler. The operating parameters of #1 and #2 loops of the residual heat removal system during the test were shown in Figure 4.

The test began when the operator manually closed the inlet and outlet damper of #1 air cooler at the time point of 8h, and ended when the operator manually opened the inlet and outlet damper of #1 air cooler at the time point of 14h. From the operating parameter curves of the residual heat removal system during the single loop run test, it can be seen:

(1) Due to the loss of a loop of heat load, both the inlet and outlet temperatures of the water cooling wall of the two loops of the residual heat removal system increased with the conduct of the test, and only began to decrease approximately 4 hours after the re-commissioning of the #1 air cooler with a certain time lag.

(2) The cooling water flow and heat load of #1 air cooler decrease rapidly when the inlet and outlet damper is closed, and the wall temperature of the pressure vessel, cooling water flow and heat load of #2 air cooler increase slightly with a certain time lag.
(3) Under the 3 MW stable power working condition of the reactor, the maximum heat load for the single loop of the residual heat removal system is approximately 100 kW, the maximum outlet temperature of the #2 water cooling wall is 68.6°C, and the maximum wall temperature of the pressure vessel is approximately 155 °C. The operating parameters and operating limits have a large margin. Historical records show that even if after the emergency shut-down of the 10 MW full power operation, the maximum temperature of the wall of the pressure vessel is approximately 197 °C, and the maximum temperature of the outlet of the water cooling wall is 80 °C, which has a large margin based on the assumption of thermal hydraulic calculation. Therefore, the single loop run can meet the requirements of the safe operation of passive residual heat removal.

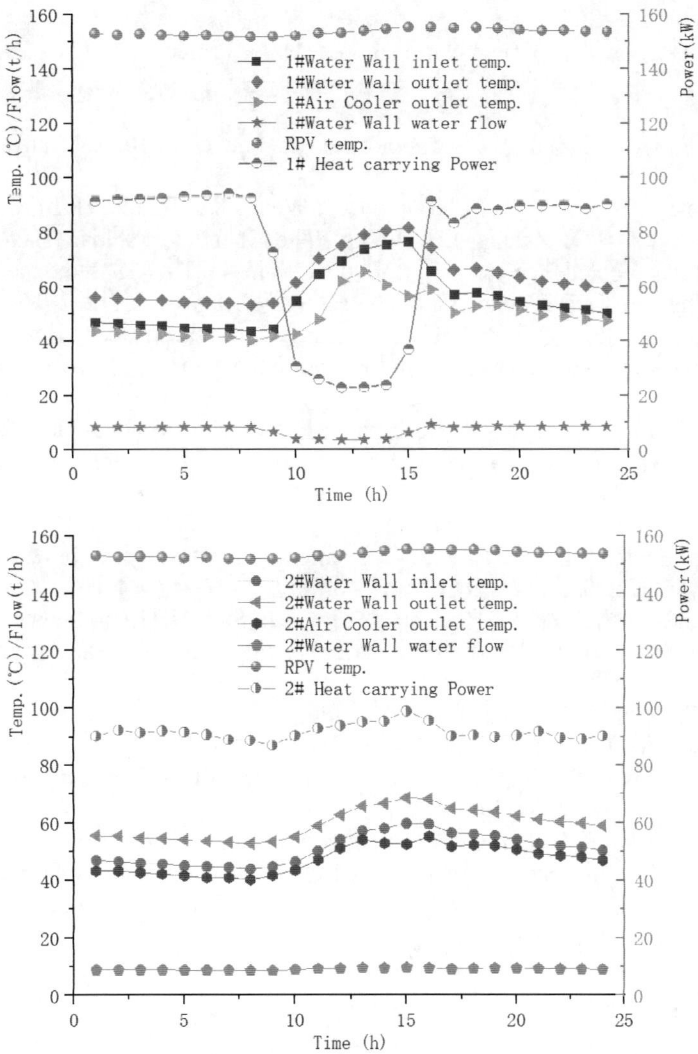


**Figure 4.** Single loop operating parameter curves of the residual heat removal system under stable power operation.

## 4. Conclusion

As a reactor safety-related system, the residual heat removal system of HTR-10 has been verified through the thermal hydraulic design calculation, test verification and operation tests, which prove that the design has sufficient heat load capacity following the single failure criterion. The system operation tests under different working conditions, different ambient temperature and a single loop run mode have been performed successfully. The main parameters and variables affecting the performance of the system are analyzed and verified. It is confirmed that the residual heat removal system of HTR-10 meets the design and safe operation requirements and possesses sufficient heat removal capacity to ensure the safety characteristics of the reactor under normal operation and accident conditions.

Considering that the HTR-10 residual heat removal system adopting passive natural circulation has many complex factors which can affect the cooling water circulation in the water cooling wall and the air flow in the air cooling tower, the performance of the residual heat removal system of HTR-10 and its improvement still need to be further tested and studied.

**Acknowledgement**

This work was supported by the Chinese National S&T Major Project (Grant No. ZX069).

## References

[1] Z.X. Wu, D.C. Lin, D.X. Zhong, The design features of the HTR-10, Nuclear Engineer and Design, v218, p.25, 2002.

[2] Z.Y. Zhang, Y.J. Dong, F. Li, Z.M. Zhang, H.T. Wang, X.J. Huang, H. Li, B. Liu, X.X. Wu, H. Wang, X.Z. Diao, H.Q. Zhang, J.H. Wang, The Shandong Shidao Bay 200 MWe High-Temperature Gas-Cooled Reactor Pebble-Bed Module (HTR-PM) Demonstration Power Plant: An Engineering and Technological Innovation, Engineering, v2, p.112, 2016.

[3] X.Y. Yun, Y.H. Zheng, X.Q. Jing, F. Li, Uncertainty Analysis on Decay Heat of Pebble-bed High Temperature Gas-Cooled Reactor, Atomic Energy Science and Technology, v47, No.7, p.1121, 2013.

[4] X.W. Li, X.X. Wu, L. Zhang, S.Y. He, Analysis of Passive Residual Heat Removal System of Modular High Temperature Gas-Cooled Reactor, Atomic Energy Science and Technology, v47, No.7, p.790, 2011.

[5] L.H. Chen, Y.H. Zheng, T. Ma, X.M. Chen, Y.Z. Ma, Modeling and Computation of Residual Heat Removal System of HTR-10 with Experimental Verification, Atomic Energy Science and Technology,v50, No.10, p.1771, 2016.

[6] D.F. Zhang, Q.S. Su, Y.J. Zhang, H. Chen, J.F. Lu, S.L. Sun, The Experimental Study for Residual Heat Removal System in 5MW Nuclear District Heating Plant, Nuclear Power Engineering, v12, No.2, p.56, 1991.

[7] M.Z. Peng, D.J. Wan, Y. Gao, Analysis for residual heat removal system with natural circulation, Journal of Tsinghua University (Sci& Tech), v36, No.12, p.51, 1996.

[8] H.X. Li, Y.J. Zhang, Z.S. Li, HTR-10 primary cavity cooling system and its features, Journal of Tsinghua University (Sci& Tech), v38, No.5, p.99, 1998.

[9] D.Y. Wang, Ch. Hao, F. Li, Operating Characteristic Analysis of Passive Residual Heat Removal System of HTR-PM, Science and Technology Review (special Issues), v30, No.20, p.33, 2012.

[10] K. Kugeler, Z.Y. Zhang, Modular High-temperature Gas-cooled Reactor Power Plant, First Edition, p.418, Tsinghua University Press, Beijing, 2019.

[11] Z.Y. Gao, Sh.Y. He, M. Zhang, Afterheat Removal for HTR-10 Test Module under Accident Conditions, Decay heat removal and heat transfer under normal and accident conditions in gas cooled reactors, Jülich, Germany, 6-8 July 1992.

[12] W. Rehm, H. Barthels, W. Jahn, Analytical and Experimental Investigations of the Passive Heat Transport in HTRs under Severe Accident Conditions, Decay heat removal and heat transfer under normal and accident conditions in gas cooled reactors, Jülich, Germany, 6-8 July 1992.

# Modelling of FPGA-based Reactor Protection Systems of an Experimental Power Reactor

**T J Suryono, Sudarno, S Santoso, R Maerani**

*Center for Nuclear Reactor Technology and Safety, National Nuclear Energy of Indonesia (BATAN), Gd. 80, Kawasan Puspiptek Serpong, Tangerang Selatan, Banten, Indonesia*

E-mail: suryono@batan.go.id

**Abstract.** The reactor protection system of nuclear power plants including an experimental power reactor which will be built by Indonesia is a safety system that actuates the control rods to be inserted in the reactor core to absorb the neutron to stop the fission reaction and then shut down the reactor (reactor trip). The reactor protection system (RPS) is actuated when the level of signals from the sensors of important components in the reactors deviates from the setpoint determined in the bi-stable processor of the RPS. RPS for the experimental power reactor has 3 redundant channels for reliability and to minimize fake signals from the sensors due to electrical noise. It can be done by selecting the channels in local coincidence logic in the RPS by voting 2 of 3 channels which are eligible to generate actuation signals to trip the reactor. Recently, the RPSs are based on the programmable logic controller (PLC). However, now the trend changes to FPGA-based RPS because of its simplicity and reliability. This paper investigates the model of the FPGA-based RPS for an experimental power reactor and the functionality of each component of the model. The results show that the model can represent the functionality of RPS for the experimental power reactor.

## 1. Introduction

Nuclear Energy Agency of Indonesia (BATAN) as a technical support organization, has functions to conduct research and development of reactor safety and technology. For the first project and to increase the public acceptance, BATAN plants to build a non-commercial experimental power reactor (RDE) of 10 MWth to provide electricity around Puspiptek area [1], [2]. The design of RDE is based on the 10 MW High Temperature Gas-cooled Test Reactor (HTR-10) which is a modular pebble-bed type reactor. Unlike light water reactors, which use water as a cooler and a moderator, the HTR uses graphite for moderator and helium gas for cooling the reactor. One of the important components of the experimental power reactor is instrumentations and controls. The instrumentations including some main components such as pumps, valves, and motors. All the components should be monitored and controlled to make sure that the reactor is operated safely. The controls can be conducted by automatic systems or by human actions.

Reactor protection system (RPS), an example of an automatic system, will break the current source to the control rod drive mechanism and drop the control rods into the reactor core to stop the fission reaction and trip the reactor if some monitored process variables exceeded the safety operation criteria of the plant. Then, the human actions are needed to cool the reactor by removing the residual heat and to prevent the release of radioactive material to the environment.

Currently, most of the RPSs are based on the computer and programmable logic controller (PLC) [3][4][5]. However, because of the complexity of new design of RPSs that difficult to handle by the PLC, and the high maintenance cost of old RPSs [5], field programable gate array (FPGA)-based RPS are developed. FPGA-based RPS system offers some advantages compared with PLC-based systems. FPGA is easy to verify and validate, and also retain to cyberattacks because it is not based on an operating system (OS) [8][4]. Although FPGA has not been widely used in nuclear industries, it offers reliability especially for handling complex systems [8].

An HTR-10-based RDE, a new generation of NPP, will implement FPGA-based RPS. Therefore, in order to design the RPS, a good understanding of the principle and the functionality of FPGA-based RPS is important. This paper discusses the modeling of the FPGA-based RPS for the RDE as one of the methods to achieve that goal. The model is based on the functional analysis of the RPS and the requirement analysis of designing the FPGA and RPS. In addition, the model uses simple components that can represent the functionality of the RPS including the inputs (initiation level), the FPGA-based components (logic level), and the outputs (actuation level). Moreover, the functional analysis of the model is also discussed.

## 2. Overview of RPS of an Experimental Power Reactor

The RDE is equipped with the RPSs that are used to monitor critical plant process variables throughout the operation of the plant and to initiate a reactor trip if a limiting safety system setting (a trip setpoint) of those process variables is exceeded. Table 1 shows the example of process variables of the RDE and their trip setpoints. It can be seen from Table 1, for example, if the helium hot temperature is more than 740°C, the initiating and actuating signal to trip the reactor is generated in the RPS.

**Table 1.** Process variables of RDE and their measure value range [6]

| No | Process variable | Description | Trip setpoints |
|---|---|---|---|
| 1 | Neutron flux | Indication of spatial and temporal levels and variations of neutron flux<br>Guidance for operators to the critical approach<br>Reactor power measurement | ≥ 120% (power measuring range<br>≥ 200% (middle measuring range) |
| 2 | Helium temperature | Measurements of cold and hot helium temperatures | ≥ 740°C (hot)<br>≥ 290°C (cold) |
| 3 | Pressure sliding rate | Measurements of differential pressure in the primary system and secondary system<br>Indication of system components or structures failure | ≥ 0.03 MPa/min |
| 4 | Flow rate | Calculation of the amount of heat removed from the core | ≤ 0.75 or ≥ 1.3 |

Figure 1 shows the block diagram of the RPS of an RDE. It consists of 3 redundancy channels, each channel has bistable processors (BP), local coincidence logic (LCL) processors, and initiation logic. The BPs and LCLs are connected with a cross channel communication both in the same channel and to other channels. The inputs of the RPS are the conditioned signals of the process variable from the transmitter and measured in the sensors. The signals are converted from analog to digital (represented by the voltage signal with the value 0 V to 5 V) so that they can be processed in the digital RPS.

The digital signal is processed and then compared with the trip setpoint in the BP in each channel. If the value is exceeded the safety limit setting, the signal is considered as an initiating signal. The initiating signal, together with those from other channels are forwarded to the LCL processor through the cross-channel communication link. The LCL processors vote 2 out of 3 (2oo3) signals that indicate trip status to generate an actuation signal to trip the reactor. This process is conducted parallelly in each LCL processor in each channel (reactor trip A, reactor trip B, and reactor trip C).

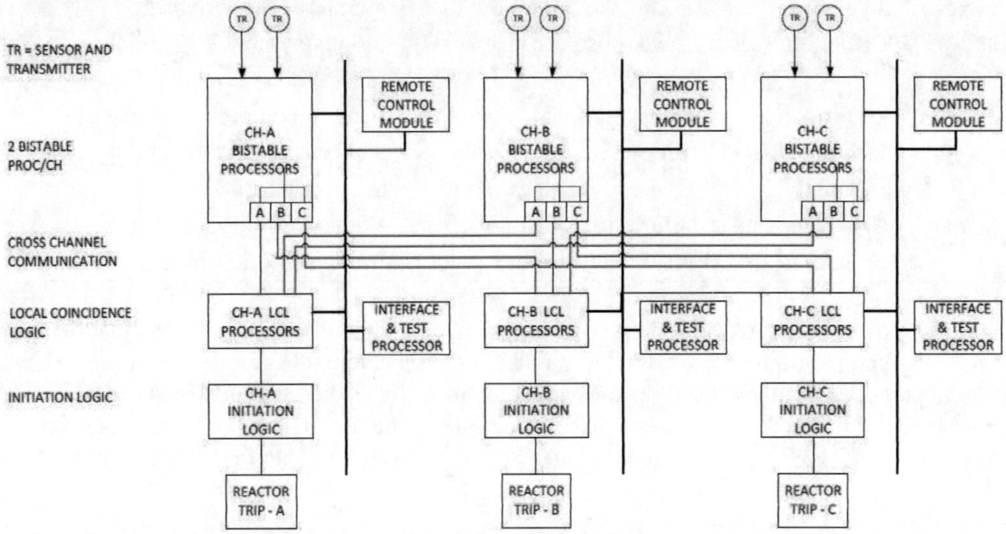


**Figure 1.** Block diagram of RPS of the RDE [7]

## 3. Overview of FPGA

Nowadays, nuclear power plants are equipped with computer-based instrumentation and control (I&C) systems and digital-based RPS [9]. Most of them used a microcontroller-based system such as a programmable logic controller (PLC) [8][5][4]. However, due to the complexity of new RPSs that needs higher integrity level and higher demands of verification and validation activities that are difficult to conduct in PLC, and high maintenance cost of PLC-based RPS [10], the FPGA-based RPS is developed.

Compare with the PLC, FPGA is a less complex system, easy to be verified and validated, and resistant to cyberattack because it is not based on the operating system (OS) and other applications. Literature [8] summarizes the comparison between PLC and FPGA in terms of strength, weakness, opportunity, and threat as can be seen in Table 2. The design of FPGA is based on the system engineering approach: need/system analysis, requirement analysis, functional analysis, design synthesis, and design verification and validation [8]. The need analysis is based on the strength, weakness, opportunity, and threat of the FPGA as in Table 2. Although the FPGA still has weakness compare with the PLC, it can handle the complexity of the new RPS, increase plan reliability, and resistance to cyberattacks. The requirement analysis includes regulatory and performance requirements. In the design process of FPGA, some standards and regulatory guides should be referred such as IEC 62566 (Development of hardware development language HDL-programmed integrated circuits for systems performing category A functions). The performance requirements include the identification of the performance parameters such as technical, operation, and response time of the RPS. The functional analysis is related to defining the allocation of hardware and software including some algorithms and logic.

The design should be synthesis by elaborating and optimizing the algorithms and the datapath of the design. The FPGA is designed using VHDL or Verilog code and should be verified by using VHDL or Verilog simulator and validated by mapping it into the FPGA board and test the design. VHDL (very-high-speed integrated circuit hardware description language), that will be used in this research, is a hardware description language that is used to design an FPGA-based system. The guidance for using the VHDL is provided in IEEE 1076 (IEEE Standard VHDL Language reference manual) [12].

**Table 2.** Comparison between PLC and FPGA [8]

| Items | PLC | FPGA |
|---|---|---|
| Strength | Experienced (it has been used for more than 3 years) | Less verification and validation load, long term supportability |
| Weakness | Difficult to verify, quick obsolescence | Relatively new in the nuclear industry, less experience |
| Opportunity | Performance and computational capability with large data handling | Less complex, increase plant availability and reliability, resistance to cyber attack |
| Threat | Common cause failure to software error, complexity, cyberattack vulnerability | Vulnerability to radiation (if static RAM-based FPGA is used |

Figure 2 shows the FPGA design flow. The design starts with the design entry by writing code VHDL/Verilog into the design. It also includes making the schematic diagram of the design. Then, the design is synthesized using VHDL/Verilog simulator to analyze the behavior of the design. In the mapping place and route phase, the map, place, and route of the design are validated using simulation and timing analysis. The last phase is generating bitstream and mapping into the FPGA board for testing.

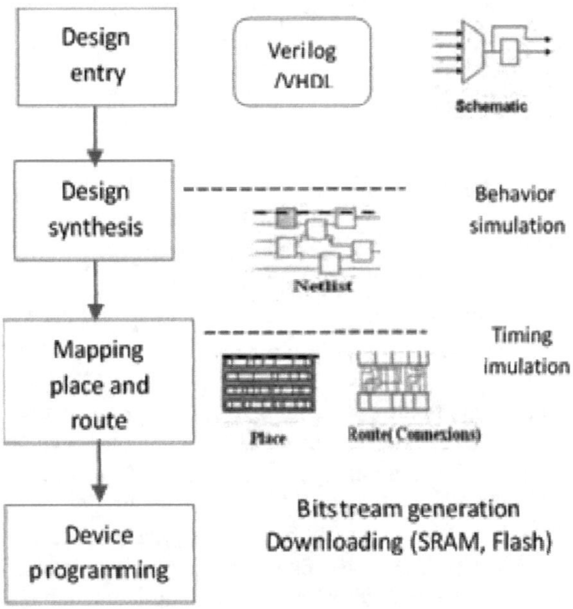


**Figure 2.** FPGA design flow [11]

## 4. Methodology

The modeling of FPGA-based RPS includes some processes such as functional analysis, requirement analysis, modeling, and feasibility analysis. The functional analysis involves the identification of the components of RPS of the RDE and their functions. In addition, the classifications of RPS based on the signal/information generated that are initiation level, logic level, and actuation level is conducted. The next step is the components analysis that includes identification of hardware and software to model the RPS that meets the RPS design criteria. Then, the model of FPGA-based RPS is created using the components identified from the previous step. Finally, the model should be analyzed using a case study to investigate the feasibility so that it can represent the functional of FPGA-based RPS of the RDE.

## 5. Results and Discussions

### *5.1. Functional analysis*

The RPS can be classified into three functional blocks: input (initiation level), logic process (logic level), and outputs (actuation level).

*Initiation level*

The initiation level includes the generation of initiation signals that indicate a trip state. It involves the data acquisition and the signal conditioning of the process variable measured by the sensor and transducer, the conversional of the signal into a digital value, and the comparison of the value with the predefined safety limit (trip setpoint) in the bistable processor.

*Logic level*

The initiation signals from the bistable processor are sent to the all LCL processor in the redundancy channels. Then the LCL processors conduct the voting and gating logic of the 2 out of the 3 coincidence initiation signals (2oo3) to generate the actuation signals.

*Actuation level*

It includes the conversion of the actuation signals into trip signals to activate the protective action. In the case of the reactor trip, it will break the electric current flowing through the control rod drive mechanism that will cause the control rods dropped into the reactor core and trip the reactor.

### *5.2. Component analysis*

The components analysis includes the analysis of hardware and software of the RPS model. The hardware includes the inputs (sensor, transducer, and analog to digital converter/ADC), logic process (bistable processor and LCL processor), and outputs (relay or LEDs). While the software is the hardware description language (HDL) to design the FPGA.

### *5.3. Hardware analysis*

#### *5.3.1. Inputs*

*Sensors and transducers*

In industrial applications, the process variables are generated by the components of the plant and measured in sensors and converted into voltage signals. Then, the transmitter (transducer) transforms the signals into electrical current 4-20 mA and delivers them to the receiver (controller, ADC, or display unit) through the wire for further processing, as can be seen in Figure3. The reasons are that the electrical current can be transmitted through the media over a distance, and resistant to the noise [13]. Therefore, this model implements the 4-20mA current source generator as the source of the process variable signals.

The value of the process variable is proportional to the range of current 4-20 mA. A 4 mA represents 0% of the scale of the process variable, while the 20 mA represents 100% of scale, as can be seen in Figure 4. The formula for converting the process variable to the current 4-20 mA follows the linear correlation

$$y = mx + c \qquad (1)$$

where y = output from instrument, m = slope, x = input of instrument, c = y-intercept point.

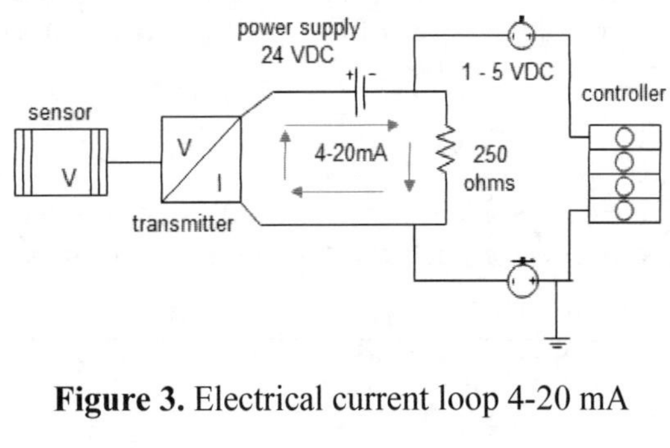


**Figure 3.** Electrical current loop 4-20 mA

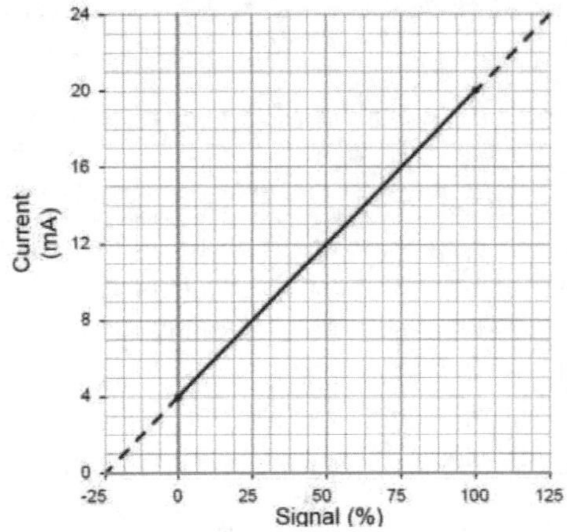


**Figure 4.** Current 4-20 mA and the corresponding scale [14]

The value of m can be calculated as follows:

$$m = \frac{(20-4)}{(100-0)} = \frac{16}{100}$$

$$y = \frac{16}{100}x + c$$

For the value of scale, x = 0, y = 100, c = 4, therefore

$$y = \left(\frac{16}{100}\right)x + 4 \quad (2)$$

The scale means that if the measurement range of hot helium gas temperature of the EPR is from 0 to 850°C, as mentioned in [15], the percentage value of 100°C will be equal to

$$\frac{100}{(850-0)} x100\% = 11.76\%$$

and the current related to the scale is

$$y = \left(\frac{16}{100}\right) 11.76 + 4 = 5.88\ mA$$

*Current to voltage converter*

As in Figure3, the 24 VDC power supply is used to supply the current loop 4-20 mA and delivered through the wire for a distance. In order to be processed in the receiver (output side), such as display unit and other controllers (usually digital systems), the current should be converted into voltage value (1-5 V or 1-10 V). It can be conducted by connecting a resistance to the loop, as can be seen in Figure3. The value of R can be determined by applying formula V = I x R. For the output voltage 1-5 V, the resistance value is 250 ohms.

*Analog to digital converter*

Figure5 shows the simple concepts of 16 bits ADC. Based on [16] 16 bits ADC means that the ADC can detect 2^16 or 65536 discrete analog levels. In other words, the resolution of the ADC is 65535 (the last value of the 16 bits). This ADC value can be related to the voltage input using the following formula:

$$\frac{resolution\ of\ ADC}{system\ voltage} = \frac{ADC\ reading}{analog\ voltage\ measured}$$

In the case of the model system of this paper, the system voltage is 5V and the resolution of ADC is 65535 (5V is related to 65535)

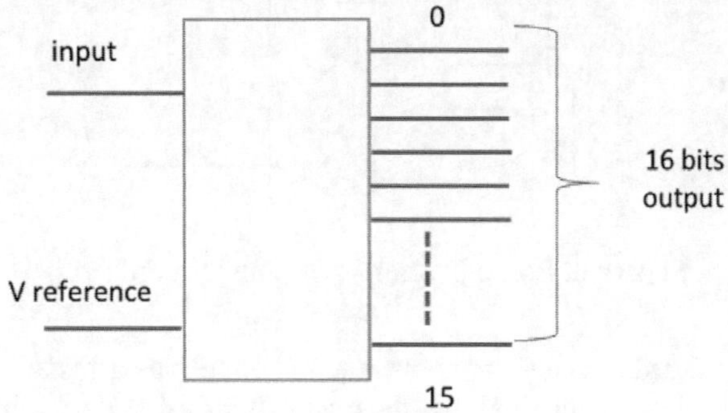


**Figure 5.** A simple 16 bits ADC

**Table 3.** Conversion of process variable into ADC value

| Process variable | Current value | Voltage value | ADC value |
|---|---|---|---|
| 740°C | 17.926 mA | 4.48 V | 59647 (dec)<br>1110100011111111 (bin) |
| 290°C | 17.26 mA | 4.315 V | 56557 (dec)<br>1101110011101101 (bin) |

As an example, let consider the value of the process variable (trip setpoint) of hot helium temperature and cold helium temperature provided in Table 1, which are 740°C and 290°C, respectively. First, the value should be converted into the current 4-20mA using eq.1 and eq.2. Then, the resulted current value is converted into a voltage value by multiplying it with resistance 250 ohms. Finally, the voltage is correlated with the ADC value. The results are shown in Table 3. The ADC values of the process variables will be processed by the bistable processor and compared with the trip setpoints to generate the initiating signals.

*5.3.2. Logic process*

*Bistable processor*

The bistable processor stores predefined safety limits of process variables that cause a reactor trip if the value is violated (trip setpoint). The trip setpoint is set based on the design basis accident analysis. For the EPR, the setpoints are provided in Table 1. In order to be processed by the bistable processor, the trip setpoints should be converted into a digital value (the results of calculation of section V.A) and the examples are provided in Table 3. The process variable from the sensor is compared with the trip setpoint in the bistable processor. If the value reaches or beyond the threshold, the signal is considered as an initiating signal. Therefore, the functionality of the bistable processor is similar to the logic comparator.

Figure 7 shows the logic diagram of a 1-bit comparator. The diagram consists of an inverter, AND, and OR gates and there are 3 possible outputs. It is considered that A is the measured process variable and B is the trip setpoint. In the case of cold helium temperature, the sensor measured that the value is 290°C or 56557 (from Table 3). It will be an input A of the comparator. Then, the value is compared with the input B (trip setpoint = 290°C or 56557). It can be seen that the value of A is equal to B (A=B). In other words, the value of the process variable reaches the trip setpoint value. Therefore, the process variable (cold helium temperature) is set as an initiating signal for the reactor trip.

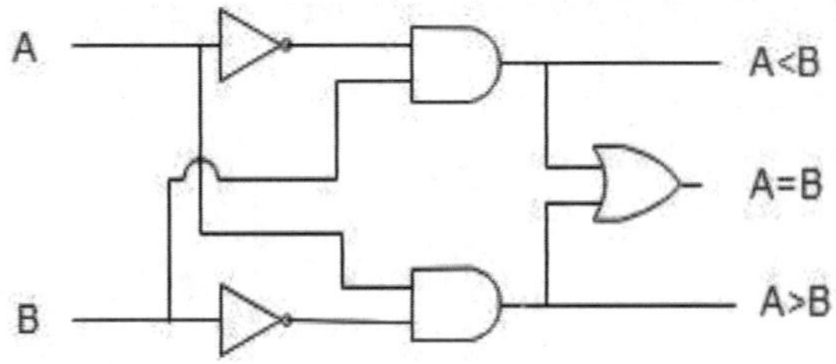


**Figure 6.** Logic diagram of a comparator (1 bit)

*LCL processor*

The RPS of the EPR has 3 redundancy channels, each channel has a bistable processor and an LCL processor. The initiating signal generated by the bistable processor will be delivered to all LCL processors (3 LCL processors) through cross channel communication. However, not all the 3 signals are used to produce the actuation signal, only 2 coincidence signals are needed. This process is called the 2 out of 3 (2oo3) method and conducted by the LCL processor.

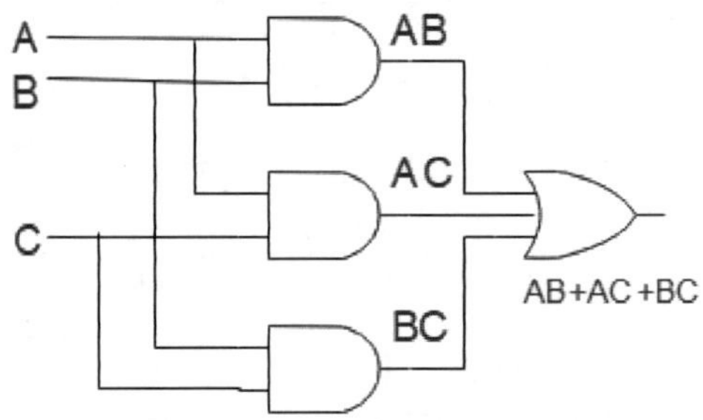


**Figure 7.** Logic diagram of 2 out of 3 (1 bit)

The functionality of the LCL processor can be represented by the logic 2 out of 3, as can be seen in Figure 7. The diagram consists of 3 AND gates and one OR gate. The logic AB, AC, and BC represent the coincidence logic of process variable from the sensor of channel A&B, channel A&C, and channel B&C. Table 4 shows the truth table of the logic. It can be seen that output 1 is achieved if the 2 input values are 1.

**Table 4.** Truth table of logic 2oo3

| A | B | C | AB | AC | BC | AC+AC+BC |
|---|---|---|---|---|---|---|
| 0 | 0 | 0 | 0 | 0 | 0 | 0 |
| 0 | 0 | 1 | 0 | 0 | 0 | 0 |
| 0 | 1 | 0 | 0 | 0 | 0 | 0 |
| 0 | 1 | 1 | 0 | 0 | 1 | 1 |
| 1 | 0 | 0 | 0 | 0 | 0 | 0 |
| 1 | 0 | 1 | 0 | 1 | 0 | 1 |
| 1 | 1 | 0 | 1 | 0 | 0 | 1 |
| 1 | 1 | 1 | 1 | 1 | 1 | 1 |

Figure 8, based on the method mentioned in [17], shows the process of voting the 2 out of 3 initiating signals from the bistable processor. It can be seen that there are 3 possible coincidence logics: AB, AC, and BC. The bistable processor delivers the resulted initiating signals to all LCL processors in the RPS. Therefore, in each LCL there is a matrix trip: [AB1, AB2, AB3], [BC1, BC2, BC3], or [AC1, AC2, AC3] that will generate a reactor trip path that consists of the series of matrix output. For example, trip path 1 consists of a series connection of [AB1, BC1, AC1].

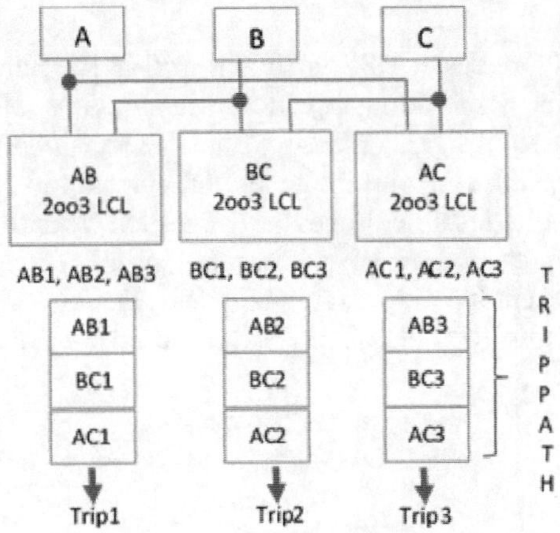


**Figure 8.** 2oo3 LCL outputs and trip path

*FPGA hardware*
Based on the description of the bistable processor and LCL processor in the previous section and the research on the hardware to design the FPGA, the suitable FPGA board for this model is Digilent Basys 3, as can be seen in Figure 9. Although the FPGA board is simple and for beginner, it is reliable and has some features such as switches to represent the inputs, and LEDs and seven-segment displays to represent the outputs.

**Figure 9.** FPGA board Digilent Basys 3

*Outputs*
As the outputs of the model, the relay that is connected to the FGA board that functions as the LCL processor. Another way is by using the output ports of the FPGA board such as LEDs and seven-segment displays to represent the value of the process variable. Regarding the relay or switch, it will change the state (from OFF to ON) when the actuation signal is sent to the relay. On the other hand, for the same case, the LEDs on the FPGA board will be ON and the seven segments will display the value of the process variable. The relay or the LED can represent the controller of the control rod that will be triggered to drop the control rods if the actuation signal is sent to the controller.

*5.4. Software analysis*
There are some VDL that are commonly used in designing the FPGA-based system such as VHDL (Very High Speed Integrated Circuit Hardware Description Language) and Verilog. Based on the research, the most commonly used HDL for the chosen FPGA-board is VHDL. Therefore, this research implements VHDL. However, this paper only discusses the model of the FPGA-based system and investigates the feasibility of the model to represent the functionality of the FPGA-based RPS. Therefore, the implementation of the design including the VHDL code writing and applied to the FPGA board is not discussed. It will be the future works of this research

### *5.5. Model*

The proposed model of the FPGA-based RPS is shown in Fig 10. Below are the descriptions of the components of the model and the assumptions used to design and investigate the model

1. Inputs that provide initiation signals (sensors/transducers, signal conditioners, analog to digital converter) are represented by the current generator, current to voltage generator, and ADC.
2. A comparator to model the bistable processor using FPGA board Digilent Basys 3
3. A logic 2 out of 3 to represent the LCL processor using FPGA board Digilent Basys 3
4. Relay or LEDs to represent the output (actuated device)
5. This model is for a single RPS channel. For the purpose of analysis, the two other identical models are used.

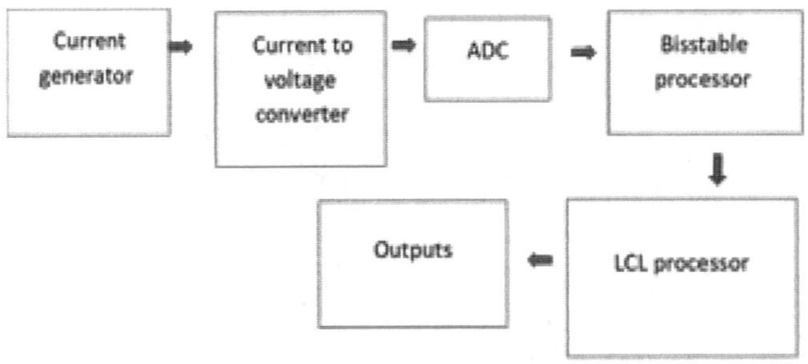


**Figure 10.** Model of the FPGA-based RPS

### *5.6. Case study*

As a case study, a simple simulation is used to investigates the functionality of the model. It is considered that sensors in each channel measured the process variables such as hot helium temperature (channel A and B) and cold helium temperature (channel C) as can be seen in Table 5.

**Table 5.** Process variables measured in 3 channels of the RPS

| Channel | Process variable | Value °C | Current mA | Voltage V | ADC value |
|---|---|---|---|---|---|
| A | Hot helium temp | 760 | 18.3056 | 4.5764 | 59983 |
| B | Hot helium temp | 750 | 18.1184 | 4.5296 | 59369 |
| C | Cold helium temp | 300 | 17.7136 | 4.4284 | 58043 |

The signals are converted into the electrical current value by the transducer. In this case, the signal generator is set to 18.3056 mA (A), 18.1184 (B), and 17.7136 9C). At the receiver of the input, the currents are converted into voltage value and then to a digital value by the ADC. The bistable processor examines the digital value of the process variable with the predetermined trip setpoint value stored in a bistable processor. The results are provided in Table 6. It can be seen that the process variable value is more than the trip setpoint. Therefore, the process variables are set as the initiation signals.

**Table 6.** Comparison of process variable with the trip setpoint

| Channel | Process variable | Value | Trip setpoint |
|---|---|---|---|
| A | Hot helium temp | 59983 | 59647 |
| B | Hot helium temp | 59369 | 59647 |
| C | Cold helium temp | 58043 | 56557 |

The resulted initiating signals from the bistable processor are sent to all LCL processors (2oo3 logic processor) and produced 3 matrix trips ac can be seen in Table 7. It can be seen that there is one matrix trip that indicates the coincidence logic that is AB. Therefore, this signal is set as an actuation signal.

**Table 7.** Matrix trips and actuation signal

| Matrix strip | Process variable | Actuation signal |
|---|---|---|
| AB | Hot helium temp, hot helium temp | yes |
| AC | Hot helium temp, cold helium temp | No |
| BC | Hot helium temp, cold helium temp | No |

The last step is, in the actuation level, the actuation signal is converted to a trip signal that in the model is represented by a signal that change the state of the relay from "OFF" to "ON" or the LEDs from "OFF" to "ON".

## 6. Conclusions

The modeling of FPGA-based RPS using simple equipment has been conducted. The results of the preliminary investigation of the model show that the model can represent the functionality of the RPS. The process variables are converted into current loop 4-20 mA and transformed into digital value before processing in the bistable processor. The bistable processor acts as a comparator that examines the process variable value with the trip setpoint. Then, amongst the 3 initiating signals from the bistable processor, in the LCL processor, the two coincidence signals are set as an actuated signal to turn on the relay or a LED that represents the reactor trip. Future work is related to the implementation of the model and some experiments to verify the model.

**Acknowledgments**
This work is funded by DIPA of PTKRN-BATAN and Insinas Ristekbrin of Ministry of Research and Technology of the 2021 fiscal year.

**References**

[1] M. Subekti, S. Bakhri, and G. R. Sunaryo, "The Simulator Development for RDE Reactor," *J. Phys. Conf. Ser.*, vol. 962, no. 1, 2018.
[2] BATAN, "Experimental Power Reactor (RDE)." .
[3] J. G. Choi and D. Y. Lee, "Development of RPS trip logic based on PLD technology," *Nucl. Eng. Technol.*, vol. 44, no. 6, pp. 697–708, 2012.
[4] I. Ahmed, J. Jung, and G. Heo, "Design verification enhancement of field programmable gate array-based safety-critical I&C system of nuclear power plant," *Nucl. Eng. Des.*, vol. 317, pp. 232–241, 2017.
[5] J. Yoo, J. H. Lee, and J. S. Lee, "A research on seamless platform change of reactor protection system from PLC to FPGA," *Nucl. Eng. Technol.*, vol. 45, no. 4, pp. 477–488, 2013.
[6] G. Zuying and S. Lei, "Thermal hydraulic transient analysis of the HTR-10," *Nucl. Eng. Des.*, vol. 218, no. 1–3, pp. 65–80, 2002.
[7] S. Sudarno, A. Cahyono, D. F. Atmoko, and S. Santoso, "Detail Engineering Design Reaktor Daya Eksperimental: Sistem Proteksi Reaktor." Badan Tenaga Nuklir Nasional (BATAN), [in Indonesian], 2018.
[8] J. Jung and I. Ahmed, "Development of Field Programmable Gate Array-based Reactor Trip Functions Using Systems Engineering Approach," *Nucl. Eng. Technol.*, vol. 48, no. 4, pp. 1047–1057, 2016.
[9] C. A. Verrastro *et al.*, "IGORR Conference 2014 FPGA Based Reactor Protection System Architecture Instrumentación y Control - Centro Atómico Ezeiza - Comisión Nacional de Energía Atómica systems to guarantee that design specifications are not exceeded . The RPS has priority over T," no. May, 2015.
[10] J. Yoo, J. Lee, and J. Lee, "A RESEARCH ON SEAMLESS PLATFORM CHANGE OF REACTOR PROTECTION SYSTEM FROM PLC TO FPGA," *Nucl. Eng. Technol.*, vol. 45, no. 4, pp. 477–488, 2013.

[11] C. Tanougast, A. Dandache, M. Salah, and S. Sadoudi, "Hardware Design of Embedded Systems for Security Applications," *Embed. Syst. - High Perform. Syst. Appl. Proj.*, no. May 2014, 2012.

[12] I. C. Society, *IEEE Standard VHDL Language Reference Manual. IEEE Std 1076-2008*, vol. 2008, no. January. 2009.

[13] T. Witt, R. Mena, and E. Cornell, "Single chip, 2-wire, 4-20mA current loop RTD temperature transmitter design," *IECON Proc. (Industrial Electron. Conf.*, vol. 10, pp. 2380–2383, 2014.

[14] O. Barrière, A. Echelard, and J. L. Véhel, *Lessons In Industrial Instrumentation*, vol. 17, no. January. 2012.

[15] Sudarno, S. Santoso, K. Santosa, R. Maerani, and Deswandri, "Assessment of Input Parameters and Architecture of RDE Reactor Protection System," *J. Phys. Conf. Ser.*, vol. 1198, no. 5, 2019.

[16] SparkFun, "Analog to Digital Conversion." [Online]. Available: https://learn.sparkfun.com/tutorials/analog-to-digital-conversion/all. [Accessed: 25-Aug-2020].

[17] USNRC, "Plant Protection System," *Usn. Tech. Train. Center, Westinghouse Technol. Syst. Manual. Usn. HRTD. Rev 10/08.*, p. https://www.nrc.gov/docs/ML1125/ML11251A044.pdf.

# MUF Calculation of Indonesian 10-MWt RDE Experimental HTGR Using Combined Uncertainty Approach

**Arief S. Adhi, Mohamad S.F. Husein, Pertiwi D. Winastri**

*BATAN (National Nuclear Energy Agency of the Republic of Indonesia)*
*Building 20, PTBBN-BATAN, Serpong Nuclear Research Complex, Puspiptek, Tangerang Selatan 15314, Indonesia ,phone: +62-21-756-2860 ext.2021,*

Corresponding author's e-mail : ariefsa@batan.go.id

**Abstract** – A safeguards assessment for the 10-MWt RDE Experimental HTGR needs to be established in order to fulfill the requirements needed to construct it. Methods and instruments used for the RDE's nuclear material accounting and safeguards system are reviewed in this paper. Material unaccounted for (MUF) is calculated using the uncertainty of each method and instrument. The effectiveness of the safeguards system is examined by comparing the resulting MUF with the number of SQ (= significant quantity, i.e. the approximate amount of nuclear material for which the possibility of manufacturing of a nuclear explosive device cannot be excluded). The total uncertainty from each KMP showed a number less than 10%. The number of MUF in each KMP according to total uncertainty showed a number below 1 kg of U-235 in one inventory period (~12 months). According to the number of MUF counted, it is impossible to reach 1 SQ if the diversion done is only by taking the advantage of MUF in the measurement. The result of total uncertainty and MUF calculation showed that the safeguards system and the material measurement designed for RDE is amendable. The sets of instruments and measurements designed will give a comprehensive data of each nuclear material in the RDE. The low number of MUF in comparison with the SQ showed that the RDE has a high proliferation resistance.

## 1. Introduction

BATAN has designed a 10-MWt high- temperature gas-cooled reactor (HTGR) named RDE. The reactor was planned to be built in its Serpong Nuclear Research Complex in Tangerang Selatan, Indonesia. A site permit has been issued by the national regulatory body, and to facilitate the issuance of a construction permit, a basic safeguards system for the reactor had been designed in 2016 and 2017 to complement the detailed engineering design. A detailed DIQ from the IAEA and a construction permit from Indonesian Nuclear Regulatory Agency (BAPETEN) are needed for RDE to begin its construction. RDE safeguards system amenability, including methods and instruments used, needs to be confirmed in order to complete the final design of RDE [1, 2].

The RDE will have 10-MWt of power with 27,000 TRISO-pebbles in the reactor. The reactor fuel is capable in both once-through-then-out (OTTO) cycle and multipass system [3]. A pebble-bed type HTGR uses pebbles with the diameter of 6 cm. The small size of the fuel and large number of pebbles in one reactor makes HTGR resembles a bulk handling facility rather than an item facility. The bulk characteristic of the nuclear material is present both in fuel storage and inside the reactor. The pebbles will have a bulk flow when each pebble is taken from the bottom of the reactor [4].

The pebble-bed type HTGR that uses fuel recycle system will utilize neutron economy and fuel burnup (reduced leakage) [5]. The recycle system will introduce partly burned fuel into the reactor that keeps the criticality in a steady level. The mixed state of pebble fuels makes a unique identification hard to be implemented on each pebble.

### *1.1. Key Measurement Points (KMPs) and RDE Safeguards System*

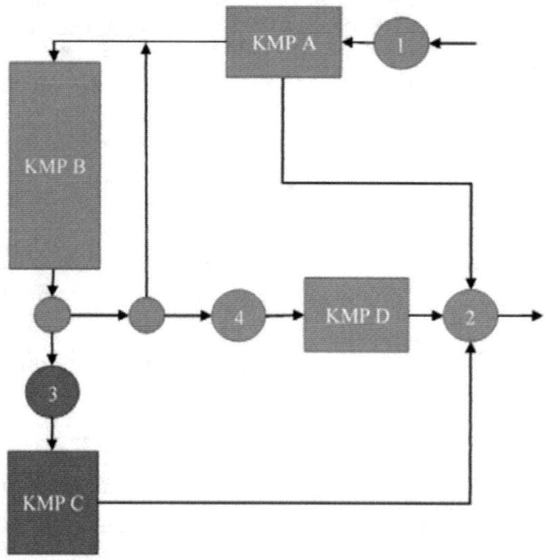


**Figure 1.** Key Measurement Points of RDE; KMP A: Fresh Fuel Storage; KMP B: Reactor; KMP C: Damaged Fuel Storage; KMP D: Spent Fuel Storage; 1: Receiver KMP; 2: Shipper KMP; 3 & 4: Flow Monitors [6]

The bulk characteristic of RDE will make a diversion of nuclear material possible. The diversion of nuclear material can be done in the fresh fuel and spent or broken fuel storage. The pebble diversion problem addresses a safeguards-by-design to be implemented in the facility. A safeguards system for RDE is designed to control and supervise nuclear material in every sector of the RDE. There are four key measurement points (KMPs) located inside the RDE. Figure 1 shows each KMP in RDE along with the function and measurements that takes place inside the KMP.

KMP A will have fresh fuel stored. The storage of fresh fuel is filled with pebbles that each contains 5 g uranium with 17% enrichment [6]. The bulk characteristic of each pebble in the storage will limit unique identification of each pebble. All unidentified items (including fuel pebbles) can be an easy target for diversion [7]. HTGR reactor core uses semi- automatic recycling system that reduces human interaction with nuclear material. The flow of pebbles inside the recycling system is in linear state. The linear flow of pebbles makes it possible to use gamma multi-channel analyzer with a short measurement time. KMPs C and D have the same characteristic. Spent fuel pebbles will be stored in the storage cask. The cask is stored in a dry storage facility. Unique identification will be implanted on each cask.

### *1.2. Method and Instrument in RDE Safeguards System*

The methods and instruments that will be in the safeguards system have the goal to give the same knowledge of nuclear material mass and other information. The knowledge is important for both operator and inspector related to safeguards activity. Each KMP in RDE have their own characteristic and unique method to measure nuclear material.

Fresh fuel storage in KMP A has uranium-235 which emits gamma radiation. The bulk characteristic of KMP A drives the measurement to use a sampling method. Some number of samples will be taken to do the measurement of uranium-235 concentration and material weight (i.e., pebble weight). The uranium- 235 measurement will be done by using miniature multichannel analyzer with NaI(Tl) detector. The measurement will take 300 seconds for each pebble. The activity of measuring uranium-235 concentration depends on the calculation of radiation counted in the specific gamma energy of uranium-235. Uranium- 235 emits gamma radiation with energy ranged from 143.8 keV to 205.3 keV with total probability of 78.07% and highest probability 57.2% in the energy 185.7 keV. Measurement of uranium-235 concentration needs a high efficiency detector to capture uranium gamma radiation due to the gamma energy falls in the region of noise radiation that can also be captured by the detector. A scintillation NaI(Tl) detector has a high efficiency which enables isotope identification and attribute verification of uranium, plutonium, thorium, and americium isotopes [8].

Burn-up analysis in fuel handling system coupled with the reactor will be done using NaI(Tl) multichannel analyzer. The use of NaI(Tl) detector is chosen because of the high efficiency and simple detector construction. The simple construction of NaI(Tl) detector makes customization of detection system easier to do. The NaI(Tl) detector will be coupled with burn-up calculation program.

Damaged and spent fuels in KMPs C and D have the same characteristic. Both fuels will be stored in the storage cask. Measurement of material weight will be done using load-cell-based weighing system (LCBS), measurement of isotopes concentration will be done using NDA with neutron counting for plutonium and gamma spectrometry for uranium. LCBS will count the weight of a bulk material inside a medium by comparing the cord's stress signal given by the load cell (reference weight) and signal given by the cask containing bulk material (measured weight). The uncertainty of LCBS comes from the environment and the weighing system. The sample cask will be hanged to measure the overall (bulk) weight of sample inside the container. Wind and atmosphere conditions are a natural cause that contributes to LCBS measurement due to the hanging position of sample [9]. The systemic parameter is hysteresis of the system and linearity of the cord that accommodates the sample cask.

Neutron multiplicity counter is also used in KMPs C and D. Neutron counter will measure total plutonium mass appeared within the sample. Total plutonium mass will be measured by measuring number of neutrons produced by plutonium in spontaneous fission. The spontaneous fission will produce high energy neutrons that will be measured using plutonium-scrap multiplication counter (PSMC). A neutron multiplication counter will count neutrons from single, double, and high order coincidence events simultaneously while coincidence counter only count single and double neutron events [10]. The PSMC has a better performance in measuring the total mass of plutonium in a dirty sample (high impurity) compared with coincidence neutron counter [10, 11].

Spent fuel in KMP D needs to be analyzed comprehensively. The plutonium in spent fuel can give so many information about the characteristic and material attractiveness of the spent fuel. The composition of plutonium-238 to total plutonium in weight percentage can give information about heat generated from each fuel. The isotopic composition of plutonium-239 to total plutonium weight percentage can determine the attractiveness of spent fuel that can determine proliferation resistance of the facility. The composition of plutonium-240 and plutonium-242 to total plutonium in weight percentage can determine number of spontaneous neutrons expected to be measured per period of time. A detailed isotopic composition of plutonium is also needed to count total plutonium weight in bulk sample before the measurement with PSMC takes place [12]. The isotopic composition of plutonium can be measured with gamma spectrometry multi- channel analyzer. The detector used in measurement of isotopic composition must have high resolution in order to produce better spectrum that can distinguish each isotope correctly [13]. High-purity germanium (HPGe) detector is used for its performance in producing high resolution spectra. The measurement will be done to the storage cask filled with spent fuel pebble. Each isotopic composition will be used to count total mass of plutonium-239 that will be reported for safeguards purpose.

### *1.3. Measurement Uncertainty and Safeguards System Amenability*

Safeguards are a set of technical measures that are established in a nuclear facility to verify a state's legal obligation that nuclear facilities will only be used for peaceful purposes and will not be diverted. One of the important parameters to verify the amenability of safeguards system is the ability to derive material that cannot be accounted in a facility. The derivation of "material unaccounted for" (MUF) can be done by determining a statistical limit error for each measurement and combined uncertainty in the facility [14,15].

An item facility such as an LWR reactor is normally expected to have almost zero MUF due to the characteristic of the nuclear material that can be exactly known for each item. A high-temperature gas- cooled reactor is a type of reactor that resembles a bulk-handling facility rather than an item facility. The lowest expected MUF in an HTGR is equal to total uncertainty in the facility [16]. The calculated MUF can give a number of nuclear materials that have the possibilities to be diverted.

## 2. Description of the Actual Work

### *2.1. Parameters in Uncertainty Calculation*

The uncertainty of each instrument can be counted using two indicators random error ($U_r$) and systemic error ($U_s$). Random error ($U_r$) is a divergence of measurement value that is obtained with the same method and instrument used to measure identical item. Random error characteristic is when value of measurement varies in an unexpected manner in repeatable conditions. Systemic error ($U_s$) is a variance in measurement resulted due to the inability of a system or instrument to measure the actual value, for example the difference of efficiency of HPGe detector and NaI(Tl) detector. Random error and systemic error are both present in each measurement done and must be calculated in the determination of combined uncertainties [17, 18]. The combined uncertainty of a key measurement point using number of instruments can be counted using equations (1) to (3) below.

$$U_c(r) = \sqrt{\sum_i U_i^2(r)/n_i} \tag{1}$$

$$U_c(s) = \sqrt{\sum_i U_i^2(s)} \tag{2}$$

$$U_c = \sqrt{U_c^2(r) + U_c^2(s)} \tag{3}$$

The combined uncertainty calculated from random error is shown by equation (3) symbolized as $U_c(r)$. The combined random error uncertainty is counted by dividing random error known for each measurement ($U_i(r)$) with the number of sample or repetition done in the measurement ($n_i$). The division must be done because random error is affected by the number of repetitions taken to determine the true value of measurement. On the other hand, combined uncertainty from systematic error is counted by adding each value of error and does not have to be divided by the number of sample nor the repetition of measurement. The total combined uncertainty ($U_c$) is the number that shows how big the divergence of value can be produced by series of measurement in one system, for this case in one KMP.

The value of $U_r$ and $U_s$ of each instrument used for combined uncertainty calculation is taken from International Target Values (ITV) 2010 for measurement uncertainties in safeguarding nuclear material [17]. The value of each error shown in ITV document can be used to calculate and estimate the value of combined uncertainty of a safeguard design when no other reliable performance values available. Every error value will then be calculated using equations (1) to (3) above.

### *2.2. MUF Calculation Using Total Uncertainty*

The value of "material unaccounted for" (MUF) can be determined using the value of combined uncertainty ($U_C$) [19]. Value of MUF can be counted by multiplying the combined uncertainty ($U_C$) with number of pebbles in a period of time. The period of time used in calculation can be one inventory period ranged about 12 months. The value of MUF can also be determined in unit of uranium mass or uranium- 235 mass by further multiplying the MUF in number of pebbles with the data of uranium mass in a pebble and isotopic composition of uranium-235 in each pebble. The calculation of each MUF is shown in equation (4) for MUF in number of pebbles, equation (5) for MUF in uranium weight, and equation (6) for MUF in uranium-235 weight. The information of MUF shown in uranium-235 weight can be used to determine the number percentage of MUF to uranium significant quantity (SQ) and to calculate the time needed to reach 1 SQ by diverting nuclear material as much as the MUF in each period. The SQ for uranium used is SQ for low-enriched uranium, the value is 75 kg of uranium-235.

$$MUFpebble = U_C \times number\ of\ pebbles\ in\ KMP \quad (4)$$

$$MUFU - total = MUFpebble \times mass\ of\ uranium\ in\ pebble \quad (5)$$

$$MUFFissile = MUFU \times \%fissile\ material \quad (6)$$

$$\%SQ = MUFFissile / SQFissile \quad (7)$$

## 3. Results

### *3.1. Combined Uncertainty of Each KMP*

The calculation of combined uncertainty was done using the data of each step, method, and instrument taken from IAEA ITV 2010. The data is distinguished by steps or parameters measured. $n_i$ is the number of samples taken or measurement repeated, $U^2(r)$ and $U^2(s)$ are parameter used to count combined uncertainty. The complete data are shown in Table 1.

*Uncertainty in KMP A:* KMP A has two parameters measured, the weight of nuclear material and the concentration of uranium-235. Every measurement in KMP A was done by sampling pebbles in KMP A. The samples taken are 10 pebbles for both weight measurement and uranium-235 concentration. The sampling must be done because pebbles in KMP A have the characteristic of bulk material due to unavailability of unique identity for each pebble. The sample needs to be taken for the measurement to represent the population of pebbles. The sampling step (activity of choosing sample for measurement) also contribute to combined uncertainty and have both random error and systemic error. The random error of sampling can appear due to the different properties such as weight or number of uranium contained in each pebble. Each pebble in KMP A has 5 grams uranium in the form of TRISO particle spread inside every space inside the pebble. A difference of uranium mass can always present but not in significant values, therefore contributing to both random and systemic error.

The weighing in KMP A will be done using electronic balance with random error and systemic error have been calculated for combined uncertainties. The uranium-235 concentration measurement will be done using miniature multi- channel analyzer with NaI(Tl) detector (MMCN). NaI(Tl) detector is chosen because the energy that needs to be measured is exactly known (185.4 keV). The fresh nuclear fuel in KMP A only has uranium as its dominant radiation emitter, so the energy spectrum will not have much noise except from the background and backscatter. The fresh pebble is classified as LEU pure material or the same as pellet as a pure and stable nuclear fuel. This classification of measured material gives the value of measurement random error value of 3 and measurement systemic error value of 2. The final result of combined uncertainty from KMP A is 2.215%, making it the lowest value of combined uncertainty compared to other KMPs.

*Uncertainty in KMP B:* KMP B is a reactor where the only measurement done is burn-up measurement. The pebble bed reactor has high temperature.

**Table 1.** Calculation of Combined Uncertainty

| KMP | Measurement (Step) | Method/ Instrument | $n_i$ | $U_r$ | $U_s$ | $U_i^2(r)/n_i$ | $U_i^2(s)$ |
|---|---|---|---|---|---|---|---|
| A | Pebble Sampling | | 10 | 0.05 | 0.05 | 0.00025 | 0.0025 |
| | Weight | EBAL | 10 | 0.05 | 0.05 | 0.00025 | 0.0025 |
| | U-235 Concentration | MMCN (NaI(Tl)) | 10 | 3 | 2 | 0.9 | 4 |
| | Sum of Variance | | | | | 0.901 | 4.01 |
| | Combined Standard Uncertainties ($U_c(r)$ and $U_c(s)$) | | | | | 0.949 | 2.001 |
| | Combined Uncertainties (%) | | | | | 2.215 | |
| B | MCA (burnup) | MMCN (NaI(Tl)) | 1 | 15 | 5 | 225 | 25 |
| | Sum of Variance | | | | | 225.000 | 25.00 |
| | Combined Standard Uncertainties ($U_c(r)$ and $U_c(s)$) | | | | | 15.000 | 5.000 |
| | Combined Uncertainties (%) | | | | | 15.811 | |
| C | Bulk Weight | LCBS | 1 | 0.05 | 0.05 | 0.0025 | 0.0025 |
| | Total Pu Mass | PSMC | 1 | 5 | 1 | 25 | 1 |
| | U-235 Conc | IMCG | 1 | 10 | 2 | 100 | 4 |
| | Sum of Variance | | | | | 125.003 | 5.003 |
| | Combined Standard Uncertainties ($U_c(r)$ and $U_c(s)$) | | | | | 11.180 | 2.237 |
| | Combined Uncertainties (%) | | | | | 11.402 | |
| D | Bulk Weight | LCBS | 1 | 0.05 | 0.05 | 0.0025 | 0.0025 |
| | Pu-238 | IMCG | 1 | 1 | 2 | 1 | 4 |
| | Pu-240 | IMCG | 1 | 1 | 1 | 1 | 1 |
| | Pu-241 | IMCG | 1 | 1 | 1 | 1 | 1 |
| | Total Pu Mass | PSMC | 1 | 5 | 1 | 25 | 1 |
| | U-235 Conc | IMCG | 1 | 10 | 2 | 100 | 4 |
| | Sum of Variance | | | | | 128.003 | 11.003 |
| | Combined Standard Uncertainties ($U_c(r)$ and $U_c(s)$) | | | | | 11.314 | 3.317 |
| | Combined Uncertainties (%) | | | | | 11.790 | |

According to design it can reach above 700°C in steady state operation condition. The high temperature and random distribution of pebbles inside the reactor make measurement hard to do. The burn-up measurement will be done in the fuel handling system of the pebbles. Each pebble will be measured one by one when they go through the fuel handling system. The burn-up measurement will measure isotopic composition of uranium-235 and other radionuclides such as cesium as the fission product. The isotopic composition will be used to calculate burn-up of each pebble by using burn-up calculation code. High resolution detector may be needed to distinguish each energy thoroughly, but to achieve the desired construction of detector coupled with burn-up calculation system.

Nuclear material in KMP B is classified as high impurity material because of other radionuclides produced in the fission process. The fission product will also emit gamma radiation that will interfere with each other increasing both random and systemic error. The value of random error is 15 and systemic error is 5, the combined uncertainty value in KMP B is 15.811%.

*Uncertainty in KMP C:* KMP C is a storage for damaged fuel from the reactor. The damaged fuel in KMP C have similar radioactivity as spent fuel. The damaged fuel pebble can range from low burn-up high burn-up because of the multipass system. The damaged fuel will send directly from fuel handling system to fuel storage cask without human interference. Every measurement will be done with damaged fuel located inside the cask.

The bulk weight measurement will be done using LCBS with random error and systemic error of 0.05. The systemic error from LCBS can come from the respond of load cell and the effect of hysteresis in the system [21]. Uranium concentration measurement along with determination of plutonium will be done using Inspector 2000 multichannel analyzer with HPGe detector (IMCG). High-purity germanium (HPGe) detector is selected because of its high resolution. Uranium-235 concentration measurement with IMCG have the random value of 10 and systemic error value of 2. High value of random error is present due to the characteristic of damaged fuel which also have a lot of radioactive impurities that will interfere with the measurement process. The determination of plutonium will then lead to plutonium total mass measurement using plutonium scrap multiplication counter (PSMC). The PSMC will determine total mass of plutonium in each case that can be divided by number of fuels inside each cask and give mass of plutonium in each pebble. The measurement of plutonium total mass has random error value of 5 and systemic error value of 1. The combined uncertainty in KMP C is 11.402%

*Uncertainty in KMP D:* KMP D is a storage for spent fuel that have reached maximum burn-up allowed in the reactor. The irradiation inside RDE reactor will reduce the uranium-235 enrichment from 17% to 3% or will reduce uranium-235 in each pebble as much as 0.7 g uranium-235 per pebble [5]. Uranium-235 concentration, bulk weight, and total plutonium mass will be measured once again in KMP D. Plutonium isotopic composition will be determined in this KMP. Isotopic composition of plutonium will be used to determine heat generation, material attractiveness, and neutron coincidence produced to support the calculation and determination of actual plutonium-239 mass in each spent fuel cask. The plutonium-239 mass is needed for detailed burn- up calculation and safeguards report.

KMP D have similar value of combined uncertainty but slightly higher. The measurement of isotopic composition not only help in calculating detailed mass of each plutonium isotopes but also increase combined uncertainty. The increased number of instruments used in KMP D affect the value of combined uncertainty in KMP D that give the result of 11.790%.

### *3.2. MUF to SQ Ratio of Indonesian 10-MWt RDE*

Material unaccounted for (MUF) in RDE have been calculated according to the design of RDE pebble fuel, expected burn-up, and combined uncertainty of each KMP. Calculating MUF using the expected combined uncertainty need to be done using several assumptions due to unavailability of actual fuel and burn-up properties. The assumption and data in calculating MUF in RDE facility are as follows:

a. Every pebble in fresh fuel has the same amount of uranium and exact same enrichment;
b. The burn-up in KMP C is the same as burn- up in KMP D decreasing U-235 enrichment from 17% to 3%;
c. KMP C and KMP D have 0.15 gram of uranium-235 in spent fuel;
d. 20% of uranium in pebble turned into plutonium-239;

e. The SQ of low-enriched uranium (LEU) is 75 kg of uranium-235 and SQ of plutonium is 8 kg [20]

The complete data of MUF and MUF to SQ ratio calculation from each KMP are shown in Table 2.

KMP A has a possible MUF of 515.775g of uranium-235 in one inventory period. The small number of MUF expected makes the MUF to SQ ratio below 1%. The data shows that it is impossible to reach 1 SQ if the diversion done only by taking the advantage of MUF uncertainty. This calculation shows that the measurement instruments and methods are amendable.

KMP B has a possible MUF of 3682.013g of uranium-235 that accounts to 4.9% of LEU SQ. The number is far higher than MUF in KMP A. The different characteristic of each KMP contributes to the value of combined uncertainty making each KMP has different possible number of MUF. KMP A has the lowest number due to assumption that sample will represent all pebbles population while KMP B has larger uncertainty and larger MUF due to the assumption that irradiated fuel will increase radiation impurity that will interfere burn-up measurement. KMP B shows the highest number of MUF in fissile material because KMP B has the highest pebble inventory with a high combined uncertainty

**Table 2.** MUF and MUF to SQ Ratio of Every KMP in RDE

| KMP | Total Uncertainty | Inventory (Pebble) | MUF (Pebble) | $MUF_{U\text{-}total}$ (gram) | $MUF_{U\text{-}235}$ (gram) | $MUF_{Pu}$ (gram) | $\%SQ_{U}$ | $\%SQ_{Pu}$ |
|---|---|---|---|---|---|---|---|---|
| **A** | 2.215% | 27000 | 598 | 2990.000 | 515.775 | 0.000 | 0.688% | 0.000% |
| **B** | 15.811% | 27000 | 4269 | 21345.000 | 3682.013 | 0.000 | 4.909% | 0.000% |
| **C** | 11.402% | 2250 | 257 | 1285.000 | 38.550 | 257.000 | 0.051% | 3.213% |
| **D** | 11.790% | 9000 | 1061 | 5305.000 | 159.150 | 1061.000 | 0.212% | 13.263% |
| | **Total MUF** | | | | 4395.488 | 1318.000 | 5.861% | 16.475% |

KMPs C and D will have both MUF calculations of uranium and plutonium because both KMPs are storage for irradiated fuel pebbles. The data in Table 2 show that KMP D has a possibility of Pu MUF as much as 1 kg in one inventory period which adds up to 13% of SQ for each inventory period which is the biggest %SQ among other KMPs in RDE. The SQ of plutonium is only 8 kg, therefore making the %SQ of plutonium higher than uranium.

The overall results of MUF calculation show that the RDE has a total MUF possibility of uranium-235 as much as 4395.488 g and plutonium-239 as much as MUF 1318 g. Ratio of MUF to SQ for uranium- 235 is 5.861% and for plutonium-239 is 16.475%. IAEA Innovative Nuclear Energy System Assessment in Proliferation Resistance [22] states that the ratio of a total MUF to SQ below 10% score very high in proliferation resistance and a total MUF to SQ ratio above 10% but below 50% score high in proliferation resistance. Table 2 shows that both uranium-235 and plutonium-239 have MUF to SQ ratio lower than 50% that confirms that the measurement used in RDE safeguards system is amendable and accountable.

## 4. Conclusions

"Material unaccounted for" (MUF) of Indonesian 10-MWt RDE has been calculated using combined uncertainty from IAEA International Target Value. KMP A show the lowest value of uncertainty because of the pebble characteristic in KMP A that contains LEU with low impurities making the measurement easier and has less interference. The reactor in KMP B has the highest uncertainty among all KMPs because the pebbles have more radioactive impurity that interfere with the measurement in KMP B. The biggest MUF to SQ ratio (%SQ) is in KMP D where spent fuels are stored. The total MUF to SQ ratio in RDE both for uranium and plutonium are below 50% which indicates strong proliferation resistance and amendable measurement system. The improvement of RDE safeguards system might be needed in the spent fuel storage. The spent fuel storage needs strong containment and surveillance in order to prevent the possible diversion in KMP C and D that will add up to 16% MUF to SQ ratio.

## References

[1] B. Farawan, M.S.F. Husein, A. Sunarto, A.S. Adhi, Proliferation Resistance Assessment of Indonesian 10-MWt RDE Experimental Power Reactor, Urania, v26, p.57, 2020.

[2] International Atomic Energy Agency, INPRO Assessment of The Planned Nuclear Energy System of Belarus (IAEA-TECDOC-1716), IAEA, Vienna, 2013.

[3] S. Kuntjoro, P.M. Udiyani, Analisis Inventori Reaktor Daya Eksperimental Jenis Reaktor Gas Temperatur Tinggi, Urania, v22, p.53, 2016. (in Indonesian)

[4] N. Gui, Z. Li, Z. Zhang, X. Yang, J. Tu, S. Jiang, Numerical Study of Pebble Recirculation in a Two-Dimensional Pebble Bed of Stationary Atmosphere Using LB-IB-DEM Coupled Method, Annals of Nuclear Energy, v124, p.58, 2019.

[5] P.H. Liem, T.M. Sembiring, H-N. Tran, Evaluation on Fuel Cycle and Loading Scheme of Indonesian Experimental Power Reactor (RDE) Design, Nuclear Engineering and Design, v340, p.245, 2018.

[6] Badan Tenaga Nuklir Nasional, Pengembangan Desain Seifgard Reaktor Daya Eksperimental, BATAN, Jakarta, 2018. (in Indonesian)

[7] C. Listner, I. Niemeyer, M. Canty, C. Murphy, G. Stein, A. Rezniczek, Acquisition Path Analysis Quantified – Shaping the Success of IAEA's State-Level Concept, Journal of Nuclear Materials Management, v43, p.49, 2015.

[8] R. Carchon, M. Moeslinger, L. Bourva, C. Bass, M. Zendel, Gamma Radiation Detectors for Safeguards Application, Nuclear Instruments and Methods in Physics Research Section A, v579, p.380, 2007.

[9] A.M. Amaral, F.R. Cabral Filho, L.M. Vellame, M.B. Teixeira, F.A.L. Soares, L.N.S. dos Santos, Uncertainty of Weight Measuring Systems Applied to Weighing Lysimeters, Computers and Electronics in Agriculture, v145, p.208, 2018.

[10] D.L. Chichester, S.J. Thompson, M.T. Kinlaw, J.T. Johnson, J.L. Dolan, M. Flaska, S.A. Pozzi, Statistical Estimation of the Performance of a Fast-Neutron Multiplicity System for Nuclear Material Accountancy, Nuclear Instruments and Methods in Physics Research Section A, v784, p.448, 2015.

[11] International Atomic Energy Agency, Safeguards Techniques and Equipment IAEA/NVS/1/2011 Rev.2, IAEA, Vienna, 2011.

[12] C. Dubi, S. Croft, A. Favalli, A. Ocherashvili, B. Pedersen, Estimating the Mass Variance in Neutron Multiplicity Counting – A Comparison of Approaches, Nuclear Instruments and Methods in Physics Research Section A, v875, p.125, 2017.

[13] A. Apostol Andrei, I. Maliuk, Uranium Isotopic Composition Analysis Using Gamma Spectrometry: Applications in Nuclear Forensics, Romanian Reports in Physics, v68, p.822, 2016.

[14] International Atomic Energy Agency, INPRO Collaborative Project: Proliferation Resistance Acquisition Diversion Pathway Analysis/PRADA (TECDOC-1684), IAEA, Vienna, 2012.

[15] E. Bonner, et al, Ensuring Effectiveness of Safeguards Through Comprehensive Uncertainty Quantification, Journal of Nuclear Materials Management, v44, p.53, 2016.

[16] P.D. Winastri, B. Farawan, H. Wahyono, Tinjauan Umum Material Accounted For (MUF) pada Desain RDE (Proc. Sem. Nasional Infrastruktur Energi Nuklir) 1-6, 2018. (in Indonesian)

[17] W. Bich, M.G. Cox, R. Dybkaer, C. Elster, W.T. Estler, B. Hibbert, H. Imai, W. Kool, C. Michotte, L. Nielsen, Revision of the 'Guide to the Expression of Uncertainty in

Measurement', Metrologia, v49, p.702, 2012.
[18] International Atomic Energy Agency, International Target Values 2010 for Measurement Uncertainties in Safeguarding Nuclear Materials (STR-368), IAEA, Vienna, 2010.
[19] J. Disser, E. Arthur, J. Lambert, Preliminary Safeguards Assessment for the Pebble-Bed Flouride High-Temperature Reactor (PB-FHR) Concept, INL/CON-16-38642, 2016. Preprint
[20] International Atomic Energy Agency, IAEA Safeguards Glossary (IAEA/NVS/3), IAEA, Vienna, 2002.
[21] C.D.S. Schmidt, F.A.C. Pereira, A.S. Oliveira, J.F.G. Junior, L.M. Vellame, Design, Installation and Calibration of a Weighing Lysimeter for Crop Evapotranspiration Studies, Water Resources and Irrigation Management, v2, p.77, 2013.
[22] International Atomic Energy Agency, Guidance for the Application of an Assessment Methodology for Innovative Nuclear Energy System Vol.5 Proliferation Resistance (IAEA-TECDOC-1575), IAEA, Vienna, 2007.

# Shear Wave Velocity ($V_s$) at Reactor Building, Experimental Power Reactor Indonesia

**Eko Rudi Iswanto[1], Theo Alvin Ryanto[2], Abimanyu BW Setiaji[2], Hadi Suntoko[2]**

[1] *Center for Nuclear Energy System Assessment, National Nuclear Energy Agency Jl. Kuningan Barat, Mampang Prapatan, Jakarta 12710 phone: +62-21-5204243,*
[2] *Center for Nuclear Energy System Assessment, National Nuclear Energy Agency Jl. Kuningan Barat, Mampang Prapatan, Jakarta 12710*

Coresponding author's e-mail : ekorudi@batan.go.id

**Abstract**. Experimental Power Reactor (RDE) is a Gen IV Reactor type with Hydrogen Gas Cooler. Despite this type of reactor has high safety performance, earthquake hazard should be demonstrated. Detail Engineering Design Activity on RDE has been conducted in the past 3 years. In the end of this phase, preliminary parameter design such as shear wave velocity ($V_s$) should be defined. This parameter correlated with subsurface condition which has high uncertainty. This study is conducted in order to estimate values of $V_s$. Generally, the data collection is carried out through geotechnical investigation but this method cost more time and resources. In the recent decades, another method has been widely introduced which is geophysical passive source Microtremor Array Measurement (MAM) with Spatial Auto Correlation (SPAC) method. This method can be used to estimate values of $V_s$ and can be used as preliminary reference to define the position of borehole before construction phase getting started. The result shows, the location of reactor building is estimated to have 5 soil layers with varying $V_s$ value. The $V_s$ value of the first soil layer is about 152 m/s started from the surface to 8 m depth. The second soil layer has 169 m/s $V_s$ value started from 8 m to 20 m depth. The third soil layer, started from 20 m to 36 m depth, has 384 m/s $V_s$ value. The next layer as the fourth layer of soil, started from 36 m to 70 m depth with a value of $V_s$ around 526 m/s. The last soil layer with a depth 70 m to 100 m, has $V_s$ value of 667 m/s. Based on these $V_s$ value estimation from surface to 30 m depth, the average value of the shear wave velocity ($V_{s\,30}$) is m/s. Thus, reactor building is located in the site class SD with medium soil categories according to SNI 1726-2012. The foundation design and excavation planning phase, this information is needed.

Keyword*: RDE, shear wave velocity, SPAC*

## 1. Introduction

The Serpong PUSPIPTEK area in South Tangerang, Banten Province is planned as the location of the Experimental Power Reactor (RDE). RDE is a Gen IV Reactor type with Hydrogen Gas Cooler. The site permits of this reactor are granted from the Regulatory Body (BAPETEN) in January 2017. The site evaluation phase was conducted for two years by considering several aspects including seismic, volcanic, geotechnical and foundation, meteorological, hydrological, human-induced events, dispersion and distribution of population aspects [1].

Despite RDE has high safety performance, earthquake hazard should be demonstrated. Considering the site is located on the high seismicity area, which is strongly influenced by the Cimandiri fault, so it needs an in-depth study of the site's acceptance of all external hazards, especially seismic aspects. In order to assess seismic hazards, the local site effects should be addressed.

Detail engineering design activity on RDE has been conducted in the past three years. At the end of this phase, preliminary parameter design, such as shear wave velocity ($V_s$) should be defined. This parameter correlated with the subsurface condition, which has high uncertainty. $V_s$ is an important parameter in calculating the amplification of the site caused by an earthquake. This earthquake generates seismic waves that pass through the ground so-called ground shaking. Two significant factors affect the level of ground shaking, which are the softness of the surface lithology and the thickness of surface sediment [2], [3].

Estimated values of $V_s$ can be obtained from analysis of geotechnical or geophysical data. There are several methods in order to get these data. For geotechnical data can be obtained by performing geotechnical surveys which considered as direct methods such as geotechnical core drilling. However, this direct method will require a lot of time and money.

Besides the direct method described above, $V_s$ can also be obtained from the geophysical survey. This survey is considered as indirect methods where consume less time and money. As indirect methods, it used two kinds of sources, which are active and passive sources. The active source such as Multi channel Analysis of Surface Wave (MASW), crosshole and downhole seismic testing while the passive source referred as Microtremor Measurements (MM) and Microtremor Array Measurement (MAM). These two kinds of measurements are widely used [4].

The fundamental resonance frequencies of the sites were obtained from the MM using Horizontal to Vertical Spectral Ratios (HVSR) method. This method records the ambient noise and estimates the ratio of the vertical component Fourier spectrum to the horizontal component. Regions that have low to moderate seismic activities recommended utilizing this method [5]. While the phase velocities of the Rayleigh waves were estimated from the MAM using the spatial autocorrelation (SPAC) method where calculates the dispersion curves [6]. The present study is carried out by using MAM. This study aims at calculating the value of $V_s$ as an important parameter in understanding site characteristics [7]. SNI 1726-2012 regulates the site class where the value is determined based on the average value of the shear wave velocity for a depth of 30 m ($V_{s\,30}$) [8].

## 2. Geological Setting

This RDE site is located on the Sunda Mainland, between the Eurasian plate with a southeastward movement of 0.4 cm / year and the Indo-Australian Ocean plate with a northward movement of 7 cm/year [7]. These two plates, together with the Pacific plate, interact by producing one of the most complex active tectonic zones on earth. This is indicated by the presence of volcanic activity and earthquake that is relatively high enough. Seismic records say that there have been several major earthquake events with magnitudes above 7 (M> 7). An example is an earthquake with a magnitude of 9.1 that occurred in the Indian Ocean on 26 December 2004[1], [7], [9].

The kinematic scenario or the real velocity of the plate vector provides information on the relative motion of the Sunda Land and its surroundings shown in Figure 1. Geologically, material in the area study is a young volcanic product from Mount Gede Salak. The underlying stratum of this location is the Serpong Formation ($T_{pss}$), the Bojongmanik Formation ($T_{mbl}$), the Genteng Formation ($T_{pg}$), Alluvial ($Q_a$), Alluvial Fan ($Q_{av3}$) and Young Mountain Rocks ($Q_{v1}$) as can be seen in Figure 2.

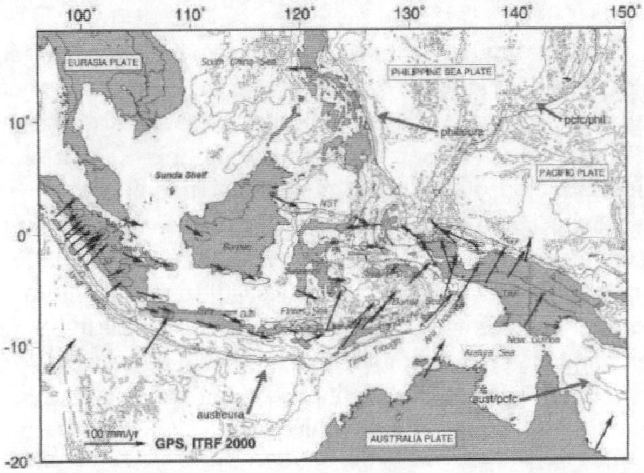


**Figure 1.** Map of Sundanese and Surrounding Kinematic Scenarios [1]

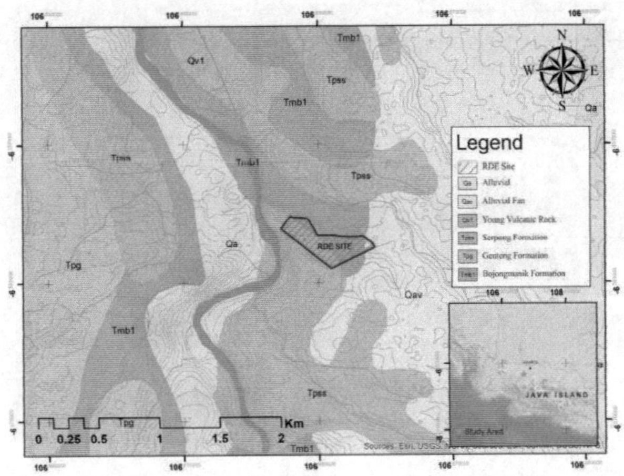


**Figure 2.** Regional Geological Map Nearby Area Study [9]

The detail information of each formation is explained as follows, the Serpong Formation ($T_{pss}$) is composed of coarse tuff interruptions with rock conglomerates, bright white, open, good sorting, dominant matrices, 2-5 cm rock fragments, rough tuff matrices, alternating with coarse tuffs, gradual contact, having direction and slope of the N 130 E bedding layer/7.

The Bojongmanik Formation ($T_{mbl}$) is composed of sandstone, claystone and limestone intervals. Limestone, white gray, bright, very hard, crystalline, alternating with sandstone limestone, there are sandstone inserts, dark gray, carbon, medium to coarse sand, have a thickness of about 20 cm, have a direction and slope layer N 35° E/20 and in some places, there is a thin layer of carbon or lignite. The Genteng Formation ($T_{pg}$) is dominated by volcanic rocks, and their weathering is very distinctively red to brownish red and shows horizontal bedding as a result of the repetition of volcanic material deposited on land or litoral areas. This formation is composed of tuffs, dark browns, smooth tuffs, rough and lapilli tuffs, horizontal layered, between coarse and fine ones, scoria and pumice, medium-high weathering.

Alluvial ($Q_a$) is founded along the Cisadane River and surrounding streams with piles of material such as clay, silt, sand, gravel, crust, and lumps. Alluvial fan ($Q_{av3}$) is a material from the deposition of volcanic material that previously existed and deposited (rework) flowing from south to north following the sloping topography. Alluvial fans are composed of conglomerates, tuffs, and sandstones.

Young mountain rocks ($Q_{v1}$) are composed of volcanic breccias, black-gray, dominant matrix, components of the crust, lumps, monomict, consisting of basalt, poor sorting, medium porosity and tuff, yellowish-reddish, smooth, medium hardness.

## 3. Methods

The methodology in this study is divided into three stages, which are data acquisition, analysis, and interpretation. The data collection phase is carried out through a geophysical investigation using a passive source, namely the measurement of MAM by the SPAC method. Furthermore, the value of Vs can be predicted at the analysis stage. These results will be compared with similar parameters from the results of previous studies conducted, namely geotechnical and geophysical investigations. Geotechnical investigation is carried out with 100m deep geotechnical drilling, which recorded as a bore log with a detailed description of each layer of soil. Geophysical investigations consist of investigations with active and passive sources. Active source investigation consists of cross hole and down hole seismic testing. From these two tests, parameter values of $V_s$ are predicted. Whereas passive source investigations which is MM. MM is able to calculate the predominant frequencies that correlate directly with the value of Vs. The final stage is the interpretation stage, which interprets and correlate all the data as so get the final parameter value of Vs. Figure 3 illustrates the flow chart for the shear wave estimation in this study.

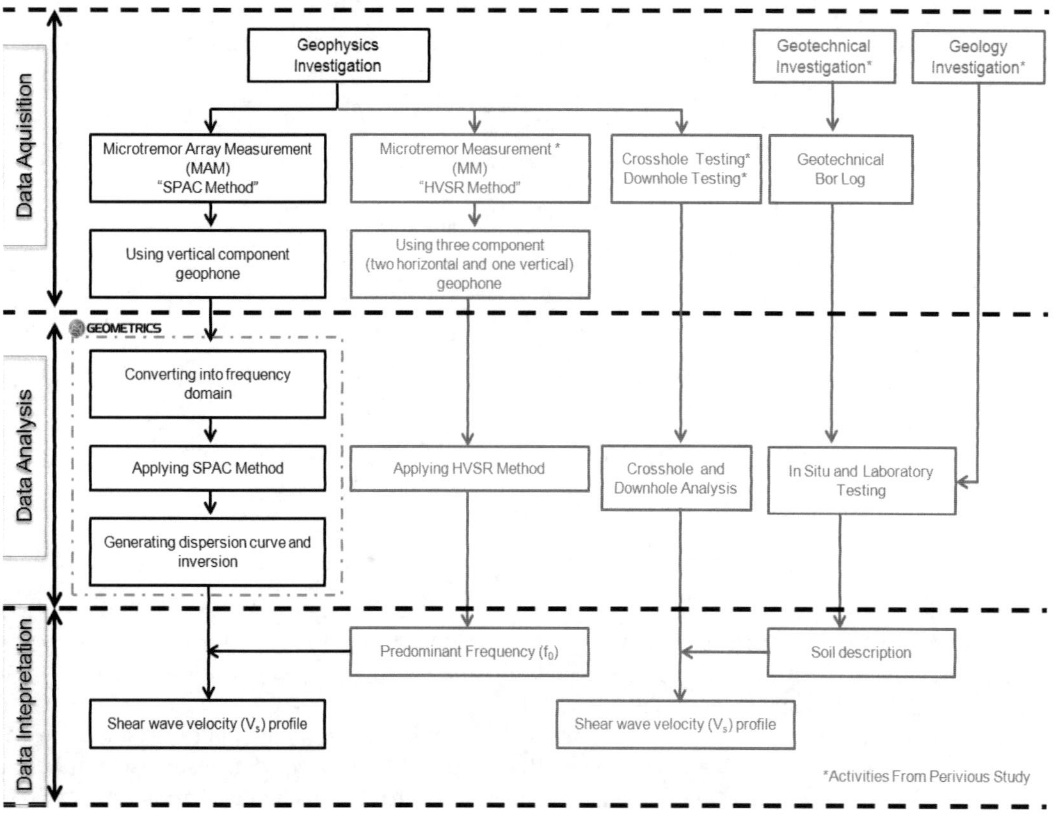


**Figure 3.** The Flow Chart for The Shear Wave Estimation in This Study

### *3.1. A. SPAC Method*

Microtremor is a very small and continuous ground vibration from various sources of vibration in the form of artificial disturbances and natural resources. Artificial disturbances in the form of human activities, industrial machinery and so on, while natural resources can be in the form of wind and sea waves. This ground vibration has an amplitude displacement of 0.1-1 microns and an amplitude velocity of 0.001-0.01 cm/s [10]. The recorded data generated from ambient noise can provide a picture of the ground spectral response of the area study [11]. In hard rocks, the motion of particles in the horizontal component (H) and vertical component (V) approaches the same value, whereas in soft rocks the horizontal component experiences reinforcement.

Mathematically, the basic frequency of a location can be calculated through the comparison of H with V of the natural vibrational spectrum, where ω is the angular frequency, S is the secondary wave, NS is the north-south direction and EW is the east-west direction as written in equation 1[12].

The SPAC method utilizes a circular array configuration. Microtremor measurement data from each of these sensors are still in the form of time domain, so it needs to be transformed into the frequency domain [13], [14], [15]. The correlation between time domain and frequency domain are calculated for each pair of the sensor. The harmonic waves of frequency of microtremors by the velocity waveform and which are observed simultaneously at the center of the array and at the point of the array, the SPAC function can be determined as follows [16]:

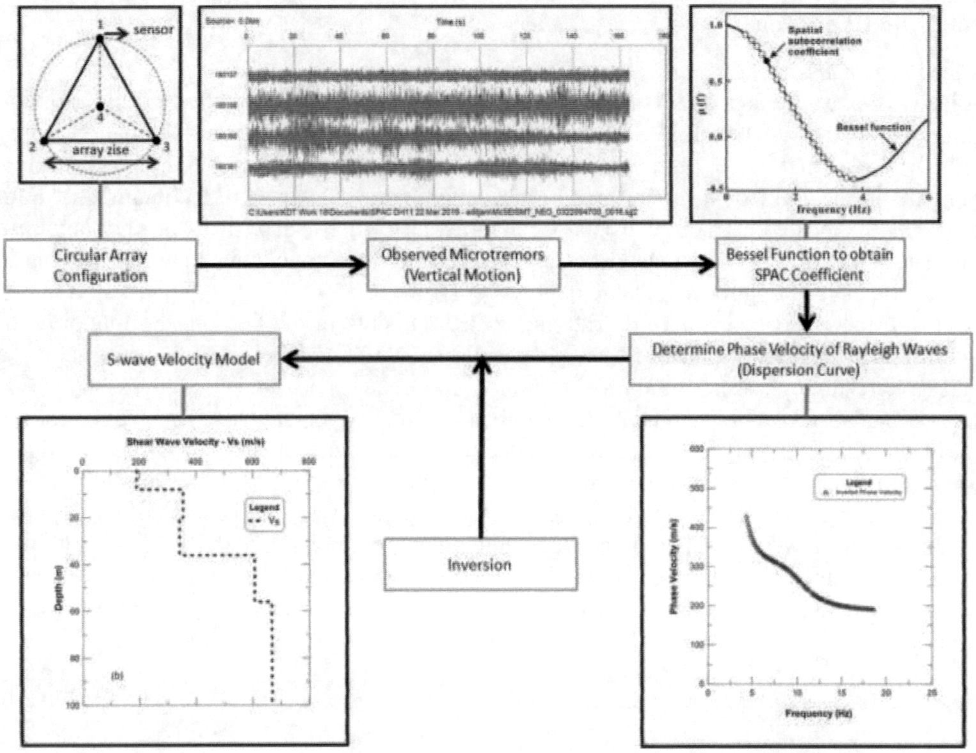


**Figure 4.** The Flow Chart of SPAC Analysis Methodology [13]

$$\emptyset(r,\theta,\omega) = \overline{u(0,0,\omega,t).u(r,\theta,\omega,t)} \tag{1}$$

where u(t) is the average velocity of the waveform in the time domain. The SPAC coefficient is defined as the average of autocorrelation function in all direction over the circular array, which calculated as follows [16]:

$$\rho(r,\omega) = \frac{1}{2\pi \times \emptyset(0,\omega)} \int_0^{2\pi} \emptyset(r,\theta,\omega)d\theta \tag{2}$$

where ω is the SPAC function at the center, of the circular array. The equation number 2 can be expressed as [16]:

$$\rho(r,\omega) = J_0\left(\frac{\omega \times r}{c(\omega)}\right) \tag{3}$$

where $J_o$ (x)is the zero-order Bessel function of the first kind and c ω is the phase velocity at frequency ω. The SPAC coefficient r,ω is calculated by using the Fourier Transform of the observed microtremors, which is in the frequency domain [16]:

$$\rho(r,\omega) = \frac{1}{2\pi}\int_0^{2\pi} \frac{Re[S_{cx}(\omega,r,\theta)]}{\sqrt{[Sc(\omega)]\times[Sx(\omega,r,\theta)]}}d\theta \tag{4}$$

where $Sc(\omega)$ is the power spectral densities of microtremors at site and $Sx(\omega,r,\theta)$is the power spectral densities of microtremors at site, while $S_{cx}(\omega,r,\theta)$is the cross-spectrum between ground motions at site C and site X.

## 4. Result And Discussion

### *4.1. Microtremor Array Measurement (SPAC method)*

Geologically, the reactor area and its surroundings are in the Serpong Formation (Tpss), Bojongmanik Formation (Tmb) and Alluvial Deposition Formation (Qav). The Serpong Formation consists of sedimentary rocks that have been deposited by volcanic deposits deposited in a swampy river environment, in the form of tuffs and sandstone conglomerates, while the Bojongmanik Formation where DH11 is located, which consists of sedimentary rocks deposited in the lagoon-marine environment in the form of sandstones, claystone and a little limestone, which is relatively harder than sedimentary rocks resulting from volcanic deposits [17],[18].

Physically, the presence of tuff material and rock fragments in the Serpong Formation will cause rocks with lower acoustic impedance than sedimentary rocks in the Bojongmanik Formation, so that they will have relatively lower Vs values as well.

Phase velocity can be estimated by looking at the pattern of SPAC coefficient values or coherence in the plot of the phase velocity values at each frequency. The pattern of SPAC coefficient values in the study area is shown in the dispersion curve graph, as can be seen in Figure 5 (a). Based on the results of the dispersion curve, the phase velocity values for each frequency can be generated. In the study area, phase velocity values were obtained in the frequency range of 1.56 hz to 6.25 hz. Phase velocity values are found in the range 188 m/s to 427 m/s. The value of phase velocity is relatively decreased with respect to the magnitude of the frequency value because in general, the increasing depth of rock will be denser and harder. The denser the rock will increase the value of the phase velocity [19].

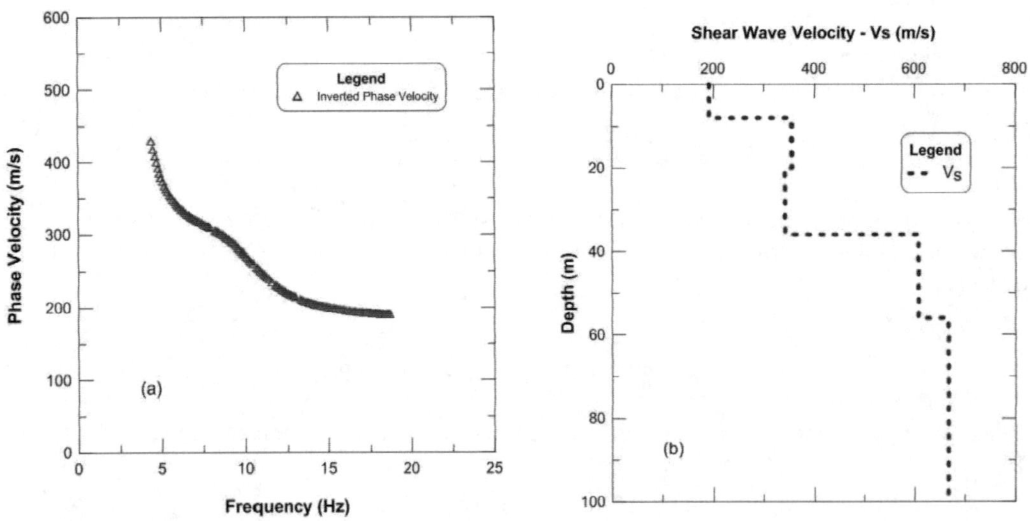


**Figure 5.** (a) Dispersion Curve (b) Model of Shear Waves Velocity Profile ($V_s$) DH-11

The shear wave velocity can be modeled from the dispersion curves that have been obtained. The value of the phase velocity at each frequency can be inverted into the value of the shear wave velocity at each depth. Figure 5 (b) illustrates the shear wave velocity profile model in DH11. The stratigraphic column at this measurement point is modeled as five layers of soil with $V_s$ values varying from 190 m/s to 667 m/s. The first layer can be found at a depth of 8 m, which has value of $V_s \leq 175$ m/s is. The second layer is started from a depth of 8 m to 20 m while the third layer is started from a depth of 20 m to 36 m. These two layers are considered as very solid soil layer which have value of 350 m/s $\leq V_s \leq$ 750 m/s.

The last two layers which are the fourth and fifth layer, it has value of $V_s \geq$ 600 m/s. From this analysis, the engineering bedrock with $V_s \geq$ 760 m/s cannot be found yet to a depth of 100 m. The analysis founds that the average value of the shear wave velocity for a depth of 30 m ($V_{s\ 30}$) is 286.6 m/s. According to the Indonesian National Standard (SNI) 1726-2012 in site classification, DH11 as the location of the reactor, is located in the site class SD with medium soil categories. This site has features in term of value of 175 m/s $\leq V_s \leq$350 m/s and 15 $\leq$ N SPT value $\leq$50.

### 4.2. *Verification value of shear wave velocity*

The value of $V_s$ from MAM analysis results are then correlated with the predominant frequency from MM. Then after that, it compares with the value of $V_s$ from the crosshole, downhole testing and geotechnical drill that already done.

As site area measurement, a total of 15 microtremor measuring points were conducted at the site with intervals ranging from 100-300 m using the OYO brand McSEIS-MT NEO type seismometer. The results of the HVSR method show that the predominant frequency values vary from 3.06 Hz to 23.27 Hz. The plot of the predominant frequency value distribution shows the highest predominant frequency value is at the southern part of the site, while the lowest predominant frequency value is at the western part of the site as can be seen in Figure 6.

The description of the soil at the southern part of the site is a tertiary rock zone composed of hard rock. From the geological point of view, this area belongs to Bojongmanik Formation ($T_{mbl}$), which is composed of intertwined sandstone, claystone and limestone. On the other hand, at the western part of the site with the lowest predominant frequency value, is accounted as the Alluvial Fan ($Q_{av3}$) which is a deposited material from volcanic material composed by conglomerates, tuffs and sandstone. This means that this area has a thicker sedimentary layer compared to other areas. According to SNI 1726-2012 for the soil classification, the western part of the site is classified as soil types III, meaning that the soil is an alluvial rock formed from delta, mud or other very soft sedimentation [9].

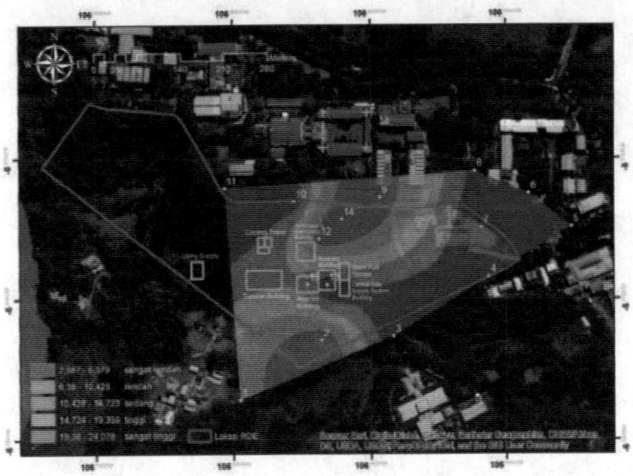

**Figure 6.** Distribution of predominant frequencies at the RDE Site

The predominant frequency does not only depend on the sediment thickness but also controlled by the value of $V_s$ [20]. As we can see at Figure 6, the predominant frequency of DH11 is found at value of 8.75Hz. Based on the soil classification from analysis microtremor, this soil is considered as Type 2

Journal of Physics: Conference Series **2048** (2021) 012040 doi:10.1088/1742-6596/2048/1/012040

which has diluvium rock with a thickness of 5 m and consists of sand-gravel, sand hard clay and loam. The sediments are predicted to be 5 up to 10 m. This condition correlates with the result of MAM which is founded the value of $V_s$ relatively low compare to the area with no sediments with higher predominant frequency value.

Borehole data was collected in the previous survey by conducting soil investigation and geophysics surveys. Soil investigation through geotechnical core drilling is conducted using the rinse method which is generally well known for its use in soils and rocks. The purpose of the geotechnical core drilling is to determine the condition of the subsurface soil layer. This information is very important in order to perform geotechnical hazard analysis. DH11 is a geotechnical core drilling point as the center of the reactor building with 100m of depth. The position and result of DH11 core drilling that stored in the core box can be seen in Figure 7 (a) and (b). As the drilling process kept up, SPT testing and sampling were taken using the undisturbed method. The results of the geotechnical core drill are a description of the core drill that will be used in making the stratigraphy. Then it recorded into the borehole log as shown in Figure 7 (c).

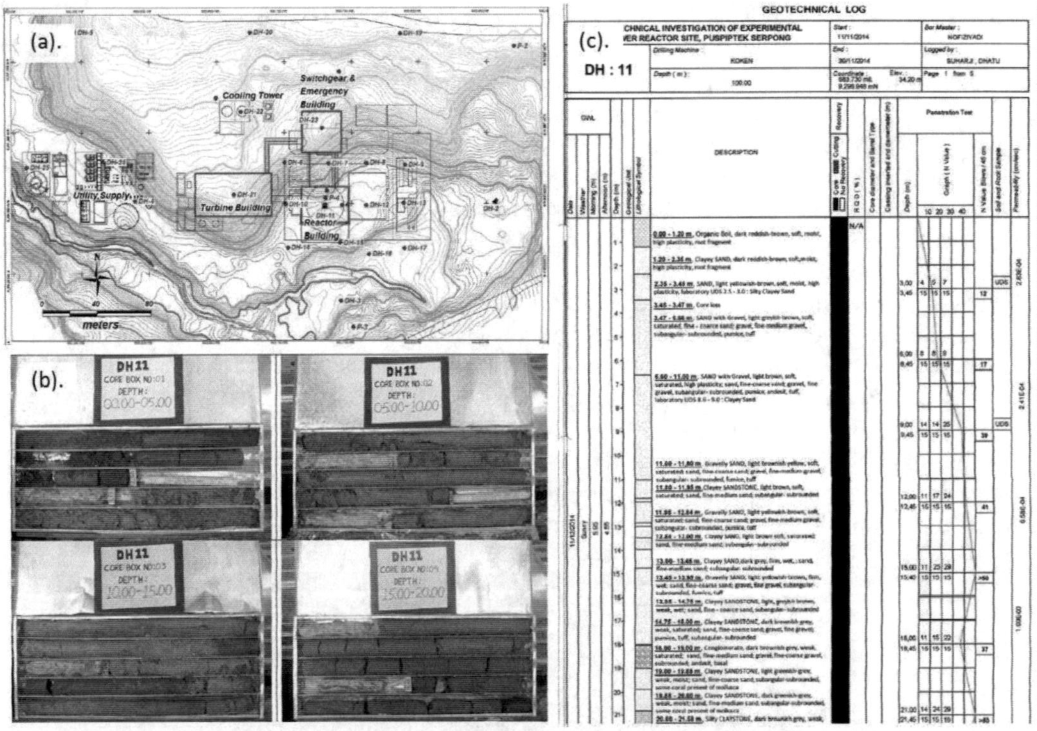


**Figure 7.** Soil Investigation at Reactor Building (a) Map of Geotechnical Core Drilling (b) Core box of DH11 (c) Borehole log of DH11

Geophysics surveys in term of crosshole and downhole seismic testing is conducted in order to estimate the value of shear wave velocity. Figure 8 shows the comparison of shear wave velocity from the field measurements which are MAM, crosshole and downhole seismic testing.

Figure 8 illustrates the shear wave velocity profile from various testing methods at each soil layer. The soil stratigraphic column in DH11 is divided into five layers of soil. In general, the mean value of $V_s$ at each soil layer from the MAM results appears to have the same pattern compared to the value of $V_s$ from the crosshole and downhole testing.

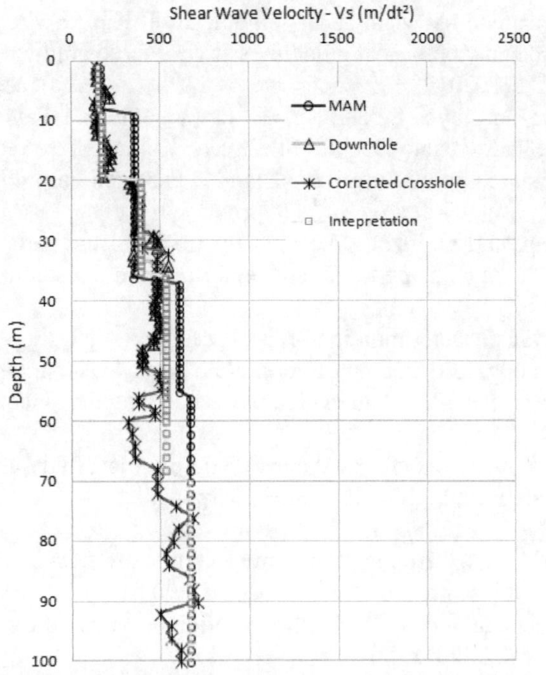


**Figure 8.** Shear Wave Velocity Profile of Reactor Building from Various Testing Methods, RDE Site

The MAM result shows that the first layer only up to 8 m depth while the second layer is founded at depth of 8 m to 20 m. These two layers, from the surface to 20 m of depth, is interpreted as a soft sediment layer that consists of loose sediment. Because of the limitation of MAM especially for the shallow zone, the crosshole data is mostly used for the first two layers of $V_s$ interpretation. In the third layer, from 20 m to 37 m of depth, the MAM result and crosshole data are quite similar with $V_s$ value of 384 m/s. This layer was interpreted consists of soft rocks that have relatively low $V_s$. In the fourth and fifth layer, the crosshole data is rather unstable with many $V_s$ lense. Therefore, the MAM results show that these layers have relatively stable $V_s$. For the last two layers, the interpreted $V_s$ layers have value of 526 m/s and 667 m/s respectively. The value was obtained from the crosshole data normalization with the MAM data. As for the fifth layer, the MAM results are in accordance with the downhole data, thus considered to give a better interpretation. Therefore, the MAM $V_s$ result was chosen for this layer. This interpretation also implies that the MAM gives better results in the depth zone analysis.

MAM is not only able to be used as a preliminary reference in order to define the value of $V_s$ of reactor building which on the foundation design and excavation planning phase, but also this information is needed to choose the position of borehole before construction phase getting started.

## Acknowledgments

This research was supported by the 2019 Research Funding of Center for Nuclear Energy System Assessment, National Nuclear Energy Agency.

## References

[1] BATAN, " Site Evaluation Report on Geotechnical Aspect and Foundation at RDE Site, Serpong," Jakarta, 2016

[2] A Singh, " Seismic hazar evaluation in Anjar city area of western India : Microtremor array measurement," Soil Dyn. Earthq. Eng., vol. 71, pp. 143–150, 2015.

[3] J. Saita an et al, "On Relationship Between The Estimated Strong Motion Characteristics Of Surface Layer And The Earthquake Damage," in 13 th World Conference on Earthquake Engineering, 2004, no. 905, pp. 1–7.

[4] S. Moon, P. Subramaniam, Y. Zhang, G. Vinoth, an T Ku, "Bedrock depth evaluation using microtremor measurement : empirical guidelines at weathered granite formation in Singapore," J. Appl. Geophys., vol. 171, 2019.

[5] Z. L. Kyaw, S. Pramumijoyo, S. Husein, T. F. Fathani, and Kiyono, " Seismic Behaviors Estimation of the Shallow and Deep Soil Layers Using Microtremor Recording and EGF Technique in Yogyakarta City, Central Java Island ," Procedia Earth Planet. Sci., vol. 12, pp. 31–46, 2015.

[6] Y. Guney, E. Pekkan, and O. Ozel, "An investigation into the bedrock depth in the Eskisehir Quaternary Basin ( Turkey ) using the microtremor method ," Gepohysical J. Int., pp. 589–607, 2016.

[7] H Suntoko an S. Sriyana, "Determination of Bedrock Depth by Using Microtremor Array Survey at The RDE Site Serpong," J. Pengemb. Energi Nukl., vol. 18, no. 2, pp. 87–92, 2017.

[8] BSN, Tata Cara Perencanaan Ketahanan Gempa untuk Bangunan Gedung dan Non Gedung, vol. 726. 2012.

[9] E. R. Iswanto, Y. Indrawati, and T. A.Riyanto, "Microtremor Study using Horizontal to Vertical Spectral Ratio (HVSR ) Method in RDE Site , Serpong," J. Ekplorium, vol. 40, no. 2, pp. 105–14, 2019.

[10] M Mirzaoglu an Ü Dýkmen, "Application of microtremors to seismic microzoning procedure," J. Balk. Geophys. Soc., vol. 6, no. No. 3, pp. 143–156, 2003.

[11] M. Sutrisna, C. Sulaeman, and N. D. Ardi,"Microtremor Metho e for Microzonation in Cilacap City," J. online Fis., vol. 3, no. 2, 2015.

[12] Lane et al, "Estimation of Be rock Depth Using the Horizontal- to- Vertical (H/V) Ambient- Noise Seismic Metho ," in Environmental and Engineering Geophysical Society, 2009, pp. 490–502.

[13] C. Kuo, C. Chen, C. Lin, K. Wen, J. Huang, and S.-Chang, " S-wave velocity structure and site effect Parameters derived from microtremor arrays in the Western Plain of Taiwan," J. Asian Earth Sci., vol. 128, pp. 27–41, 2016.

[14] M W Asten, "On bias an noise in passive seismic data from finite circular array data processe using PA metho s," J. Geophys., vol. 71, no. 6, pp. 153–162, 2006.

[15] O. Karagoz, K. Chimoto, S. Citak, O. Ozel, H. Yamanaka, and K. Hatayama, "Estimation of shallow -wave velocity structure and site response characteristics by microtremor array measurements in Tekirdag region , NW Turkey," Earth, Planets Sp., pp. 1–17, 2015.

[16] B. Setiawan, M. B. Jaksa, and M. C. Griffith, "Analysis of microtremor array measurement using the spatial autocorrelation ( SPAC ) method across the Adelaide City by School of Civil , Environmental , and Mining Engineering The University of Adelaide Research Report No R 96 November 6," 6

[17] H. Syaeful and A. G. Muhammad, "Interpretation of Depositional Environment of Rock Formations using Electrofacies Analysis in the Puspiptek Site, Serpong," J. Ekplorium, vol. 38, no. 1, pp. 29–42, 2017.

[18] P. Soe, S. Pramumijoyo, K. Sri, and J. Kiyono, "Estimation of S-wave velocity structure for Sedimentary layered media using Microtremor array measurements in Palu City , Indonesia," Procedia Environtmental Sci., vol. 28, pp. 595–605, 2015.

[19] E. R. Iswanto, H. Suntoko, T. A. Ryanto, and A Bon an, " Shear Wave Velocity Profile of Rector at RDE Site, Serpong," in Prosiding Seminar Nasional Infrastruktur Energi Nuklir 2019, 2019, p. 187–194.

[20] Sungkono an B. Santosa, "Horizontal-toVertical Spectral Ratio: Literature Study and Modeling," J. Neutrino, vol. 4, no. 1, pp. 65–85, 2011.

# V&V Methods Used in the Development of FPGA-based I&C Systems for HTR-10

**R Maerani[1], TJ Suryono[1], S Santoso[1], JC Jung[2]**

*[1]Centre for Nuclear Reactor Safety and Technology, National Nuclear Energy Agency of Indonesia (BATAN), Kawasan Puspiptek Serpong Gd. 80 Tangerang Selatan 15310 – Indonesia*
*[2]KEPCO International Nuclear Graduate School, Department of NPP Engineering 658-91 Haemaji-ro,Seosaengmyeon, Ulju-gun, Ulsan 45014, Republic of Korea*

E-mail: maerani@batan.go.id

**Abstract** – Currently, in few countries, there have been many projects related to the development of Field Programmable Gate Array (FPGA)-based Instrumentation and control (I&C) system designs for their nuclear power plant (NPP), whether for modernization or the new development of NPPs. Indonesia already develops a study related to High Temperature Gas Cooled Reactor as the generation IV for NPPs type for these few years with a specific type which is High Temperature Reactor–10 MW (HTR-10). Since the FPGA-based technology is new in the field, and both the international standards and guidance, from national and international has not defined provisions this issue, therefore verification and validation (V&V) activities for this HTR-10 are mandatory to be included in the design life cycle of I&C system development to get license approval from the national regulatory body. The FPGA-based system needs concentration both in hardware and software development, but commonly only software-related standards that usually included in the design and V&V in the previous computer-based I&C system. Therefore, in this study the V&V plan needs to be developed to state the methods to be required regarding the correctness of the applications of FPGA based I&C system. By arranging this V&V method, we will see whether they are easily applicable to actual systems, had the result to reach the requirement to have reliability, availability, maintainability and safety aspects, and has shortened and easier V&V step than computer-based I&C system. From the results of this study, it can be seen that the results of the method used for V&V between Programmable Logic Controller (PLC)-based and FPGA are almost the same because both have almost the same requirements, especially in software design. Some testing is not mandatory for FPGA-based because of the reduced system complexity. The use of FPGA can shorten the V&V process which can also reduce costs.

## 1. Introduction

High Temperature Gas-cooled Reactor-Test Module (HTR-10) which has the first digitalize Reactor Protection System (RPS) in China, was developed by Tsinghua University of China in 2000 with their own design. The reasons for changing the analog RPS design to the digital RPS design because analog devices have many components that need a lot of space, to reduce the connection line, to avoid failure probability and the ability to online self-checking and self-diagnosis, and a friendly man-machine interface [1]. After years, microcontroller technology has disadvantages because of high complexity and rapid obsolescence. Therefore, Field Programmable Gates Array (FPGA) has become an alternative option since FPGA has a large-scale integrated circuit without an operating system, so that FPGA-based system can be more safe from cyber-attacks [2]. International Atomic Energy Agency (IAEA) also publishes the recommendation of the use of FPGA for Instrumentation and Control System (I&C

System) for Nuclear Power Plant (NPP) in the IAEA Nuclear Energy Series document No. NP-T-3.17 [3]. Since there is no specific recommendation for FPGA development from the regulatory body, the industrial International Standards can be used for the recommendation [4].

Currently, Badan Tenaga Nuklir Nasional (BATAN) as the national nuclear agency of Indonesia, are interested to study related to High Temperature Gas Cooled Reactor (HTGR), especially to the specific HTR-10 the 10 MW reactor. Initially, the early design of HTR-10 was equipped with a digital computer-based system. However, as the increasing of the complexity of systems, the use of computer-based systems have some drawbacks, such as high development cost of modern I&C systems, software common cause failure (CCF), difficult and expensive cost of Verification and Validation (V&V) process, and regarding the obsolescence issues, it will need to retraining operational staff after installing the new software [5]. Therefore, in this study, BATAN can considers FPGA as an alternative for I&C System-based design.

Nowadays, FPGA becomes one of the alternatives to be implemented into Instrumentation and Control System (I&C) of Nuclear Power Plant (NPP). Therefore, in this study, the development of Verification and Validation (V&V) plans that are used to fulfill all the requirements of the I&C based system for the HTR-10 reactor is conducted. The V&V methods should combine the process from the requirements of the design specification of the HTGR / HTR-10 and related to the implementation of FPGA based design for I&C system.

The reasons to develop V&V plan is to ensure that the methods implemented in FPGA-based I&C system can be shorter, more accurate and can reduce costs than computer-based I&C System. The V&V methods of FPGA-based I&C System will be compared with computer-based RPS design which is developed by Tsinghua University. The V&V method still has to follow the requirement for software V&V for NPP, even though FPGA is hardware design but developed with Hardware Description Languages (HDL) and related tools used to implement the requirements in a proper assembly of the pre-developed micro-electronic resources [6]. There are similarities in requirements and processes between HDL and the software development process, syntax, or logic errors can cause the implementation errors [3]. For implementing the FPGA-based I&C system, the national regulatory body should review the design process, both hardware and software, the methodology for V&V, device failure mode information, and the result of validation related to reliability and failure analysis [3]. Therefore, this study is intended to simplify and facilitate the licensing process in the future.

## 2. Theory

### *2.1. HTR-10 I&C System*

HTR-10 is a helium-cooled, pebble-bed with 10 MW power reactor, located at Tsinghua University in Beijing, China, that has similar to Siemens design for an HTR module [7]. HTR-10 took over a 10 year runtime to ensure that the system built with a high protection precision, flexible configuration, ability to self-inspection, maintainability, has stability, and reliability [8]. For the HTR-10 reactor, safety important systems are primarily the following to the RPS and its related instrumentations and power supplies, reactor shutdown systems and decay heat removal system, primary coolant pressure boundary, and its pressure relief system [9]. Figure 1 shows that the digital safety I&C system developed by Tsinghua University has many advantages, which are it is designed with a simple structure, flexible configuration, and small volume [8]. FPGA which is the latest technology than the Programmable Logic Controller (PLC) and micro-controller, comes with the promise to reduce the complexity of the developed system because the end product is a traditional analog electronics that can be designed only consisting of hardware[2].

Generally, the development of the I&C system for NPP should follow the life cycle process. The development process of the FPGA-based I&C systems has two design life cycle process: overall I&C architecture life cycle, and software development process. There are several life cycles models that can be used. However, V model is the most common life cycle process which correlates with the V&V

activities. From recommendation IAEA Safety Standards, Specific Safety Guide No.SSG-39 the development of the I&C system should follow the V&V activities that had been stated in Figure 2.

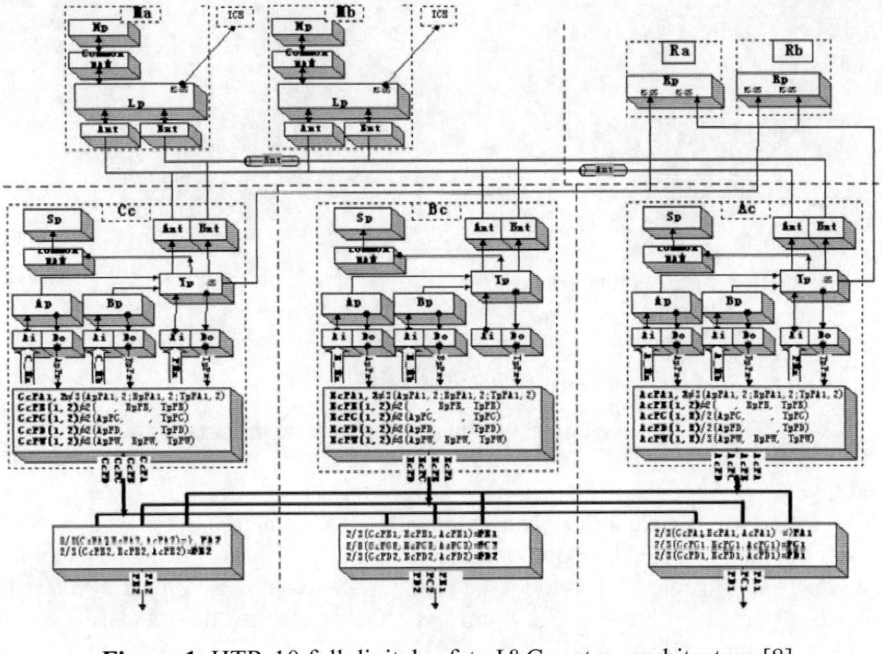

**Figure 1.** HTR-10 full digital safety I&C system architecture [8].

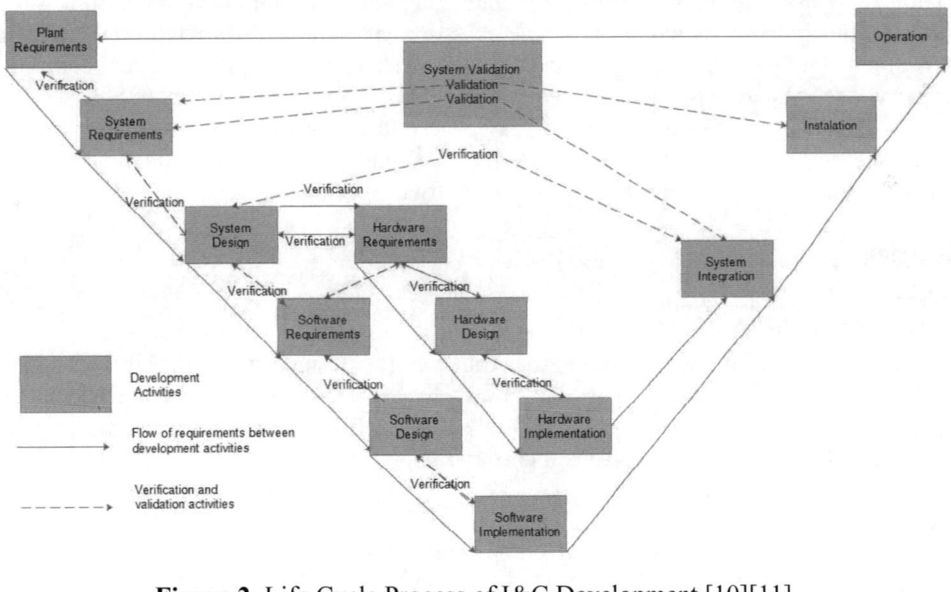


**Figure 2.** Life Cycle Process of I&C Development [10][11].

*2.2. FPGA-based Instrumentation and Control System*

FPGA-based I&C system is developed with the Hardware Description Language (HDL) and related tools used to implement requirements in the micro-electronics field that has been developed previously. This device is called HDL-Programmed Devices (HPD) [6]. The international standard IEC 62566, that also has a life cycle V model design as shown in Figure 3 is used to design the FPGA-based system related to the safety. Although the FPGA is hardware-based systems, and constructed using HDL language, the design must follow the software and hardware design requirements as shown in Figure 2.

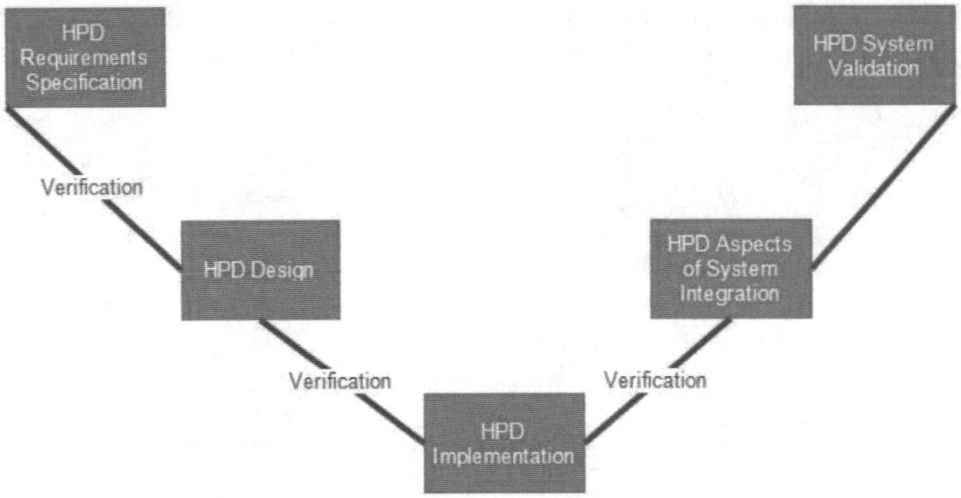


**Figure 3.** Development of the HPD life cycle process [6].

## 3. Methodology

V&V processes are used to maintain the management and development process whether for software, and hardware development to meet the requirements and user needs. The software development process should refer to the IEEE Standard 1074-2006 Standard for Developing a Software Project Life Cycle Process. And the system and software V&V process should refer to the Standard for System and Software Verification and Validation, IEEE Std 1012-2012. For the plant requirement, the design specification of HTR-10 should be made by conducting the traceability analysis from the top tier documents. All this process, including the implementation and integration should be verified. The last step is to validate the implementation design to ensure whether the design meets the requirement and work properly. The validation methods can refer to IEEE Std 1012-2012 and IEC 62566.

Although, the final product of the FPGA-based system is hardware, but since the development process uses the software tools to design and verify the application, then the validation process should be developed to check the reliability of the complex software [12].

## 4. Discussion

### *4.1. Requirement Traceability Analysis*

Requirement traceability analysis is the first step verification process at the management system, to verify whether the design of the I&C system has followed the design criteria for NPP. General Design Criteria (GDC) commonly developed by the law of the nuclear regulatory commission which is a mandatory requirement for NPP development. Table 1 is the general design criteria from I&C system which is stated in GDC 13 of 10 CFR Appendix A to 50.

**Table 1.** General Design Criteria for NPP [13]

| Criteria | Requirement from General Design Criteria for NPP |
|---|---|
| 10 CFR<br>Appendix A to 50<br>GDC 13 for I&C System | Instrumentation and Control System<br>Instrumentation shall be provided to monitor variables and systems over their anticipated ranges for normal operation, for anticipated operational occurrences, and for accident. Appropriate controls shall be provided to maintain these variables and systems within prescribed operating ranges. |

Since HTR-10 is a Non-Light Water Reactor (Non-LWR), we must refer to the non-LWR design criteria. By these reasons, US. Department of Energy (DOE) with US. Nuclear Regulatory Commission (US. NRC) consider to develop a regulatory framework for non-LWR reactor which is Advanced Reactor Design Criteria (ARDC) [14]. From this report, DOE published their guidance to develop principle design criteria on December 2015 [15], and US.NRC with their Regulatory Guide (RG) 1.232 Rev.0 on April 2018[16]. This document can be used as the guidance for the reactor designers, applicants or licenses to develop non-LWR.

There is a specific design criteria related to the I&C system for the High Temperature Gas-Cooled Reactor (HTGR), by reference from RG 1.232 of US.NRC and as well as described in Figure 4, some criteria will not be different from Light Water Reactor (LWR) [11]. Table 2 compiled based on criteria from 10 CFR 50 Appendix A and guidance from RG.1.232 Rev.0.

**Table 2.** Principle Design Criteria for Non-LWR from 10 CFR 50 Appendix A, ARDC and Appendix C - Modular High-Temperature Gas-Cooled Reactor Design Criteria

| DC | Requirement for Non- LWR | Reg. Guide | Standards | Ref |
|---|---|---|---|---|
| MHTGR-DC-10 | Reactor design, same with GDC 10, modified for MHTGR-DC. Shall be designed with an appropriate margin. | RG 1.232. Rev.0<br>RG 1.153 | IEEE Std 603-1991 | [16]<br>[17] |
| MHTGR-DC-13 | Instrumentation and control, shall be provided to monitor variables and systems over their anticipated ranges for normal operation, for anticipated operational occurrences, and for accident conditions. | RG 1.153 | IEEE Std 603-1991.<br>IEEE Std 497-1981 | [17] |
| MHTGR-DC-15 | Reactor coolant design, same with GDC 15, modified for MHTGR-DC 15. All systems that are part of the reactor helium pressure boundary, such as the reactor system, vessel system, and heat removal systems, and the associated auxiliary, control, and protection systems, shall be designed with sufficient margin. | RG 1.153 | IEEE Std 497-1981 | [17] |
| GDC 19 | Control Room, shall be provided from which actions can be taken to operate the nuclear power unit safely under normal conditions and to maintain it in a safe condition under accident conditions. | RG 1.97 | IEEE Std 603-1991 | [17]<br>[18] |
| GDC 20 | The protection system shall be designed to initiate automatically the operation of appropriate systems, including the reactivity control systems. | RG 1.153 | IEEE Std 603-1991 | [17]<br>[19]<br>[20] |

| DC | Requirement for Non- LWR | Reg. Guide | Standards | Ref |
|---|---|---|---|---|
| GDC 21 | The protection system shall be designed for high functional reliability and in-service testability commensurate with the safety. | RG 1.22<br>RG 1.171<br>RG 1.118<br>RG 1.153 | IEEE Std 603-199,<br>IEEE Std. 7-4.3.2-2003,<br>IEEE Std 379-2000<br>IEEE Std 338 | [21]<br>[22]<br>[23]<br>[17] |
| GDC 22 | The protection system independence, shall be designed to assure that the effects of natural phenomena and normal operating, maintenance, testing, and postulated accident conditions on redundant channels. | RG 1.153<br>RG 1.97 | IEEE Std 603-1991.<br>IEEE Std 497-1981 | [17] |
| GDC 23 | The protection system shall be designed to fail into a safe state or a state demonstrated, (Failure Modes). | RG 1.153 | IEEE Std 603-1998.<br>IEEE Std. 379-2000 | [17] |
| GDC 24 | The protection system shall be separated from control systems, interconnection of the protection and control systems shall be limited, shall be designed to ensure that specified acceptable system radionuclide release design limits are not exceeded during any anticipated operational occurrence, accounting for a single malfunction of the reactivity control systems. | RG 1.75<br>RG 1.152<br>RG 1.153 | IEEE Std 603-1991,<br>IEEE Std 379-2000 | [17] |

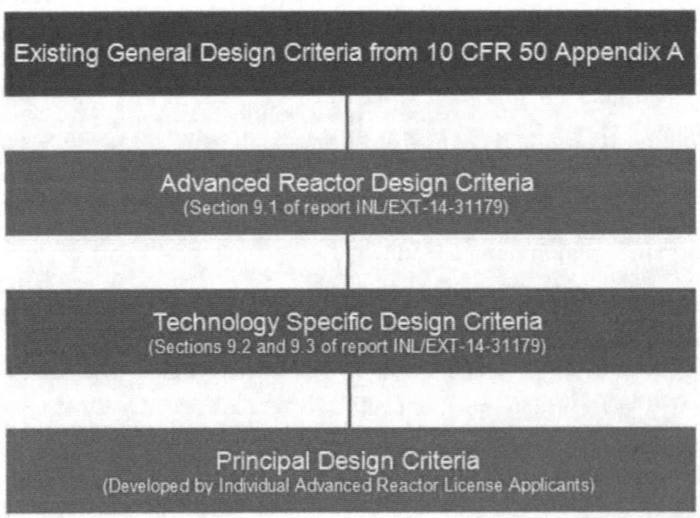


**Figure 4.** Design Criteria Relationship [14][24].

*4.2. Verifying and Validating I&C Design Development.*

Figure 5 is a computer-based I&C system for HTR-10 developed by the Institute of Nuclear and New Energy Technology (INET), Tsinghua University. They show general development from verifying design criteria, preliminary design, prototype integration, and testing before continuing to the engineering phase. Figure 6 is the design flow for FPGA-based system recommendation from NUREG/CR-7006, it shows that the development process requires hardware and software V&V.

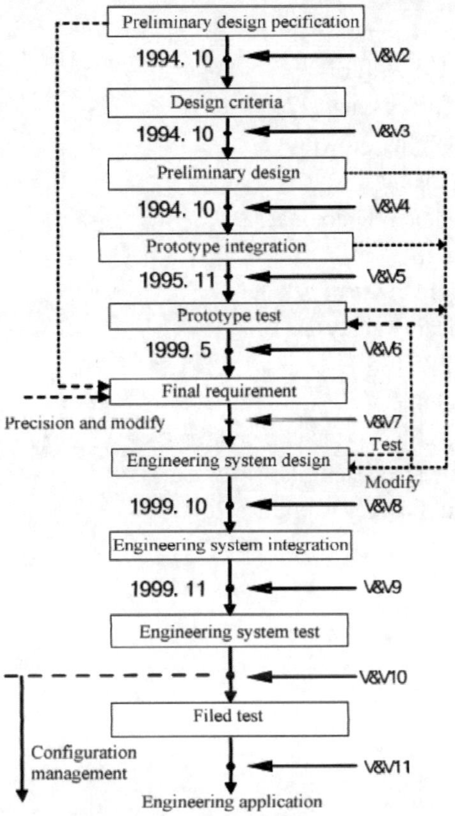


**Figure 5.** HTR-10 digital I&C system development and V&V developed by INET [8]

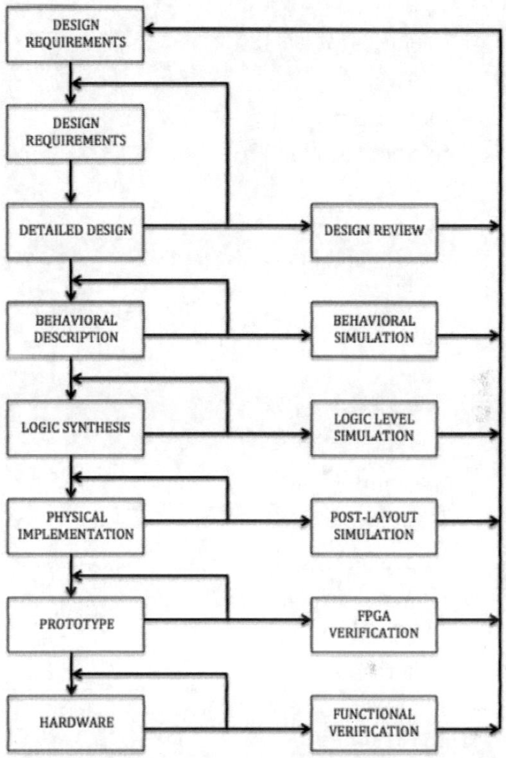


**Figure 6.** FPGA Design Flow by NUREG/CR-7006 [25]

From the different of software-based and hardware-based design for I&C system, the validation methods used will be different based on the characteristics of the component, programming language, complexity of the system and the environments.

Table 3 shows the V&V methods that should be complete during I&C development. Since the I&C system are related to software and hardware development, and computer-based that used in safety system of NPP and the uses of FPGA and PLC or micro controller, therefor Table 3 are referring to the international standards to develop V&V activities. Some standards are finds from the regulatory guide, and for the specific software and hardware development.

**Table 3.** Comparing V&V Methods between Programmable Logic Controller (PLC)/micro-controller and FPGA-based for I&C System

| No | Verification | PLC | FPGA | Validation/Testing Methods | PLC | FPGA |
|---|---|---|---|---|---|---|
| 1. | User requirements. [26] | ✓ | ✓ | White-box Testing. [6] [26] | ✓ | ✓ |
| 2. | System requirements.[26] | ✓ | ✓ | Functional black box testing. [12][26][27] [28] | ✓ | ✓ |
| 3. | Design specification.[26] | ✓ | ✓ | Static Timing Analysis. [6][10][25][26] | ✓ | ✓ |
| 4. | Criteria analysis.[26] | ✓ | ✓ | Module testing. [12] | ✓ | ✓ |
| 5. | Software requirement.[26] | ✓ | ✓ | Reliability growth models.[26] | ✓ | ✓ |
| 6. | System test plan.[26] | ✓ | ✓ | Periodic functional tests. [26][28] | ✓ | ✓ |
| 7. | Software design specification.[26] | ✓ | ✓ | Failure mode effect and criticality analysis.[10] [12][25][26] | ✓ | ✓ |
| 8. | Software Coding.[26] | ✓ | ✓ | Fault tree analysis. [10][25][28] (recommend for hardware system, for software should handle carefully [26]) | ✓ | ✓ |
| 9. | System Integration. [26] | ✓ | ✓ | Event Tree Analysis [26] | ✓ | ✓ |
| 10. | Load testing [26] | ✓ | ✓ | | | |
| 12. | Acceptance testing (formal verification)[28] | ✓ | ✓ | | | |
| 13. | MC/DC (Coverage Criteria) [4][27] | ✓ | ✓ | | | |

## 5. Conclusion

Based on the V&V process carried out on a computer-based I&C system compared to those based on FPGA, the software design process on a computer-based system has more requirements that must be met. Remembering Tsinghua University's journey as well, they took over 10 years to develop digital based I&C systems. Regarding the design flow analysis for HTR-10, the longest process was in the verifying final requirement analysis. It can be happened because the licensing process actually takes more time than process engineering, because there are so many requirements that must be met to satisfy the regulatory body. The validation testing methods for the micro-controller/PLC and the FPGA-based I&C system use the same methods, they should refer to the IEEE Std 1012-2012 for implementing the V&V process. Both micro-controller and FPGA should have a good result as the requirements from the design criteria, especially to meet the reliability, availability, maintainability and safety. To reduce the development process of FPGA-based I&C system is possible for changing the obsolete components, or for the safety reasons to avoid cyber-attacks that must be replaced from computer–based system to hardware –based system. By replacing the old one, the design requirements verification process has been carried out, so that the reverse engineering can be carried out based on the previous operational records, and develop the software requirement specification for FPGA-based system, develop design synthesis for FPGA-based system, implementation and integration. This study explains that although FPGA is a different platform from PLC and other software based, since it related to components that are important for safety, they have the same mandatory of requirements.

**Acknowledgments**
This research is funded by DIPA of the Centre for Nuclear Reactor Technology and Safety (PTKRN - BATAN) and INSINAS Ristek-BRIN the Ministry of Research and Technology of 2021 fiscal year.

**References**

[1] Li F, Yang Z, An Z and Zhang L 2002 The First Digital Reactor Protection System in China *Nucl. Eng. Des.* **218** 215–25
[2] Mayaka J and Jung J C 2018 Complexity reduction of the Engineered Safety Features Component Control System *Nucl. Eng. Des.* **331** 194–203
[3] IAEA 2016 *IAEA Nuclear Energy Series No. NP-T-3.17, Application of Field Programmable Gate Arrays in Instrumentation and Control Systems of Nuclear Power Plants*
[4] Maerani R, Mayaka J K and Jung J C 2018 Software Verification Process and Methodology for the Development of FPGA-based Engineered Safety Features System *Nucl. Eng. Des.* **330** 325–31
[5] IAEA 1999 *Technical reports series No. 387, Modern intrumentation and control for nuclear power plants: A Guidebook* vol 1
[6] IEC 2012 *IEC 62566, Nuclear Power Plants - Instrumentation and Control Important to Safety - Development of HDL - Programmed Integrated Circuits for Systems Performing Category A functions*
[7] Mcdowell B, Mitchell M, Pugh R, Nickolaus J and Swearingen G 2011 *High Temperature Gas Reactors : Assessment of Applicable Codes and Standards*
[8] Wei L, Liu L and Yang Z 2011 Design, application and maintenance of HTR-10 full digital safety I&C system *Proc. 2011 Int. Conf. Mechatron. Sci. Electr. Eng. Comput. MEC 2011* 450–3
[9] International Atomic Energy Agency 1998 *Safety related design and economic aspects of HTGRs*
[10] IAEA 2016 *IAEA Safety Standards, Specific Safety Guide No.SSG-39, Design of Instrumentation and Control Systems for Nuclear Power Plants*
[11] Maerani R, Suryono T J and Subekti M 2019 Requirement Analysis of Computer-Based Instrumentation and Control System for Reaktor Daya Eksperimental *J. Teknol. Reakt. Nukl. Tri Dasa Mega* **21** 39
[12] Flink B and Killian C 2009 *EPRI TR-1019181, Guidelines on the Use of Field Programmable Gate Arrays (FPGAs) in Nuclear Power Plant I&C Systems*
[13] Anon NRC: 10 CFR Appendix A to Part 50—General Design Criteria for Nuclear Power Plants
[14] Holbrook M R 2015 *Summary of The Advance Reactor Design Criteria (ARDC) Phase 1 Activities, Including the Development of Final Report and the Advanced Reactor Technology*
[15] Kinsey J and Hobrook M 2015 *Guidance for Developing Principal Design Criteria for Advanced ( Non-Light Water ) Reactors*
[16] US.NRC 2018 *Guidance for Developing Principal Design Criteria for Non-Light Water Reactor, Regulatory Guide 1.232. Rev 0*
[17] U.S.NRC 1996 *Regulatory guide 1.153 - Critetria for Safety Systems*
[18] US.NRC 1980 *Regulatory Guide 1.97, Instrumentation for Light Water-Cooled Nuclear Power Plants to Assess Plant and Environs Conditions During and Following and Accident*
[19] US.NRC 2003 *Regulatory Guide 1.196, Control Room Habitability at Light-Water Nuclear Power Reactors*
[20] US.NRC 2003 *Regulatory Guide 1.197, Demostrating Control Room Envelope Integrity at Nuclear Power Reactors*
[21] US.NRC 1972 *Regulatory Guide 1.22, Periodic Testing of Protection System Actuation Functions*
[22] US.NRC 2013 Software Unit Testing for Digital Computer Software used in Safety System of Nuclear Power Plants *Regulatory Guide 1.171* vol 17 pp 1–14
[23] US.NRC 1978 *Regulatory Guide 1.118, Periodic Testing of Electric Power and Protection Systems*
[24] Holbrook M R 2015 *Summary of the Advanced Reactor Design Criteria ( ARDC ) Phase 2*

*Activities*
[25] Bobrek M, Bouldin D, D.E H, S.M K, S.F S, C W and Wood R T 2009 *NUREG/CR-7006, Review Guidelines for Field-Programmable Gate Arrays in Nuclear Power Plant Safety Systems*
[26] IAEA 1999 *IAEA Technical Report Series No.384, Verification and Validation of Software Related to Nuclear Power Plant Instrumentation and Control*
[27] Ahmed I, Jung J and Heo G 2017 Design Verification Enhancement of Field Programmable Gate Array-Based Safety-Critical I&C System of Nuclear Power Plant *Nucl. Eng. Des.* **317** 232–41
[28] IEEE 2012 *Standard for System and Software Verification and Validation, IEEE Std 1012-2012*

# Management of Site Evaluation: A Lesson Learnt of 10 MW HTGR Experimental Power Reactor (RDE) Project Site Licensing

**Yarianto S Budi Susilo**[1]

*Center for Nuclear Mineral Technology, National Nuclear Energy Agency, PTBGN BATAN, Jl/ Lebak Bulus Raya No 09 Pasar Jumat, Jakarta, Indonesia*

phone: +62 -21-7691775, yarianto@batan.go.id

**Abstract**. In 2013, a pre-project activity of Experimental Power Reactor (RDE Project) was started. The reactor type is a High Temperature Gas-cooled Reactor (HTGR) with a 10 MWth capacity. At present the project has been postponed due to some reason, however, there was an important stage that has been achieved, regarding the site evaluation process to obtain site permits from the Regulatory Body (BAPETEN). Site evaluation is an critical activity that will guarantee the safety of nuclear facilities from natural and human induced external events as well as the safety of population and the environment due to nuclear facility accidents. Site evaluation for the RDE project has the same process as a large NPP project, considering that at the time of the site evaluation process there were no specific regulations that considered a graded approach for a mini-scale NPP. The site evaluation process includes two stages, namely 1). Site Evaluation Program (SEP) and Management System of Site Evaluation (MSSE) Approval and 2) Site Evaluation Approval. SEP is intended to establish the scope and criteria for site evaluation safety. Whereas the Site Evaluation Management System is a managerial instrument that makes site safety as the top priority in each activity and process of RDE site evaluation. BATAN as the project owner delivered the SEP document and MSSE to BAPETEN on March 10, 2014. These documents was intensively discussed by BAPETEN and BATAN to determine agreement on the scope of site evaluation, criteria and management aspects based on site safety considerations. The technical aspects that must be evaluated are seismicity, volcanic hazard, geotechnical and foundation, meteorology, hydrology, human induced events, dispersion and population distribution. This document was approved by BAPETEN on March 2, 2015. Considering the very wide scope with various fields of competence and need supporting data for evaluation, this can not be done only by BATAN experts, it must collaborate with various institution that have competence related to the site aspect. The experts that involved in the site evaluation come from Meteorology and Geophysics Agency (BMKG) for seismic and meteorological aspects, Geospatial Information Agency (BIG) to support geospatial data and ground movements/deformation, Geological Survey Center (PSG) to support geological data and geological structures, Center for Volcanology and Geological Disaster Mitigation (PVMBG) to support volcanic catalog data and volcanic hazard, University to support geotechnical, foundation and hydrology evaluation. BATAN experts from various Centers involved for evaluating topography, human induced events, dispersion, dose assessment, population distribution, emergency preparedness, and technology aspects. Data acquisition activities such as geophysics, drilling, geological mapping, volcanic mapping, hydrology, satellite imagery and digitizing processes are contracted through third parties with guidance developed by the BATAN Expert Team. Considering the very limited time and financial resources availability, in order to achieve the effectiveness of all activities, a special organization was formed to control site evaluation with the BATAN Chairman as Top Management. The Site evaluation document was submitted in two stages. The first stage is administrative completeness and it was declared administratively complete on November 15, 2015. The second step is BAPETEN assessed and evaluated the technical documents submitted to determine the acceptability of the site. The process of evaluating the site evaluation document lasts quite a long and intensive. Finally, the site permit was issued on January 23, 2017. The valuable lessons during the site evaluation project are: 1) It require the same understanding and perception between applicant and regulator regarding the site licensing process; 2) The establishment and implementation of an effective organization; 3) controlling the project schedule.

## 1. Introduction

The RDE Project is a project to build an experimental power reactor with main objectives to conduct experiment, demonstrating safety and performance of reactor and increasing human resource capacity. The idea of the project was started in 2013, and implementing of the pre project activities started in 2014. The RDE to be built is a High Temperature Gas-cooled Reactor (HTGR) reactor type with a capacity of 10 MWth [1]. At present the project has been postponed due to some reason, however, there was a crucial stage that has been achieved during the pre-project activities. Site evaluation process has been carried out successfully resulting a site permits from the Regulatory Body (BAPETEN) on January 23, 2017. This is the first experience for both applicant (BATAN) and regulatory body (BAPETEN) in the process of nuclear reactor site licensing.

Good data management is important not just for selecting and licensing the best site, but also to help to resolve possible future issues that arise during operations and require further justification [2].

## 2. Problems

Site licensing process for nuclear power involves a lot of technical and non-technical problems that must be well managed to achieve site permit in a proper time. From a technical point of view, availability data on site is very limited, so it needs hard work in data acquisition and analysis. The scope of study includes:

a. Seismic hazard evaluation needs a lot of supporting data such as detail topographic map, satellite imagery, detailed geological maps, confirmed geological structure, geophysical data, earthquake catalogs, ground deformation with the objective to ensure that there are no capable faults in the site vicinity as well to build a proper seismotectonic models as a basis for seismic hazard analysis for both deterministic and probabilistic method [3]. To meet the Indonesia regulation for site permit, it must be proven that the level of seismic (peak ground acceleration-PGA) on the site should be still meets the acceptance criteria, which is 0.6 g for a 10,000-year return period. If the PGA level on the site exceeds 0.6 g, the site will be rejected [4].
b. Geotechnical hazard evaluation requires supporting data such as depth of bed rock, lithology, drilling data with in situ tests and laboratory tests for soil characteristics of each lithology layer [5], stratigraphy, slope analysis based on detail topography map and the layout of nuclear facilities to be built. Soil characteristic (i.e. shearwave velocity, Vs) should be able to support the reactor building load and there will be no geotechnical hazards such as liquefaction in the event of an extreme earthquake. Therefore, a systematic drilling (with geophysical logging) is needed to ensure site safety from geotechnical hazards and also to provide input data for the design of foundations and building structures, especially for nuclear reactors. Other geotechnical hazards such as sinking, ground collapse, land subsidence, landslides in the site must be proven not to occur in the site area. This requires data support through geophysical investigation [6].
c. Evaluation of volcanic hazard is conducted within radius 150 km from the site. The site is located in the geological area of volcanic products. Within a 25 km radius of the site there are several old volcanoes (Mt. Pengki, Mt. Sodong, Mt. Dago, Mt, Pagutan and Mt. Sudamanik), which have to be proven by identification of their eruption age through K/Ar dating analysis. The results of the dating, they have age > 7 ma [7]. While active volcanoes within a radius of 150 km there are 90 volcanoes with an age of early Miocene to Holocene. For the site evaluation

purpose, it had been selected 2 nearest active volcanoes (agreement with regulatory body) from the site that have the most significant potential impacts on the site, namely Gede Volcano and Salak Volcano. The evaluation should prove their capabilities and impacts from any volcanic phenomenon (pyroclastic flow, lava flow, lahar flow, volcanic ash, bombs, debris avalanches, groundwater anomalies, opening new vents etc.) to the site [8] [9]. Volcano mapping is made in detail to identify all volcanic products (both of primary and secondary) around the site. Other phenomena such as hot spring (9 km distance) are also analyzed through geochemistry analysis to ensure that the occurrence of hot spring is not influenced by gas release from magma system which is indicated by low concentration of magmatic chemical component (sulfate and fluoride).

d. Evaluation of hydrological hazards. River flooding (the site location is near the Cisadane River) is one of the potential hazards that can threat the safety of the nuclear reactor, so it must be proven that the site meets with the criteria of extreme river flooding. Factors that may influence the magnitude of river flooding are extreme rainfall (based on long term data from nearest meteorological station), river configuration in the upstream area to determine the catchment area, river dimensions (hydro-morphology), topography around the site, site platform (based on design) [10] [11]. Simulations were carried out for extreme flood with 1000 and 10,000 years return period and described areas affected and inundated by floods, to evaluate site acceptance. Floods that have come suddenly due to structural failures in the upstream area must also be carried out, so that the collection of all structural data is also required. River floods are also analyzed based on past events with regard to sediment deposits. It was also measured groundwater levels at the determined monitoring wells, to ensure that the probable maximum ground water level is still acceptable
e. Meteorological aspects. Meteorological data collection (i.e., temperature and its temperature lapse rate, relative humidity, wind speed, wind direction, air pressure, solar radiation, lightning) was conducted through a) secondary data collection (minimum 30 years) from meteorological stations closest to the site (owned by Meteorological, Geophysical and Climatological Agency-BMKG) and b) from primary data through on-site meteorological station monitoring. Meteorological evaluation is carried out for 3 purposes, namely 1) to evaluate the hazard of meteorological rare events phenomena (such as tropical cyclones, tornadoes, storms, etc.), 2) to determine the design basis parameters with a certain return period (such as probable maximum temperature, probable maximum rainfall, etc.) and 3) to determine the atmospheric dispersion parameters due to radionuclide release from reactor from both normal operation and worst-case accident scenario. On site meteorological monitoring is carried out continuously until the reactor operation is complete.
f. External Human Induced Events (EHIE) aspect. Around the RDE site there are sources of human activity that have the potential to threat the safety of the nuclear reactor. In principle, it can be divided into fixed source (such as airports, industries, military bases, fuel stations, oil and gas depots, etc.) and mobile sources (including air traffic, gas pipelines, railway, highways). Potential hazards of fixed sources were evaluated based on potential of explosions, fluid releases, cloud releases, toxic vapors, etc. The analysis was carried out through the Screening Distance Values (SDV) and Screening Probability Level (SPL) approach [12]. The determination of the radius of SDV used in initial screening is based on references and discussions result with regulators. Furthermore, the analysis of the acceptability of all EHIE sources within the SDV radius is based on simulations taking into account the potential sources, intensity of accident (i.e., explosion) protection systems, distribution zone of the accident impacts (missile, toxic fluid, flammable material, etc.) to the reactor site.
g. Dispersion and Population distribution Aspect. Dispersion analysis was carried out for both normal operation and accident postulated releases (by using worst case accident). The purpose of the evaluation of dispersion and radiation dose assessment is to prove that the radionuclide release due to the both normal operation and accident of the RDE will remain safe for the worker, population surrounding the site and environment [13]. Data that needed for the evaluation

Journal of Physics: Conference Series **2048** (2021) 012042 doi:10.1088/1742-6596/2048/1/012042

among other meteorological data (statistic of wind speed, wind direction, temperature lapse rate, stability of atmosphere, solar radiation, etc., which is supplied by meteorological aspect), population distribution, land and water use, topography, dietary habit, etc. The data of population distribution was collected from Statistical Agency, interpretation of satellite imagery and ground survey for validation [14]. For evaluation purposes it was supported by some software for source terms calculation and dispersion analysis. Dose assessment is carried out by considering the initial (existing) dose received by the population and then added by radiation dose due to the release of radionuclides from RDE. In the calculation of radiation doses, it was considered existing nuclear facilities around the site such as the GA Siwabessy research reactor (30 MW), radioisotope production, nuclear fuel installation, and radioactive waste treatment.

To ensure the quality of processes and results, all activities were conducted by referring to the Management System of Site Evaluation (MSSE) and the results of its implementation are reported in the Site Management Evaluation System Implementation Report, which includes internal and external audit reports (BAPETEN), inspection reports, management review, etc. MSSE will be as control and verification system for all RDE site evaluation activities which will impact to the quality (process and product) as well safety aspect [15].

Based on the non-technical side, the obstacle and challenges are as follows:

a. The project milestone has been determined by BATAN Leader, with a very tight schedule, including site evaluation and site permit that should be implemented in time manner. Time management is the key factor in measuring the success of the project.
b. Interaction between Site Team and Design Team (carried out by consultants and work in parallel) to determine the drilling point, need to be mutually agreed upon and interdependent of each other. This is a technical and management issue, and need an effective communication.
c. The location of the site had been determined to be located within the Science and Technological Research Park (PUSPIPTEK), therefore the option of locations is limited only on the vacant land available on Puspiptek. Several areas within PUSPIPTEK then proposed to the authority (Ministry of Research and Technology) to select one.
d. Considering that there has not been a comprehensive site study before in the study area that follows site evaluation standards and regulations, so that many sites evaluation items, installation of equipment for data acquisition, surveys for primary data collection and monitoring must be carried out in a short time.
e. There are still many different perceptions between the applicant (BATAN Team) and regulatory body (BAPETEN Team) regarding the site evaluation process both in substance and scope. The interaction between the applicant and the regulatory body is one of the key factors in the success of the site permit process.
f. BEPETEN regulations related to site evaluation have never been used before for the site permit process, and this evaluation process actually becomes a validation test for the implementation of regulations.
g. Management system of a complex project.

## 3. Objective

The purpose of this paper is to share experiences in managing site evaluation projects and its permit which are very complex processes, as a lesson learned in developing nuclear installation projects.

## 4. Methodology

The methodology used in this paper is to identify, study, analyze, and evaluate the empirical experience of each evaluation process and the licensing process so that it can be a valuable lesson in project management evaluation and licensing processes. This experience is very important as a feedback for the improvement of the system and the process of site permits and other permits in the developing of nuclear facilities, so that the licensing process can be managed properly and efficiently without reducing the safety factor.

## 5. Result and Discussion

### *5.1. Site Licensing Process*

The site licensing process is divided into 2 phases. The first is Site Evaluation Program approval phases, where the applicant must submit 2 documents, namely site evaluation program (SEP) and management system of site evaluation (MSSE) [16]. Both documents then evaluated by BAPETEN until they are approved by Chairman of BAPETEN. The second phase is site permit process, where the applicant must submit a site evaluation report (SER) for all aspect, implementing report of MSSE, and a number of administrative documents. The process can be seen in Figure 1 and Figure 2.

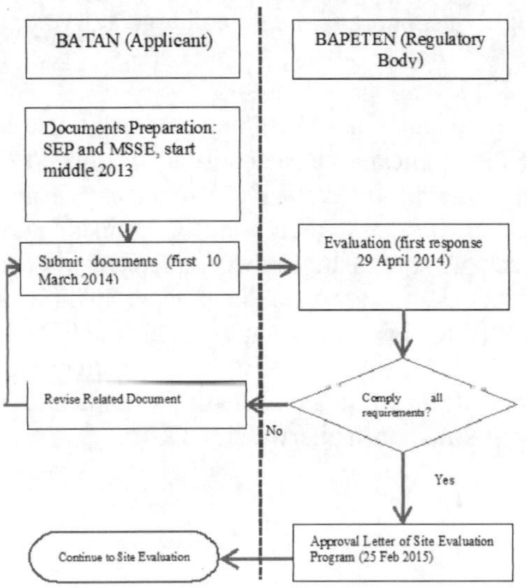


SEP: Site Evaluation Program
MSSE: Management System of Site Evaluation

**Figure 1.** Approval process for site evaluation program (SEP)

In practice, the SEP approval process takes a long time, from submitting documents until approval it was almost one year. The site evaluation program is crucial phase because it will determine the scoping and acceptance criteria that must be met and have an impact on the item and volume of site evaluation work and site acceptance. The process that takes a long time is caused by:

a. Both applicant and regulator are the first time to carried out a site permit, therefore in order to make a crucial decision regarding the critical issue, it take a long time and it usually delay a predetermined target.
b. Existing regulations are adopted from IAEA standards which are the requirements more suitable for larger commercial Nuclear Power rather than for experiment small scale nuclear power. The selected technology (high temperature reactor 10 MW) was also an obstacle from licensing process view because all this time the basis for regulation is light water nuclear power plants. Existing regulation is also not adopted graded approach yet. A long discussion regarding the acceptance criteria and scope of work also cause time to get longer.
c. During the discussion of the scope of the study, there were still differences in perceptions between the applicant and the regulator regarding the ultimate goal of site evaluation. Applicants assume that the purpose of site evaluation is to demonstrate site safety, but technical experts (TSO) from the regulator emphasize that the site evaluation objective is to provide data used for construction design. For example, for the geotechnical aspect, this difference of opinion causes the volume of work to be several times larger with regard to number and spacing of boreholes, drill depth, volume of in situ tests and lab tests, kind of in situ test, etc.

Lesson learnt:

a. Human resources who have technical competence and experience in site evaluation is really needed both for regulator and applicant.
b. Regulations need to accommodate the graded approach, including requirements and acceptance criteria, so that the evaluations carried out will not be excessive which will have consequences for longer completion times and higher costs.
c. Communication regarding the technology to be used must be delivered as earlier as possible.
d. It is needed a nuclear energy master plan, as a reference for regulator and applicant in preparing regulatory infrastructure.
e. It is also necessary to prepare TSO capability both to support applicant and regulatory body to improve quality of site evaluation.

For the second phase of site licensing process, Applicant should submit the administrative requirements first including proof of establishment of the applicant's legal entity, conformity to the spatial plan, proof of land rights, proof of site evaluation payment, site evaluation document (8 aspects), site evaluation system implementation document, reactor main data (RMD) and Preliminary Design Information Questionnaire (DIQ). This document was declared administratively complete on November 15, 2015. Furthermore, BAPETEN assessed and evaluated the technical documents submitted to determine the acceptability of the site. The process of evaluating the site evaluation document lasts quite a long and intensive. The meeting was held between BATAN and BAPETEN at the management level, the overall technical team and the special aspects technical team. Besides evaluating documents, field verification is also carried out. Finally, the site permit was issued on January 23, 2017.

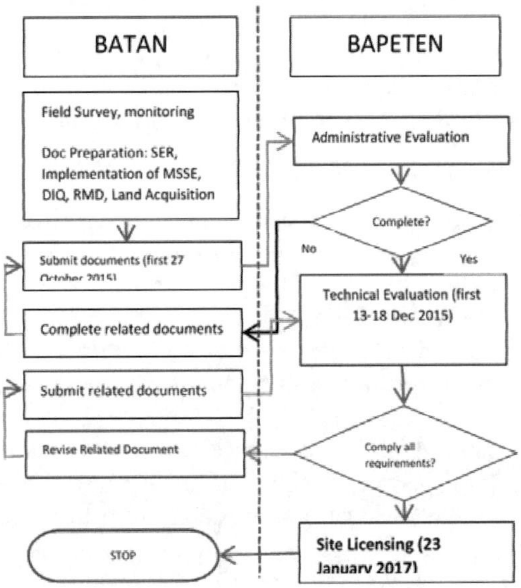


SER: Site Evaluation Report
MSSE: Management System of Site Evaluation
DIQ: Design Information Questionnaire
RMD: Reactor Main Data

**Figure 2.** Approval Process for Site Permit

On 13-18 December 2015 a technical evaluation of the findings (Preliminary Finding of BATAN Site Evaluation Report) has been conducted by IAEA through the PRE SEED (Site and External Events Design) Mission. As a follow up, BATAN improves by completing the data and analysis according to the evaluation results. Document revisions were made several times both after the plenary meeting and meeting of each specific aspect or issue. In addition, there is also a management level meeting to accelerate the site permit process. Field activities continue during the evaluation process and BAPETEN staff always monitor and inspect the field activities. Finally, the RDE site permit was granted through the Decree of the Head of BAPETEN Number 001 / IT / Ka-BAPETEN / 23-I / 2017. The process of site permits from entering the application (27 October 2015) until the site permit issued takes 1 year 2 months. If the time is calculated from sending SEP and MSSE, the time needed to get a site permit is 2 years 10 months. If the preparation of the SEP and MSSE documents is calculated, it becomes 3 years and 4 months (from the target of 2 years). Time used for site permit can be seen at Figure 3.

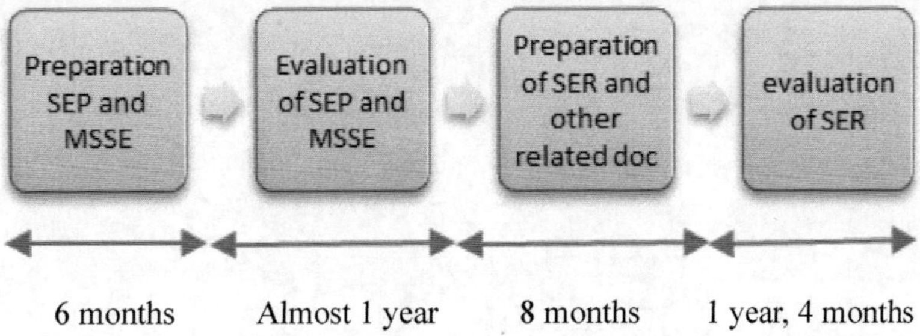


**Figure 3.** Time used for Site Permit

Lesson learnt:

a. In the nuclear facility construction project cycle, the time to complete the site permit is too long, so that it will complicate the project implementation and disrupt the milestone. Regulators need to prepare technical guidelines for SEP especially the acceptance criteria that can be directly used by the user.
b. The parameters for site evaluation with the aim of site permit differ in terms of depth and density of the data with the site parameters required for construction design. In the process of site permits that have been carried out, this has not yet been distinguished, so that at the site evaluation stage for site permits it must meet the data completeness requirements for construction design. This resulted in prolonged discussions and site permits being delayed. Site permits should be more focused on in-depth study of site parameters that affect reactor safety.

*5.2. Organization of Site Evaluation*

Since the site evaluation work is very complex and the budget is limited, effective special organizations are needed [17]. The purpose of establishing this organization is to prepare all resources, technical documents, legal and cooperation frameworks, site evaluation activities, preparation of Design Information Questionnaire (DIQ) documents and Reactor Main Data (RMD) as well as other documents required in the site permit process.

After the SEP and the MSSE document have been approved by BAPETEN, field survey activities are carried out in accordance with a mutually agreed schedule. BATAN prepares a master schedule and detailed schedule for each aspect

Considering that the technical scope is very broad and its competence is spread in several Technical Centers in BATAN and other Institutions outside BATAN, so for activities to be effective, a special organization needs to be formed with the top manager being the BATAN Chairman. Operational management is under the control of the Center for Nuclear Energy System Assessment, which manages and controls project operations. There are 7 Technical Centers and 1 Administrative Bureau in BATAN is involved in site evaluation activities. Other institutions involved are the Geology Agency (with technical centers: the Center for Geological Survey and the Center for Volcanology and Geological Disaster Mitigation), the Geospatial Information Agency (geospatial and GPS Geodetic data support), the Meteorology, Climatology and Geophysics Center (BMKG), University of Indonesia (hydrology), Bandung Institute of Technology (geotechnics), Gadjah Mada University (Geophysics). All experts and supporting staff involved more than 100 people. Some of the field work (mapping, geophysics) is contracted out to third parties with internal supervision carried out by experts in this particular organization and external supervision by BAPETEN.

Journal of Physics: Conference Series **2048** (2021) 012042 doi:10.1088/1742-6596/2048/1/012042

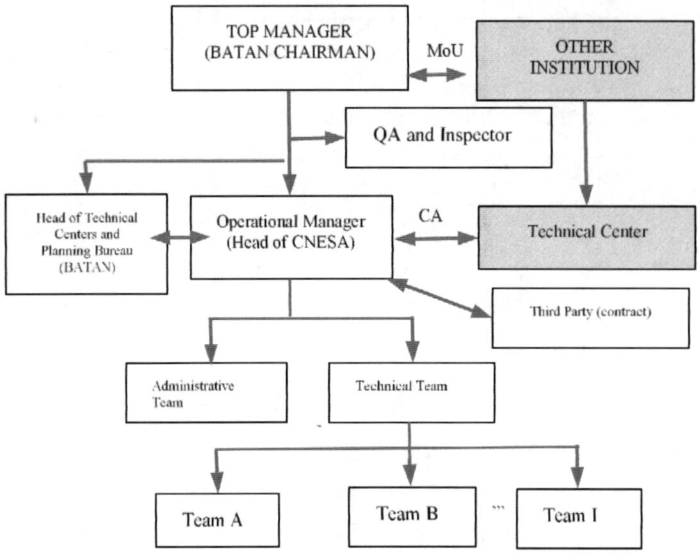


MoU: Memorandum of Understanding
CA: Cooperation Agreement
CNESA: Center for Nuclear Energy Assessment

**Figure 4.** Organization of Site Evaluation [15]

To anticipate that work involving external institutions can run on time according to schedule and in accordance with the scope of work, project management instruments in the form of memorandum of understanding are needed between BATAN and the related Institution. Top management level in each institution will participate in monitoring the work carried out by experts under their authority.

Lesson learnt:

Site evaluation work involving many parties. requires a very strong top management commitment, synergy both within BATAN and between institutions, intensive coordination, providing benefits for all parties involved, (especially in the development of research and competence), as well as strong, accountable and open administrative support. Strong commitment and communication must be built before the site evaluation begins

*5.3. Time Handling of Technical Aspects*

Considering many limitations (available existing data, human resources according to competency requirements, budget), normally, it will be difficult to meet the 2-year target from applying a SEP until a site permit. This is due to external factor dependence (BAPETEN) and interdependent work sequences. For this reason, it is required to perform a multi-level schedule consisting of the project milestone (overall RDE development plan), a master schedule for each site permit activity, a detailed schedule of each aspect and a detailed schedule of sub-activities in each aspect. The most difficult in controlling time is activities that involve external parties, related to synchronizing the implementation of activities that are at the same time with their internal activities. The agreed schedule is the key in controlling the activities.

During the survey activity there is a delay/hold point that gives BAPETEN an opportunity to evaluate the validity of the methods and data that have been taken. In this time delay period, the BATAN Team is not allowed to conduct survey activities. After being verified by BAPETEN, survey activities can be continued. In order the survey implementation not to be hampered by the result of BAPETEN Inspection during the hold point, all method and standard operational procedure (SOP) have been well prepared and consulted with BAPETEN Technical Team. During site evaluation activities, BATAN has an internal quality assurance team that conducts internal audits, inspections, surveillance to ensure the quality of the site evaluation process. BAPETEN also periodically conducts external audits.

In practice, from submitting an SEP application to obtaining approval from BAPETEN, it takes one year. Discussion of items and work volumes as well acceptance criteria are the most critical factors and require a long period of time in discussion until they are mutually agreed upon. The lesson to be learned is that before submitting SEP, the acceptance criteria must be communicated first. Alternatively, BAPETEN already has acceptance criteria in their guidelines, as a reference for the preparation of the SEP.

For survey work that involves a lot of support staff, some of the work is done through contracts with consultants to save time. The consultant work based on the terms of reference (TOR) provided by BATAN. The TOR was prepared in detail by competent experts and discussed with BAPETEN in order to be in sync with the proposed SEP. The contracted work includes geological and volcanological mapping and geophysical work, where points and trajectories have been determined in the TOR. Data interpretation and analysis are not included in the contract, but are carried out by the Expert Team. In addition, drilling activities are also carried out by third parties.

The technical aspects that are crucial in managing time are as follows:

a. Seismic aspects, where the required data is very complex and its acceptance greatly affects the site feasibility results. Seismic analysis was compiled and based on regional geological maps, DEM, satellite imagery interpretation, verified structural data, paleosesimic, geodetic GPS, geophysical data interpretation (geoelectric, geomagnetic, georadar, seismic reflection, gravity), earthquake catalog, micro earthquake record (primary data), microzonation, stratigraphy, and seismotectonic models. Determination of wave propagation from bed rock to the surface is very dependent on the soil bedding model obtained from in situ testing during geotechnical drilling and microtremor survey [3] [4] [18]. External parties involved in data acquisition, analysis, and interpretation activities are the Center for Geological Survey, the Meteorology, Climatology and Geophysics Agency, the Geospatial Information Agency, consultants, and Gadjah Mada University. The process of analysis, interpretation and integration and the process of making conclusions are very time and energy consuming.
b. Geotechnical aspects, especially for drilling planning. Prior to drilling, a topographic survey is carried out to provide a detailed topographic map with a scale of 1: 500 for the initial determination of the RDE layout planned by design consultants working in parallel. Determination of drilling points is carried out jointly between geotechnical experts and designers taking into account slope cross sections and potential geotechnical hazards (sinks, liquefaction obtained from geophysical surveys and some previous initial drilling points). This synchronization requires handling and management intervention, so that the planned drill points already represent the needs of foundation analysis and are in accordance with the conceptual design of RDE.

<u>Lesson learnt:</u>

a. Internal progress review meeting is a management tools that to be done at least every two weeks
b. Coordination with the RDE designer is required to be synchronized between site evaluation and RDE design activities.
c. It is required a periodically communication and consultation with Regulatory Body and hold special meetings if there are problems that must be resolved immediately
d. It is needed focusing on solving problems and following up on the Evaluation Results Report from Regulator Team.

## 6. Conclusion

The RDE site evaluation process is a very valuable experience in controlling a complex project with all its limitations, but is demanded by the target of time and budget. Site evaluation management requires a special organization that is able to control all activities effectively and can carry out effective communication both internally and externally, must be able to make careful and very detailed planning, able to control administration and finance. Effective communication with regulators is one of the keys factors to success in site evaluation until obtaining site permission.

**Acknowledgement**
The Author would like to thank all the parties that have involved and supported in the RDE site evaluation activities until to obtain site licensing from BAPETEN.

**References**
[1] BATAN, Blue Print of Experimental Power Reactor Development 2014-2020, p.4, p.27, BATAN, Jakarta, 2014
[2] IAEA, IAEA Nuclear Energy Series No NG-G-3.1 (Rev.1), Milestones in the Development of a National Infrastructure for Nuclear Power, p.45-46, IAEA, Vienna, 2015
[3] IAEA, IAEA SSG-9, Seismic Hazard in Site Evaluation for Nuclear Installation, IAEA, Vienna, 2010
[4] BAPETEN, BAPETEN Chairman Regulation No 8, year 2013 Regarding Seismic Hazard in Site Evaluation of Nuclear Installation, BAPETEN, Jakarta, 2013
[5] IAEA, IAEA NS-G-3.6, Geotachnical Aspects of Site Evaluation and Foundations for Nuclear Power Plants, IAEA, Vienna, 2004
[6] BAPETEN, BAPETEN Chairman Regulation No 4 Year 2008 Regarding Site Evaluation and Foundation of NPP, BAPETEN, Jakarta, 2008
[7] BATAN, Site Evaluation Report of RDE on Volcanological Aspect, PKSEN BATAN, Jakarta, 2016.
[8] BAPETEN, Regulation of BAPETEN CHAIRMAN Number 2 Year 2008 regarding Site Evaluation for Power Reactor for the Volcanological Aspects, Jakarta, 2008.
[9] IAEA, IAEA SSG-21 Volcanic Hazard ins Site Evaliation for Nuclear Installations, IAEA, Vienna, 2012
[10] IAEA, IAEA SSG-18 Meteorological and Hydrological Hazards in Site Evaluation for Nuclear Installation, IAEA, Vienna, 2011
[11] BAPETEN, BAPETEN Chairman Regulation No 6 Year 2014 regarding Nuclear Installation Site Evaluation on Mataoeological and Hidrological Aspects.
[12] IAEA, IAEA NS-G-3.1. External Human Indiced Events in Site Evaluation for Nuclear Power Plants Safety Guide, IAEA, Vienna, 2002
[13] BAPETEN, BAPETEN Chairman Regulation N0 3 Year 2008 Regarding Dispersion of Radioactive Material in Air and Water and Consideration of Population Distribution in NPP Site Evaluation, Jakarta, 2008
[14] BATAN, Site Evaluation Report of RDE on Dispersion Aspect, PKSEN BATAN, Jakarta, 2016,
[15] BATAN, Management System of Site Evaluation for Experimental Power Reactor at Puspiptek Area, Serpong, BATAN, Jakarta, 2014.
[16] Khoirul Huda, Requirement and Mechanism of NPP Licensing in Indonesia, Proceeding of National Seminar XII, NPP Technology and Safety and Nuclear Facility, p.313, p.318 12-13, Yogyakarta, September 2006.
[17] Sriyana, Imam Bastori, Suparman, Yarianto SB Susilo, Assessment of Organization for Experimental Power Reactor Project, Proceeding of Nasional Seminar of Nuclear Technology Energy, vol 1/2015 p.11, Denpasar, Bali 15 - 16 Oct 2015.
[18] BATAN, Site Evaluation Report of RDE on Seismic Aspect, PKSEN BATAN, Jakarta, 2016.

# Study on the DLOFC accident of the GEMINI+ conceptual design of HTGR reactor with MELCOR and SPECTRA

**M Skrzypek[1], E Skrzypek[1], M Stempniewicz[2] and J Malesa[1]**

[1] *National Centre for Nuclear Research, A.Soltana 7, 05-500 Otwock, Poland*
[2] *NRG, Utrechtseweg 310, Arnhem/Westerduinweg 3, Petten, Netherlands*

E-mail: eleonora.skrzypek@ncbj.gov.pl

**Abstract.** The work presented in this paper was performed within the Euratom Horizon 2020 GEMINI Plus project. Behavior of the HTGR reactor under severe accident conditions was investigated and the maximum fuel temperature was observed. Due to application of the TRISO particles and SiC layers in the fuel element, no damage of the fuel is expected up to 1600°C. Under the cooperation in the project between Nuclear Research Group (NRG) and National Centre for Nuclear Research (NCBJ) a code-to-code calculations were carried out between the SPECTRA and MELCOR codes. SPECTRA code, developed by the NRG is a thermal hydraulic analysis code and MELCOR 2.1.6342 used by NCBJ developed by SANDIA National Laboratory is fast running severe accident code. Both codes have already HTGR specific models build in. The following accident was analyzed and will be presented: Depressurized Loss of Forced Circulation (DLOFC) with 65 mm break at the top of reactor vessel. The scenario was calculated applying following sets of assumptions: best estimate and conservative. Plant behavior was analyzed including primary and secondary side of the reactor. As the results of applying conservative assumptions, it was found that fuel temperature excides the acceptable limit of 1620°C. Therefore, changes in the core design were proposed by project participants. Analyses of the new core showed acceptable temperatures. In the paper the results of code-to-code comparison are presented. Both codes have shown a good agreement of presented following characteristics on maximum fuel temperature, relative power and Reactor Cavity Cooling System power, primary pressure and break flow.

## 1. Introduction

The work presented in this paper was performed within the GEMINI Plus project, WP1, Task 1.6: Transient Analyses. This work provides a description of analyses of selected accident scenarios for an innovative reactor design, which is considered for the Polish industry utilizing process heat in various sectors of production. Two following accidents were analyzed: Depressurized Loss of Forced Circulation (DLOFC) with 65 mm break in the primary system.

Due to the nature of the project and the investigatory character of the performed analyses presented here, both scenarios were calculated applying two sets of conditions Best Estimate (BE) and Conservative (C) and considering uniform radial peaking factor (flat).

## 2. HTR-GEMINI

HTR reactor specified for Polish end-users is designed as reactor which produces 251 t/h of live steam (138 bar, 540°C). Thermal power that was estimated as the most suitable for the end user corresponds to 165 MWth and 15$MW_{th}$ was dedicated for internal power needs.

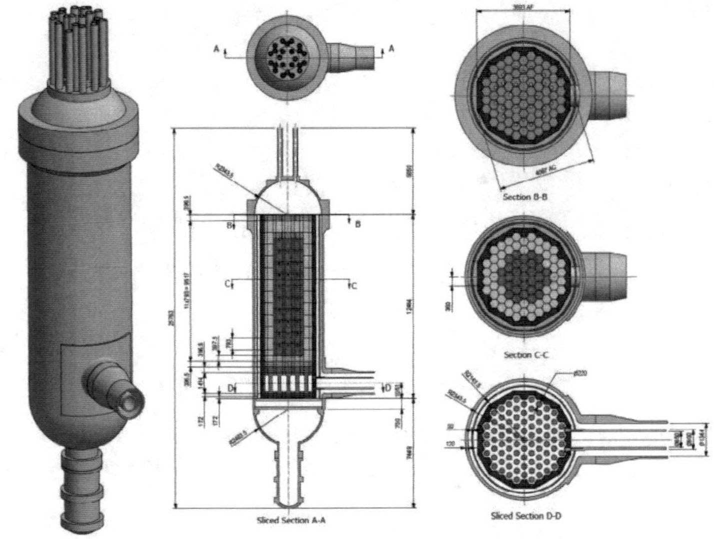


**Figure 1.** Design of reactor core and reactor pressure vessel.

During the project few designs were taken under investigation and the final decision was done on the basis of the extensive calculation campaign. The main interest was to keep the maximum temperature under limit of 1600°C, which in the literature is considered the fuel integrity limit for short period lasting temperature spikes and 1620°C in modern small HTRs [1].

Developed GEMINI+ HTR core (presented in the Figure 2) consists of prismatic graphite blocks, 800 mm height and 360 mm across the flat cross section. Two types of the blocks can be distinguished: one fully fueled and second one with a large channel serving as a duct for the absorber rods Figure 2 and Figure 3 respectively.

Fuel compact is produced with TRISO particles, pressed together in the graphite matrix into a small cylinder, with a diameter of 12.5 mm and a height of 50 mm. There are approximately 3760 particles in a compact which results with the packing fraction of around 0.25. For TRISO particle, the $UO_2$ fuel were used with an enrichment of 14%. Each fuel hole is filled by fuel pin which consist of 15 compacts and graphite plugs are cemented into the tops of the fuel hole enclosing the fuel compact into stacks.

The version of design, which is analyzed is called Configuration AY [2], with the active core height of 8.8 m. This translates to 11 axially prismatic blocks to create an active core region. There are two reflectors, on the top and bottom of the core, situated with dimensions of 1.2 and 1.6 m respectively. Active core is surrounded by the permanent reflector. Details are being presented in Figure 4 below.

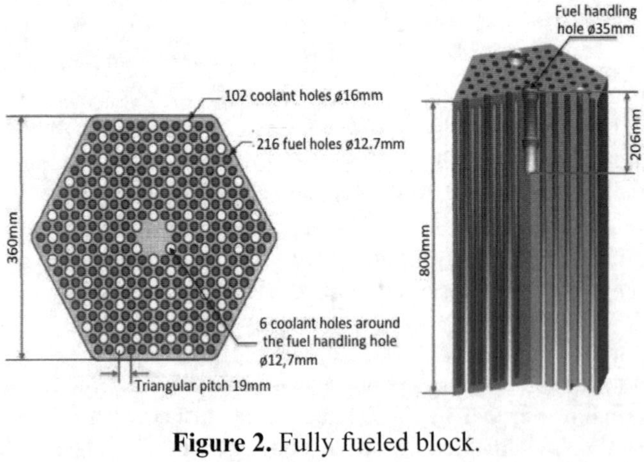


**Figure 2.** Fully fueled block.

Journal of Physics: Conference Series **2048** (2021) 012043 doi:10.1088/1742-6596/2048/1/012043

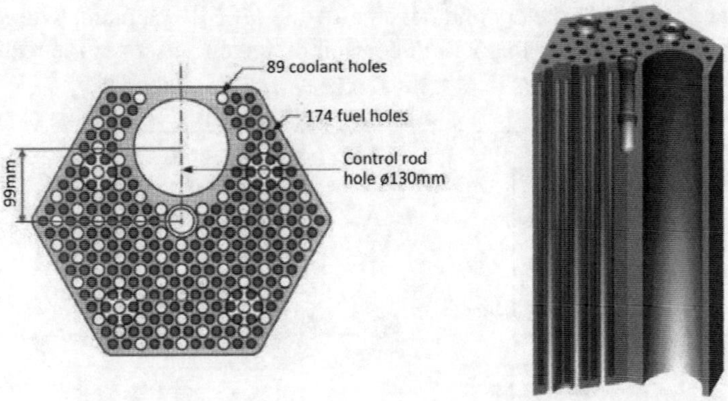


**Figure 3.** Block with control rod hole.

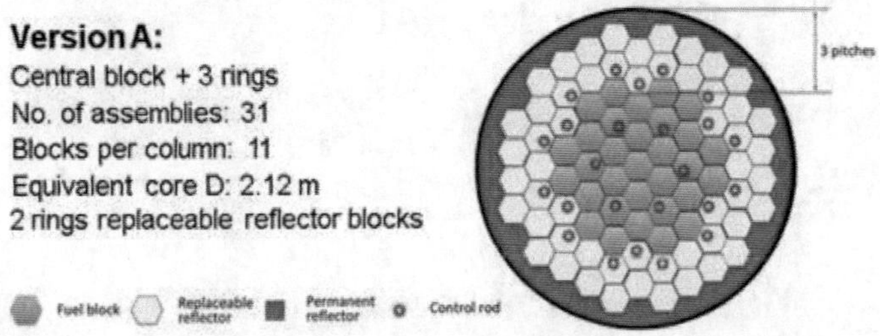


**Figure 4.** Core configuration AY.

**Table 1.** Main parameter of the reactor for normal operating conditions.

| | |
|---|---|
| Thermal power | 180 MW |
| Core inlet temperature | 325°C/598 K |
| Core outlet temperature | 750°C/1023 K |
| Primary pressure | 6 MPa |
| Number of blocks in column | 11 |
| Number of fully fuel loaded blocks in the core | 275 |
| Number of fuel blocks with control rods in the core | 66 |
| Number of reflector blocks with control rods in the core | 198* |
| Number of reflector blocks in the core | 396* |
| Number of reflector blocks- upper | 255 |
| Number of reflector blocks- lower | 340 |
| Gap between blocks: | 2.0 mm |
| Secondary steam pressure | 13.8 MPa |
| Feedwater inlet | 200°C/473 K |
| Steam outlet temperature | 540°C/813 K |

*Only core region, without lower and upper permanent reflector

Figure 5 shows the main parameters and scheme of the GEMINI+ plant. The scheme presents the concept of the steam production line that would be used by the end-users of the reactor.

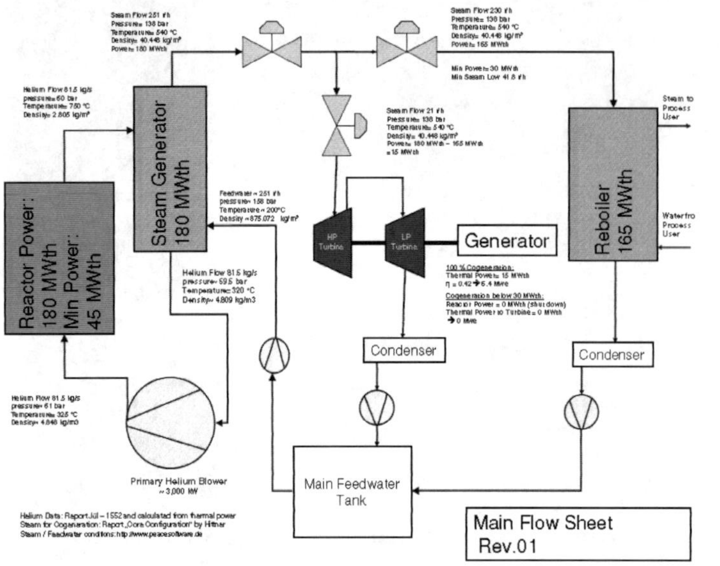


**Figure 5.** Reactor reference parameters and scheme.

## 3. Code introduction

### *3.1. MELCOR*

MELCOR [3] is a fully integrated, engineering-level computer code developed by Sandia National Laboratories for the U.S. Nuclear Regulatory Commission, that models the progression of severe accidents in nuclear power plants.

The structure of the code is package-based organization, which allows the user to decide upon the use of case specific physics to be modelled. This structure of the code enables the calculations to be more flexible and less time consuming in instances of extensive sizes of input.

A broad spectrum of severe accident phenomena, in both boiling and pressurized water reactors, is treated in MELCOR in a unified framework. The most important one is the ability to model thermal-hydraulic response in the reactor coolant system [3], which is the main focus for the application of the HTR in the GEMINI+ project. In terms of specific HTR designs features the MELCOR framework is also adopted, there is possibility of using specific modules, allowing the modelling of prismatic and pebble bed HTR reactors. The most interesting one is the model of the Radial Conduction in the HTGR, which involves the Radial Effective Conductivity of Graphite Blocks with the Tanaka and Chisaka expression for a continuous solid system [3]. This expression does take into account the discontinuous character of the domain (presence of the pores), which are affecting the conductive heat transfer in the block greatly. The expressions are given below:

$$k_{eff} = k_s \left\{ A + (1 - A) \cdot \frac{ln\left[1 + 2 \cdot B \cdot \left(k_{por}/k_s - 1\right)\right]}{2 \cdot B \cdot \left(1 - k_s/k_{por}\right)} \right\} \quad (1)$$

$$k_{rad} = 4 \cdot \varepsilon_r \cdot \sigma \cdot T^3 \cdot D \quad (2)$$

$$k_{er} = \frac{1}{\dfrac{1}{h_{gap} \cdot D_{blk}} + \dfrac{1}{k_{blk}}} \quad (3)$$

$$h_{gap} = \left(k_{He} + 4 \cdot \varepsilon_r \cdot \sigma \cdot T^3 \cdot \sigma_{gap}\right) \quad (4)$$

$A = 2\,(1 - \varepsilon) / (2 + \varepsilon)$,

$B = (1 - \varepsilon) / 3$,

$\varepsilon$ = porosity,

$k_s$ = thermal conductivity of solid material [W/m-K],

$k_{por}$ = thermal conductivity of pores [W/m-K],

$k_{rad}$ = radiative conductivity [W/m-K],

$\varepsilon_r$ = emissivity in pores (channels walls),

$\sigma$ = Stefan-Boltzmann constant [W/m2-K4],

$D$ = effective diameter of pores [m],

$k_{er}$ = effective radial block conductivity [W/m-K],

$h_{gap}$ = gap heat transfer coefficient [W/m2-K],

$D_{blk}$ = effective radial diameter of a block [m].

### *3.2. SPECTRA*

The SPECTRA code developed at NRG, the Netherlands, is a computer program designed for thermal-hydraulic analyses of nuclear or conventional power plants [4]. The code's main applicability is in the area of Light Water Reactors, High Temperature Reactors, Liquid Metal Fast Reactors, and Molten Salt Reactors. The code can be used for thermal accident scenarios, involving loss-of-coolant accidents (LOCAs), operational transients, and other accident scenarios in nuclear power plants. The code structure is based on packages that contain models on a given topic. The available models include multidimensional two-phase flow, non-equilibrium thermo-dynamics, transient heat conduction in solid structures, and general heat and mass transfer, with natural and forced convection, condensation, boiling. SPECTRA was applicable in past to many Generation IV rectors and analyses:

- PBMR: thermal-hydraulics (TH), dust and fission product analyses, Reactor Cavity Cooling System (RCCS).
- NGNP: (pebble) TH dust and fission product analyses.
- HTR-PM: safety analyses, including [5]:
  - DLOFC (comparison with the TINTE code)
  - PLOFC (comparison with the TINTE code)
  - water ingress.

## 4. Calculation model and scenario description

This section will firstly focus on the calculation models developed under the GEMINI+ project, with the use of two described codes in the Section III – MELCOR and SPECTRA. It will be followed by the description of the scenario, which was performed and is the interests of this comparative study. This scenario will be the DLOFC accident, which is crucial from safety point of view for HTR reactors.

### *4.1. Calculation model*

For the purpose of the proper investigation of the proposed design and elimination of the user effect (due to the choice of nodalization), the model for each code was prepared using the same nodalization scheme [6], [7]. The schemes are presented in the following figures: Figure 6 – Figure 9.

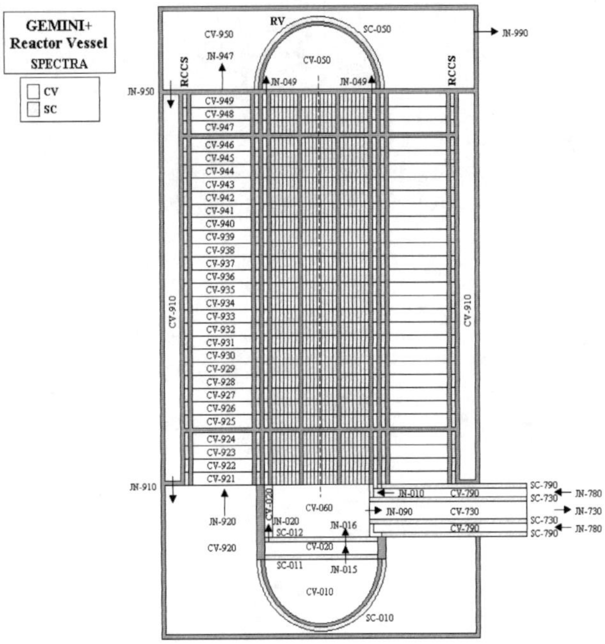


**Figure 6.** Reactor pressure vessel -SPECTRA model.

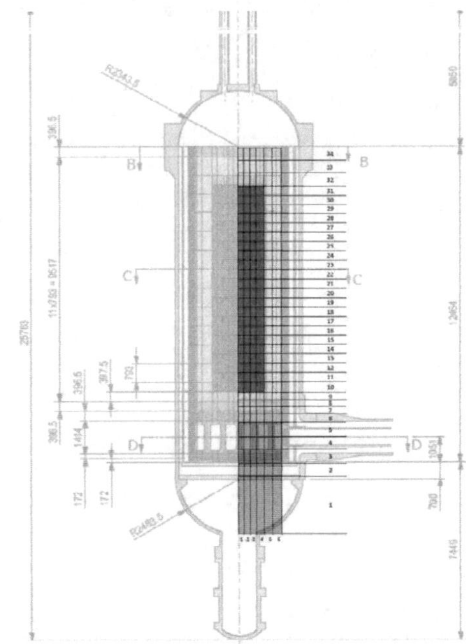

**Figure 7.** Reactor pressure vessel – MELCOR model.

The description on the model on the example of the MELCOR code model is given in the following way:

- Reactor Pressure Vessel was divided into 34 axial and 6 radial nodes, see Figure 7.
- First two bottom levels are dedicated to the lower plenum, next three are corresponding to supporting structures zone.
- Sixth to ninth levels are the lower reflector.
- Tenth to thirty-one level is the active core region and last four are upper reflector.
- In axial levels 1-9 and 32-34 the radial meshes are the same for all rings (graphite material for the reflector).
- In 10-31 the two zones can be recognized 1-4 the active core region and 5-6 surrounding reflector.

Outer volume of the vessel represents a riser and heat structures of the vessel wall (modeled only by CVH package in MELCOR). Exterior of the vessel - reactor cavity is also modelled with the RCCS, what is important for the long-term lasting heat exchange during accident scenarios. The heat exchange at the cooling side of the RCCS was decided to be modelled with heat exchange coefficient h=1000 W/m$^2$-K and temperature of T=373 K (100 °C). Detailed scheme of the RCCS is presented in Figure 8.

Figure 9 presents steam generator (SG) nodalization, where primary and secondary side are modelled. Primary side is modelled by inlet plenum of the hot helium, SG-tubes bundle region, lower plenum, riser with upper plenum and blower, and outlet plenum. Flow of the helium is forced by helium blower located on the top of SG. Secondary side (water) consists of feedwater inlet, pump and isolation valve; inlet header, helical tubes, outlet header, steam line including the isolation valve, as well as the SG drain system, which is used in case of SG tube rupture to minimize the water ingress into the primary system by draining the SG water. The 2200 SG tubes walls are represented by the heat structures.

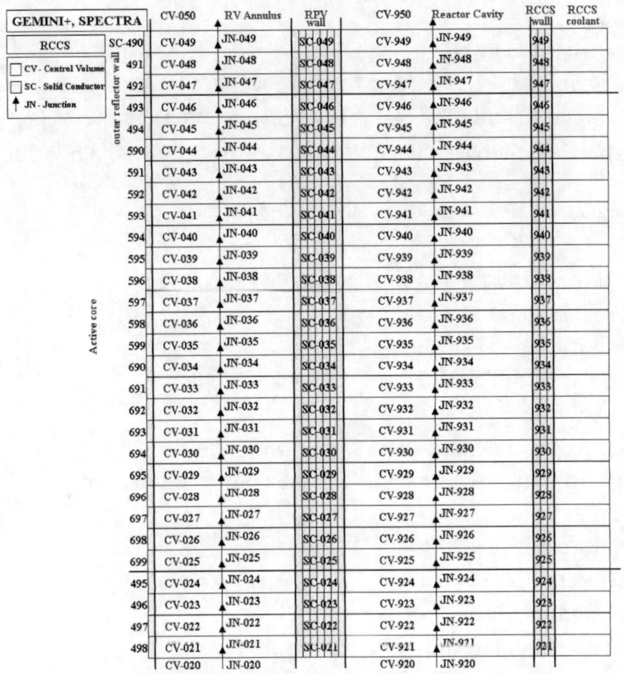

**Figure 8.** Reactor pressure vessel – MELCOR model.

The SCRAM signals modelling is important part of the logic in the developed model. During propagation from the steady state (SS) to transient (T) situations the following SCRAM signals are used in the model:

- dP/dt < –1000.0 (Pa/s) - Fast primary pressure drop.
- T > 1073 K (800°C) - High gas exit temperature.
- W(1) / W(2) < 0.7 - Low ratio of primary mass flow to secondary mass flow.

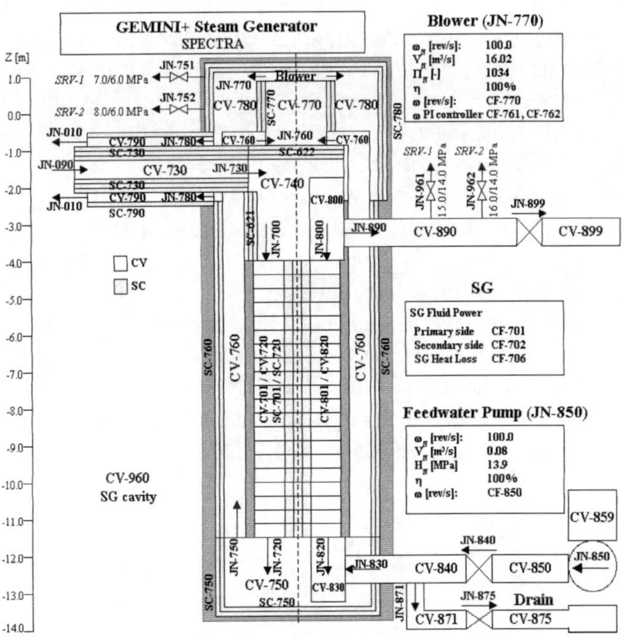

**Figure 9.** Steam Generator MELCOR and SPECTRA models.

Journal of Physics: Conference Series **2048** (2021) 012043 doi:10.1088/1742-6596/2048/1/012043

### *4.2. Scenario description*

In this section the transient scenario will be described.
The following accident was analyzed:

Depressurized Loss of Forced Circulation (DLOFC), 65 mm break in the primary system.

The scenario weas calculated for radially uniform (flat) power profile applying following sets of assumptions:

- Best Estimate (BE) and
- Conservative (C)

The following assumptions were made for the Best Estimate runs:

- Core power: 180 MW (100%)
- RV inlet gas temperature 325°C
- RV outlet gas temperature 750°C
- RV/RCCS wall emissivity 0.9
- RV/RCCS natural convection default (best estimate) models

Based on [8], the following assumptions were made for the conservative runs:

- Core power: 189 MW (105%)
- RV inlet gas temperature 355°C (+30 K)
- RV outlet gas temperature 800°C (+50 K)
- RV/RCCS wall emissivity 0.54
- RV/RCCS natural convection multiplier of 0.7 (–30%)
- Conservative decay heat curve: approximately 10% higher

Both DLOFC scenario is detected by the protective system due to the signal of "low ratio of primary mass flow to secondary mass flow". After that the blower and feedwater pump are tripped and control rods are dropped.

## 5. Calculation results

In this section the results of the comparative work will be summarized for performed scenario and both codes.

### *5.1. DLOFC scenario*

DLOFC accident is a typical Design Basis Accident (DBA) and one of the most serious for the reactor safety barriers to withstand. It receives high attention, because it results in the higher maximum fuel temperature in comparison to other DBAs. With such large 65 mm break, the reactor will depressurize quickly (as shown in Figure 10), causing coolant medium to escape the reactor coolant loop and decrease the ability of cooling heated structures of the reactor core.

Within 500 seconds the system is almost depressurized and the flow through the break is almost zero Figure 11. For both scenarios and codes, the results are very similar and the progression of the accident happens with a good agreement. The two assumptions (BE and C) show the same behavior of the system depressurization and the break mass flow characteristics.

Reactor power after SCRAM depends on the decay heat curves, which are based on data from NRG, obtained using 11-group calculations [7]. Those calculations were the effect of neutronic calculations based on the SERPENT code simulations (done by GEMINI+ project partner), which enabled to obtain the neutron precursors group constants. Later on, the constants were used to update the decay heat data available from [10] by group constants modified in SPECTRA.

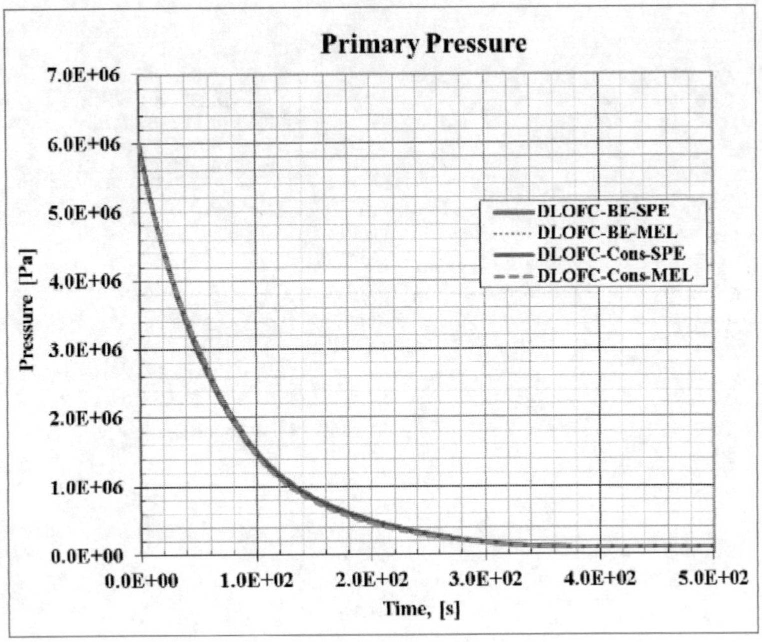


**Figure 10.** DLOFC primary pressure.

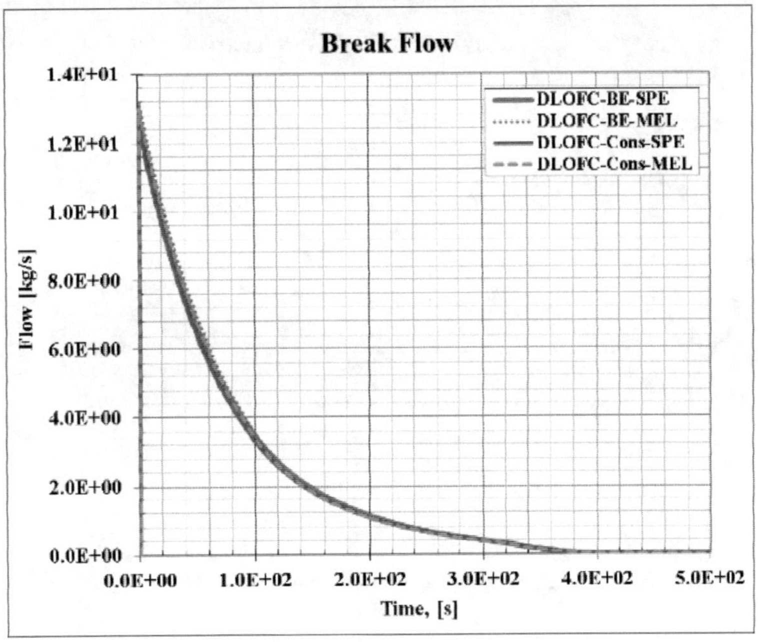


**Figure 11.** DLOFC break flow.

After reactor shutdown, the decay heat is transferred from the core to the RPV via heat conduction, convection and radiation. In terms of the HTR cores the dominating mechanism of heat transfer is conduction and in comparison, to the water reactors the solid structures in the core are responsible for heat extraction from the core. The graphite blocks are heated up by the fuel pellets and later on they are transferring the heat through the helium gaps to the outer walls surrounding the core. Thanks to the RCCS the reactor vessel is cooled. Due to high heat capacity of the graphite, the core heat relatively slowly and the maximum fuel temperature is reached around 20-30h of simulation Figure 13.

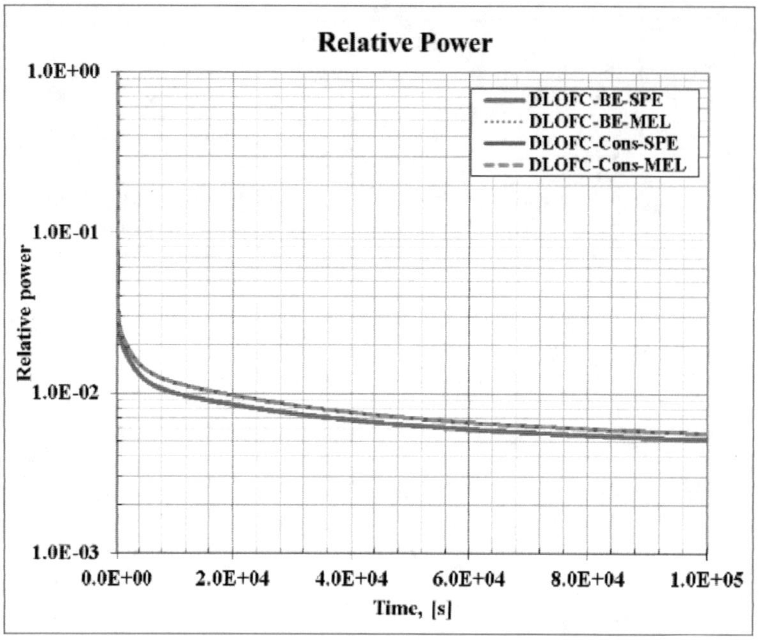


**Figure 12.** DLOFC relative power - long term.

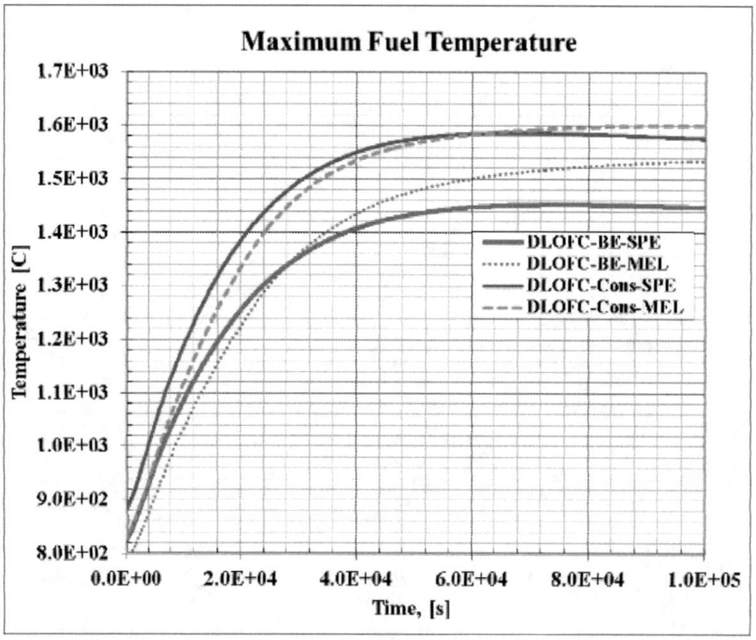


**Figure 13.** DLOFC maximum fuel temperatures.

Depending on the code and assumptions the maximum fuel temperature is predicted around 1450°C and 1600°C for best estimate and conservative assumptions respectively. Detailed data with the results for DLOFC scenario is presented in summarizing Table 2.

| GEMINI+ Core Temperatures SPECTRA | Time: 80000.2 s 22.2 hr | Temperature limit, °C: 1600 / 1599 | | | | | | | | | |
|---|---|---|---|---|---|---|---|---|---|---|---|
| | FA-01 | FA-02 | FA-03 | CA-04 | FA-05 | RA-01 | RA-02 | Outer reflector | | RV wall | RCCS wall |
| UR-01 | 389°C | 385°C | 374°C | 377°C | 363°C | 376°C | 354°C | 304°C | 277°C | 206°C | 101°C |
| UR-02 | 437°C | 429°C | 403°C | 416°C | 386°C | 379°C | 354°C | 305°C | 278°C | 205°C | 101°C |
| UR-03 | 556°C | 540°C | 482°C | 512°C | 452°C | 393°C | 363°C | 310°C | 285°C | 210°C | 101°C |
| Core-01 | 798°C | 769°C | 677°C | 709°C | 623°C | 530°C | 467°C | 368°C | 319°C | 231°C | 102°C |
| Core-02 | 1015°C | 984°C | 823°C | 956°C | 755°C | 557°C | 482°C | 377°C | 334°C | 240°C | 102°C |
| Core-03 | 1169°C | 1131°C | 955°C | 1083°C | 874°C | 687°C | 587°C | 440°C | 372°C | 265°C | 102°C |
| Core-04 | 1268°C | 1221°C | 1030°C | 1144°C | 935°C | 699°C | 594°C | 444°C | 378°C | 270°C | 102°C |
| Core-05 | 1344°C | 1294°C | 1094°C | 1215°C | 992°C | 754°C | 636°C | 469°C | 391°C | 279°C | 102°C |
| Core-06 | 1381°C | 1324°C | 1125°C | 1218°C | 1015°C | 761°C | 641°C | 472°C | 395°C | 282°C | 102°C |
| Core-07 | 1416°C | 1359°C | 1154°C | 1257°C | 1043°C | 791°C | 665°C | 487°C | 404°C | 269°C | 102°C |
| Core-08 | 1441°C | 1385°C | 1170°C | 1295°C | 1058°C | 794°C | 667°C | 488°C | 406°C | 290°C | 103°C |
| Core-09 | 1445°C | 1390°C | 1173°C | 1301°C | 1062°C | 799°C | 672°C | 491°C | 408°C | 291°C | 103°C |
| Core-10 | 1432°C | 1378°C | 1163°C | 1289°C | 1053°C | 797°C | 671°C | 490°C | 407°C | 291°C | 103°C |
| Core-11 | 1404°C | 1350°C | 1138°C | 1263°C | 1030°C | 771°C | 649°C | 477°C | 400°C | 286°C | 103°C |
| Core-12 | 1370°C | 1318°C | 1113°C | 1233°C | 1008°C | 763°C | 644°C | 474°C | 394°C | 282°C | 102°C |
| Core-13 | 1329°C | 1279°C | 1083°C | 1198°C | 983°C | 749°C | 636°C | 474°C | 398°C | 286°C | 103°C |
| Core-14 | 1278°C | 1231°C | 1048°C | 1155°C | 953°C | 744°C | 634°C | 473°C | 397°C | 285°C | 103°C |
| Core-15 | 1218°C | 1173°C | 999°C | 1101°C | 910°C | 707°C | 606°C | 458°C | 389°C | 280°C | 102°C |
| Core-16 | 1156°C | 1115°C | 955°C | 1047°C | 872°C | 698°C | 601°C | 456°C | 385°C | 277°C | 102°C |
| Core-17 | 1089°C | 1050°C | 898°C | 987°C | 821°C | 644°C | 558°C | 431°C | 373°C | 269°C | 102°C |
| Core-18 | 1022°C | 986°C | 850°C | 928°C | 779°C | 631°C | 550°C | 427°C | 367°C | 265°C | 102°C |
| Core-19 | 951°C | 919°C | 797°C | 867°C | 733°C | 599°C | 527°C | 415°C | 361°C | 261°C | 102°C |
| Core-20 | 878°C | 850°C | 748°C | 806°C | 692°C | 592°C | 524°C | 414°C | 359°C | 260°C | 102°C |
| Core-21 | 796°C | 773°C | 689°C | 735°C | 642°C | 562°C | 504°C | 405°C | 354°C | 256°C | 102°C |
| Core-22 | 700°C | 682°C | 623°C | 654°C | 587°C | 561°C | 506°C | 406°C | 355°C | 257°C | 102°C |
| LR-01 | 582°C | 567°C | 515°C | 544°C | 485°C | 435°C | 402°C | 341°C | 309°C | 236°C | 102°C |
| LR-02 | 529°C | 518°C | 478°C | 499°C | 455°C | 433°C | 402°C | 341°C | 308°C | 234°C | 102°C |
| LR-03 | 508°C | 498°C | 466°C | 482°C | 445°C | 432°C | 402°C | 341°C | 308°C | 234°C | 102°C |
| LR-04 | 501°C | 492°C | 463°C | 477°C | 443°C | 432°C | 402°C | 341°C | 308°C | 234°C | 102°C |

**Figure 14.** DLOFC (BE) maximum fuel temperatures in core rings for SPECTRA code.

| GEMINI+ Core Temperatures MELCOR | Time: 100000.0 s 27.8 hr | Temperature limit, °C: 1600 / 1599 | | | | | | | | |
|---|---|---|---|---|---|---|---|---|---|---|
| | Ring 1 FA-01 | Ring 2 FA-02 | Ring 3 FA-03/4 | Ring 4 FA-05 | Ring 5 RA-01/3/4 | Ring 6 RA-02/5/6 | Outer reflector | | RV wall | RCCS wall |
| 34 (UR) | 581°C | 575°C | 561°C | 541°C | 484°C | 266°C | 240°C | 230°C | 183°C | 100°C |
| 33 (UR) | 621°C | 613°C | 596°C | 571°C | 503°C | 273°C | 240°C | 226°C | 174°C | 100°C |
| 32 (UR) | 721°C | 711°C | 684°C | 646°C | 538°C | 291°C | 255°C | 237°C | 178°C | 100°C |
| 31 (C) | 954°C | 940°C | 902°C | 849°C | 613°C | 305°C | 257°C | 238°C | 177°C | 100°C |
| 30 (C) | 1149°C | 1132°C | 1085°C | 1014°C | 716°C | 333°C | 272°C | 250°C | 182°C | 100°C |
| 29 (C) | 1284°C | 1264°C | 1212°C | 1129°C | 818°C | 376°C | 298°C | 270°C | 192°C | 100°C |
| 28 (C) | 1379°C | 1359°C | 1302°C | 1212°C | 904°C | 421°C | 323°C | 288°C | 203°C | 100°C |
| 27 (C) | 1446°C | 1425°C | 1366°C | 1271°C | 967°C | 469°C | 352°C | 310°C | 215°C | 100°C |
| 26 (C) | 1491°C | 1469°C | 1409°C | 1311°C | 1010°C | 504°C | 373°C | 326°C | 225°C | 100°C |
| 25 (C) | 1518°C | 1496°C | 1435°C | 1335°C | 1037°C | 530°C | 389°C | 337°C | 208°C | 100°C |
| 24 (C) | 1531°C | 1509°C | 1448°C | 1348°C | 1052°C | 546°C | 398°C | 344°C | 239°C | 100°C |
| 23 (C) | 1534°C | 1512°C | 1450°C | 1350°C | 1057°C | 557°C | 402°C | 347°C | 241°C | 100°C |
| 22 (C) | 1527°C | 1505°C | 1444°C | 1345°C | 1054°C | 558°C | 402°C | 347°C | 241°C | 100°C |
| 21 (C) | 1512°C | 1490°C | 1430°C | 1332°C | 1044°C | 553°C | 398°C | 345°C | 239°C | 100°C |
| 20 (C) | 1490°C | 1468°C | 1409°C | 1313°C | 1028°C | 542°C | 390°C | 339°C | 236°C | 100°C |
| 19 (C) | 1461°C | 1440°C | 1382°C | 1288°C | 1006°C | 526°C | 382°C | 333°C | 232°C | 100°C |
| 18 (C) | 1424°C | 1404°C | 1347°C | 1257°C | 979°C | 506°C | 368°C | 323°C | 225°C | 100°C |
| 17 (C) | 1381°C | 1361°C | 1307°C | 1220°C | 945°C | 482°C | 357°C | 315°C | 221°C | 100°C |
| 16 (C) | 1333°C | 1313°C | 1261°C | 1178°C | 907°C | 454°C | 340°C | 302°C | 213°C | 100°C |
| 15 (C) | 1277°C | 1259°C | 1209°C | 1131°C | 865°C | 424°C | 327°C | 293°C | 208°C | 100°C |
| 14 (C) | 1215°C | 1197°C | 1151°C | 1079°C | 819°C | 396°C | 311°C | 281°C | 201°C | 100°C |
| 13 (C) | 1142°C | 1126°C | 1084°C | 1019°C | 770°C | 371°C | 299°C | 272°C | 197°C | 100°C |
| 12 (C) | 1058°C | 1044°C | 1006°C | 950°C | 720°C | 352°C | 287°C | 263°C | 192°C | 100°C |
| 11 (C) | 956°C | 944°C | 914°C | 869°C | 674°C | 337°C | 281°C | 258°C | 190°C | 100°C |
| 10 (C) | 829°C | 821°C | 799°C | 769°C | 639°C | 331°C | 277°C | 256°C | 189°C | 100°C |
| 09 (LR) | 743°C | 737°C | 721°C | 699°C | 630°C | 332°C | 278°C | 257°C | 193°C | 100°C |
| 08 (LR) | 704°C | 699°C | 686°C | 667°C | 611°C | 340°C | 285°C | 262°C | 196°C | 100°C |
| 07 (LR) | 678°C | 673°C | 662°C | 644°C | 591°C | 356°C | 298°C | 273°C | 204°C | 100°C |
| 06 (LR) | 661°C | 656°C | 645°C | 624°C | 570°C | 384°C | 329°C | 298°C | 221°C | 100°C |

**Figure 15.** DLOFC (BE) maximum fuel temperatures in core rings for MELCOR code.

As it can be seen in the Figure 14 – Figure 15 no exceedance of the temperature limit for the both codes SPECTRA and MELCOR was reached for the case of the DLOFC scenario with best estimate assumptions. The hottest areas are determined to be in the center of the core. The following peak values are observed in MELCOR calculations:

- BE: 1807 K (1534°C) at 100,000 s,
- C: 1873 K (1600°C) at 98,600 s.

The following peak values are observed in SPECTRA calculations:

- BE: 1718 K (1445°C) at 80,000 s,
- C: 1850 K (1577°C) at 72,000 s.

The highest temperature is observed FA 1 (ring 1) - Figure 14 and Figure 15, which represents a single fuel assembly, 3.2% of the whole core fuel mass.

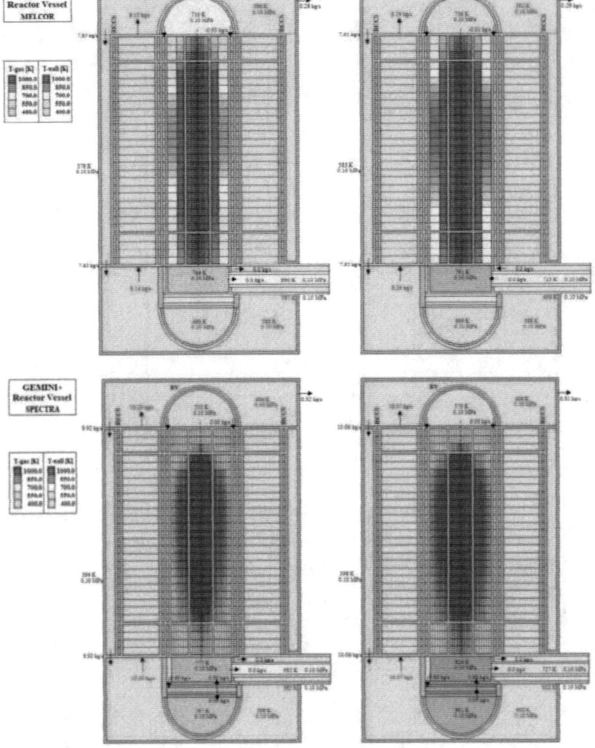


**Figure 16.** Steam Generator MELCOR and SPECTRA models.

The differences in the maximum fuel temperatures are 90 K in the BE case and 23 K in the conservative case. Investigation of the code modeling and input assumptions showed the following main differences:

- Use of separate effective conductivity correlations in fuel and reflector in SPECTRA. Sensitivity calculations showed that this gives roughly 40 K difference in the maximum fuel temperatures [9].
- Different correlations for natural convection, as well as different characteristic dimensions that are being used with these correlations. Consequently, clearly larger heat transfer to RCCS in SPECTRA (Figure 17) than in MELCOR (Figure 18). The differences in default natural convection correlation were pointed out in [7]. Differences in the characteristic dimensions are a consequence of using a single value in MELCOR and separate values for natural and forced convection in SPECTRA. The hydraulic diameter is typically applied for forced convection; surface height is applied for the natural convection. Due to those differences the convective heat transfer coefficients observed on the RV and RCCS surface were approximately twice larger in SPECTRA than in MELCOR. A sensitivity calculation was performed [9], where a multiplier of 0.5 was applied on the HTC correlations to get approximately twice smaller convective HTC on the RCCS and RV. The resulting maximum fuel temperatures were:
    - o BE: 1733 K (1460°C),
    - o C: 1866 K (1593°C).

  In this case the difference compared to MELCOR is 74 K in the BE case and 7 K in the conservative case.

- Other differences include: in MELCOR the core is composed of 4 rings, in SPECTRA there are 5 different assembly types, which come from 1/12 core symmetry), and
- small differences in core component masses, which are a consequence of different input (SPECTRA input model is based on geometrical dimensions; MELCOR model is based on component masses).

It is considered that for the current conceptual state of the reactor design, the agreement is satisfactory. Some changes of the design were recently implemented that are not even fully implemented in both models, e.g., the gas riser channel, discussed in [9]. This will have to remain as eventual future work. For now, the agreement of 6 K on the maximum fuel temperature in the most conservative case is considered as very good.

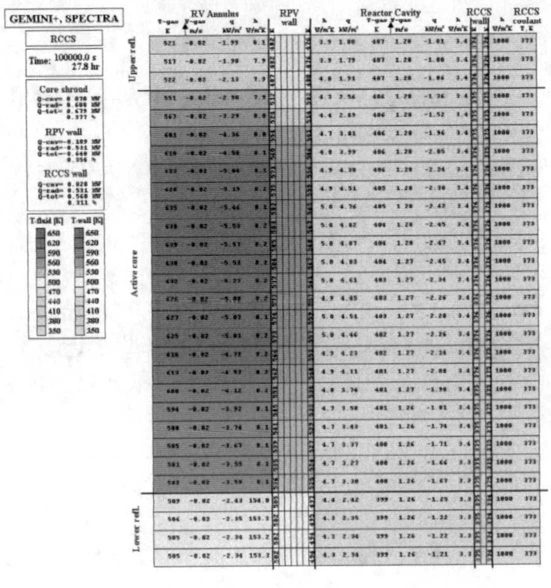


**Figure 17.** DLOFC/PLOFC with BE/C SPECTRA power extracted by RCCS.

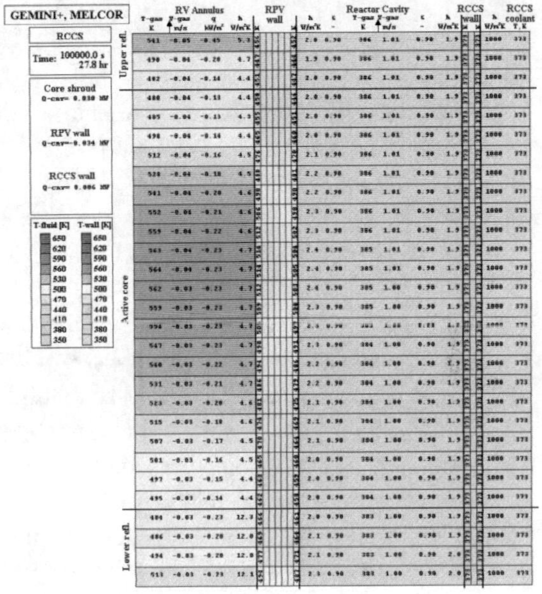


**Figure 18.** DLOFC with BE/C MELCOR power extracted by RCCS.

## 6. Summary of results

In DLOFC scenario calculated maximum fuel temperatures do not exceed the acceptable level of 1600°C and it is far from limit 1620°C specified in [1]. Any fraction of the fuel is not overheated and the design fulfil safety criteria for operation specified in [2]. Safety margin varies between assumptions from 20 to 296 degrees for MELCOR code and 57 to 452 degrees for SPECTRA code. Some result differences will need more model investigations and further results will be published.

**Table 2.** Summary of DLOFC results

| Assumption | BE | | C | |
|---|---|---|---|---|
| Code | MELCOR | SPECTRA | MELCOR | SPECTRA |
| Thermal power | 180 MW | | 189MW | |
| Maximum fuel | 1807K<br>1534°C | 1718K<br>1445°C | 1873K<br>1600°C | 1850K<br>1577°C |

## 7. Results discussion

In the two models, the peak values of the maximal fuel temperature are below the HTR TRISO fuel element temperature limitation 1620°C [1]. For MELCOR conservative calculations it is predicted as 1600°C and for SPECTRA 1577°C, which give the relatively small safety margin.

## Acknowledgments

This project has received funding from the Euratom research and training program 2014-2018 under the grant agreement n°755478.

Scientific work was financed from financial resources for science of The Ministry of Science and Higher Education in Poland in the years 2017-2020 granted for the implementation of an international co-financed project.

## References

[1] International Atomic Energy Agency, "High Temperature Gas Cooled," Sales and Promotion, Publishing Section International Atomic Energy Agency, Vienna, 2010.

[2] D. Hittner, „GEMINI+, Task 2.2: Data on block type HTGR core configuration, RA0004, Rev. 2,," 2017.

[3] M.M. Stempniewicz, NRG, „Thermal Hydraulic Model of the GEMINI+ HTR Plant, Safety Analyses WP1.6," 2019.

[4] N.Kohtz, „Consideration of unfavorable initial conditions and safety margins for input parameters of thermal hydraulic analyses of passive heat removal scenarios. GEMINI+ Task 1.6," 2019.

[5] M.M. Stempniewicz, "Thermal-Hydraulic Model of the GEMINI+ HTR Plant (8.8 m), Safety Analyses, WP1.6", 24203/20.171610, 30/04/2020.

[6] SNL, „MELCOR Computer Code Manuals, Vol. 1: User's Guide, Vol. 2: Reference Manuals, Vol. 3: Assessment Problems," 2019.

[7] NRG, „SPECTRA Sophisticated Plant Evaluation Code for Thermal-Hydraulic Response Assessment, Version 3.61, October 2019, Vol. 1 – Program Description, Vol. 2 – User's Guide, Vol. 3 – Verification and Validation," 2019.

[8] M.Skrzypek, E.Skrzypek, NCBJ, "TH Analyses of GEMINI+ HTR Plant (8.8m) Results of PLOFC and DLOFC Scenarios," 2020.

[9] Y. Zheng, M. M. Stempniewicz, C. Zhipeng and S. Lei, "Study on the DLOFC and PLOFC accidents of the 200 MWe pebble-bed modular high temperature gas-cooled reactor with TINTE and SPECTRA codes," Annals of Nuclear Energy, p. 763–777, 2018.

[10] Y. Zheng, L. Shi and Y. Dong, "Thermo-hydraulic transient studies of the Chinese 200 MWe HTR-PM for loss of forced cooling accidents," Annals of Nuclear Energy, p. 742–751, 2009.

# Developing a Preliminary Design of FPGA Based Control Rod System for a High Temperature Experimental Power Reactor

**Sigit Santoso, Tulis Jojok Suryono[1], Restu Maerani[1], Dian Fitri Atmoko[2], Auralius Manurung[3]**

[1] *Center for Nuclear Reactor Technology and Safety-BATAN, Puspiptek Area, Setu, South Tangerang, 15310, Indonesia*

[2] *Center for Engineering of Nuclear Facility-BATAN 3, Puspiptek Area, Setu, South Tangerang, 15310, Indonesia*

[3] *Department of Mechanical Engineering, Universitas Pertamina, Jakarta Selatan, 12220, Indonesia*

Coresponding auhor's e-mail : sigitsan@batan.go.id

**Abstract.** An Experimental Power Reactor (*Reaktor Daya Experimental*, RDE) which is based on high-temperature gas-cooled reactor technology is being developed in Indonesia during recent years. As an advanced reactor design type, a fully digital- based I&C would be employed in the design of RDE reactor monitoring and control including the control rod drive system. On the other hand, some of the major issues discussed in the licensing process for such digital I&C are the possibility that a common cause failure can undermine the reactor protection function and the vulnerable to cyber-attack possibility. Therefore, a number of the defense in depth measures need to be applied to I&C systems design help to mitigate those issues. This paper discusses the design process for employing FPGA based digital system in the control rod drive system of RDE. The methodology follows the life cycle process of instrumentation and control architecture and software development which is presented in the V shape model. A generic control rod system prototype which consists of a control rod motor driver, control rod handling system, magnetic handling, and the motor system was prepared and would be used as an object in the FPGA implementation. The result of the process design conducted in this current phase study shows the implementation of FPGA-based digital technology will enable to minimize the lack of a digital based control rod drive system. However, appropriate testing and verification of the design developed are required to ensure better performance of the control rod drive system.

## 1. Introduction

Categorized as a system important to safety, the control rods system (CRS) used to perform reactor shutdown, that is one of the most important safety functions in nuclear reactor. The design of CRS applied to Experimental Power Reactor (RDE) was developed to bear that safety function and power control adjusting system as well. RDE is a 10 MWth pebble bed HTGR type reactor utilizing spherical fuel elements with ceramic-coated fuel particles [1]. As an advanced reactor design type, a fully digital-based I&C would be employed in the design of RDE reactor monitoring and control including the control rod drive system. The CRS design type was varied based on drive control system type, motor drive, control rod assembly and its position, and others. Reactor operation experience showed that some reactor accidents are contributed by the failure of control rod systems. Hence several types of research were performed to conduct the performance test of the control rod designs and to create a more reliable CRS design [2][3][4]. In general, during the emergency operation where the reactor scram is required the control rods would be drop naturally into the rod channels by gravity. The approaches to enhance the reliability of the control rod system was developed, such as by the use of advance digital I&C system [2][5][6]. The implementation of digital I&C systems offers many benefits, such as improved control accuracy, a more user-friendly interface for the human computer and a higher level of automation, although the reliability of embedded software often presents a challenge [6-8].

Due to embedded software, the risk of unintended malware and latent CCF on the device should be minimized and predicted in the design process. With regard to these issues, the FPGA digital based system provides several considerations. Their technology showed the ability as a counter measure to minimize the issue according vulnerability and security of the digital I&C system [7][9]. Moreover, FPGA technology can be applied in the design as a diverse and redundant system of other control system equipment.

This paper discusses the design process for the application of FPGA based digital system to control a motor driver used in a control rod system of RDE preliminary design. The methodology for designing the process applied in this research follows the generic I&C lifecycle and software development lifecycle process presented in a V Model [9][10]. The method is started with a document review to identify plant/system requirements and operational characteristics. The analysis was carried out to identify the functionality and system requirements of the control rod and control rod drive systems, and to synthesize the corresponding solution. Finally, a preliminary design presented in a block diagram was developed based on system requirements. The result of this study is necessary for providing a tentative design of the CRS for RDE. Moreover, the result offers another approach to minimize the lack of vulnerability that may arise in the implementation of a digital control system.

## 2. Theory

### *2.1. I&C Development Life Cycle*

An appropriate development plan and the process should be applied to obtain a reliable and suitable digital controls system. The development process of the I&C system will follow the life cycle process. There are some models of the lifecycle process, one of them which is generally used in the digital based I&C development is a V Model [10-11]. The approach is an advanced waterfall model in which testing functionality is added at each stage of the project development. This V model is considered most suitable for conducting the process systematically [10-12]. Moreover, the development phase applied in the model can be used simultaneously for conducting the verification and validation process. The implementation of the V model to the design of I&C for NPP was also described in the Specific Safety Guide of IAEA, SSG- 39 [12].

FPGA based digital I&C system consists of a hardware system with software implemented in the system. The development process of the implemented software in the form of Hardware Description Language (HDL) should be verified and validated to ensure that the obtained I&C system has good conformity toward the defined design requirements [10-12]. The design development process of the CR drive system for RDE in this study employed the V model since its simplicity in implementation and ability in detecting and removing the error early, which means the design process would be more effective. The software development process in the V model is presented in Figure 1.

### *2.2. RDE Control and Operation*

RDE is a 10 MWth pebble bed HTGR type reactor utilizing spherical fuel elements with ceramic-coated fuel particles. The reactor core has a diameter of approx. 1.8 m and an average height of approx. 2 m and is cooled by helium gas [1][13]. The core containing spherical balls is surrounded by graphite, and graphite reflectors are surrounded by a layer of boronated carbon bricks. Mean power density during nominal power operation of the core is limited to 2 MW/m3 and the mean core outlet temperature to 700 °C [1].

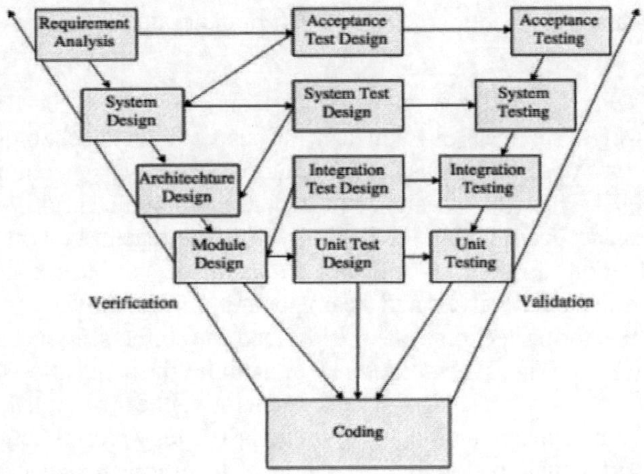


**Figure 1.** Software development process life cycle in V Model [10].

RDE operation is essentially divided into start-up, power operation, and shutdown modes. Each operation mode has a particular procedure that consists of a series of task steps and the conditions needed. Start-up operation is initiated by starting the primary gas blower. Two independent and diverse shutdown systems perform the reactor control and shutdown systems, that are control rod (reflector rod) and absorber ball. However, only the first shut-down system is controlled by the reactor protection system, while the second shut-down system using the absorber ball can be operated manually if necessary.

The core and its geometry are developed that the reactor can be shut down merely by the insertion of absorbers in reflector columns [1][13]. Moreover, under all operating and accident conditions, residual heat can only be removed by thermal conduction, thermal radiation and natural convection to the surface coolers outside the reactor pressure vessel. Even without the active removal of residual heat from the core, the maximum fuel temperature limit for maintaining the coated fuel particle integrity is not exceeded [1][13][14]. The shutdown system specification of RDE is given in Table 1.

**Table 1.** The shutdown system device of RDE.

| | | |
|---|---|---|
| **1$^{st}$ Shutdown System (Reflector Rods)** | | |
| Rods | 10 | pcs |
| Absorber length | 2,200 | mm |
| Absorber diameter | 100 | mm |
| Maximum travel | 2,600 | mm |
| Normal speed | 1 | cm/s |
| Absorber material | $B_4C$ | |
| **2$^{nd}$ Shutdown System** | | |
| Shutdown unit | 7 | pcs |
| Small ball shutdown element diameter | 5 | mm |
| No. of small ball shutdown elements per unit | $2.7 \times 10^5$ | pcs |
| Absorber material | $B_4C$ in graphite matrix | 25% $B_4C$ by volume |

The signals for reactor shutdown were generated based on the RDE safety parameters. There are process variables categorized as reactor safety parameters, such as Neutron flux, Hot gas temperature, Cold gas temperature, Moisture in the primary system, Pressure in the primary system, Pressure in the secondary system, and Earthquake acceleration. All of the initiation criteria derived from these safety

Journal of Physics: Conference Series **2048** (2021) 012044 doi:10.1088/1742-6596/2048/1/012044

variables are used by reactor protection systems (RPS) to generate trip signals and actuate protective actions [8][13].

### *2.3. I&C for Reactor Protection and Shutdown System*

The design of the RDE I&C system was developed on the basis of digital technology. The I&C equipment of RDE is categorized into operational systems, limitation systems, protection systems and accident monitoring systems [1][14]. The RPS is designed in such a way that it can fulfill its safety function even when failure initiating events occur within the RPS or within the reactor system. The protection system of RDE includes the actuation equipment of reflector rods, primary gas blower, primary system isolation valves, secondary system isolation valves, and steam generator relief valves.

The circuitry of the reactor protection system is divided into three sections, that are initiation level, logic level and actuation level. The RPS initiation level includes the acquisition of data from the sensors to the limit value monitors. Logic level responsible for generating the limit signal, voting and gating logic of the limit signals to produce the actuation signals. The last level which is actuation level responsible in conducting a process of actuation signals from the logic level to actuate safety equipment [13][14]. The logic level of RPS design in general is presented in Figure 2 [14]. The RPS carries out two types of logic: Bistable logic and Local Coincidence Logic (LCL) [14-16].

Control rod drive system is a part of I&C system of RDE which has a function in controlling the movement of control rod, monitoring the position of CR and conducting a reactor scram. Design concept of control rod regulating system of this reactor is developed based on type, mechanisms, criteria and the number of the specified control rod. In general, the reactor control panel has control rod control buttons to control reactor power, reactor safety buttons used to secure reactor operation in the event of an emergency (scram) and parameter monitoring used to display the height parameters of the reactor control rod, as well as panel locks used as interlock guards [11][12][15].

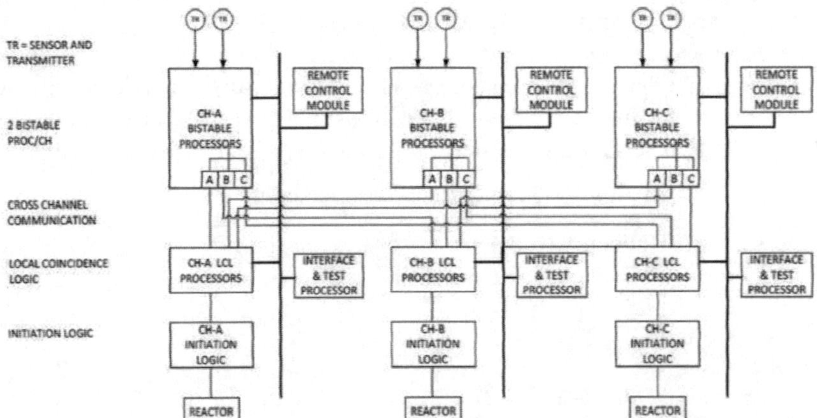


**Figure 2.** The logic level of RPS design, in general [14]

## 3. Methodology

Design development of FPGA based digital system for the RDE control rod drive system basically follows the V Model that is generally applied in both of development of I&C systems and software development process. The method is started with a document review to identify plant/system requirements and operational characteristics [1][14]. Design a basic document and design concept of experimental power reactor developed previously are considered. The following step was to define the functional requirements of the control rod and control rod drive systems and to synthesize the corresponding solution [18]. Identify requirements of CRD systems were conducted through some techniques which include discussion and interviews with process system team, simulations, and technical documents review. Finally, a preliminary design presented in a block diagram was developed based on the functions and physical solution to satisfy the system requirement.

## 4. Results and Discussion

The results in the current phase study include identification of control rod operation system characteristics and design requirements. Moreover, the architecture design of CRS in a block diagram and software requirement were also developed.

### *4.1. Operation Characteristics and Design Requirements of CRD System*

The preliminary and basic requirements of the previous research's result was compiled and refined in the analysis by incorporating the information collected through discussion and updating the data and specification as well. The criteria from 10 CFR 50 Appendix A and guidance from RG.1.232 Rev.0 was used as reference. The design requirements of CRS for RDE were formulated and some of them listed as follows:

- CRS of RDE covers two main functions, the first is to execute scram signal from RPS by releasing and dropping the control rod in the defined reflector area. The second function was related to control the reactor power (Reactor Regulating System - RRS) through the temperature regulating system which conducted by adjusting control rod position.
- Modes of CR controls in CRS include automatic scram generated by RPS or manual switches, automatic control for sequential movement, manual control for sequential CR movement, and Standby. Table 2. shows the actuation method of the CR system.
- The aim of the RRS is to regulate the temperature of the setpoint program as a function of the turbine load. Hot leg temperature (Th), cold leg temperature (Tc), Turbine load, and reactor power signals are the main inputs of the RRS. The main outputs of this system are control rod (withdraw, insert, and hold) and control rod (high low) speed. There are the feedback and feed-forward loops in the RRS.
- Main Control Room and the Remote Shutdown Room are designed to support CRS man-machine interface devices, and other safety channel and control channels. CRS provides outputs for operator monitoring of the CR status and operation mode and receives manually entered input from operators using provided switches.
- The CRS provides status alarm signals to the alarm system of the MCR for the following types of conditions: bistable trips, bistable pre-trips, bypass operation.
- The CRS design completed with a test capability equipment for determining operability status and diagnostic testing as well.
- The movement equipment of the control rod should be reliable, has acceptable accuracy and satisfy safety requirement.
- CR status (drop or no-drop) and height position was determined by core protection calculation system and reactor regulation system. The calculation system has redundant channels that determine this CR position. When a safety limit exceeded, a trip signal is transmitted to the protection system using hardwired cables.
- The core protection system also produces a control rod withdrawal prohibit signal for the CRS when pre-trip conditions or associated CR conditions, such as power reduction or control rod deviation are reached.
- Controlled components of the power control system in RDE consists two main components that are helium circulator pump and related valves, and control rod system. Controlled parameters include Reactor coolant temperature, reactor pressure, position level of CR (direction and rate), and speed of blower.
- The power control system interfacing with the reactor regulating system, the power cutback systems, and the CR system, and other systems as shown. The Reactor regulating system receives Helium temperature and flow rate, and neutron flux from the measurement system; and sends control rod withdrawal, and control rod insertion status to the digital control rod control system. Steam control system provide the signal to confirm the withdrawal motion status to the CR control system.

**Table 2.** Actuation control provision of CR of RDE.

| Mode | Description | Activated Via |
|---|---|---|
| Automatic scram | Automatic actuation to trip reactor generated by safety parameters | Reactor Protection system |
| Manual scram actuation switch | Manual scram actuation by operator. Manual scram can be conducted through CR drop and small absorber ball release. | Hardware switches located at MCR and RSR |
| Manual system operation switch | Manual adjusting of CR height position by operator | CR manual control switch located at MCR |
| Automatic operation | Automatic CR height regulation system, includes automatic stop when achieving CR max/min height position. | CR automatic drive system |

### *4.2. Preliminary Design of CRS of RDE*

We consider three types of mechanism system for CR movement applied in RDE, that are 1). spindle with screw moved by stepping motor, 2). chain and sprocket with stepping motor, and 3). circular coils and latch-style jack with the armature. In this current study-phase we apply the first mechanism type which generally applied to the research reactor in Indonesia. The aim is to simplify the mechanical aspect of CRS mode, since the focus was on the implementation process of FPGA based digital control system.

The components of CRS would be similar to other CR drive system design, such as applied to the PWR [14][17]. The main component of the CRS design consists of:

1. Logic cabinet, power cabinet, interfaces and other supporting systems/components such as reactor process control, reactor protection system, control rod position monitoring and power source.
2. The spindle equipped with screw, motor driver, CR grip system, shock absorber, and switches.

The operation scenario and operation requirement of CRD in RDE design were formulated, some of them are listed in below:

- The control rod can be operated (motion up or down) if the interlock signal is in normal condition.
- To raise and down the control rod can be done by pressing the corresponding button provided in control room manually, and automatically by the system.
- Control rods are only allowed to move up individually (not allowed to be raised simultaneously), on the other hand the control rod is allowed to go down simultaneously.
- If the up button and the down button of one of the control bars are pressed simultaneously, then the action of the control rod motion is the motion down.
- If the position of the control rod carrier magnet has reached the upper limit (fully-Up) or lower limit (fully-down) then the control rod drive motor will automatically stop.

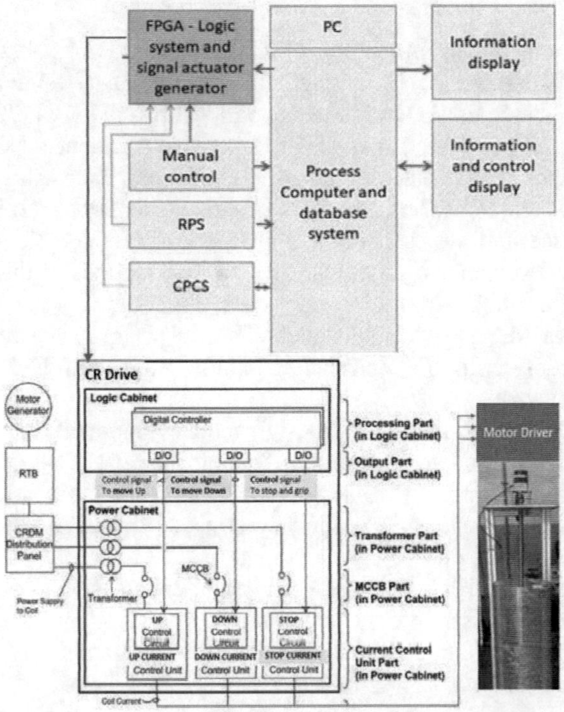


**Figure 3.** Schematic diagram of CRS design for RDE.

Presented in Figure 3, the control rod movement was generated by stepping motor provided in each CR drive system. The control can be move up and move down by changing the direction of motor rotation. The logic signal to operate the motor stepper was supplied by CRS installed in the logic cabinet. The control rod design mechanism applied in PWR was adopted in the CRS design with some adjustments [17].

In the case of emergency or accident situation when the reactor should be scram, the signal scram was supplied by RPS which directly connected to reactor trip breaker-RTB in a reactor trip switchgear system to cut off the current power and to drop the control rod. The reactor trip switchgear system receives the reactor trip signals from the RPS, and manual reactor trip switches through hardwired cables. The reactor trip switchgear disconnects the power to the CRS for dropping control rod element into the reflector by RPS signals or manual reactor trip signals from the main control room or remote shutdown room.

## 5. Conclusions

A fully digital-based I&C would be employed in the design of RDE reactor monitoring and control including the control rod drive system. The process design follows the V model which applied the phase systematically to enable detecting possible error immediately. The design requirements of CRS for RDE were formulated and obtained in this study. The schematic diagram was developed and CRS prototype was prepared. The result of this current phase study shows that the use of FPGA-based digital technology will enable to minimize the lack of digital based control rod drive system. Appropriate testing and verification of the design are required to ensure better performance of the control rod drive system.

## Acknowledgements

This research was a part of research project supported and funded by the Nuclear Research & Development Program (DIPA 2020) at the Center for Nuclear Reactor Technology and Safety of the National Nuclear Energy Agency, and research grant from Ministry of High Education and Science Technology of Indonesia.

Journal of Physics: Conference Series **2048** (2021) 012044 doi:10.1088/1742-6596/2048/1/012044

## References


[1] Conceptual design, general design features of RDE, PTKRN BATAN 2015.

[2] W. Yuanqiang, D. Xingzhong, Z. Huizhong, and H. Zhiyong, "Design and tests for the HTR-10 control rod system," Nucl. Eng. Des., vol. 218, no. 1–3, pp. 147–154, 2002.

[3] H. M. Saad, A. M, and M. H.M, "Analysis of Reactivity Accident for Control Rods Withdrawal at the Thermal Reactor," Int. J. Recent Adv. Phys., vol. 3, no. 2, pp. 21–40, 2014.

[4] A.I. Oludare, M.N. Agu, A.M. Umar, et al, "Control Rods Drop Failure On Reactors Stability And Safety", Advances in Physics Theories and Applications, Vol. 27, pp.58-73, 2014.

[5] J. H. Lee, CRDM performance tests of PGSFR," in Transactions of the Korean Nuclear Society Spring Meeting, Jeju, Korea, 2018 .

[6] Z. Ma, H. Yoshikawa, M.Yang, "Module level reliability performance evaluation of digital reactor protection system considering the repair and common cause failure." Annals of Nuclear Energy no 110, pp. 805–817, 2017

[7] C. Guo, H. Xiong, X. Huang, and D. Li, "Design and Development Framework of Safety-Critical Software in HTR-PM," J. Sci. and Technol of Nucl. Install.2017, 1-9.

[8] Sudarno, S. Santoso, K. Santosa, R. Maerani, and Deswandri, "Assessment of Input Parameters and Architecture of RDE Reactor Protection System," J. Phys. Conf. Ser., vol. 1198, p. 052007, 2019.

[9] I. Ahmed, J. Jung, and G. Heo, "Design verification enhancement of field programmable gate array-based safety-critical I&C system of nuclear power plant," 2017.

[10] ISO/IEC/IEEE, 15288-2015, International Standard-Systems and Software Engineering– System Life Cycle Processes, 2015.

[11] IEC, IEC 62566, Nuclear Power Plants- Instrumentation and Control Important to Safety Development of HDL Programmed Integrated Circuits for Systems Performing Category A functions. IEC 62566, Edition 1.0, 2012.

[12] IAEA, IAEA Safety Standards, Specific Safety Guide No.SSG-39, Design of Instrumentation and Control Systems for Nuclear Power Plants, no. SSG-39 Specific Safety Guide. 2016.

[13] D. E. Holcomb, S. J. Ball, and S. M. Cetiner, HTGR Measurements and Instrumentation Systems 1, ORNL, UT-Batelle, AS. May.2012.

[14] Basic Engineering Design of RDE, Arsitektur Sistem Instrumentasi dan Kendali, PTKRN-BATAN 2017.

[15] S. Santoso, Sudarno, R. Maerani, J. Situmorang, and A. Cahyono, "Software requirement analysis for digital based reactor protection system of RDE design," J. Phys. Conf. Ser., vol. 1198, p. 022046, 2019.

[16] J. Mayaka and J. C. Jung, "Complexity reduction of the Engineered Safety Features Component Control System," Nucl. Eng. Des., vol. 331, no. January, pp. 194–203, 2018.

[17] Roslund, et al., United States Patent No. US 8,670.515 B2 (Mar. 11, 2014).

[18] IEEE Std. 1233, 1998c. IEEE Guide for Developing System Requirements Specifications, 1998

# AUTHOR INDEX